D1294971

NEW HORIZONS
IN EDUCATION

Pan American's Guide to
Schools and Universities Abroad

Prepared by

PAN AMERICAN AIRWAYS

Simon and Schuster, New York

Note: Part II of this book first appeared in pamphlet form under the title "A Guide to Boarding Schools Abroad," published by Pan American World Airways, Inc., copyright © 1963. Pan Am, New Horizons and Clipper, Trade Marks Reg. U.S. Pat. Off.

ACKNOWLEDGMENTS

THE ASSEMBLING OF THE INFORMATION in this book was made possible through the co-operation and invaluable advice and guidance of cultural counselors of various countries and the cultural attachés of foreign embassies. Our special thanks go to Miss Lily von Klemperer and Maria Jacobson of the Institute of International Education in New York, Mrs. Geraldine Thompson of the International Schools Services in New York and the authorities of the universities and schools abroad who have painstakingly checked the facts presented. Stanley Washburn, Jr., and Craig Ludlow served as editors for Pan American, with Maxine R. Bullard as Associate Editor.

Inquiries and comments should be addressed to Gerald W. Whitted, Manager Publications, Pan American Airways, Pan Am Building, New York, N. Y. 10017.

Note: While we have made every effort to provide the most current and accurate information on education abroad, there are continual changes being made in universities and schools everywhere in curriculum, cost of living and entrance requirements. In view of this, we cannot accept responsibility for inaccuracies and omissions.

Contents

PART I

A Guide to Colleges and Universities in Africa, Europe, the Middle East, the Far East and Latin America

Foreword

THE FUTURE OF THE WORLD *depends upon the knowledge and understanding by the peoples of all countries of the customs, language, ideals and aspiration of other countries. Through the ages students have pioneered the way for others to follow, removing the barriers of doubt, suspicion and fear which are the root of international misunderstanding and a constant threat to peace. American students studying in foreign universities can be most effective ambassadors in spreading the ideals and democratic way of our country.*

Until recently students traveling abroad to take courses or degrees in foreign universities have been limited largely to scholars on fellowships or on special grants financed by foundations or subsidized by governments. But now we are on the threshold of a new educational era which, for the first time, truly makes possible new horizons in education for a large number of students. Jet transportation with its low cost and high speed has made it possible for the average American student who is qualified for admission to one of the many fine universities abroad to carry out his studies on his own budget without recourse to a scholarship or subsidy.

The cost of tuition and lodging in many foreign universities, including the round trip air transportation, is often less than the cost of a year in an American university. But the great value to the student, and the nation, is the new perspective gained of other countries. Moreover, the valuable personal, lifetime friendships achieved with foreign students, as well as fluency in a modern language, are increasingly important to any educated person in today's shrinking world.

Parents of students planning to study abroad can rest assured that their sons or daughters are never more than a day's journey from home, even though they may be enrolled in the most distant foreign universities listed in this book.

JUAN T. TRIPPE, *Chairman of the Board, Pan American Airways*

The Benefits of Study Abroad

by SENATOR J. W. FULBRIGHT, *Chairman, Committee on Foreign Relations, United States Senate, Author of the Fulbright International Scholarship Program* •

FROM THE BEGINNINGS OF universities, centers of learning have attracted scholars from beyond national boundaries.

The interdependence of all the world's peoples in the jet age is now greater, more complex, and more manifest than ever before and gives redoubled emphasis to the promise inherent in "cross-fertilization" of cultures, and multiplies opportunities for the advancement of human welfare in every corner of the earth. Unfounded prejudices can be softened and destroyed, fundamental education advanced, conditions of health and labor improved, material resources developed.

All these possibilities flow from exchange of students, teachers, and technicians between countries of differing cultures and diverse stages of economic and scientific development.

But the exchange of students in the jet age today need not be restricted to scholars in the higher reaches of advance study and research. The opportunity and practicability for the average American college boy or girl to enrich his college courses by taking a year or more in a foreign university is now available . . . but practically unknown to those who would be most interested . . . the students themselves and their parents.

Young students or industrial apprentices can be greatly enlightened by experience away from the homeland, even though their individual motives may be scarcely more than a dilettante wish to "see the world" or a vague feeling that "travel is broadening." These attitudes, characteristic of youth, may be trite, but they hold vast possibilities for good. In the past they have been suppressed and frustrated for millions of young people on account of economic and political barriers; but freedom of movement comes to be recognized as the fundamental right of man, and it will have an ever-increasing place in the practical world, as the speed and increasingly low fares of jet transportation have placed long distance travel to foreign universities within the budget of college students.

Americans Need More Fluency in Foreign Languages*

by DR. JAMES B. CONANT, *former President, Harvard University, U.S. High Commissioner of Germany, Ambassador to Germany* •

IT IS HARDLY NECESSARY TO ARGUE the importance of a foreign language in a world which has been so constricted by the invention of the airplane. Since, however, I have met some resistance among school people to my recommendation that all the academically talented youth should study four years of one foreign language, it may be well to remind the reader of the arguments in favor of this recommendation.

In the first place, unless a person has acquired something approaching mastery of one foreign language, he has missed an educational experience of the first importance. Such people never know what it means to *know* another language. They either think that acquiring mastery is an impossible hurdle to surmount, or else they believe that the ability to understand and speak a few words, perhaps enough to order a meal in a hotel, is a working knowledge. In short, a door is closed to them forever.

The second argument is the one usually put forward by foreign language teachers; that a real knowledge of a foreign language makes available a new approach to human problems. By reading the literature of another culture, one understands not only something of the culture, but realizes that ideas which English-speaking people accept as a matter of course may never have been formulated in a comparable way in another language and vice versa. It is particularly important for applied scientists to realize that, while mathematics is an international language, there are many words which are almost untranslatable from one language to another because the concepts they convey are somewhat alien.

The third and fourth arguments are practical ones and not unrelated to the highly constricted and deeply divided world in which we live. It is agreed by foreign language teachers that a person who has mastered one foreign language is in a position to learn a second with far greater ease than would otherwise be the case. This fact is true even if the second language is unrelated to the first. Therefore, a student who enters college with a considerable degree of mastery of one foreign language is able to pick up a second much more rapidly than he could otherwise. For example, one finds people in United States missions overseas who have the greatest difficulty learning the language of the country because they have never learned any foreign language.

Finally, it seems quite clear that a small fraction of our youth have those special talents which are needed for making rapid progress in the study of a foreign language. Unless such youth have an opportunity to find out that they are indeed highly gifted in this respect, their talents will never be developed. One hardly need argue that such boys and girls will find fruitful and rewarding careers in the modern world. That the nation badly needs young people who can quickly master a foreign language for missions overseas, both official and private, is evident to all who read the daily news. The grim competition with the Soviet Union in newly developing countries turns quite as much on an adequate supply of competent linguists as on our ability to send competent engineers and business men to these nations.

* Quoted with permission of the author from *The American High School Today* (McGraw-Hill; New York, 1959), pp. 70–72.

Foreign Travel and Foreign Education

by THOMAS C. MENDENHALL, *President of Smith College, formerly Director of Foreign Area Studies, Yale University ·

FOREIGN TRAVEL AND FOREIGN EDUCATION in themselves are both profitable and praiseworthy. Though obviously related, there is an unhappy tendency to confuse the two, to argue that foreign travel, because it is educational in its own way, is identical with formal education either at home or abroad, or that education in a European university conveniently parallels American higher education in arrangement or purpose.

The possible role of travel in the education of the individual can be quickly defined in Mark Twain's inimitable words: "Travel is fatal to prejudice, bigotry and narrowmindedness, all foes to real understanding. Likewise, tolerance or broad wholesome charitable views of men and things cannot be acquired by vegetating in one little corner of the earth all one's lifetime." These and many other admirable qualities, which should all be present in anyone with a pretension to a liberal education, more than justify foreign travel, but it is wrong to consider them in and of themselves as the equivalent of formal education, no matter how much of a bonus they may represent for the student who travels abroad. Let us assume these benefits as given and turn to some of the problems the individual will face as a student in a foreign land.

This last year thousands of American youth who had finished high school were continuing their formal studies abroad. If their work was to count as the equivalent of the same amount of academic work at home, what were some of the difficulties which had to be resolved? The first problem is that of language facility. Unless the prospective foreign student is considering a university where the instruction is in English, to seek an education abroad without an adequate foundation in the language of the country is most inadvisable. By adequate would be meant sufficient competence so that the student can handle academic work in his field at his level of preparation. An intensive refresher program before the beginning of formal classes may prove desirable, but when the latter begin, the student should be able to cope with lectures and reading, especially if he is to be abroad only for a year. Surely any student who is significantly lacking such a level of language ability might better rest content with the role of a traveler rather than that of a student abroad.

A second difficulty which must be resolved in arranging a substantial year of foreign study concerns the inevitable differences which prevail between the American system of education and that of a particular country where the student wishes to study. The American system is in every way unique; its pattern and purpose, its parts and its whole are so different that transfer into that of a foreign country at any point from kindergarten through college will call for understanding and flexibility. Such problems as how the year fits into his plans and needs, the educational system of the foreign country, the background and training of his fellow students abroad, the point in each educational system whereat the year abroad can best be taken easily and successfully in his particular case—these are just a few of the factors in this equation. If the student has not anticipated and weighed them in advance, the likelihood of his having a happy, let alone a profitable year, is seriously imperiled.

Finally, much of the value of the educational experience abroad will depend on the maturity of the individual, on his readiness physically, intellectually, and emotionally to derive maximum profit from the experience. This is perhaps the hardest factor to judge, for individuals mature at such different rates. Yet its importance cannot be overemphasized, for without it the individual may in fact do himself more harm than good by choosing to study abroad at a particular moment in his life.

The above comments may sound too discouraging. Though the writer through personal experience and conviction is profoundly persuaded of the lasting value of foreign study properly planned and seriously pursued, he is equally sure that an ill-conceived venture in education abroad can prove well nigh disastrous. The unhappy effects may involve far more than the individual student. Never before in our history has the reputation of the United States abroad been so important and so controversial. And just as ill-prepared, immature students from the United States who journey abroad to study will do neither themselves or their country any good, so the mature student, well prepared in language and training for the level of work he is seeking, aware of the necessity both to defend his country and its actions as well as to preserve a balanced yet critical perspective on it from afar, such a student at this moment can be one of the nation's most effective envoys to the world.

Note: Smith College was one of the pioneers of the Year Abroad program.

Institute of International Education

The Institute of International Education, founded in 1919, is a private non-profit agency that initiates and administers exchange of persons and programs between the United States and more than a hundred countries of the world. Approximately six thousand students, teachers, technicians and specialists train or study in a country other than their own each year through its programs. The Institute is financially supported by contracts with governmental and private organizations for which it administers exchange programs and by contributions from foundations, corporations, colleges and universities, and individuals.

Through its publications and information services, I. I. E. acts as a central clearinghouse of information in the field of international education. Each year the Institute answers more than a hundred thousand inquiries. Publications on various phases of international educational exchange are issued by the Institute. A free descriptive folder describing the work of the Institute and its regional offices is entitled *What Is I. I. E.?* The basic facts and statistics on educational exchanges, including data obtained in a yearly census of foreign students and scholars in the United States and U.S. students and scholars overseas, are published annually in the publication *Open Doors,* which sells for two dollars.

In addition to its New York world headquarters, the Institute maintains regional offices in Chicago, Denver, Houston, San Francisco, Washington, D.C., and overseas offices in Nairobi, Kenya; Lima, Peru; and Bangkok, Thailand.

The Counseling Division of the I. I. E. answers questions on all phases of international education through correspondence and personal interviews. A library of foreign university catalogues and other pertinent literature is available for reference. Descriptions of the university systems and enrollment procedures of many countries, an annual listing of summer courses offered abroad, a list of organizations that arrange teaching and employment opportunities abroad are among the materials available for distribution to those planning a period abroad. Miss Lily von Klemperer is the Head of the Counseling Division.

In addition to the above activities of the I. I. E., the Institute administers the following summer programs:

UNITED KINGDOM

University of Birmingham, Stratford-upon-Avon—Shakespeare and Elizabethan Drama—80 students
University of London—Victorian Literature—125 students
University of Oxford, Exeter College—England, 1870 to the Present Day—120 students
Scottish University: Edinburgh—British History, Philosophy and Literature, 1688–1832—110 students

AUSTRIA

Salzburg Summer School, Salzburg and Klessheim—Introductory and Advanced German Language, History of Austrian Art, European Music, and Foreign Policy—100 students
University of Vienna, Strobl—Law and Political Science, Liberal Arts, German Language—85 students.

For further information, write to The Counseling Division, Institute of International Education, 809 United Nations Plaza, New York, N. Y. 10017.

See Summer Sessions, page 179.

How To Choose a Foreign University

by KENNETH HOLLAND, *President, Institute of International Education* •

THERE ARE MANY COMPLEX FACTORS that a college-bound student has to consider when he selects an institution of higher learning. A successful choice depends on the student's preparation, his educational potential, his academic and professional plans, and his financial resources. In choosing a foreign university all these factors and many more must be considered. This chapter contains information of help to those preparing for a period of foreign study.

The U.S. student must realize that he is a product of a unique educational system, which differs in philosophy, content and techniques from that of every country of the world. His foreign study plans, therefore, should not be based on home-grown concepts, since measuring foreign educational facilities with an American yardstick would lead only to misunderstanding and disappointment.

Meaningful study abroad demands thorough fact-finding and careful planning and preparation. The student should in the first place discuss matters with his faculty adviser. He should consult reference works, both national and international, which explain other educational systems. There are many books describing foreign centers of learning and containing information on entrance requirements, course and degree prerequisites and related matters. A list of reference works may be found on page 22. There are also various organizations here and abroad, such as the Institute of International Education at 809 United Nations Plaza, New York, N. Y. 10017, that have been set up to deal with all types of inquiries related to foreign study. Foreign students and professors on U.S. campuses and American students and professors who have had foreign study and teaching experiences are usually excellent and willing sources of information.

Advance planning should also include a close look at the financial requirements. Students must be able to pay for international travel. Living expenses vary with each country and city. Housing is limited in most major foreign cities. Tuition fees are low compared to American standards. However, the practice of working one's way through college is not known abroad and is legally impossible for most Americans. There are scarcely any scholarships for undergraduate study abroad and a limited number for graduate study. Scholarship competitions usually close a year before the award becomes tenable.

Once the student has acquired the necessary background information and has acquainted himself with a given foreign educational system, his next task is to relate the information to his own situation to see whether or not he fits into the foreign system. Is he adequately prepared to go abroad at that particular point? Would it be more advisable to postpone his foreign study until a later date? This is the time for him to discuss his plans with his faculty adviser. If he is an undergraduate, will his home institution consider granting credit for study abroad? If he is a graduate student, will his foreign study count toward a graduate degree? Will foreign professional study be acceptable for professional certification in the United States? Would it perhaps be advisable to spend the summer abroad rather than the full academic year? A listing of summer school opportunities may be found on page 179.

The student's choice of country will frequently be decided by his foreign language competence. With few exceptions, the language of the country is the language of instruction. That the student be proficient in the language of the country concerned cannot be stressed enough. Students who have not heeded this recommendation have found their educational experience abroad unrewarding. Opportunities for foreign language study (with no academic prerequisites) are offered by most European universities. A list may be found on page 25.

As far as institution affiliation is concerned, this choice depends on where the student's particular field is taught. The student should know that foreign universities, as such, offer courses in the traditional disciplines, i.e., philosophy, law, science and medicine, rather than work in applied fields. The latter are generally taught at special university-ranking institutions. Thus, musicology and history of art figure in university curricula, whereas music and art are taught at conservatories and art academies respectively. The student interested in attending a particular institution must make sure that courses in his specialty are available.

Since admission procedures vary from country to country and university to university, it is advisable to write to the university concerned for their instructions regarding application procedure and documents to be submitted with the application. The student should use American terminology in describing his educational background, since free translations often lead to misinterpretation. For example, if he tells the French authorities that he holds a *baccalauréat,* in France this means a secondary school-leaving credential. The French, however, are fully familiar with the term "Bachelor's degree." On the other hand, the American student who hopes to obtain a Master's degree from a British university should not feel insulted or offended if it is suggested that he undertake a program leading to a B.A. Honors degree. This degree requires a minimum of two years of solid work for the well-prepared American B.A.

Even after arrival in the foreign country the American student must be prepared to cope with problems. Selecting appropriate courses and enrolling officially in a foreign university will prove an experience in itself. Since there are almost no dormitories abroad, he will need to find housing and eating facilities. The student will discover that he is truly "on his own" and will have to make decisions without the aid of a faculty adviser, for whom no foreign counterpart exists.

The foreign university structure places greater demands on the student's initiative and affords him no direct guidance. This is one of the reasons why U.S. undergraduates are often encouraged to join one of the "junior year" study programs under the auspices of an American college or university. The student who joins such a group receives the benefits of academic supervision and, even more important, can usually arrange to receive credit from his home institution. Since the credit system does not operate at foreign universities, undergraduates who study abroad independently have frequently encountered difficulty in having their foreign study translated into American credit terms. Any credit an American student will receive for his foreign study must be determined by the U.S. university to which he returns. Before joining any group program, the student and his academic adviser should make sure that the offering is educationally sound. A list of U.S. college-sponsored undergraduate programs abroad may be found on page 26.

The well-prepared and well-informed student, once settled in his work, will find foreign study a fruitful experience. Study abroad is becoming an integral feature of American higher education. All over the world study in a country other than one's own is increasingly becoming the order of the day. In addition to providing for their own ever-growing student populations, developed countries are also playing an important role in educating students from less-developed areas of the world. Most universities are overcrowded; their facilities are highly taxed. It is, therefore, all the more important that those students who do go abroad take full advantage of the opportunity. There is no room in this day and age to accommodate the "student-tourist." Well-prepared, mature Americans who go abroad for serious study, for interchange of ideas and skills, will return home not only enriched by their experience but also with the satisfaction of having made a contribution to the field of international understanding and education.

Some Major Reference Works on Higher Education Abroad

Many of the following publications are available in university and reference libraries. Prices, however, have been indicated whenever the information was available.

INTERNATIONAL

Handbook on International Study: for U.S. Nationals. Institute of International Education, New York, 1964. $3.50.

Commonwealth Universities Yearbook. Association of Commonwealth Universities, London. Annual. Distributed in the U. S. by the American Council on Education, Washington, D. C. $13.00.

International Handbook of Universities. International Association of Universities, Paris, 1962. (Third edition appeared in 1965.) Distributed in the U. S. by the American Council on Education, Washington, D. C. $6.00. (This is a companion volume to the *Commonwealth Universities Yearbook* and therefore does not include Commonwealth countries.)

The World of Learning. Europa Publications Ltd., London. Annual. $23.50.

REGIONAL AND COUNTRY GUIDES

AUSTRALIA ... *A Brief Guide to Australian Universities,* 4th Edition. Australian Council for Educational Research, Victoria, 1964.

AUSTRIA ... *Austria: A Survey of Austrian Education and Guide to the Academic Placement of Students from Austria in Educational Institutions in the U.S.A.* AACRAO, 1961. Distributed by the American Council on Education, Washington, D. C. $1.00

CANADA ... *Canadian Universities and Colleges, 1962.* Canadian Universities Foundation, Ottawa.

University Study in Canada. Canadian Universities Foundation, Ottawa, 1962. Distributed in the U. S. by Canadian embassies and consulates. Free.

DENMARK ... *Education* (reprint from *Denmark*). Press Department, Ministry of Foreign Affairs, Copenhagen, 1961. Distributed in the U. S. by the Danish Information Office, New York. Free.

FRANCE ... *Education in France* by George A. Male. U. S. Office of Education, 1963. 75¢. Available from U.S. Government Printing Office, Washington, D. C.

Guide de l'Enseignement Supérieur Universitaire Français. Office National des Universités et Écoles Françaises, Paris, 1963.

GERMANY ... *Deutscher Hochschulführer.* Verlag Hochschuldienst, Bonn. Annual.

The Foreign Student in Germany. Deutscher Akademischer Austauschdienst, Bonn, 1961.

Vademecum Deutscher Lehr—und Forschungsstatten. Stifterverband für die Deutsche Wissenschaft, Essen, 1964.

INDIA ... *Handbook of Indian Universities.* U.S. Educational Foundation in India, New Delhi. $5.00.

ITALY ... *Guide for Foreign Students to Universities and Art Schools in Italy.* Ministry of Public Instruction, Rome, 1960. 80¢.

JAPAN ... *Guide to Study in Japan.* Japanese National Commission for UNESCO, Tokyo, 1962. $1.00.

LATIN AMERICA ... *Instituciones Latinoamericanas de Enseñanza Superior.* Pan American Union, Washington, D. C., 1960. 25¢.

MEXICO ... *A Guide to the Academic Placement of Students from Mexico in Educational Institutions in the U.S.A.* AACRAO, 1961. Distribution by the American Council on Education, Washington, D. C. $1.00.

Study in Latin America: Part I, 1960 Regular Academic Year. Pan American Union, Washington, D. C. 25¢.

Study in Latin America: Summer. Pan American Union, Washington, D. C. 1962. 25¢.

MIDDLE EAST ... *Institutions of Higher Learning in the Middle East.* Middle East Institute, Washington, D. C., 1961. $1.00.

NETHERLANDS ... *The Netherlands: A Guide to the Academic Placement of Students from the Netherlands in Educational Institutions in the U.S.A.* AACRAO, 1961. Distributed by the American Council on Education, Washington, D. C. $1.00.

Study in Holland—A Guide for Prospective Students. Netherlands Information Service, New York, 1961. Free.

SPAIN ... *Estudios en España,* 6th Edition. Instituto de Cultura Hispanica, Madrid, 1964.

SWEDEN ... *Studying in Sweden. Hints and Suggestions for Foreign Students.* The Swedish Institute and the Swedish National Union of Students, Stockholm, 1961. Distributed in the U. S. by the American-Scandinavian Foundation, New York. Free.

Travel, Study and Research in Sweden. Sverige-Amerika Stiftelsen, Stockholm, 1962. Distributed in the U. S. by the American-Scandinavian Foundation, New York. $2.00.

SWITZERLAND ... *Schweizerischer Hochschulkalender.* Verlag Leemann, Zurich. Annual. 95¢.

UNITED KINGDOM ... *Higher Education in the United Kingdom: A Handbook for Students from Overseas and Their Advisers.* Longmans Green for the British Council and Association of Universities of the British Commonwealth, 1964. Distributed in the U. S. by the British Information Services, New York. $1.50.

The Counseling Division of the Institute of International Education has prepared individual booklets on university study in Africa, Australia, Austria, Belgium, Denmark, Finland, Germany, Greece, India, Italy, Ireland, Israel, Japan, Latin America, the Middle East, Netherlands, New Zealand, Spain and Sweden, which are available free upon request. Other free pamphlets are *Some Notes for the Guidance of Overseas Students Who Wish to Study at British Universities,* available from the British Information Services, New York; *Advanced Study in France* and *Summer and Undergraduate Courses for Foreign Students,* available from the French Cultural Services, New York; and *Study in Switzerland,* available from the Swiss Consulate, New York.

The U.S. Office of Education, Department of Health, Education and Welfare, Washington, D. C., has prepared an extensive series of pamphlets on aspects of higher educational systems throughout the world, which can be obtained from their Publications Distribution Unit.

Summer Study Abroad

During the summer months educational institutions abroad suspend their regular academic programs and offer instead special courses of interest to foreign students.* In most cases the courses, which are general in nature, provide an opportunity for studying the language and culture of the country concerned. The language courses are divided into beginning, intermediate and advanced sections. Some institutions offer special courses for teachers of foreign languages or programs concentrating on a particular field of study such as music, art, law, political science and sociology. Although a few programs are conducted in English, instruction is generally in the language of the country concerned. Programs usually include visits to nearby sites of interest.

Some schools provide special living accommodations for students at the summer session. Most do not; students attending these institutions must make their own arrangements. The schools will, however, assist students in finding a suitable place to live and frequently supply a list of suggested residences.

The cost of a summer program varies greatly, depending upon the country, length of stay, the school, and whether or not room and board are included. There are almost no scholarships for summer study, but tuition costs are considerably lower than in the United States.

The summer-study-abroad programs are not set up according to the American college credit system. However, by special arrangement, American colleges and universities may grant credit for attendance at one of these summer schools. It is important for those who wish to receive credit to make prior arrangements with their own educational institutions.

A booklet listing summer study opportunities, called *Summer Study Abroad,* is available from the Institute of International Education, 809 United Nations Plaza, New York, N. Y.

* Note: See page 179 for a list of the universities in this book that offer summer sessions.

10017, and may be obtained upon request. Other sources of information regarding summer opportunities abroad are:

Invest Your Summer. Information on international service projects, including work camps. Available through the Commission on Youth Service Projects, National Student Christian Federation, 475 Riverside Drive, New York, N. Y. 10027. 25¢.

Scholastic Teacher (March 20, 1964, issue). Contains a listing of courses abroad and study tours. Available from the Scholastic Teacher, 50 West 44th Street, New York, N. Y. 10036. 10¢.

Students Abroad. Information on international programs sponsored by members of the Council on Student Travel. Available from the Council on Student Travel, 777 United Nations Plaza, New York, N. Y. 10017. Free.

Summer Study in Latin America. Information on opportunities for study-work projects and vacation tours in Latin America. Published by the Pan American Union, Washington, D. C. 20006. 20¢.

Vacations Abroad. Information on short study tours arranged by national groups and youth-center activities. Published by UNESCO and available through the UNESCO Publications Center, 317 East 34th Street, New York, N. Y. 10016. $1.75.

Work, Study, Travel Abroad. Information on courses arranged by U. S. educational and travel groups, which may or may not include a period of study. Published by the U.S. National Student Association, 265 Madison Avenue, New York, N. Y. 10016. $1.

Undergraduate Study Abroad. Report of the Consultative Service on U. S. Undergraduate Study Abroad. Information on U. S. college-sponsored summer programs abroad. Published by the Institute of International Education, 809 United Nations Plaza, New York, N. Y. 10017. $2.50.

Some Opportunities for Foreign Language Study in Europe

Many universities in Europe offer special courses for foreigners during the academic year (or some part of it) in the language and culture of their respective countries. Generally, there is no academic prerequisite for these courses and in most cases application in advance is not required. Details regarding dates, hours during which instruction is given, etc., should be obtained *direct* from the school or institution concerned. Listed below are some opportunities for studying French, German, Italian and Spanish.

FRANCE

The Universities of Aix-Marseille, Besançon, Bordeaux, Caen, Clermont-Ferrand, Dijon, Grenoble, Lille, Lyons, Montpellier, Nancy, Nice, Rennes, Strasbourg, Toulouse and Tours. In *Paris,* French may be studied at Cours de Civilisation à la Sorbonne, École des Professeurs de Français à L'Étranger, Institut Catholique de Paris, Institut de Phonetique, and the École Partique de L'Alliance Française.

A brochure describing these courses may be obtained from the French Cultural Services, 972 Fifth Avenue, New York, N. Y. 10021. Inquiries that are sent direct to the universities should be marked for the attention of the Cours pour Étudiants Étrangers.

GERMANY

The Universities of Berlin, Bonn, Cologne, Frankfurt, Freiburg, Giessen, Heidelberg (Dolmetscher Institut), Mainz, Marburg, Munich, Münster, Tübingen, Würzburg; the Institutes of Technology of Aachen, Darmstadt, and Stuttgart.

Inquiries regarding these courses should be sent to the Deutsche Sprachkurse für Ausländer at the respective institutions.

The Goethe Institute, Lenbachplatz 3/1, Munich, offers 8-week introductory and advanced German courses for foreigners. The courses are conducted at schools of the Goethe Institute in various towns throughout Germany. Applications for this program should be submitted at least four months in advance.

ITALY

The Italian University for Foreigners (Università Italiana per Stranieri), Perugia; Centro di Cultura per Stranieri, Florence; and the Società Dante Alighieri, Rome.

SPAIN

Spanish universities and educational institutions offer Spanish language and literature courses at all levels for various periods of time and at various locations during the academic year. A complete listing of Spanish language study opportunities is contained in the publication *Learn Spanish in Spain,* which may be obtained from The Office of Cultural Relations, Spanish Embassy, 1477 Girard Street, N.W., Washington, D. C. 20009.

In addition to the language courses mentioned above, a special one-year program in Spanish language and culture has been established at the Universities of Barcelona, Granada, Madrid and Saragossa. A Diploma in Hispanic Studies is awarded for the successful completion of this program. Details regarding the Diploma in Hispanic Studies may also be obtained from the Spanish Embassy (see above address).

SWITZERLAND

Courses in French language and literature are offered at the Schools of Modern French at the Universities of Fribourg, Geneva, Lausanne, and Neuchâtel. There are no German language courses for foreign students at the German-speaking universities.

U.S. Colleges with Programs for Undergraduate Study Abroad

The various programs of foreign study sponsored by U.S. colleges and universities offer an undergraduate the opportunity of a period of study abroad for which he is reasonably assured of receiving credit toward his degree. Programs vary in length from a quarter or a semester to a full academic year; there are also many during the summer months. Some programs include courses at a foreign university, others have courses that are specially arranged.

Much information on foreign study opportunities is given in a report published in May 1964 by the Consultative Service on U.S. Undergraduate Study Abroad, of the Institute of International Education.* According to this report, there were 103 college-sponsored programs in the academic year 1963–64. Approximately twenty-four new programs were added during that period. Descriptive information about these programs is included in the report.

Although many colleges limit enrollment in their foreign study programs to their own students, the following colleges admit students from other institutions as well. Further information may be obtained by writing directly to them. Unless otherwise indicated, the programs are for a full academic year, co-ed, and primarily emphasize languages and humanities studies.

ACADEMIC YEAR PROGRAMS SPONSORED BY U.S. COLLEGES FOR THEIR OWN AND OTHER STUDENTS

EUROPE

AUSTRIA

University of Notre Dame, Notre Dame, Indiana (Vienna)
Wagner College, Staten Island, New York (Bregenz)

DENMARK

Washburn University, Topeka, Kansas (Copenhagen, spring semester)
Whittier College, Whittier, California (Copenhagen, fall semester)

* The Consultative Service's report *Undergraduate Study Abroad: U.S. College-Sponsored Programs* is available from the Institute of International Education at $2.50.

FRANCE

Hamilton College, Clinton, New York (Paris)
La Sierra College, Riverside, California (Collonges-sous-Saleve)
University of Michigan, Ann Arbor, Michigan, and University of Wisconsin, Madison, Wisconsin (joint program at Aix-en-Provence)
University of North Carolina, Chapel Hill, North Carolina (Lyons—open to students in southeastern U. S.)
Sarah Lawrence College, Bronxville, New York (Paris, women only)
Smith College, Northampton, Massachusetts (Paris, women only)
Sweet Briar College, Sweet Briar, Virginia (Paris)
Syracuse University, Syracuse, New York (Poitiers, fall semester)
Vanderbilt University, Nashville, Tennessee (Aix-en-Provence, fall or spring semester)
West Chester State College, West Chester, Pennsylvania (Besançon)

GERMANY

Brethren Colleges, Joint Program Administrative Co-ordinator at Manchester College, N. Manchester, Indiana (Marburg—limited outside enrollment)
DePauw University, Greencastle, Indiana (Freiburg, spring semester)
Heidelberg College, Tiffin, Ohio (Heidelberg)
Millersville State College, Millersville, Pennsylvania (Marburg)
University of Oregon, Eugene, Oregon (Oldenburg—music)
Pepperdine College, Los Angeles, California (Heidelberg)
Smith College, Northampton, Massachusetts (Hamburg)
Wayne State University, Detroit, Michigan (Freiburg and Munich)

GREAT BRITAIN

University of Michigan, Ann Arbor, Michigan (Sheffield—teacher education)

ITALY

Gonzaga University, Spokane, Washington (Florence)
Loyola University, Chicago, Illinois (Rome)
Portland State College, Portland, Oregon (Pavia—Oregon State System of Higher Education Program)
Rhode Island School of Design, Providence, Rhode Island (Rome—art)
Sarah Lawrence College, Bronxville, New York (Rome, women only)

Smith College, Northampton, Massachusetts (Florence)

Syracuse University, Syracuse, New York (Florence, one semester)

Tufts University, Medford, Massachusetts (Naples)

SPAIN

Georgetown University, Washington, D. C. (Madrid)

Indiana State College, Indiana, Pennsylvania (Valladolid, June to December)

Mary Baldwin College, Staunton, Virginia (Madrid)

Smith College, Northampton, Massachusetts (Madrid)

SWITZERLAND

Georgetown University, Washington, D. C. (Fribourg, men only)

La Salle College, Philadelphia, Pennsylvania (Fribourg, men only)

Rosary College, River Forest, Illinois (Fribourg, women only)

Sarah Lawrence College, Bronxville, New York (Geneva, women only)

Smith College, Northampton, Massachusetts (Geneva, women only)

AFRICA

TUNISIA

University of Southern California, Los Angeles, California (Tunis)

ASIA

REPUBLIC OF CHINA

Stanford University, Stanford, California, and several other participating universities (Taipei)

INDIA

University of Wisconsin, Madison, Wisconsin (several cities)

JAPAN

Stanford University, Stanford, California, and several other participating universities (Tokyo)

LATIN AMERICA

BRAZIL

New York University, New York, N. Y. (São Paulo, February to December)

CHILE

Fordham University, Bronx, New York (Santiago, men only, May to December)

COLOMBIA

Rollins College, Winter Park, Florida (Bogotá, spring semester)

COSTA RICA

University of Kansas, Lawrence, Kansas (San José, February to November)

GUATEMALA

Syracuse University, Syracuse, New York (Guatemala City, spring semester)

MEXICO

Antioch College, Yellow Springs, Ohio (Guanajuato, one quarter)

College of St. Thomas, St. Paul, Minnesota (Cuernavaca, spring semester)

University of Nebraska, Lincoln, Nebraska (Mexico City)

Washington University, St. Louis, Missouri (Guadalajara)

PERU

Indiana University, Bloomington, Indiana (Lima, February to December)

Great Lakes Colleges Association Administrator of program is at Antioch College, Yellow Springs, Ohio (Guadalajara, Mexico, and Bogotá, Colombia)

THE MIDDLE EAST

ISRAEL

Brandeis University, Waltham, Massachusetts (Jerusalem, July to December)

LEBANON

Princeton University, Princeton, New Jersey (Shimlan, summer and following academic year)

University Education in Latin America

The universities of Latin America are a complete contrast to the universities in the United States. Invariably the Latin American university is located in the heart of a metropolis with its various faculties scattered throughout the city. There is generally no campus, no dormitory or eating hall. Sports are absent or de-emphasized and university clubs or organizations are uncommon. Students are more interested in public affairs and national politics than in developing social activities within the university. Their strong interest in politics does, however, manifest itself in the form of strikes and riots within the university when they champion a particular cause.

The full-time professor or administrator is the exception in Latin American universities. Since salaries are quite low, university teaching is provided largely by practicing professional and business men. They come to the university for about two or three hours a week to give formal lectures. Because of this system, professors have little time to conduct seminars and laboratory work or give individual counsel to their students. Since this is the present situation, a student must be prepared to study independently.

Although the Latin American universities are, with a few exceptions, government financed, they are autonomous in the sense that their internal administration is not subject to government interference. They are usually composed of nine basic faculties: Philosophy and Letters, Commerce and Economic Sciences, Law and Political Science, Physical and Natural Sciences, Agronomy and Veterinary Science, Medicine, Engineering, Pharmacy, and Education. The liberal arts college as we know it in the United States generally does not exist in Latin America. Therefore when a student enters a university, he enrolls in a specific faculty and starts immediately on a program of pre-scribed and specialized subjects. Should he wish to further his studies on an advanced level, he continues with a series of electives within the framework of the faculty in which he is enrolled. There are no special schools for graduate study such as exist in the United States.

The United States student who wishes to enter a Latin American university on an undergraduate level is admitted on the same basis as the nationals of the country concerned, and becomes subject to the same regulations and examinations. The student who has completed several years of college in the U. S. may find that he will lose credits in transferring to a Latin American university. Therefore it is advisable for the student to become a member of an accredited college or university group

program with the advance approval of his own institution in the U. S. before attempting a period of study in Latin America. However, if an American student does not intend to study for a degree, he may be admitted as a special student and attend courses for credit to be transferred to a school in the United States. Arrangements should then be made in advance with the U.S. institution.

The academic year usually runs anywhere from February and April to November and December, since the seasons are reversed in Latin America. During our summer, many universities and institutes in Latin America offer courses in language, literature, culture and other selected topics of interest to foreign students. As in the case of university study during the academic year, it is suggested that the student arrange in advance with his college or university here for recognition of courses taken at one of the Latin American summer schools.

At this time, the following U.S. university group programs are designed for students in their junior year with a knowledge of the host country's language. (Students from other colleges and universities can participate.)

New York University, New York, N.Y. (São Paulo, Brazil); *Fordham University,* New York, N.Y. (Santiago, Chile, men only); *Rollins College,* Winter Park, Florida (Bogotá, Colombia, one semester only); *College of Liberal Arts and Sciences, University of Kansas,* Lawrence, Kansas (San José, Costa Rica); *Syracuse University,* Syracuse, New York (Guatemala City, Guatemala, one semester only); *Antioch College,* Yellow Springs, Ohio (Guanajuato, Mexico); *University of Nebraska,* Lincoln, Nebraska (Mexico City, Mexico); *College of St. Thomas,* St. Paul, Minnesota (Cuernavaca, Mexico, one semester only, no language requirement).; *Washington University,* St. Louis, Missouri (Guadalajara, Mexico); *Indiana University,* Bloomington, Indiana (Lima, Peru).

FOR FURTHER INFORMATION

In order to assure the quickest and most accurate replies to your questions, always supply the following information:
—Your year in college (minimum requirement is two years)
—Language ability
—Field of study
—Countries of interest
—Age at time of overseas study (minimum requirement is 18).

PART I

*A Guide to Colleges and
Universities in Africa, Europe,
The Middle East, The Far East,
and Latin America*

ALASKA

FAIRBANKS •

ALASKA

ANCHORAGE •

Note: Even though this book is concerned primarily with foreign universities, we have included schools in Alaska, Hawaii and Puerto Rico since they are "abroad" in the sense of being outside the continental United States. In these schools, entry requirements, transfers of credits, curriculums and methods of study are similar to those of all U.S. universities.

HOW TO GET THERE ... By Pan American Jet Clipper, nonstop service from Seattle to Fairbanks, 3 hours flying time; or nonstop jet service from Seattle to Anchorage, 3 hours flying time. Cruise ships operate during the summer. The Alaska Highway, now partially paved, is reached through Alberta, Canada, or the Hart Highway through British Columbia.

ALASKA METHODIST UNIVERSITY, ANCHORAGE

The campus of Alaska Methodist University is located just a few minutes from downtown Anchorage in the rolling foothills of the Chugach Mountains. Grant Hall, the academic center of the growing campus, is designed to accommodate more than 400 students. This building houses classrooms, laboratories, a library of more than 30,000 select volumes, a student union area, bookstore, lounges, auditorium and administrative offices. A student union building and additional residence halls are under construction for completion in 1965–66.

Alaska Methodist University was established as a liberal arts college. It is a private college founded by church leaders to foster higher education under Christian auspices. After years of planning and study of educational needs in the Alaska Territory, the University was chartered on February 4, 1957. On June 27, 1958, the day prior to the achievement of statehood by Alaska, the campus was dedicated. Construction of the first buildings was begun in 1959. On September 30, 1960, the doors of the college opened for the first students.

Anchorage, Alaska, a growing, prosperous community of 100,000 in the Greater Anchorage area, is readily accessible—7½ hours nonstop to New York, 6 hours from Chicago, and only 3 hours from Seattle—to every point in the United States. There is regular nonstop service from the Orient and Europe.

SIZE ... The 1964 enrollment was 318 students, an increase of 23 per cent over 1962–63.

CALENDAR ... The academic year begins in September and ends in May. There are two semesters. The summer sessions offer courses in the liberal arts and in education for both graduate and undergraduate credit. The graduate work is offered on the A.M.U. campus in co-operation with the University of Puget Sound.

COURSES OF STUDY ... The University offers a 4-year liberal arts program with undergraduate studies in the humanities: English and comparative literature, speech, religion, philosophy, music, art, drama, French, German, Russian; the natural sciences: mathematics, physics, chemistry, biology, geology; and social sciences: history, political science, economics and business, sociology and anthropology, education, psychology, physical education. Teacher education and pre-professional training are offered within the liberal arts program.

TUITION ... Tuition for the academic year is $850; board and room run about $950. There are no other required fees at the University, but a student must budget funds for his books and personal expenses, e.g., private lessons, entertainment, clothes, travel, etc.

ADMISSION REQUIREMENTS ... Graduates of accred-

ited high schools or preparatory schools with a grade average of C or better are eligible to apply for admission.

ACCOMMODATIONS ... Gould Hall, the campus residence facility, houses 96 students. There are also four faculty apartments, guest rooms, lounges, recreation rooms and laundry facilities in this building. On the ridge overlooking Anchorage, with a view of the mountains, are nine homes accommodating thirteen faculty families. The master planner for the campus is the internationally famous architect Edward Durrell Stone.

STUDENT LIFE ... Students will find the cosmopolitan-international atmosphere of Anchorage filled with excitement the year round: Fur Rendezvous, Music Festival, exhibitions and theater. At the same time the advantages of a modern city are available, the vast natural beauty of outdoor, recreational Alaska is accessible by foot, horseback, dog team, car, boat, train or plane. Nearby skiing, boating, hunting and fishing opportunities are ideal.

HOW TO ENROLL ... For complete information on Alaska Methodist University, write to the Office of the Registrar, ALASKA METHODIST UNIVERSITY, Anchorage, Alaska.

UNIVERSITY OF ALASKA, FAIRBANKS

The University of Alaska is located in College, Alaska, about four miles northwest of Fairbanks, Alaska's second largest city, the hub of the gold mining industry and gateway to Alaska's arctic lands. A few miles from the city one can see huge gold dredges operating round the clock and giant hydraulic hoses seeking gold hidden under centuries of muck accumulations. Fish wheels flip salmon from the mighty Alaskan rivers and sled dogs can be seen on the trails and in kennels along the highways.

A week-long Winter Carnival in March offers the North American Sled Dog Racing Championships; the Golden Days celebration in July commemorates the discovery of gold in the Tanana Valley; the 700-mile Yukon River marathon covers the Memorial Day weekend activities, starting at the historical gold-rush city of Circle, Alaska, and ending in Fairbanks. On the longest day of the year, June 21st, a midnight baseball game is played in the eerie natural glow of the midnight sun. Northern lights—the aurora borealis—spray bands of color across the winter skies, providing the most spectacular school colors in the world for the northernmost university in the world, the University of Alaska.

Collegians on this campus in the subarctic often trade the usual term of freshman for the Alaskan word "cheechako" and, of course, an oldtimer is a "sourdough." The University of Alaska, a land-grant institution, dates from 1915, when Congress voted land for the Alaska Agricultural College and School of Mines. Classes began on September 18, 1922. In 1935 the Alaska Territorial Legislature changed the AACSM to the University of Alaska.

SIZE ... About 1,250 students attend classes on the main campus at College and approximately 2,700 more are registered in college-credit courses conducted in other University of Alaska facilities about the state. The on-campus student population is approximately 80 per cent Alaskan; 18 per cent are from other states and 2 per cent from other nations. The ratio of men to women is about two to one. A small percentage of the students are married.

CALENDAR ... The academic year runs from the second

week in September to the end of May. An examination period is scheduled for the final week of each semester following the end of classes. Summer sessions and special institutes are conducted from early June through early August; a post-session one-week college-credit Workshop on Alaska is given in August.

COURSES OF STUDY ... The University of Alaska is composed of six colleges, a Division of Statewide Services, five community colleges and several institutes for advanced research. The academic colleges are College of Arts and Letters; College of Biological Sciences and Renewable Resources; College of Business, Economics and Government; College of Earth Sciences and Mineral Industry; College of Mathematics, Physical Sciences and Engineering; College of Behavioral Sciences and Education. The Division of Statewide Services includes classes on military sites, evening classes, extension courses, Co-operative Extension Service (in agriculture and home economics), correspondence study, audio-visual communications, summer sessions, conferences and short courses. Community colleges, which offer the first two years of college-credit courses, are located at Anchorage, Juneau-Douglas, Ketchikan, Sitka and Palmer. Research units include the Agricultural Experiment Station at Palmer and farm at College; the Geophysical Institute; Institute of Marine Science; Institute of Arctic Biology; Arctic Research Laboratory and the Arctic Research Laboratory Ice Island in the Arctic Ocean; Institute of Business, Economics and Government; the MIRL satellite tracking station operated under contract with the National Space and Aeronautics Agency (NASA) and the Alaska Co-operative Wildlife Research Unit, co-sponsored and financed with the Alaska Department of Fish and Game, the U.S. Fish and Wildlife Service and the Wildlife Management Institute.

SUMMER COURSES ... Several summer programs are offered, including a 2-week workshop session in June and the regular session from the end of June to early August, which includes the summer institute for junior and senior high school teachers of science and mathematics. A post-session Workshop on Alaska is held the second week of August; a 9-week course in mining offers lectures, laboratory work and demonstrations in geology, mining and milling and mineralogy and is given on the main campus during the fall months. A Mining Extension Course covering the same subjects as the Mining Short Course adds an intensive 4-week study session in the villages and towns of Alaska. There is also an annual short course for homemakers in June and a Leadership Conference the first week of August.

TUITION ... Residents of Alaska do not pay tuition if carrying seven or more semester credit hours; non-residents taking seven or more semester credit hours pay tuition fees of $150 per semester. All students taking seven or more semester credit hours pay a consolidated fee of $75 to cover matriculation, registration, course fees, library deposit and incidentals. A student activity fee of $37 per year covers Associated Students organization fee, yearbook and health and accident insurance. Special fee schedules have been established for part-time students and special programs, including summer sessions, institutes, workshops and off-campus courses. These fee schedules will be furnished by the Office of the Registrar upon written request.

ADMISSION REQUIREMENTS ... Students must consult the current University of Alaska catalogues for full details of admission requirements. To enter as a freshman, certain secondary school requirements must be met including study of English, mathematics, history of the United States, one foreign language and certain sciences. College credits of students wishing to transfer will be evaluated by the director of admissions and the registrar. Certain grade point averages and examinations are required as specified in the catalogue. No special academic credentials are required for some summer sessions and non-college-credit courses. See the How to Enroll heading at the end of this section for where to write for this information.

LANGUAGE OF INSTRUCTION ... English.

ACCOMMODATIONS ... The University of Alaska maintains several residence halls on the main campus. All students under 21 who do not live at home must live in the residence halls except by special permission of the dean of students. A double room in a dormitory, including laundry privileges, runs about $160 per semester. A $25 refundable room deposit is also charged and must be paid in advance. Food service in the University of Alaska cafeteria is $95 per month and averages about $800 per year. Apartments are available on campus for a limited number of married students and rent for $120 per month plus electricity.

AVERAGE COSTS ... In addition to regular academic fees and room and board, students at the University of Alaska average about $300 per year for other expenses. For resident Alaskans taking seven or more credit hours, an average budget for the academic, two-semester school year is about $1,750; for the non-resident student, the average, academic year cost will be approximately $2,050 minimum.

STUDENT LIFE ... The Associated Students of the University of Alaska (ASUA) publishes the *Polar Star*, the weekly student newspaper; prepares and edits the *Denali*, the yearbook; supports and promotes intramural and intercollegiate athletics; provides a strong student legislative type of government; and organizes social, cultural and intellectual events and clubs. All students are welcome to participate in such extracurricular activities as band, community orchestra and chorus, drama workshop, and sports such as skiing, dog-sled team mushing, snowshoeing, riflery, basketball and drill teams. In Constitution Hall, the building where the 49th state's Constitution was drafted, student union activities are centered. Facilities include offices for the student government, the *Polar Star*, the *Denali*, the University Alumni Association and the student placement service; transmitting facilities for an FM educational broadcasting station, a drama lounge, a faculty lounge, snack bar, bookstore, cafeteria, barber shop, a game room and a television viewing room. The University of Alaska colors are blue and gold and the mascot is the polar bear, which is called *nanook* in Eskimo. The motto of the northernmost university in the world is "Ad Summum," to the heights.

HOW TO ENROLL ... For complete information on the University of Alaska, write to the Office of the Registrar, UNIVERSITY OF ALASKA, P.O. Box 1003, College, Alaska.

University of Alaska

ARGENTINA

UNIVERSITIES OF ARGENTINA ... Argentina has nine official universities. They are the University of Buenos Aires, University of Córdoba, University of La Plata, National University of the Litoral, University of the South, National University of Cuyo, National University of Tucumán, National University of the Northeast and National University of the South. In addition, there are also private and religious universities; the most important are the Catholic University of El Salvador and the Argentine Catholic University—Saint Mary of Buenos Aires.

ARGENTINE UNIVERSITY SYSTEM ... The universities in Argentina are supported by the national government but are completely independent both economically and politically. In other words, they establish their own rules, plan their budget, elect their own authorities and prepare their programs of study with no interference from the federal government.

The universities are organized in schools and faculties each having its own authorities, and generally the Director is the school representative at the University's Superior Council. The University Government is composed of:

  a) The University Assembly—comprises representatives from the student body, professors and directors
  b) The Superior Council
  c) The President or University Director.

ADMISSION REQUIREMENTS ... There are several steps to be followed when applying to a university in Argentina. A student must:

  a) Submit proof of a minimum of two years of college for validation by the Argentine Consul and the university.
  b) Complete a health certificate issued by the university or National Health Department.
  c) Take an entrance examination or a course (one year for medicine and engineering) depending on the school's policy and regulations. Some schools do not require the previous examination for admittance.

There is no limit to the number of students, either Argentine or aliens, that can be admitted to a university in Argentina. Alien students are required to have a visaed passport. The student's visa is valid for the entire duration of courses and for multiple entries.

REGULATIONS ... For student visa and entrance procedure, see the For Further Information heading at the end of this section.

CREDIT TOWARD AN AMERICAN DEGREE ... Graduation certificates issued by Argentine universities are not valid in the United States. Therefore, Argentine graduates must repeat the entire course all over again at a U.S. university in order to qualify for a degree.

University of Buenos Aires, School of Law

TUITION ... Tuition is free at all Argentine universities. A student must pay, however, a small fee for legalization of certificates. This amounts to very little.

LIVING COSTS ... The average cost of a room at a hotel or in a boardinghouse is 40 cents to $2.40 per day. This does not include meals. One should plan to spend 15 cents for breakfast and between 40 cents and $1.20 for lunch and approximately the same for dinner.

COMMON COURTESIES AND LOCAL CUSTOMS ... Office hours in Buenos Aires are from 9:00 to 12:00 and 2:00 to 6:00. Street doors to apartment houses are locked after 9:00 p.m. The dinner hour is from 9:00 on. Argentineans usually dine and entertain in their homes.

HOW TO GET THERE ... By Pan American Jet Clipper from New York nonstop to Buenos Aires in 10½ hours or via the east coast of South America. You can also travel by jet from New York via Washington and Miami by National, Pan American and Panagra with no change of plane down the west coast of South America to Buenos Aires. By ship, 19 days from New York or New Orleans.

FOR FURTHER INFORMATION ... See How to Enroll at the end of each individual university listed in this chapter. Be sure to read page 28 regarding necessary qualifications before writing. For travel particulars and documentation, write to Educational Department, NHE, Pan American Airways, Pan Am Building, New York, N. Y. 10017.

UNIVERSITY OF BUENOS AIRES

The University of Buenos Aires was created by decree of the Governor of the Buenos Aires Province, General Martin Rodriquez, on August 9, 1821. In 1833 the University Code was finally ratified, and it became effective the following year. In 1854 the University was reorganized with the study programs and the organization of the different institutes being greatly improved. When the city of Buenos Aires was declared capital of the Republic in 1881, the University of Buenos Aires became a national university.

During the recent 12-year period of Juan Perón's rule, the University was controlled by the government. When Perón was deposed in 1955, the University regained its autonomy from the federal government. Today the University has its own governing council composed of the president, the dean and vice-dean of each faculty. Although the University governs itself, it does receive money from the national government for its operation and administration.

SIZE ... There are 72,370 students enrolled in the University's ten schools. The total number of professors at the various schools is 560.

CALENDAR ... The school year begins in March and ends in November. There is a vacation of 1–2 weeks in July. As in other Latin American countries, the seasons are reversed—winter begins in June and summer in December. Buenos Aires has a mild climate all year round.

ADMISSION REQUIREMENTS ... A student must take an entrance examination or a one-year preliminary course, depending on the requirements of the particular school of the University. See also "a" and "b" under the Admission Requirements section in the opening summary on Argentina.

COURSES OF STUDY ... The University of Buenos Aires offers courses of study in the Schools of Agriculture, Architecture, Economic Sciences, Physics and Mathematics, Medicine, Law and Social Sciences, Pharmacy and Biochemistry, Philosophy, Engineering, and Odontology. The Cultural Relations Department of the University offers special courses in the theater and the movie industry. In addition, the various schools also offer special courses, meetings, conferences, etc.

TUITION ... The courses at the University of Buenos Aires, as in other official universities in Argentina, are given free of charge. The students must pay only very small fees for legalization of certificates, diplomas, etc.

LANGUAGE OF INSTRUCTION ... All subjects are taught in Spanish.

ACCOMMODATIONS ... At present there are no dormitory facilities at the University. Students must therefore live in boardinghouses or with private families in Buenos Aires. In the future University City, however, which is under construction in the northern riverside district of Buenos Aires, housing facilities will be built for the students.

AVERAGE COSTS ... A student should plan to spend approximately $12 a month for a room in a boardinghouse. Apartments of 1–2 rooms generally cost between $24–$40 per month. Breakfast is about 15 cents, lunch and dinner average 40 cents–$1.20 each. Bus fare is 2 cents.

STUDENT LIFE ... Each school of the University organizes its own cultural and social activities. The most important student associations at the University are those affiliated to the Federación Universitaria de Buenos Aires, which is closely tied to the Argentine University Federation. One remarkable aspect of the student's life is his firm purpose in participating in the political, economic and social problems affecting the University and the country as a whole.

HOW TO ENROLL ... For complete information on the University of Buenos Aires, write to the UNIVERSIDAD NACIONAL DE BUENOS AIRES, Viamonte 444, Buenos Aires, Argentina.

UNIVERSITY OF CÓRDOBA

The University of Córdoba, the oldest university in Argentina, was founded in 1613 by a Catholic bishop as a college of Latin, Arts and Theology. In 1621 the college became a university by the order of Pope Gregory XV. Three years later King Philip IV authorized the School-Master of the University to confer degrees on university graduates. In 1680 this function was transferred to the University Director.

On December 1, 1800, by royal decree, the government of the University was handed to the secular clergy and the University was officially called Royal University of St. Charles and of Our Lady of Monserrat. In 1820 the University was placed under the supervision of the Government of the Province of Córdoba and by 1854 it was returned to the national jurisdiction. This meant that now the national treasury would provide financial support for the University. By this time the number and scope of courses given at the University had increased, and additional schools were being founded. Therefore, in 1883 the national government established general rules governing the organization of the Universities of Buenos Aires and Córdoba. These rules provided that the University Director was to be elected by the University Assembly and that the University was free to plan and establish its own statutes.

During the Perón administration the University was subordinated to the authority of the national government, which established that the University Director was to be elected by the national government. Today, under present regulations and a new national government, the University of Córdoba, as well as other universities in Argentina, is free to elect its own authorities and to establish its own rules of organization and government.

The University is ruled by:

1) the General Assembly composed of the executive councils of the various schools or faculties.

2) the Superior Council composed of the University Director and Vice Director, directors of the different faculties, four undergraduate student representatives and two graduate student representatives.

3) the Director, who is the highest representative in the University.

SIZE ... The University of Córdoba has 7 schools or faculties and 4 high schools. 23,939 students are enrolled in

Córdoba University, Director's Office Building

university courses. The total number of full-time professors is 852 and in addition there are 213 substitute professors.

CALENDAR ... Regular courses at the University begin the first of March and end in the middle of December. The minimum period of instruction required by the University Statutes is 7 months.

ADMISSION REQUIREMENTS ... No previous examination is required for admission to the University of Córdoba. Alien students, however, must present, together with their application for admission, a statement from the university of their country that no examination for admission is required. In the case where an exam is required, the foreign student will have to take an equivalent exam in order to be admitted to the school he chooses. The application for admission will be filed with the University no later than March 15 each year, and if an examination is required it will be given not later than April 15. See also the Admission Requirements section in the opening summary on Argentina.

REGULAR COURSES OF STUDY ... The University offers courses in the following schools and institutes: School of Arts; Graduate School of Classic and Modern Languages; Institute of Mathematics, Astronomy and Physics; Chemical Sciences; Astronomical Observatory of the University of Córdoba; School of Architecture; Economic Sciences; Natural and Physical Sciences; Medicine; Law and Social Sciences; Philosophy; and Odontology.

TUITION ... The courses at the University of Córdoba as well as at the other Argentine universities are free.

LANGUAGE OF INSTRUCTION ... All courses are given in Spanish.

ACCOMMODATIONS ... The University does not have dormitory facilities for its students. Therefore, it is necessary for a student to live in a boardinghouse or in an apartment. The University does, however, have a cafeteria which can accommodate 2,200 students for daily meals.

AVERAGE COSTS ... A room in a boardinghouse in Córdoba costs about $12 a month. This does not include meals. If a student wishes to rent an apartment, he should plan to spend $24–$40 a month. Lunch or dinner generally costs between 40 cents and $2.40.

STUDENT LIFE ... As in other universities in Argentina, the students of the University of Córdoba participate in the University Government as members of the Superior Council. The student associations, such as the Reformist Union, Reformist List, the University Federation of Córdoba, promote very important social and cultural activities.

HOW TO ENROLL ... For complete information on the University of Córdoba, write to UNIVERSIDAD NACIONAL DE CÓRDOBA, Obispo Trejo & Sanabria 242, Córdoba, Province of Córdoba, Argentina.

UNIVERSITY OF LA PLATA

The University of La Plata was created by the House of Representatives of the Province of Buenos Aires on January 2, 1890. Courses began in the year 1897.

In accordance with an agreement signed between the Province of Buenos Aires and the federal government, the properties of the University were handed to the latter in 1906 and the University then became known as the National University of La Plata. Today the University is governed by:

a) The University Assembly—the highest authority. It has the right to reverse or modify the University Code with the approval of two-thirds of the Assembly members; elect the President of the University; suspend or dismiss the President; approve creation of new schools or institutes, etc.

b) Superior Council—creates the rules and issues University decrees; elects the University Vice President among the Council members; decides to intervene in the different faculties or school governments whenever circumstances so require. The members of the Superior Council are the directors of the different faculties and schools of the University.

c) The President—the highest university representative in all academic, civilian or administrative acts. He is elected by the Assembly for a period of 3 years, which can be extended for 3 more years.

SIZE ... There are approximately 49,760 students enrolled in various schools and institutes of the University. Six per cent of these students are aliens. The University has nine faculties, one Institute of Teacher Training, one Normal School, four special schools, one Primary School and three high schools.

CALENDAR ... Courses at the University begin the first of April and last until the end of November. The seasons are reversed in Argentina—winter begins in June and summer in December.

ADMISSION REQUIREMENTS ... In addition to the requirements listed under the Admission Requirements section in the opening summary on Argentina, students must present the following documents when applying to the University of La Plata:

a) Application for admission
b) Certificate of identity by the police
c) Two photographs (front) 2″ x 2″.

An entrance exam is also required by certain schools of the University.

COURSES OF STUDY ... The following institutes and schools are under the supervision of the University of La Plata: School of Agriculture; Physics and Mathematics; Law and Social Sciences; Medicine; Philosophy; Veterinary; Chemistry and Pharmacy; Economic Sciences; Natural Sciences; Astronomy; Advanced School of Arts; Obstetrics; Administration; Journalism; and High School. There are also special courses given to doctors at the Medical School as well as special courses given at the Schools of Agriculture, Pharmacy, Economic Sciences, Veterinary, Physics and the School of Social Sciences and Law.

TUITION ... The education at the University of La Plata, as at the Universities of Córdoba and Buenos Aires, is free. Students must pay only very small fees such as examination fee—10 cents per subject; examination certificate—12 cents; authentication of certificates—15 cents; certification of diplomas—25 cents; diplomas of different schools—80 cents–$2.40; revalidation of diplomas issued by foreign universities—$10; insurance—25 cents per year.

LANGUAGE OF INSTRUCTION ... All courses are taught in Spanish.

ACCOMMODATIONS ... At present the University does not provide housing facilities for the students. Authorities are presently considering the possibility of building dormitories to accommodate the students who do not have their permanent residence in the area.

AVERAGE COSTS ... It is comparatively inexpensive to live in a boardinghouse in La Plata. A room without meals costs about $6.50 per month. The University has its own restaurant where a student can have a complete meal for about 5 cents. The average cost of meals at restaurants in the city of La Plata is 40 cents.

STUDENT LIFE ... The students of the different schools have their own "centers" such as the center for medical students.

These centers are considered to be both cultural and educational associations because they contribute to the student's social life as well as to his education by providing at very reasonable prices mimeographed bulletins on the different subjects of each course. Most of the students at the University belong to the Federación Universitaria de la Plata, and the Federación Universitaria del Interior. Students may also join a theater group, play in the school orchestra, use the radio station and the central library.

HOW TO ENROLL ... For complete information on the University of La Plata, write to the UNIVERSIDAD NACIONAL DE LA PLATA, 7 no. 776, La Plata, Province of Buenos Aires, Argentina.

NATIONAL UNIVERSITY OF THE LITORAL, SANTA FE AND ROSARIO

The National University of the Litoral was originally founded in 1889 as the University of Santa Fe. In 1909 the national government gave recognition to the degrees being awarded by the University. The Provincial University of Santa Fe was converted into the National University of the Litoral in 1919. The University is an autonomous institution governed by a Superior Council, a University Director, and a General Assembly composed of students, professors and directors.

SIZE ... The University has eight schools located in the cities of Santa Fe and Rosario, as well as several institutes and a Popular University in each city. The total student enrollment is approximately 21,250.

CALENDAR ... The courses at the University generally begin in March and continue through October or the early part of November.

ADMISSION REQUIREMENTS ... In general, no previous examination is required for admission. See also "a" and "b" in the Admission Requirements section in the opening summary on Argentina.

REGULAR COURSES OF STUDY ... The National University of the Litoral maintains faculties in both Santa Fe and in Rosario. The following schools are located in Santa Fe: Law and Social Sciences; Chemical Engineering; Master School of Industries; Commerce; Health Technicians; Institute of Basic Teaching; Music; Cinematography; and the Popular University of Santa Fe.

The schools located in Rosario are Medicine; Mathematics; Natural-Physical-Chemical Sciences for Industry; Economic-Commercial-Political Sciences; Philosophy-Literature-Educational Sciences; Institute of Arts; Music; Master School of Industries; and the Popular University of Rosario.

TUITION ... The courses at the National University of the Litoral, as well as in other Argentine universities, are free.

LANGUAGE OF INSTRUCTION ... All courses are given in Spanish.

ACCOMMODATIONS ... The University offers accommodations in apartments and rooms for a limited number of students and professors as well as cafeteria service in both Rosario and Santa Fe. Plans for extending these services to a larger number of students are presently being considered.

AVERAGE COSTS ... A student should plan to spend approximately $12 a month for a room without meals; $24–$40 a month for a 1–2 room apartment; 40 cents–$1.20 per day for lunch or dinner; and about 4 cents a day round trip bus fare from the University to his home.

STUDENT LIFE ... The students actively participate in the government of the University, as they nominate representatives to the University's Superior Council and to the directive councils of the different schools. They also participate in conferences and seminars which are sponsored by the University Cultural and Social Department. The Institute of Music also prepares excellent concerts for the student body. Sports play a very important role at the University. Tournaments are often arranged between the different schools of the University.

HOW TO ENROLL ... For complete information on the National University of the Litoral, write to the UNIVERSIDAD NACIONAL DEL LITORAL, Boulevard Pellegrini 2750, Santa Fe, Argentina.

AUSTRALIA

University education in Australia is undergoing a period of great expansion. Enrollments during the past decade have increased by over 100 per cent and several new universities have been created since World War II. The universities are not only providing for increasing numbers of Australians who wish to embark on university education but also welcome many young people from other countries. More students from overseas, particularly from Asia, are coming to Australia each year.

These students receive a very warm welcome here, for our universities have come to know that their presence broadens and enriches university life.

Generally in Australia there is an awakened interest in Asian and Pacific countries. The development of courses in their culture, language and history is one of the features of recent university activity. Another is the increasing provision for post-graduate students exemplified in the Institute of Advanced Studies at the Australian National University in Canberra.

Each Australian university makes a distinctive contribution to the pattern of Australian education, but in each one a student from overseas will find the same friendly greeting that Australia traditionally extends to visitors. Those who plan to come here will find universities happy to advise them about their courses, facilities and entrance requirements.

Wm. J. Weeden, M.A., Dip.Ed.
Director, Commonwealth Office of Education

UNIVERSITIES IN AUSTRALIA . . . There are ten universities in Australia, three in New South Wales, two in Victoria and one in each of the other states and in the Australian Capital Territory (Canberra). There are also three university colleges, which do not award their own degrees but prepare students for degrees from the sponsoring universities. There are various technical, teachers and agricultural colleges administered by the states.

The universities in Australia have been established by governments; the older institutions were established by colonial governments and the more recently established ones have been set up by the state or Commonwealth governments. All are modeled on the lines of the Scottish and English provincial universities that were established during the nineteenth century.

They are mainly non-residential, secular—all being created by the state and not by any religious body—they are autonomous and accept all students possessing the prescribed qualifications for entry. There are some faculty restrictions on student enrollments at some universities, however.

Faculties of the universities represent the broad areas of human knowledge: arts, architecture, economics and commerce, science, law, engineering, agriculture, education, medicine, dentistry and veterinary science.

Foreign students in recent years have studied to advantage such fields as agriculture, dairy science, soil science, irrigation, genetics (animal breeding), forestry, geology, meteorology, paleontology, plant sciences, food technology, wool technology, chemistry, sociology, economics, anthropology, geography, education and guidance, mining and metallurgy engineering, political science, public administration, international relations, Far Eastern studies and oceanography.

Following is a list of the universities in Australia:

NAME AND LOCATION

	Approximate Enrollment
Australian National University, Canberra, Australian Capital Territory	1,900
University of New England, Armidale, New South Wales	3,300
University of New South Wales, Kensington, New South Wales	9,900
University of Sydney, Sydney, New South Wales . . .	14,600
University of Adelaide, North Terrace, Adelaide, South Australia	7,400
University of Melbourne, Parkville N 2, Victoria	13,100
Monash University, Clayton, Victoria	1,600
University of Queensland, St. Lucia, Brisbane, Queensland	11,500
University of Tasmania, Hobart, Tasmania	1,700
University of Western Australia, Nedlands, Western Australia	4,000
Newcastle University College, Tighes Hill, New South Wales, affiliated with University of New South Wales.	
Townsville University College, Townsville, Queensland, affiliated with the University of Queensland.	
Wollongong University College, Wollongong, New South Wales, affiliated with the University of New South Wales.	

Monash University and Townsville University College enrolled their first students during 1961. Wollongong University College was established at the beginning of 1962.

With the exception of the Australian National University and the University of New England, the universities are not residential, but hostels and colleges provide accommodation for a limited number of students.

TECHNICAL COLLEGES . . . The chief institutions for higher education other than the universities are the technical colleges, which are administered by the Education Department in five states. In New South Wales a separate Department of Technical Education has been established, and in Victoria a number of foremost technical colleges are controlled by independent councils, which, although responsible to the Minister of Education, enjoy a large measure of autonomy.

The technical colleges offer training not only in all the major industrial skills, but also in a variety of commercial, artistic and domestic occupations. Their courses may be divided into three main types: diploma courses giving advanced training in technical professions and other fields such as accountancy and art; vocational courses, usually leading to the award of a certificate, for skilled technical and semi-professional workers (many of these courses are in the fields not covered by an apprenticeship award); craftsman or artisan training in the apprenticeship trades.

TEACHERS COLLEGES . . . There are seven state teachers colleges in New South Wales, twelve in Victoria, three in South Australia and two each in Queensland, Western Australia and Tasmania.

In general, primary and infant, and in some states, junior secondary teacher trainees complete a 2-year course before appointment to government schools. Students training for service in government secondary schools are generally required to undertake a university degree course (normally 3 years' duration) followed by a one-year course of professional training qualifying them for a diploma in education. Specialist teachers of physical education, music, art, manual arts or domestic science receive from 2 to 5 years' training either entirely at a teachers college or partly at a teachers college and partly at some institution such as a technical college or a conservatorium of music.

AGRICULTURAL COLLEGES ... There are seven residential agricultural colleges in Australia. Each college offers a comprehensive course of 2 to 3 years' duration leading to a diploma of agriculture. Certain colleges also offer courses in horticulture, dairying, food technology and wine making.

OTHER INSTITUTIONS ... Other institutions of higher learning in Australia include a Forestry School in Canberra, and conservatories of music in Sydney, Melbourne, Brisbane and Adelaide.

THE AUSTRALIAN UNIVERSITY SYSTEM ... The older universities were established by the colonial governments, which provided both the initiative for their foundation and a large part of the money for their operation. The more recently established institutions have been set up by the state or Commonwealth governments. All the universities in Australia today receive substantial funds from both the state and Commonwealth governments, but they are completely autonomous and cannot be compared with the American state universities.

There is no institution corresponding to the American "college." The final year of secondary schooling and the first year of undergraduate study at the university may be considered to correspond in scope and difficulty with the work covered in the American college. The Australian student begins to specialize in his chosen field as soon as he enters the university, and by the time he has completed his university work, he has devoted a considerable amount of time to professional study. Formal lectures supplement his research, which is generally carried on independently with a minimum of professional supervision.

Because of this, it is advisable for the foreign student to complete his undergraduate work in his own country before attempting to engage in independent study in Australia.

COURSES OF STUDY ... The unit in Australian universities is an academic year of study (usually about 30 weeks) in a given subject or group of subjects. The typical subject in an Arts course involves attendance at from two to four lectures a week, each of an hour's duration. Attendance may also be required or expected at smaller tutorial classes or discussion groups. The typical Science subject involves two to four lectures and six hours or more of practical work per week. In some faculties (e.g., Arts, Economics and Commerce) credit toward the complete course may be obtained by passing in individual subjects; in other faculties (e.g., Medicine or Dentistry) the unit is the year's work in several subjects and all of these must be passed in the same academic year.

THE BACHELOR'S DEGREE ... Attainment of a First degree in Arts or Science depends on the satisfactory completion (mostly by written examinations) of a defined number of subjects and must include at least 3 years of study (in some cases 4) in the student's major subjects, accompanied usually by not less than 2 years' work in another field of study. (Calendars of the universities show the combinations of subjects which may be taken.) Four subjects are commonly the maximum allowed to be taken in one year, and nine or ten subjects are the total number required to complete a Bachelor's degree.

HONORS DEGREE ... The student who wishes to specialize and to carry his study further than is required for the ordinary degree may elect to take an honors course (3 or 4 years of study). In many faculties, the honors candidate attends the same lectures as other students. More frequently, however, honors courses involve additional reading, often additional lectures and tutorials, and almost certainly additional examination papers and usually an extra year of study.

In many faculties a First degree with at least second-class honors is required before students can proceed to work for a higher degree.

HIGHER DEGREES ... Most faculties award the degree of Master to a graduate of at least 2 or 3 years' standing who fulfills the required extra study. In addition, the candidate must present

a thesis embodying the results of original research; he may also be required to pass further examinations.

All universities have instituted Ph.D. degrees in some or all faculties. The candidate must pursue, for at least 2 years, a course of advanced study and research under university supervision, and must finally present a satisfactory thesis.

RESIDENTIAL COLLEGES ... The term "college" is applied to residences that provide tutorials in all major university subjects. They were originally church-founded, but are non-sectarian in enrollment. Tutors are appointed by the principal of the college and are under his direct supervision. Approximately 15 per cent of full-time students live in the colleges.

ADMISSION REQUIREMENTS ... Students from overseas need to obtain individual rulings on their particular cases. In general, however, students from well-known universities might expect to be admitted *ad eundem statum*. For example, the University of Sydney sets out the following provisions:

a) Persons of foreign nationality and education may be admitted by special examination.
b) The Professorial Board may admit as a matriculated student
   i) a graduate of another university, or
   ii) a student holding a certificate from another university, providing this shows that he possesses qualifications acceptable for entrance to the university.

The University of Melbourne requires an applicant for admission to produce evidence that he is qualified to enter on a degree course in a university of good standing in his own country.

CREDIT TOWARD AN AMERICAN DEGREE ... A student must make arrangements for receiving credit toward an American degree from his own university before he leaves the United States. Because of the variations in credit systems within American universities, it is not possible to generalize about the number of credit hours a student may receive. Degrees, as previously mentioned, may be earned by American students from the Australian universities.

TUITION ... Tuition and fees vary according to the faculty of study. They range from £75 to £170 per year. Since one Australian pound equals about $2.25, this would mean from approximately $169 to $382 a year.

LIVING COSTS ... Inquire from the university to which a student intends to proceed as to the latest figures on the cost of board and lodging, housing and other facilities. Generally, room and board will cost approximately $20 per week.

COMMON COURTESIES AND LOCAL CUSTOMS ... Australians are rather like Americans in their habits, so one would feel perfectly at home there. Most Australians dress quite informally when in restaurants and hotels. One thing to remember, though: there is no central heating or air conditioning in most places. Australia, however, does not have the extremes of climate experienced in the U. S. A.

FOR FURTHER INFORMATION ... write to the Registrar of the particular university. But first read pages 17 to 21 for basic requirements.

For travel particulars and documentation, write to Educational Department, NHE, Pan American Airways, Pan Am Building, New York, N. Y. 10017.

Organizations assisting students are

Australian Embassy
1700 Massachusetts Avenue, N.W.
Washington, D. C.

Australian Consulate General
636 Fifth Avenue
New York, New York

Australian Consulate General
206 Sansome Street
San Francisco, California

REGULATIONS ... A student must submit to the nearest Australian Consulate his passport and a letter of acceptance from an Australian educational institution.

HOW TO GET THERE ... By Pan American Jet Clipper via Honolulu, and the Fiji Islands or Pago Pago, Sydney is 18½ hours (elapsed time) from San Francisco and Los Angeles. Melbourne is about 1½ hours from Sydney by air. By ship, about 21 days from the U.S. West Coast.

The following three universities have been included as representative of Australian universities, since space limitations make it impossible to give similar details about them all.

UNIVERSITY OF SYDNEY

The University of Sydney is the oldest of the universities of Australia. It was established in 1850, when the Senate was empowered to purchase Sydney College, but the buildings were inadequate, and land—a block of 128 acres, later increased to 142 acres—was acquired at Grose Farm on the western edge of the city.

The University has a student body of approximately 14,600.

CALENDAR ... First term is from late February through May. Second term begins early June and ends the beginning of August, and Third term (last term) runs from the first week of September to early December.

COURSES OF STUDY ... The University has Faculties of Arts, Law, Medicine, Science, Engineering, Dentistry, Veterinary Science, Agriculture, Economics and Architecture. A Teachers College and a School of Public Health and Tropical Medicine are affiliated with the University.

TUITION ... Tuition and fees vary according to the faculty of study. For example, the Faculty of Arts costs from $169 to $338 per year; the fees for Law, Medicine or Science are $338 per year.

ADMISSION REQUIREMENTS ... See the Admission Requirements section in the opening summary on Australia.

ACCOMMODATIONS ... There are four men's and two women's residential colleges in the University. Approximately 700 students live in these colleges; the remainder either live at home or in lodgings of various kinds and suitability. The University and the student organizations have appointed housing officers to advise students on accommodation problems. Good quality low-cost meals are available in the University cafeteria and, although living costs vary according to individual taste in dwelling and eating, approximately $20 a week should be sufficient.

STUDENT LIFE ... The social life of the University is centered around the Union, which contains reading rooms, recreational rooms and a cafeteria. Student societies cater to a wide range of interests. Some are related to fields of study, others embrace wider interests. There is a great variety of sports, inter-faculty and inter-varsity. During the academic year there is an extensive program of dances, balls and dramatic programs.

HOW TO ENROLL ... At the present time, admission to this university is limited to residents of New South Wales, except for students from overseas who hold scholarships tenable at the University or who qualify for entry at the examination for matriculation in their state. Fulbright Scholarships are accepted; details may be obtained from your campus Fulbright adviser, or from the Institute of International Education, 809 United Nations Plaza, New York, N. Y. 10017. See also the For Further Information section in the opening summary on Australia.

UNIVERSITY OF MELBOURNE

The University of Melbourne is the second oldest university, being established in 1853. It is co-educational, and has a student body of approximately 13,100. It is situated in the northern section of the city on more than a hundred acres.

CALENDAR ... First term is from mid-March to the end of May. Second term begins early June and ends the beginning of August. Third term lasts from the first week of September to late October.

COURSES OF STUDY ... There are Faculties of Agriculture, Applied Science, Architecture, Arts, Dental Science, Economics and Commerce, Education, Engineering, Law, Medicine, Science, and Veterinary Science.

TUITION ... Tuition and fees vary according to the faculty and they range from approximately $169 to $382 per year.

ADMISSION REQUIREMENTS ... See the Admission Requirements in the opening summary on Australia.

ACCOMMODATIONS ... There are four men's and three women's residential colleges. Approximately 900 students live in these colleges, 1,700 live in lodgings of various kinds and suitability, and the remainder live at home. Housing officers at the University assist students to obtain suitable lodgings. International House is a residential building in which both Australian and overseas students are accommodated. The annual fee for lodging and board at International House during the academic year is approximately $585.

STUDENT LIFE ... As in all Australian universities, the Union is the hub of the student's social life. There are reading, recreational and meeting rooms, in addition to a cafeteria in which meals may be obtained at moderate cost. Student societies typical of those at American universities prevail. Sports include inter-school and inter-varsity programs, and there are dances and theatrical productions throughout the school year.

HOW TO ENROLL ... See the For Further Information section in the opening summary on Australia.

AUSTRALIAN NATIONAL UNIVERSITY, CANBERRA

The Australian National University was established in 1946 as a graduate institution for the development of advanced research in specific fields which are taught at the John Curtin School of Medical Research, the Research School of Physical Sciences, the Research School of Social Sciences and the Research School of Pacific Studies. Each department accepts a small number of graduate students of high caliber who have a Master's degree or its equivalent. Since the beginning of 1961 undergraduate students have been accepted in the undergraduate faculties of the University.

CALENDAR ... The first term begins the second week of March and ends the middle of May. The second term is from mid-June to the middle of August, and the third term is from early September to early December.

COURSES OF STUDY ... (listed above). Research work in the graduate schools is based upon a course of independent study and research under supervision. Three years of full-time work at the University are required for a Ph.D. or Master's degree. Oral examinations are based upon the student's thesis, which must be based solely upon his research.

TUITION ... The tuition in the graduate school is $118 per year. One scholarship is awarded to a U.S. student annually for advanced research. The tenure is two years with a possible extension for a third year. Particulars and application forms may be obtained from the Australian Embassy or Consulate General.

ADMISSION REQUIREMENTS ... See Admission Requirements in the opening summary on Australia.

ACCOMMODATIONS ... Students are required to live at the University in university residences. Scholarship holders are allowed living expenses for themselves and, if married, certain additional monies for dependents living at the University. Travel allowances are fixed in each case. Approximate weekly charges at the University House, including all meals, are as follows:

Single room—$21
Small flat—$23
Two-room flat—$28
Two-room flat for married couple—$41.

STUDENT LIFE ... Due to the nature of the school, student life is not as social as at other universities, although there are student societies embracing a variety of interests.

University of Melbourne

AUSTRIA

In our time mankind struggles for the achievement of one world. The United States has assumed a leading role in this struggle. The men and women who guide this great country in all fields of political, economic, scientific, and cultural endeavors must know the world in which they have to carry so heavy a burden. There is no better way to prepare for this responsibility than to go abroad and meet the challenge of a different environment. Austria is one of the countries in which such an experience can be gained.

Located in the heart of Europe, until 1918 the nucleus of a multinational empire, Austria has not only great scenic beauties and tourist attractions to offer. In its many archives, museums, and libraries are deposited, and in its universities are brought to life again, the records of a long and colorful past. The switch from an agricultural to an industrial economy after World War II has stimulated research in technology and economics. The country's rich cultural life is one of its greatest assets.

Austria has much to offer to the mature American student. He may be certain that he is welcome in the small country with the great traditions.

Dr. Wilhelm Schlag
Austrian Cultural Attaché

UNIVERSITIES IN AUSTRIA . . . Austria has four universities and a number of other institutions of higher learning accorded university rank. The University of Vienna was founded in 1365; the University of Graz was set up in 1585; the University of Innsbruck was established in 1677; the University of Salzburg was founded in 1623, its Faculty of Catholic Theology, discontinued in 1810, was re-established in 1963. In addition there are in Vienna, of university rank, the Institute of Veterinary Medicine, Vienna Institute of Technology, Institute of Agriculture, Silviculture and Horticulture, Institute of Commerce and World Trade, Academy of Fine Arts, Academy of Applied Arts, and Academy of Music and Dramatic Art; in Graz, the Institute of Technology; in Leoben, the School of Mining and Metallurgy; and in Salzburg and Graz, Academies of Music. The Austrian Ministry of Education supervises the country's educational system from primary through university level. Study of technical subjects, such as architecture and engineering, and the arts can be pursued at the university-rank institutions especially set up in each field. Financial support is given by the Ministry of Education to all these institutions. Foreign students have been welcome at Austria's universities since their inception. The University of Vienna and the University of Innsbruck hold international summer schools offering German language courses and various liberal arts courses taught in English.

AUSTRIAN UNIVERSITY SYSTEM . . . Austrian universities are composed of four faculties, namely, Faculty of Medicine, Faculty of Law, Faculty of Philosophy, Faculty of Catholic Theology. The University of Vienna also has a Faculty of Protestant Theology. The University of Salzburg has, for the time being, a Faculty of Catholic Theology and a Faculty of Philosophy only. Students who wish to study subjects outside these faculties attend on of the schools, academies, or institutes offering instruction in the chosen field. Within each university faculty are a large number of institutes, or departments, which offer courses of study. The courses may vary from one university to another; however, the standard of instruction and examination is fairly uniform at the four universities, as each must meet requirements established by the Ministry of Education. Less emphasis is placed on class attendance than is the case at American institutions of higher learning. As a rule, attendance is checked only in *Pflichtübungen* (roughly corresponding to American quiz sessions) and in seminars. Students are much more on their own than in the United States, a fact which

requires maturity and self-discipline. The number of courses normally taken during a semester is not the same in all fields but is generally somewhat higher than at American institutions, 20 to 40 hours per week. Students can work at their own pace and take examinations when they feel prepared to do so. To obtain a degree or diploma in a chosen field, certain minimum courses must be completed.

Most courses are taught by the lecture method. Advanced courses may be given in the form of seminars. Professors at Austrian universities generally arrange their lectures in cycles of 3 or 4 years—a different course is given in each of these years, so that students who attend classes for the normal 4- to 5-year period may take each course a professor offers. The language of instruction is German.

ADMISSION REQUIREMENTS . . . A thorough and complete knowledge of the German language is essential for enrollment as a regular student in an Austrian university; instruction and examinations are in German. Admission requirements are standard throughout Austria. Foreign students may be admitted to Austrian institutions of higher learning at the discretion of the rector or the dean of the faculty if they show the same degree of preparation as Austrian students. At almost all Austrian institutions of higher learning, students whose mother tongue is not German must prove in an examination, before they begin their studies, that they have a sufficient knowledge of German. Foreign students seeking admission should apply in German directly to the Austrian institution of their choice. A transcript of records, with a verified German translation, and copies of diplomas, also with German translations, should accompany such applications. Translations may be verified by the nearest Austrian Consulate or by the Austrian Institute, 11 East 52nd Street, New York, N. Y. 10022.

Persons who have received their schooling in the United States and seek admission to one of Austria's universities as regular students (*ordentliche Hörer*) should have a Bachelor's degree. In exceptional cases, two years of undergraduate study qualify for admission. Applications for admission should be made approximately six months in advance.

CREDIT TOWARD AN AMERICAN DEGREE . . . A student must make arrangements for receiving credit toward an American degree from his own university before he leaves the United States. Because of the variations in credit systems within American universities and colleges, it is impossible to generalize about the number of credit hours a student may receive. Each student should discuss with his own dean or guidance counselor the requirements for receiving credit and the number of credit hours toward his American degree that may be awarded for study in Austria. Sometimes full credit may be given for the period of study in Austria if the student passes the Austrian examinations. But each American university will make its own evaluation of the study at each Austrian university. American students seeking credit for work done in Austria should make sure their attendance is properly certified in their *Meldungsbuch* or *Studienbuch* by the *Antestur,* or certificate of enrollment, at the beginning, and by an *Abtestur,* or certificate of attendance, at the end of each semester. Students should also inform the person conducting the course, at the end of the term, that they wish to take an exam. The results of this exam are entered into a printed certificate which the student must buy at the university.

REGULATIONS . . . Students from the United States must have a valid American passport to enter Austria. Those who plan to be in the country for a continuous period lasting longer than three months must obtain an entry visa, which is available from the Visa Section of the Austrian Embassy in Washington, D. C., or from the nearest Austrian Consulate General. Those who plan to spend less than three months in Austria do not need an entry visa. Students should inform themselves of Austria currency regulations.

TUITION AND OTHER COSTS ... These vary according to the faculty; the range of tuition charges is from $10–$105 per semester for foreign students. In general, tuition fees per semester are as follows: Faculty of Theology, about $26; Faculty of Law, about $26; Faculty of Medicine, pre-clinical semesters, about $50, clinical semesters, $40; Faculty of Philosophy, $26 for humanities, $45–$70 for sciences; the study of Pharmacy or Chemistry costs about $48 to $95; the study of technical subjects costs about $55 to $105; study of the arts costs from about $10 to $16. There may be small matriculation costs in addition.

LIVING COSTS ... Most students will find that about $100 to $150 a month will be sufficient for living expenses. It is possible for a single student to live on less. Universities do not maintain dormitories and students generally live with families, in boardinghouses, or in student homes, which are maintained by various student associations or religious groups. There are university cafeterias which serve inexpensive meals, as do various restaurants in the university districts. In general, students should expect to pay about $45 to $60 a month for rent, $40 to $65 per month for meals, $10 to $20 per month for transportation, and $5 per month for laundry and other incidentals. Although students should not hope to supplement their allowance through part-time work, some small jobs may be available from time to time. Various student organizations can furnish information on such jobs as well as on living accommodations and costs. Auslandsreferat der Österreichischen Hochschülerschaft (Foreign Students' Department of the Austrian Student Association) at Führichgasse 10, Vienna 1, and the Oesterreichisches Komitee für internationalen Studienaustausch (Austrian Committee for International Educational Exchange) at Türkenstrasse 4/III, Vienna IX, with offices also in Graz and Innsbruck, try to help foreign students in these and other matters.

COMMON COURTESIES AND LOCAL CUSTOMS ... Students will find themselves the recipients of various courtesies, one being that they are entitled to a 50 per cent reduction of fares on the Austrian Federal Railways from the Austrian border to the place of their studies and return. The Austrian Student Association—or perhaps an Austrian student—will introduce newcomers to places for purchasing inexpensive books, good but inexpensive tickets for theatrical and orchestral performances, and other cultural bargains.

The relationship between instructors and students, and even between the students themselves, is not so informal at Austrian institutions as is often the case at American colleges. There is little student counseling, in the American sense, but professors who seem aloof are often very friendly and helpful when asked for advice.

HOW TO GET THERE ... By Pan American Jet Clipper, 11 hours (elapsed time) to Vienna from New York via Frankfurt. By ship, 5 to 9 days to Le Havre, France, then about 28 hours by train to Vienna. Western Austria is most easily reached by Pan Am to Munich and thence a 2½-hour train ride to either Innsbruck or Salzburg. Austrian Airlines provides frequent service by connecting with Pan Am in many European cities. During the summer there is also daily air service to Salzburg, Innsbruck, Graz, Linz and Klagenfurt.

FOR FURTHER INFORMATION ... Write to the Austrian Institute, 11 East 52nd Street, New York, N. Y. 10022. First read the basic requirements on pages 17 to 21. For travel particulars and documentation, write to Educational Department, NHE, Pan American Airways, Pan Am Building, New York, N. Y. 10017.

UNIVERSITY OF GRAZ

Graz is the second largest city of Austria; it is located in the Eastern Alps in the southeastern part of the country with the Yugoslavian hills to the south and the Hungarian plains to the east. A profusion of flowers grows in the city's numerous parks and private courtyards; Graz has been called the "Garden Spot" of Austria. The Schlossberg, a steeply rising and rocky hill in the heart of the city, offers a vantage point for a view of the city and its environs. The opera, theater, and the festivals and fairs of the city are big attractions. The Graz Festival held in late June through mid-July offers open-air performances of music and drama; the Graz Fair held in the spring and again in the autumn has outstanding agricultural and textile exhibits. The market is worth visiting, as well as the Provincial Museum, the Hunting Museum in the Eggenberg Castle, and the Schlossberg Hill Clock Tower, a landmark of Graz since 1561. The University of Graz was founded in 1585.

SIZE ... About 5,460 students, of whom 1,124 are from foreign countries.

CALENDAR ... The academic year begins in October and ends in July and consists of two semesters: the winter semester runs from the beginning of October to the end of January; the start of the summer semester varies from March to July. Summer courses are offered from mid-June through August.

COURSES OF STUDY ... The University of Graz is composed of the Faculty of Theology, Faculty of Medicine, Faculty of Law, and the Faculty of Philosophy. The Theology Faculty offers courses in Catholic Theology; the Faculty of Philosophy offers courses in both Humanities and Science, including Philosophy, Psychology, Education, Ancient History and Archaeology, Medieval and Modern History, Librarianship, Musicology, Classical Archaeology, History of Fine Arts, General and Indo-European Linguistic, Germanic Philology, Classical Philology, English Philology, Romance Philology, Slavonic Philology, Oriental Studies, Ethnology and Religion, Folklore, Geography, Mathematics, Astronomy, Physics, Meteorology, Geophysics, Geology, Paleontology, Chemistry, Mineralogy, Petrography, Botany, Zoology, and Physical Education; there are also an Institute for Translators and Interpreters and 34 additional institutes, each devoted to a special subject. Pharmacy is also included in the Faculty of Philosophy. The Faculty of Medicine offers courses from Anatomy to Zoology and includes 18 institutes and clinics. The Faculty of Law offers courses in Political Science in addition to Law. These courses are for regular students of the University.

SUMMER COURSES ... From mid-June to mid-October German language courses are offered for beginners. More advanced students are offered German language and literature and Austrian art and history. During July and August German literature, philosophy and European culture are offered to very advanced students and teachers of German.

TUITION ... See upper left of this page.

ADMISSION REQUIREMENTS ... For admission to the University of Graz as a regular student a minimum of 2 years of college is required. Knowledge of Latin is required for certain courses. Foreign students should write in German directly to the University or to the dean of the faculty indicating the course of study desired and giving an outline of all previous academic studies. The University or dean will inform each student whether he meets the admission requirements. Special students are accepted; they must, however, follow the same procedure for admission as regular students. See also the Admission Requirements section in the opening summary on Austria.

LANGUAGE OF INSTRUCTION ... German.

University of Graz, Main Building

ACCOMMODATIONS ... The University does not maintain residence halls for students; there are some privately operated student homes which offer room and board. Austrian students live in such homes or with families or in ordinary boardinghouses. The Austrian Student Association and other student and religious organizations will help students find lodgings and inexpensive places to eat.

AVERAGE COSTS ... Fees for tuition about $60 per academic year. Room and board start at about $100 per month.

STUDENT LIFE ... The Schlossberg, or Castle Hill, in the city's center offers numerous footpaths for strollers; much of the hill is in a park and the Clock Tower is located there, facing the city. Students will find themselves offered a wide variety of cultural activities: music, opera, drama, open-air festivals to attend. There are coffeehouses and espresso café-bars where students gather; there are student-organized trips to other parts of Austria; there are skiing and ice skating. Tennis, mountain climbing, bicycling and camping out are favorite activities of students.

UNIVERSITY OF INNSBRUCK

University of Innsbruck

Whether Innsbruck is seen from a vantage point reached by cable car or from a walking tour in the early morning, it is an impressive city. Its old section, with narrow Gothic houses, pointed arcades and wrought-iron signs, dates back to ancient times. Located in the Tyrol, at the crossroads of Germany, Italy, Austria, and Western Europe, Innsbruck is known as the capital of "The Land of the Mountains." In the neighborhood of the *Goldenes Dachl,* a golden-roofed Gothic balcony, there are many picturesque houses, shops and inns. Three cable car lines take one to high mountains north and south of the city. Innsbruck is a gateway to the Arlberg resorts and to Kitzbuehel where some of the world's best skiing is found. The University of Innsbruck dates from 1677.

SIZE ... About 5,700 students, 2,490 of whom are from foreign countries.

CALENDAR ... The academic year begins in October and ends in July and consists of two semesters: the winter semester runs from the beginning of October to February, the start of the summer semester varies from March to early July. An International Summer School is held from June to September.

COURSES OF STUDY ... The University has a Faculty of Law, which offers courses in Law, Political Science, Economics, International Relations, Philosophy and Sociology, Criminology, Forensic Psychiatry, Forensic Medicine and related courses; a Faculty of Catholic Theology; a Faculty of Medicine, which offers courses from Anatomy to Zoology, and about twenty clinics and institutes; and the Faculty of Philosophy, which offers courses in the fields of Science and the Humanities, an Institute for Translators and Interpreters, and nearly 35 special institutes. Pharmacy and Chemistry are also offered by the Faculty of Philosophy. These courses are for regular students of the University.

SUMMER COURSES ... Four 3-week sessions are held by the University of Innsbruck at Mayrhofen in the "Zillertal"; the village has a snow-capped peak in the background. Sessions are offered from June to September. Courses in the German language are given for beginners, intermediate and advanced students. There are also lectures on history, poetry, fine arts, music and folklore of Austria.

TUITION ... See page 39.

ADMISSION REQUIREMENTS ... For admission to the University of Innsbruck as a regular student a minimum of 2 years of college is required. Latin is required for admission to several faculties. Foreign students must write in German directly to the University of Innsbruck or to the dean of the faculty, giving an outline of their educational background and evidence of previous academic studies; the course of study one wishes to follow must be indicated in the letter. The University or the dean will inform each student whether he meets the admission requirements. Special students are accepted, but they must follow the same procedure for admission as regular students. For admission to the summer courses it is not necessary to present academic certificates; students may enter German language courses designed for their level of proficiency in the language. See also the Admission Requirements section in the opening summary on Austria.

LANGUAGE OF INSTRUCTION ... German. Summer courses are given in German, English and French.

ACCOMMODATIONS ... The University of Innsbruck does not maintain dormitories for students. There are a few independently operated "student homes" where students can have room and board. Other students live in ordinary boardinghouses or with Austrian families. See also under Living Costs, page 39. Various student groups, including a branch of the Austrian Student Association and several religious organizations, will assist foreign students to find lodgings and suitable places to eat. Summer school students are accommodated in hotels and villas and the inclusive fee of about $80 covers the cost of room and board for 20 days plus tuition and certain other expenses.

AVERAGE COSTS ... Fees for the academic year about $60. Room and board about $125 per month.

STUDENT LIFE ... Skiing is the national sport of Austria. The students of Innsbruck have several excellent skiing grounds nearby to give them not only good skiing but also an opportunity to attend ski schools. In other seasons mountain climbing, bicycling, boating and fishing are popular sports. Tennis, sailing, rowing, swimming and hiking are also popular. Various student organizations and clubs devote themselves to intellectual and cultural activities, and a foreign student can easily find a group with whom he shares interests. There are tours to historical points of interest as well as to museums and musical fetes.

UNIVERSITY OF VIENNA

Sometimes called the "Music Capital of the World," Vienna is a city where music is everywhere. The Vienna State Opera (Staatsoper), famous for grand opera, the Volksoper, for light opera, the Vienna Philharmonic Orchestra, the Vienna Symphony Orchestra, many small orchestras, choirs and chamber ensembles make it so. The Vienna Opera Ballet, the theaters, the superb National Library, the outstanding collections of the Museum of Fine Arts and of the Albertina, in the Belvedere Palace, and in the former Imperial Palace are part of the city's cultural offerings. Sidewalk cafés, numerous parks, structures like the magnificent Opera House, Schönbrunn Palace and St. Stephen's Cathedral make the city a scene of true architectural splendor and delight. The University of Vienna, the oldest university in the German language area, was founded in 1365 by charter granted by Duke Rudolph IV of Austria.

SIZE ... In 1962–63 there were 17,126 students, of whom 2,770 came from countries outside Austria.

CALENDAR ... The academic year begins in October and ends in July and consists of two semesters: the winter semester runs from the beginning of October to February; the summer semester is from March to early July. A summer session at Strobl runs from mid-July through August; at Vienna, July through September. These courses are 4-week sessions each.

COURSES OF STUDY ... The University is made up of the Faculty of Law, the Faculty of Medicine, the Faculty of Philosophy, the Faculty of Catholic Theology and the Faculty of Protestant Theology, each comprising a number of institutes and departments. The Faculty of Law offers courses in Political Science, Law, Economics, Philosophy, Sociology, Criminology, Forensic Medicine, among others. The Faculty of Medicine offers courses leading to the degree of M.D. and comprises 25 clinics and institutes. The Faculty of Philosophy offers courses in the Humanities and Sciences, from Anthropology through Zoology; this Faculty also includes an Institute for Translators and Interpreters and about 50 other special institutes. The Institutes of Pharmacy, Physics and Chemistry are also part of the Faculty of Philosophy. Courses here described are for regular students.

SUMMER SCHOOL ... The Strobl Summer School of the University of Vienna is held on the St. Wolfgang Campus of the University, a large estate on the shore of Lake St. Wolfgang, about 187 miles from Vienna and 33 miles from Salzburg. The summer school's aim is "to enable English-speaking students to become acquainted with Austrian educational and social values." A 6-week course from the middle of July to the end of August is offered in two 3-week parts; either part may be taken separately. Lecture courses are offered in Law and Political Science, including Law and State in Occidental Philosophy, International Relations since 1938, International Organization, Framework of European Economic Integration, International Economic and Financial Institutions, Social Problems and Social Politics in Central Europe, Major Trends of Modern Democratic Life in America and Europe, Geography and Geopolitics of Austria and Central Europe, and a Seminar on Current International Affairs; in Liberal Arts, including Austria's Role in Europe Today, Culture, Society and Education in an Age of Change, History of Middle Europe, Austrian Painting from the Early Middle Ages to the Present Time, History of Music, and other music and science courses and seminars; and in the German Language, classes in German for beginners, intermediate and advanced students. Physical education classes and special lectures and tours are also offered.

The University of Vienna Summer School at Vienna offers German language courses and lectures on topical subjects, Austrian culture, etc.

TUITION ... See page 39. Strobl Summer School charges include a registration fee of $20 and an inclusive price of $320 for the 6-week course; this covers tuition, room and board, conducted tours, special lectures, social activities, three visits to the Salzburg Festivals, accident insurance and some medical care. Vienna Summer School charges are $4 for registration and $28 for tuition only. Room and board are extra.

ADMISSION REQUIREMENTS ... For admission to the University of Vienna as a regular student a minimum of 2 years of college or its equivalent from a foreign school is required. Latin is required for admission to several faculties. A foreign student must write in German directly to the University or to the dean of the faculty, giving an outline of his educational background and evidence of his previous academic studies; the course of study one wishes to follow must be indicated in the letter. The University or the dean will inform the student whether he meets the admission requirements. Special students are accepted, but they must follow the same procedure for admission as regular students. For admission to the summer vacation course at Strobl, students must have completed at least 2 years of college before they enroll and must meet the prerequisites, when set up, for courses they wish to enter. The Vienna course has no academic prerequisites. See also the Admission Requirements section in the opening summary on Austria. Applications for Strobl should be sent to the Institute of International Education, those for Vienna, direct.

LANGUAGE OF INSTRUCTION ... German. Courses of the summer schools are given in English.

ACCOMMODATIONS ... Residence halls are not maintained by the University and Austrian students generally live with families, in boardinghouses, or in student homes. See the Living Costs section in the opening summary on Austria. In Vienna laundry and other incidentals will run about $4 a week or $15 a month. Students will find that about $80 to $100 a month will be sufficient for living expenses. The Austrian Student Association and various other student groups and religious organizations will help foreign students find lodgings and inexpensive places to eat. Students attending the summer schools will be housed in dormitories on the summer campuses and will have Austrian dishes served. Cost of room and board, tuition and various excursions is $140 for three weeks, or $250 for six weeks.

AVERAGE COSTS ... Fees for the academic year about $60. Room and board about $100 to $150 per month.

STUDENT LIFE ... The University of Vienna does not have a campus and there are few extracurricular activities in the American sense. But the University does offer very inexpensive and good courses, open to all students, in tennis, skiing, mountain climbing, sailing, fencing, ice skating, swimming, and field athletics. Outside the University there is a rich musical and theatrical life to share. From September first to the end of June, there are two operas performed every night, one in the Staatsoper, one in the Volksoper. The theaters offer classics of the German stage and varied international fare: one can hear O'Neill, Thornton Wilder, or Tennessee Williams in German! Every night there are concerts; the museums offer conducted tours. The Alpenverein, the Gebirgsverein, and the Touristenklub, long-established outdoor clubs, offer fine facilities and good comradeship for students at their lodges in the Austrian Alps. It is on the ski slopes and in the lodges that one finds the Austrians at their best. Even within the city of Vienna there is skiing terrain. In summer sailboats dot the waters of the Danube. Wooded paths—where once walked Beethoven and Schubert—beckon in the foothills of the Alps which cradle Vienna. The sidewalk café and its discussions must be included in any description of student life; the opinions of foreign students will always have a hearing there.

Summer school students will find the campus at Strobl a playground for sailing, swimming, rowing, fishing, tennis, badminton, volleyball, rhythmical gymnastics, sun-bathing, walking, and hiking. In the evenings there is opportunity to learn Austrian folk songs and dances.

University of Vienna

BELGIUM

The Belgian universities have always been open to students coming from other countries. Perhaps the subjects that American students have gone to Belgium to study in greatest number are history (particularly of the medieval and Renaissance periods), history of art, and philosophy. However, they have found courses in all the traditional subjects and advanced training in numerous special fields of such diverse nature as Egyptology and pre-stressed concrete.

There is a rich past and a modern spirit in Belgium and the Belgian people. Americans feel this and there is every reason why they should find that a period of study in a Belgian university is a rewarding experience in their lives.

Jan-Albert Goris
Minister Plenipotentiary
Commissioner of Information for Belgium

UNIVERSITIES OF BELGIUM ... During the past 25 years, there has been an increase of about 60 per cent in the enrollment at institutions of higher learning in Belgium. This is due to the greater importance of university degrees in many fields of work, to the increase in population in general and to the greater number of women attending the universities.

The state universities are supported entirely, and the private universities partially, by the state. The universities of Ghent and Liége are state-supported; those at Brussels and Louvain are private. There are several state agricultural institutions, a polytechnic school at Mons, a number of commercial and professional schools and academies of the arts.

BELGIAN UNIVERSITY SYSTEM ... The Belgian university system is similar to that of other European universities. Instruction is largely by lecture and seminar. The exams at the end of the year are generally oral and comprehensive in their respective fields. Curriculum and duration of studies are fixed by law for degrees which entitle their holders to practice a profession. Law degrees must also be approved by a Committee of Ratification set up by the state.

University of Brussels, School of Engineering

ADMISSION REQUIREMENTS ... Admissions examinations are required for entrance into schools of engineering and some schools of agriculture and commerce. Foreign students must present evidence of training equivalent to a Belgian secondary school. This will mean for the student from the United States a high school certificate plus two years at an accredited college.

CREDIT TOWARD AN AMERICAN DEGREE ... It is important for the student to make arrangements for receiving credit toward an American degree from his own university before he leaves the United States. There is nothing to correspond to the credit-hour system at Belgian universities, and each student should discuss with his dean the basis on which his work should be evaluated.

REGULATIONS ... A passport is required, and since a student will stay in Belgium longer than two months, a visa must also be obtained. A vaccination certificate is a requirement for re-entry into the United States.

TUITION ... Matriculation fees range from $7 to $10. Tuition varies according to university and faculty selected, from $20 to $75. Examination fees and laboratory fees will amount to from $2 to $25 and $5 to $11 respectively.

LIVING COSTS ... The cost of living in Belgium is relatively high, especially in Brussels. However, special rates for students make the living cost lower. The universities have dining halls where meals are reasonable. Some universities provide board and room in student lodgings for about $250 to $400 for the academic year.

Foreign students may find private accommodations and board for about $600 to $1,000 for the academic year.

COMMON COURTESIES AND LOCAL CUSTOMS ... It is the custom to shake hands when you meet or leave someone.

The Belgians are industrious, thrifty people who are essentially *Belgian* in spite of a constant mixing of nationalities since Roman times.

HOW TO GET THERE ... By Pan American Jet Clipper, from New York to Brussels, 8¼ hours (elapsed time). By ship, 8 to 10 days to Antwerp, depending on the steamer.

FOR FURTHER INFORMATION ... For complete information about the universities and how to enroll, write to the Secretary of the Belgian-American Educational Foundation, 420 Lexington Avenue, New York, N. Y. 10017. Before doing so be sure to read about basic requirements, pages 17–21.

For travel particulars and documentation, write to Educational Department, NHE, Pan American Airways, Pan Am Building, New York, N. Y. 10017.

UNIVERSITY OF BRUSSELS

Brussels, the capital of a country the size of Rhode Island with a population of over 9,000,000, is one of the gayest cities in Europe. It is cosmopolitan and sophisticated. The medieval part of the city lives on in the Market Place with its beautiful Town Hall, "Maison du Roi" and Guild Houses. The upper or "new" town is built in the style of the late Renaissance. Brussels has been a haven for writers: Voltaire and Byron, Victor Hugo, Baudelaire, Verlaine and Rimbaud, and Thackeray lived here. The city was founded on the banks of a marshy lake known as "Bruc-Sella." It was at a crossroads on the great trade route from Cologne to Bruges and became the capital of the Province of Brabant when the Dukes found the people of Louvain too revolutionary for their taste. The people of the lower town, around the Market Place, were Flemish-speaking from the start. Their rulers established their residences in the upper town, which was essentially French-speaking and is to this day. The University of Brussels was founded on November 20, 1834, by Théodore Verhaegen. It is a private institution governed by the Administrative Council. Its motto is "Through freedom toward science, through science toward freedom." The university is housed in five large buildings and operates extensive playing fields, an eating house, and the University City, which provides lodgings for some students.

SIZE . . . About 7,000 students are enrolled at the University of Brussels, of whom about 800 are foreigners.

CALENDAR . . . The academic year runs from mid-October through July. Examinations are held in July. A summer course for foreign students is given from late July to late August.

COURSES OF STUDY . . . The University of Brussels has Faculties of Philosophy and Letters, Law, Science, Medicine and Pharmacy, Applied Science, and Social, Political and Economic Science. It also has Schools of Commerce, Criminology, Education and Nursing; Institutes of Statistics and Labor and a Center of Physical Education.

SUMMER COURSES . . . A one-month French Language and Literature course is given starting the latter part of July. A working knowledge of French is required.

TUITION . . . A matriculation fee of $11 is charged. Tuition is about $75; laboratory fees are from $6 to $24 and examination charges are from $4 to $30. Auditors are required to pay about $15.

ADMISSION REQUIREMENTS . . . See the Admission Requirements section in the opening summary on Belgium.

LANGUAGE OF INSTRUCTION . . . French. The courses in the Law School are also given in Dutch, and Dutch is being introduced into the other schools of the University alongside of French. The thesis must be written in the language of instruction. Foreign students must present evidence of examination for aptitude in French.

ACCOMMODATIONS . . . Board and lodging at University City are available to fully enrolled students. Private rooms may be found nearby for foreign students.

AVERAGE COSTS . . . The charge for board and lodging at University City is about $400 for the academic year. Private *pension* will amount to about $700. Tuition and fees will total about $125, and an additional $25 to $40 per month should be allowed.

STUDENT LIFE . . . Brussels is a fascinating city and is noted for its art treasures and its good food and conviviality. Near the University is the beautiful Bois de la Cambre and farther on is the Forêt de Soignes, one of the grandest beech forests in Europe. Beyond is Waterloo, and all around are interesting places to visit.

University of Ghent, Library

UNIVERSITY OF GHENT

The city of Ghent once outshone Paris in importance in the time of Emperor Charles V of the Holy Roman Empire, who was born there in 1500. The city is famous for its magnificent guild houses and for the Cathedral of St. Bavon, which contains one of the great treasures of Belgium, the Beautiful "Adoration of the Mystic Lamb" by the brothers Hubert and Jan Van Eyck. The imposing Castle of the Counts of Flanders is a magnificent survival of the Middle Ages, with dungeons, crenelated battlements, a moat, banqueting halls and other marvels. The castle was begun in 868 as protection against the Normans. John of Gaunt, son of Edward III of England, was born here. Ghent is now most famous for the beautiful flowers which are grown all around. It is surrounded by acres of begonias and azaleas, by greenhouses containing world-famous orchids which are exhibited every five years.

The University of Ghent was founded in 1816. It is a state institution and is governed by the Rector-President, who is elected for four years, by the Vice-President, and by a Board of Administration, whose members are elected for four years by the different faculties.

CALENDAR . . . The academic year runs from early October to the end of July.

SIZE . . . About 4,000 students are at the University of Ghent, of whom 50 are foreigners.

COURSES OF STUDY . . . There are five faculties at the University of Ghent: Philosophy and Letters, Law, Science, Medicine, and Applied Sciences. Attached to the Faculty of Philosophy and Letters is the Higher Institute of Fine Arts and Archaeology, and the Institute of Pedagogy; attached to the Faculty of Law is the Higher School of Commercial and Economic Science, the Criminology School. Affiliated with the Faculty of Medicine is an Institute for Physical Education and a Veterinary School.

ADMISSION REQUIREMENTS . . . Foreigners must have their certificates approved by the Belgian Minister of Education as equivalent to the Belgian secondary school certificate. There are admissions examinations for the engineering program. See also the Admission Requirements section in the opening summary on Belgium.

LANGUAGE OF INSTRUCTION . . . Dutch. Theses must be in Dutch, except for foreigners.

TUITION . . . $20 an academic year. Laboratory fees, from $2 to $9. Examination fees, $8.

ACCOMMODATIONS . . . The University operates dining facilities where meals may be bought for a very low fee. Foreigners may find rooms for rent in the town.

University of Brussels, School of Philosophy and Letters

AVERAGE COSTS ... A private room in Ghent rents for about $12 a week. Meals at the university dining hall cost about 30 cents each. The student should have $20 to $30 per month for personal expenses.

STUDENT LIFE ... Ghent has a proud history and its people are strongly independent and energetic. The student will find an atmosphere of eager debate and a vigorous Flemish spirit.

University of Liége, Zoology Building

UNIVERSITY OF LIÉGE

The city of Liége lies on both banks of the Meuse in what is known as Wallonia, the southern section of Belgium as opposed to Flanders and the Flemings in the north. It is an industrial city, but also a city of churches and intellectual life. In fact, Liége was ruled for centuries by prince-bishops who ensured privileges for the townspeople and some immunity from the otherwise harsh rule of Burgundians, Spaniards, and Austrians. Nevertheless, Liége has been one of the most fought-over cities in Europe. The University of Liége occupies twenty buildings scattered over the town. It is a state university, founded in 1817, and reorganized in 1837 after Belgium had won her independence from Holland.

SIZE ... About 4,600 students are enrolled at the University of Liége, of whom 350 are foreign students.

CALENDAR ... The courses begin in October and run until May.

COURSES OF STUDY ... The University of Liége has Faculties of Philosophy and Letters, Law, Science, Medicine and Applied Science. Postgraduate studies are organized in special fields, e.g., social law, criminology, astrophysics, sanitary engineering, nuclear energy, applied mathematics.

TUITION ... For one academic year tuition fees are about $20, laboratory fees from $1 to $10, examination fees from $2 to $6.

ADMISSION REQUIREMENTS ... Foreign students must have their credentials approved by the University.

See also the Admission Requirements section in the opening summary on Belgium.

LANGUAGE OF INSTRUCTION ... French. Theses must be written in French except those in foreign literature.

ACCOMMODATIONS ... The University operates a students' hostel. Private rooms may be found in the town.

AVERAGE COSTS ... It costs about $12 per week for a private room in Liége. The University operates dining facilities where meals may be obtained for 30 cents each. The student should have $20 to $30 per month for personal expenses.

STUDENT LIFE ... It has been said that the Fleming is the artist, the poet and the mystic, while the Walloon is gay and excitable, quick to investigate anything new and challenging. Pure French is now ousting the Walloon language but the surviving traces are interesting. The student will find this a stimulating atmosphere.

UNIVERSITY OF LOUVAIN

Louvain was the capital of the Duchy of Brabant when Brussels was a mere village. It derived its wealth during the thirteenth century from the cloth trade; however, civil war led to

disaster and destruction. After peace was restored, the University was founded by Duke Jean I with the help of Pope Martin V in hopes of bringing back some of the greatness of the town. At one time it ranked second only to Paris and was one of the first Catholic universities in the world. Louvain has been enormously damaged twice in this century. It is a miracle that the beautiful Hôtel de Ville has survived. The magnificent University Library was destroyed in 1914 and rebuilt with American help. Priceless collections of manuscripts were irreparably lost but gifts of books were sent from all lands, and Germany made reparation by handing over to the University books and manuscripts equal in value and importance to those destroyed. The University of Louvain, the oldest university in Belgium, was founded in 1425 by Papal Bull. It was closed by decree of the French Directoire in 1797 and opened again in 1816 as a state institution under William I of Orange. The University was closed again just before the revolution of 1830, when Belgium gained her independence from Holland. Belgian bishops reopened it in Malines in 1834 and transferred it back to Louvain in 1835. The university was again closed from August 1914 until January 1919, during which time it suffered great destruction. Invasion and air raids between 1940 and 1944 again destroyed the University Library and damaged the town but reconstruction is well along. It is a Roman Catholic institution.

SIZE ... About 15,000 students are enrolled at the University of Louvain, of whom about 1,200 are foreigners.

CALENDAR ... The academic year begins the first of October and runs through May. Examinations are given during June, July and September.

COURSES OF STUDY ... The University of Louvain began with Faculties of Law, Medicine, Philosophy and Letters, and Natural Sciences. In 1432 Faculties of Theology and Canon Law were added, and more recently, a Faculty of Economic and Social Sciences.

TUITION ... There is a matriculation fee of $18. Tuition amounts to $80. There is a fee of $12 for examinations, a graduation fee of $3 and laboratory fees of $6 to $10.

ADMISSION REQUIREMENTS ... See the Admission Requirements section in the opening summary on Belgium.

LANGUAGE OF INSTRUCTION ... French and Dutch. The institution is divided into two complete and independent sections. Theses may be written in French, Dutch, English, German, or Italian.

ACCOMMODATIONS ... The University provides board and room for some students for a very low fee. Private accommodations may be found through the University Social Center.

AVERAGE COSTS ... Foreign students must find private accommodations for about $600 per academic year. Tuition and fees will amount to about $100, and the United States student will need about $30 per month for other expenses.

STUDENT LIFE ... Students gather in cafés to talk over the problems of the world. Belgium is so small that it is possible to visit the whole country without difficulty. It has great diversity and much interest for the student from the United States.

University of Louvain, Library

BRAZIL

UNIVERSITIES OF BRAZIL ... The university system in Brazil is relatively new. Previously, higher education was conducted by independent and specialized faculties. The first university was organized in 1920 as the University of Rio de Janeiro by merging three already existing schools. In 1934 the University of São Paulo was established followed by the University of Brazil, which incorporated the faculties of the University of Rio de Janeiro in 1937. The University of Brazil became the model for other institutions that were established.

Each university in Brazil is required to have a faculty of philosophy and letters where secondary school teachers may be trained.

BRAZILIAN UNIVERSITY SYSTEM ... The university system in Brazil is quite different from the system found in American universities. First of all, the academic year in Brazil begins in March and continues until the end of June. In July the students take a month-long vacation and return to begin their second semester on August 1. This term ends in mid-November. Exams are held in June and November.

Many university classes are conducted at 5:00 p.m. or later because so many students as well as professors work during the day. Although many universities are private, all are regulated in accordance with government requirements. Private institutions can and do receive financial assistance from the federal government because they are government controlled. All state and private institutions must be accredited by the Ministry of Education if their diplomas are to be valid. Brazilian universities are administered by a rector and a university council. The rector is appointed for a 3-year term subject to reappointment for as many terms as his faculty support him.

Universities in Brazil are divided into faculties and institutes. These divisions correspond more or less to our departments or schools in U.S. universities. Each unit is administered by a director, a council and assembly of faculty members. The director is responsible to the rector of the university for administration.

The length of time taken to graduate from a Brazilian university varies with each course of study. For example, to graduate from a Faculty of Law takes 5 years and each year's courses are prescribed, with no variation possible. An additional 2 years are required for the Doctorate in Law. A course in Medicine requires 6 years, Architecture 5 years, Engineering 5 years, Education 4 years, Agronomy 4 years, Diplomacy 3 years and Dentistry 3 years. Students who successfully complete their course of study receive a Bachelor's degree.

ADMISSION REQUIREMENTS ... Special students are admitted without examinations. It is very difficult for a foreign student to enter a Brazilian university, since the administration of each university as well as each individual student body opposes accepting foreigners because of a general lack of housing facilities. Thus an individual student, to enroll at the University of Brazil, for example, would have to come down to Rio and pass all regular entrance exams; chances of passing them are poor. On the other hand, Brazil will accept foreign students from countries with which Brazil has a Cultural Covenant (including U.S.) and assign them to universities in Brazil without the entrance exam. In case of such special visiting students, no degrees are granted to graduating students, and they are not permitted to practice their profession in Brazil. The special students can come under a Brazilian Government scholarship, a Fulbright Commission Scholarship or on their own by applying to the Brazilian Embassy. Each Brazilian Embassy receives yearly quotas of vacancies for each country, and can route the student to Brazil, where the Foreign Ministry will send the applicant to the Ministry of Education for assignment to one of the local universities.

CREDIT TOWARD AN AMERICAN DEGREE ... Brazilian universities do not give hour credits toward degrees according to courses taken. It is, therefore, impossible for a student to earn quarter or semester credits to apply to a U.S. degree unless such study is specifically accepted by an individual university in the United States.

TUITION ... Regular students pay a very small tuition fee at government universities and much higher tuition fees at private universities. Special foreign students do not pay tuition fees.

LIVING COSTS ... There are no dormitories or student houses on university campuses; therefore students must arrange to live in private homes. It is not advisable for a student to rent his own apartment, since it is quite expensive to do so. A student can plan to live comfortably on $200 a month.

COMMON COURTESIES AND LOCAL CUSTOMS ... The dinner hour is generally from 8:00 to 10:00 p.m. Dressing at the University is more formal than in the United States. Men are expected to wear tie and jacket to class. It is customary to shake hands with everyone to whom you are introduced.

HOW TO GET THERE ... By Pan American Jet Clipper 8¾ hours from New York to Brasilia, 10 hours to Rio, an hour more to São Paulo. By ship from New York, about 11 days.

FOR FURTHER INFORMATION ... See the How to Enroll section at the end of each individual university listed in this chapter.

For travel particulars and documentation, write to Educational Department, NHE, Pan American Airways, Pan Am Building, New York, N. Y. 10017.

UNIVERSITY OF BRAZIL, RIO DE JANEIRO

The first university in Brazil, the University of Rio de Janeiro, was established in 1920 by merging three already existing schools—the Law School, the Medical School and the Polytechnic School of Rio de Janeiro. In 1937 the University was reorganized, expanded and given the name of the University of Brazil. All the faculties, institutes and schools of the University are located in Rio.

University of Brazil

SIZE ... The University of Brazil has a total of 14 faculties and schools, as well as 8 specialized institutes. There are approximately 1,770 professors and 8,200 students at the University.

CALENDAR ... The first semester begins the first of March and continues until the end of June. The second semester begins the first of August and terminates in mid-November. Exams are in June and November. There is a month's vacation in July.

It is always summer in Rio. During the winter season, June to September, temperatures below 50 degrees are almost unknown.

COURSES OF STUDY ... The University is composed of the following faculties and schools: the National Faculties of Medicine, Law, Odontology, Philosophy, Architecture, Economic Science, Pharmacy, Fine Arts, Engineering, Music, Mines and Metallurgy, Chemistry, Physical Education, and Nursing.

The specialized institutes include the Electro-Technical Institute, Institutes of Psychology, Psychiatry, Biophysics, Nutrition, Neurology, Gynecology.

TUITION ... Special foreign students do not have to pay tuition fees at all.

ADMISSION REQUIREMENTS ... See the Admission Requirements section in the opening summary on Brazil.

LANGUAGE OF INSTRUCTION ... All courses are conducted in Portuguese.

ACCOMMODATIONS ... The University of Brazil has no dormitory facilities. A student, therefore, must rent a room or small flat.

AVERAGE COSTS ... A single student can live in Rio on about $200 a month.

STUDENT LIFE ... Since Brazilian students do not live in dormitories or student houses on campus and often are only part-time students, the University offers few extracurricular activities. There is, however, a national organization called the National Union of Students which functions as a co-ordinating body to local chapters. Some of its activities include publishing periodicals, providing cultural activities, and representing student interests with faculty and government.

HOW TO ENROLL ... For complete information on the University of Brazil, write to the UNIVERSIDADE DO BRASIL, Avenida Pasteur, 250, Rio de Janeiro, D.F., Brazil.

UNIVERSITY OF SÃO PAULO

The University of São Paulo was established in 1934 by incorporating several existing schools with several newly created schools. The majority of schools today are located in São Paulo with a few being situated in several of the surrounding Brazilian states. These schools are autonomous, within limits established by the decree that created the University of São Paulo.

SIZE ... The University of São Paulo is composed of 13 schools, 20 institutes and numerous complementary institutes. There are over 7,000 students enrolled in all the divisions of the University.

CALENDAR ... The school year is divided into two periods: from the first of March to the end of June and from the beginning of August to the end of November. Exams are given in June and November. School vacations are during the month of July and during the period from mid-December to mid-February.

COURSES OF STUDY ... The University of São Paulo consists of the following university institutions:

a) The Law School—with a 5-year undergraduate course and a 2-year doctorate course. The Law School Library, composed of 100,000 volumes, is considered the largest library specializing in law in Brazil.

b) The Polytechnic School—maintains regular courses for civil engineers, mechanical and electrical engineers, chemical engineers, and mining and metallurgical engineers. Each course is for 5 years except the Mining and Metallurgical course, which requires 6 years.

c) The Medical School—offers a regular basic course of Medical Science which covers a 6-year period, and a clinical course. The school maintains a modern hospital of 238 rooms with a capacity of 1,200.

In addition, there are the Schools of Philosophy, Science and Letters, Pharmacology and Dentistry, Veterinary Medicine, Agriculture, Hygiene and Public Health, Economic and Administrative Sciences, Architecture and Urbanism, Medicine, an Engineering School, and a new school of Pharmacology and Odontology.

The Faculties of Engineering and Medicine have exceptionally fine reputations.

TUITION ... The schools mentioned above are all free, whereas the institutes of the University charge a fee for the entrance examination, for laboratory work, and for the issuance of diplomas and certificates.

ADMISSION REQUIREMENTS ... The University of São Paulo gives preference to postgraduate foreign students applying for admission. However, the regular foreign student can enroll at the University under the following conditions:

a) He must present official documents proving that his secondary school certificates enable him to attend a university in his own country.

b) He must have a Brazilian consular authority or a diplomatic authority in his own country approve all his documents.

c) He must revalidate his secondary course in Brazil, for which he must apply for authorization to the Diretoria do Ensino Secundario, do Ministerio da Eucacão e Cultura, in Rio de Janeiro.

d) The revalidation requires examinations in the Portuguese language, geography and history of Brazil, and other subjects which the candidate may not have studied. It is, therefore, necessary that a foreign student attach *all* documents pertaining to his school record to his application for admission so that the Diretoria do Ensino Secundario can determine what additional exams the candidate must take.

Once a foreign student has passed the revalidation exams, he must apply directly to the faculty of the university which he has chosen in order that he may take the required entrance examination. He is subject to the same conditions as Brazilian students applying for admission.

LANGUAGE OF INSTRUCTION ... All courses are conducted in Portuguese.

ACCOMMODATIONS ... The University of São Paulo provides no dormitory facilities for its students. Therefore one must make his own arrangements to live in a boardinghouse.

AVERAGE COSTS ... A student can live in São Paulo on about $200 a month.

STUDENT LIFE ... As in other Latin American universities student life at the University of São Paulo is nonexistent. Social activities are carried on outside the university—namely within one's own family group.

HOW TO ENROLL ... For complete information on the University of São Paulo, write to the UNIVERSIDADE DO SÃO PAULO, Rua Helvetia, 49/55, São Paulo, Brazil.

University of São Paulo, Engineering School

CANADA

Canada today is in a cultural ferment. As the country approaches the centennial of Confederation in 1967, scholastic and artistic endeavors are in rapid acceleration. At all levels of society, these endeavors reflect a more conscious and more articulate search for a distinctive Canadian identity.

Certain realities, long submerged by adherence to pragmatic values, are now being faced. The viability of a dual Canadian culture in a North American environment is now being debated and the mood among Canadian thinkers is becoming more introspective.

French-speaking Canada, comprising one-third of the Canadian population and enjoying a culture and language of its own, is no longer satisfied with its right to merely survive in Quebec and expects that the bilingual and basically bicultural character of Canada will be effectively recognized.

Everywhere traditional values, both political and cultural, are being subjected to critical reappraisals

In our French- and English-speaking Canadian universities soul-searching has made common cause with the more orthodox academic pursuits. The resultant atmosphere for students is dynamic, stimulating and rewarding. It should be an atmosphere of special interest to American students to whom the warm hand of friendship and hospitality is extended. Apart from participating in provocative dialogue, American students will find in Canadian universities high academic standards and excellent facilities. They will also find a deep respect for the free exchange of ideas, concepts and values. We welcome them to our academic round table.

Honorable Maurice Lamontagne
Secretary of State of Canada

UNIVERSITIES IN CANADA ... Canada has many universities and colleges with general powers to confer degrees. Several of these have affiliated or federated colleges, and more than 300 other institutions offer courses at university level. Enrollments range from a few dozen students to more than 12,000.

Some Canadian universities and colleges are controlled by provincial governments, some by religious groups, and some are independent. In general it can be said that the method of control has no bearing on the academic standards, which are consistently high in the major institutions. Total enrollment is about 160,000 and the projection for 1970 is 230,000.

The language of instruction is English at all main universities except Laval, Montreal and Sherbrooke, where it is French. The University of Ottawa has instruction in both languages.

CANADIAN UNIVERSITY SYSTEM ... Each of the ten provincial governments is responsible for education; there is no co-ordinating national department.

The organization and procedure at most Canadian universities are similar to those in the United States. There are evidences of the British tradition of education, with an effort to give individual instruction and counsel; in the French-speaking universities in Quebec province the organization resembles the French system. In education as in other things, however, Canada has evolved a system that is distinctively its own.

Courses lead in three to five years to a Bachelor's degree in arts, pure science, and such professional fields as engineering, business administration, agriculture and education. Certain other courses are longer, such as those in law, theology, dentistry and medicine, usually requiring all or part of a course in arts or science, which is usually required as a base for these specialized studies.

Many of the Bachelor's degrees in Canada represent one year of studies beyond most Bachelor's degrees in the U.S. A general, ordinary or "pass course" in a Canadian university is equivalent to a Bachelor's degree course in most U.S. universities; an "honors course" takes a year longer. (The adjectives refer to length and extent of courses rather than grades.)

A Master's degree normally requires one year of studies beyond a Bachelor's degree from an honors course, and after that a doctorate normally requires at least two further years.

ADMISSION REQUIREMENTS ... The admission requirements vary from one Canadian university to another. Most state their requirements in terms of certificates for completion of secondary schooling, as issued by provinces. The schooling of each applicant from outside the country is assessed individually in relation to these Canadian certificates.

Admission follows 11 to 13 years of elementary and secondary schooling. Some universities admit students who have earned their junior matriculation, while others have senior matriculation as a prerequisite. The pass course for a Bachelor's degree takes three years from senior matriculation and the honors course takes four years; from junior matriculation, each takes one additional year.

Graduation from a United States high school usually is equated to junior matriculation, provided the selection of subjects and level of attainment are appropriate; and completion of the freshman year at a United States college, with the same proviso, is equated to senior matriculation. While College Entrance Examining Board tests are taken into consideration by Canadian universities, they do not have the same status as they do in the United States.

In general, suitable qualifications are required in the following subjects: English, at least one other language, mathematics, history and science (either chemistry and physics or botany and zoology).

More than 5 per cent of students in Canadian universities come from other countries. Most courses are open to all who are fully qualified, whether from Canada or elsewhere, but crowding of certain faculties in some universities has made it necessary to limit the number of applicants who can be accepted.

CREDIT TOWARD AN AMERICAN DEGREE ... A student who wishes to attend a Canadian university for only one year and who wishes to receive credit toward an American degree must make arrangements for receiving credit toward his American degree at his own university before he leaves the United States. Because of the variations in credit systems within American universities and colleges, it is impossible to generalize about the number of credit hours a student may receive. Universities in Canada, too, are organized according to a variety of systems. Each student should discuss with his own dean or guidance counselor the requirements for receiving credit and the number of credit hours toward his American degree that may be awarded for study in Canada. Sometimes full credit may be given for the period of study in Canada if the student passes the Canadian examinations. But each American university will make its own evaluation of the study at each Canadian university. Certain certificates can be earned from some Canadian universities.

TUITION AND OTHER COSTS ... Tuition fees vary from one university to another and depend upon the course of study. In general tuition charges range from $150 to $700 per year. Small miscellaneous fees (not exceeding $50) may be charged in addition. Charges for room and board run from $400 to $1,000. Total cost will be from $1,600 to $1,800 for an academic year.

REGULATIONS ... American students need neither a passport nor a visa to enter Canada. It may be necessary, however, to provide Canadian immigration authorities a copy of a birth certificate, a health certificate, a negative chest X-ray certificate, evidence of good character, and evidence of financial competence for the period of study in Canada.

COMMON COURTESIES AND LOCAL CUSTOMS ... In many ways Canada is an economic unit with the United States, so it is not surprising that Canadians and Americans are very much the same sort of people. Americans are likely to feel more at home than anyplace else outside their own country. Courtesies and customs generally are identical to those in the United States, except in the French-Canadian province of Quebec. Perhaps the most important courtesy for a visitor is to inform himself about Canada and to recognize the fact that this is neither a British colony nor an American satellite, but a proud and independent nation.

FOR FURTHER INFORMATION ... For complete information, write directly to the institution of your choice. It is advisable to begin correspondence a year in advance of the time chosen for enrollment.

For travel particulars and documentation, write to Educational Department, NHE, Pan American Airways, Pan Am Building, New York, N. Y. 10017.

HOW TO GET THERE ... By car, train, plane, boat, bike or bus from the U. S. A. Pan Am Jets serve Canada from all parts of the world, through gateway cities of New York, Boston, Chicago, Detroit and Seattle via connecting carriers.

ACADIA UNIVERSITY, WOLFVILLE

Wolfville is a town of 2,413 on Minas Basin, an inlet from the Bay of Fundy on the Atlantic Coast. Acadia University was founded here (as Queen's College) in 1838 by the Nova Scotia Baptist Educational Society, and various legislative acts have led to the present name and status.

The University is Baptist, but without credal restrictions. Governors are nominated by the Associated Alumni and the United Baptist Convention of the Atlantic provinces.

Most of the University's 35 buildings are situated on a high slope facing the Minas Basin, on a 100-acre campus.

SIZE ... About 1,000 full-time students, of whom 10 per cent are from outside Canada.

The Maritime School of Social Work, Halifax, is an associated professional school.

CALENDAR ... Mid-September to early May. Certain courses are given in a summer session from early July to mid-August.

COURSES OF STUDY ... Acadia University has the following departments: Liberal Arts, Commerce, Education, Engineering, Home Economics, Music, Science, Secretarial Science and Theology.

TUITION ... Tuition fees per year: Arts (B.A.), $425; Arts (M.A.), $360; Arts (B.A. Major in Music), $480; Commerce (B. Comm.), $425; Education (B.Ed., Jr. and Sr. Diplomas), $425; Engineering (Certificate), $500; Home Economics (B.Sc. in H.Ec.), $480; Music (B.Mus. & Licentiate), $480; Science

(B.Sc.), $450; Science (B.Sc. & Engineering), $450; Secretarial Science (B.A., & Sec. Sc. Diploma), $450; Theology (B.D. & B.Th.), $400.

ADMISSION REQUIREMENTS ... See the Admission Requirements section in the opening summary on Canada.

ACCOMMODATIONS ... Most of the students are accommodated in the University's nine residences, six for men and three for women.

AVERAGE COSTS ... Residence rates, board and room, $560 per academic year.

STUDENT LIFE ... Cultural, recreational and social events; special-interest clubs and activities.

UNIVERSITY OF ALBERTA, EDMONTON AND CALGARY

Edmonton is a city of 281,000 that has been described as the oil capital of Canada, the gateway to the north country and the air crossroads of the world. It started life as a solitary fur-trading post in 1795; its first house was built in 1874; early in the present century it was a town of only 5,000 people. Much of its commerce and industry today stems from the huge oil and gas fields that in recent years have given Alberta a new prominence in the Canadian economy. Edmonton is the capital of the province, located near its center.

Calgary, in the southern part of the province, began in 1875 as a fort of the Northwest Mounted Police and now is a city of 249,600. It is a commercial and industrial center for cattle and grain areas and also oil and gas. Its most colorful claim to fame is the Calgary Stampede, a week-long rodeo that has a national reputation.

Both cities are clean and modern, and both have professional football and other sports events. They are within short drives of the Rockies and the main resorts there—Banff, Lake Louise and Jasper. Mountain climbing and skiing are among the attractions of the majestic mountains.

The University of Alberta was inaugurated in 1906. It is the provincial university and is non-denominational. Teaching began in Edmonton in 1908 and in Calgary in 1945.

The Edmonton campus is situated on the North Saskatchewan River with a site of 133 acres. The University Farm, extending to 724 acres, is about two miles to the south. On the campus are eleven major teaching buildings, a library, facilities for administration and student activities, residences, and two affiliated colleges.

The Calgary campus is on the Banff Highway on the outskirts of Calgary. On its 240 acres are two major teaching buildings and a library.

Location of the Banff School of Fine Arts and Centre for Continuing Education is on the slopes of Tunnel Mountain above the town of Banff. It has one large instructional building, several smaller ones, and residences.

Distinctive programs among the varied courses include agriculture, northern studies, cancer research, theoretical physics, cosmic ray studies, petroleum engineering, and medical laboratory science.

Acadia University, University Hall

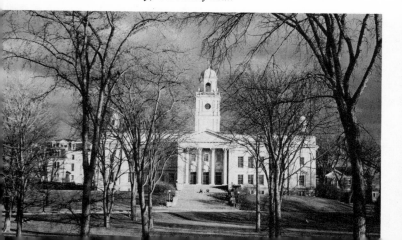

University of Alberta

SIZE ... About 6,000, of whom 2 per cent are from outside Canada.

Constituent teaching organizations are University of Alberta in Calgary, and the Banff School of Fine Arts. Affiliated are St. Joseph's College (Roman Catholic), St. Stephen's College (United Church), Camrose Lutheran College (Lutheran), Lethbridge Junior College (non-denominational) and Mount Royal College (United Church).

CALENDAR ... Mid-September to early May. Certain courses are offered at a summer session from early July to mid-August, and at an intersession (for graduate students) from early May to mid-September.

COURSES OF STUDY ... The University of Alberta has the following departments: Agriculture, Arts and Science, Commerce, Education, Household Economics, Nursing, Pharmacy, Physical Education, Physical and Occupational Therapy, Engineering, Law, Dentistry, Medicine.

TUITION ... Tuition fees per academic year, full time: (a) for First degree—Agriculture, Arts and Science, Commerce, Education, Household Economics, Nursing, Pharmacy, Physical Education, Physical and Occupational Therapy, varying between $250 and $290, according to course and year; Engineering, $340; Law, $340; Dentistry, $425; Medicine, $425–$525; (b) for Master's degree—$250 ($125 additional in second year); (c) for Doctor's degree—$500 in a 2-year program, $250 additional for third year.

ADMISSION REQUIREMENTS ... See the Admission Requirements section in the opening summary on Canada.

ACCOMMODATIONS ... The University maintains residences for a small proportion of the students, and it helps the others to find private room and board.

AVERAGE COSTS ... Residence rates, room and board per month $70–$75 (or about $560–$600 per academic year). Private room and board can be expected to be somewhat higher.

STUDENT LIFE ... Cultural, social, recreational and sports events, including intercollegiate sports; special-interest clubs and activities.

ASSUMPTION UNIVERSITY OF WINDSOR

Windsor is a city of 114,400 that lies across the Detroit River from Detroit. It is an industrial and commercial center and, as in other Canadian border cities, its people have much in common with their neighbors across the line.

Assumption University of Windsor was founded (as Assumption College) in 1857. It was affiliated with the University of Western Ontario for many years before it became independent in 1953.

The University is conducted by the Basilian Fathers, with the co-operation of community representatives on its administrative bodies, and offers its facilities to all regardless of creed.

Assumption University of Windsor

Assumption is the only Roman Catholic university in the world which has an Anglican college affiliated.

The 100-acre campus is south of the Detroit River by the Ambassador Bridge, which links Canada and the United States. There are four teaching buildings, a library, administration building, gymnasium and swimming pool, and residences.

SIZE ... About 1,500 full-time students, of whom 14 per cent are from outside Canada.

University College (Roman Catholic, Basilian) is a constituent college.

Affiliated are Canterbury College (Anglican), Essex College (non-denominational), Holy Names College (Roman Catholic, Sisters of the Holy Names of Jesus and Mary, women only) and Holy Redeemer College (Roman Catholic, Redemptorist, men only).

CALENDAR ... Mid-September to early May. Summer session is held from early July to mid-August.

COURSES OF STUDY ... Assumption University of Windsor has the following departments: Arts and Science, Commerce, Engineering, Nursing, and Theology.

TUITION ... Tuition and incidental fees per year, full time: Engineering, $550; all other courses (undergraduate), $465, (graduate), $412.50, plus $100 non-resident fee for students from outside Canada.

ADMISSION REQUIREMENTS ... See the Admission Requirements section in the opening summary on Canada.

ACCOMMODATIONS ... Residence halls are maintained for a portion of the students, and others find private lodgings.

AVERAGE COSTS ... Residence rates, board and room $700 to $715 per academic year. Private board and room are usually slightly higher.

STUDENT LIFE ... Cultural, recreational and social events; special-interest clubs and activities; intercollegiate sports.

University of British Columbia

UNIVERSITY OF BRITISH COLUMBIA, VANCOUVER

Vancouver, Canada's third largest city, is the center of commerce, industry, finance and shipping on the Pacific Coast. It has a population of 384,500 and a reputation for progress and intense civic pride. In its setting of mountains, hills and island-dotted ocean it is perhaps the most picturesque of any Canadian city, and it is in the area which has the mildest climate in the country.

After relatively slow growth during most of the 1800s, Vancouver gained impetus toward its present stature with the completion of a transcontinental railway line, cutting through the Rocky Mountains, in 1885. The city now has a wide diversity of attractions for visitors, ranging from professional sports to the Vancouver Festival of the Arts. It has a colorful Chinatown, a busy waterfront and verdant park areas.

The University of British Columbia was established in 1908. It is the provincial university and is non-denominational.

The 1,000-acre campus is situated on the peninsula of Point Grey, bounded on three sides by the Gulf of Georgia. Buildings there include 15 teaching buildings, an administration building, library, faculty club, gymnasium, auditorium, residences, student union and five affiliated colleges.

Distinctive programs among its varied courses are oceanography, fisheries, community planning, neurological research and cancer research.

SIZE ... About 14,500 students, of whom 4 per cent are from outside Canada.

Affiliated are the Anglican Theological College of British Columbia (Anglican, men only), Carey Hall (Baptist, men only), St. Andrew's Hall (Presbyterian, men only), St. Mark's College (Roman Catholic, men only), Union College of British Columbia (United Church), Victoria College (non-denominational).

CALENDAR ... Mid-September to early May. Summer session from the end of June to mid-August.

COURSES OF STUDY ... The University of British Columbia has the following departments: Agriculture, Architecture, Arts and Science, Education, Home Economics, Library Science, Nursing, Physical Education, Engineering, Forestry, Commerce, Law, Pharmacy, Social Work, Medicine.

TUITION ... Tuition fees per academic year, full time: (a) for First degree—Agriculture, Arts and Science, Education, Home Economics, Nursing, Physical Education, $346; Applied Science, Architecture, Forestry, Commerce, Law, Pharmacy, Social Work, $396; Medicine, $551; (b) for graduate studies, $346.

ADMISSION REQUIREMENTS ... See the Admission Requirements section in the opening summary on Canada.

ACCOMMODATIONS ... The University maintains residences for some of its students and helps others to find private room and board.

AVERAGE COSTS ... Residence rates per academic year, room and board, $435 to $543. Private room and board can be expected to be slightly higher.

STUDENT LIFE ... Cultural, social and recreational events; intercollegiate sports; special-interest clubs and activities.

CARLETON UNIVERSITY, OTTAWA

Carleton University is situated on a 130-acre campus on the Rideau River at Ottawa, the capital of Canada. (For information about the city, see University of Ottawa.)

Carleton College was established in 1942 as a non-sectarian institution. It became Carleton University in 1957.

A program of new buildings began in 1957 and to date an arts building, science building, library and field house have been completed. In September 1962 a classroom building, two student residences, a university student center and major additions to the present arts and science building and a cafeteria center were completed.

Among the varied courses are distinctive programs in public administration, journalism, Canadian studies and engineering.

SIZE ... About 1,550 full-time students, of whom 7.5 per cent are from outside Canada.

CALENDAR ... Mid-September to late May. Summer session is held from the first week of July to mid-August.

COURSES OF STUDY ... Carleton University has the following departments: Arts and Science, Commerce, Engineering, Journalism, Public Administration.

TUITION ... Tuition fees and incidental costs per academic year, full time: $465 to $525.

ADMISSION REQUIREMENTS ... See the Admission Requirements section in the opening summary on Canada.

ACCOMMODATIONS ... New men's and women's residences were opened in September 1962. Board and room for the academic year are $675 for double rooms and $700 for single rooms. Accommodation can also be found in private homes near the University.

Carleton University

DALHOUSIE UNIVERSITY, HALIFAX

Nova Scotia is a province of varied scenery—of rugged rock formations, tranquil fishing villages, sandy coves, grassy fields, green orchards. Halifax, its capital, is the center from which to see these surroundings. Founded in 1749 as a military and naval base, Halifax is today a busy seaport and naval base with a metropolitan population (Greater Halifax and Dartmouth) of about 200,000. Halifax has such historic landmarks as St. Paul's, the oldest Protestant church in Canada; the Citadel, a massive fortress built in 1749, now a national historic site; and the Old Town Clock, which has kept time since 1803.

Dalhousie University was founded in 1818 by the Ninth Earl of Dalhousie and it was the first Canadian institution of higher learning to be established upon the principle of religious toleration. There are now 23 buildings on two campuses. The university is affiliated with eight hospitals in the immediate vicinity, Maritime Conservatory of Music, N.S. College of Art, Bedford Institute of Oceanography, National Research Council, N.S. Research Foundation, and many other institutions. Distinctive programs, in addition to regular courses, include oceanography, engineering physics, cancer research, medical sciences and clinical medicine, law and community studies by the Institute of Public Affairs.

SIZE ... About 2,500 full-time students, of whom 10 per cent come from outside Canada. The University of King's College is associated with Dalhousie.

CALENDAR ... Early September to mid-May.

COURSES OF STUDY ... Dalhousie University has the following departments: Arts and Sciences, Commerce, Education, Engineering, Law, Nursing, Dentistry, Medicine.

The University has the only organized Faculty of Graduate Studies in the Maritimes. Ph.D. degrees are given in Biological Sciences, Chemistry, Oceanography and Physics.

TUITION ... The following fees are average. Please write to the Registrar, Dalhousie University, Halifax, N. S., for the exact cost of the courses of your choice.

Arts, Science, Education, Commerce, $465; Engineering, $520; Law, $465; Medicine, $550; Dentistry, $585; Graduate Studies, $405.

ADMISSION REQUIREMENTS ... See the Admission Requirements section in the opening summary on Canada.

ACCOMMODATIONS ... The University maintains residence halls for 157 male and 210 female students. Others find private lodgings.

AVERAGE COSTS ... Residence rates, board and room, $575 to $638. Private accommodations are usually slightly higher.

STUDENT LIFE ... Dalhousie students have a variety of sports to choose from: swimming, tennis, boating, yachting, golf, fishing, ice skating. The University has the usual cultural, recreational and social events, and special-interest clubs and activities. The foreign students have founded the International Students Association, which embraces many nationalities.

Dalhousie University

University of King's College

UNIVERSITY OF KING'S COLLEGE, HALIFAX

The University of King's College is situated adjacent to Dalhousie University in Halifax (see Dalhousie).

The University was founded in 1789 as King's College at Windsor, Nova Scotia. It was the first university founded in what is now Canada and it is the oldest university in the British Commonwealth outside Great Britain. It moved to its present location in 1923.

King's is an Anglican institution. On its 5-acre campus are classrooms, administration offices, library, residences, dining hall, chapel, President's Lodge and recreation hall.

SIZE . . . About 200 full-time students, of whom 8.5 per cent are from outside Canada.

Associated professional schools are the Maritime School of Social Work and the School of Journalism, Halifax.

CALENDAR . . . Early October to early May.

COURSES OF STUDY . . . The University of King's College has the following departments: Arts and Sciences (through Dalhousie University), Journalism, Social Work, and Theology.

TUITION . . . Tuition fees for full-time students are about $488 per year.

ADMISSION REQUIREMENTS . . . See the Admission Requirements section in the opening summary on Canada.

ACCOMMODATIONS . . . Nearly all students can be accommodated in the residence halls for men and for women. A new gymnasium with swimming pool and residential facilities for a further 100 students were completed in 1962.

AVERAGE COSTS . . . Residence rates, room and board, $575 to $625 per academic year.

STUDENT LIFE . . . Cultural, recreational, sports and social events; special-interest clubs and activities.

LAVAL UNIVERSITY, QUEBEC

Quebec City, the capital of the province of Quebec, located beside the St. Lawrence River, is a city steeped in history and tradition. It is a center of French-Canadian culture and its steep old streets, its distinctive buildings and market places, its monuments and churches, its museums, its provincial parliament buildings—all add charm to Quebec's grace and beauty. The predominant language is French in this city of 172,000.

Among the many churches and chapels of interest in Quebec are the Basilica of Notre Dame, built on the foundations of a church standing in 1647, and the chapel of Notre Dame des Victoires, built in 1688, which is a repository for art treasures. The parliament buildings date back to 1878 and are of French Renaissance architecture.

Laval University was founded in 1852 by the Seminary of Quebec. It is Roman Catholic and it is the oldest French-language university on the continent. On its two campuses are a total of fourteen buildings.

Among distinctive programs in addition to regular courses are folklore and special philosophical studies. During the 6-week summer session there are courses for foreign students who wish to learn the French language or improve their knowledge of it.

SIZE . . . About 11,000 full-time students, of whom one per cent are from outside Canada.

CALENDAR . . . Mid-September to late May. A number of courses are offered in the summer session, from July to mid-August.

COURSES OF STUDY . . . Laval University has the following departments: Agriculture, Arts and Sciences, Commerce, Education, Law, Medicine, Music, Pharmacy, Nursing and Theology.

SUMMER COURSES . . . French language at all levels and French Literature, teaching methods and philosophy; Spanish language—conducted in French and English.

TUITION . . . Tuition fees for full-time students per year: Faculty of Theology, $350; Philosophy, $350; Law, $350; Medicine, $500 (for students from outside Canada, $600); Arts: Music, $50 to $100; Education, $350; Letters, $350; Sciences, $400; Social Sciences, $350.

ADMISSION REQUIREMENTS . . . See the Admission Requirements section in the opening summary on Canada.

LANGUAGE OF INSTRUCTION . . . French.

ACCOMMODATIONS . . . Accommodations are available in residence halls for some of the students; others find private lodgings.

AVERAGE COSTS . . . Room and board cost an average of $700 per academic year.

STUDENT LIFE . . . The city of Quebec has many attractions for students, including such events as the once-weekly night of French-Canadian folk dancing along the boardwalk in front of the Château Frontenac. At the University itself there are sports, cultural, recreational and social events, along with special-interest clubs and activities.

Laval University, Faculty of Commerce

University of Manitoba

McGill University, Arts Building

UNIVERSITY OF MANITOBA, WINNIPEG

Winnipeg, the capital and metropolis of Manitoba, is a city of 265,400 population on the historic Red River in the south-central part of the province. It achieved prominence in the eighteenth and nineteenth centuries as the gateway to Canada's west and northwest. Today it retains the position of the main commercial and financial center for the agriculture of the west and the furs of the northwest.

Nearly 100 public parks, gardens and squares beautify the city. Ballet, symphony and theater are among the cultural attractions. There is a varied assortment of sports events, including professional football.

The University of Manitoba was established in 1877. It is a non-denominational provincial university, located on the Red River in the rural municipality of Fort Garry about seven miles from the center of Winnipeg. On the 1,200-acre main campus are 17 teaching buildings, the facilities of 2 affiliated colleges, and a library.

Distinctive programs among the varied courses include agriculture, community planning, interior design, Icelandic and Slavic studies.

SIZE ... About 7,000 full-time students, of whom 7.1 per cent are from outside Canada.

Affiliated are Brandon College, (non-denominational), the Manitoba Law School, Collège de Saint-Boniface (Roman Catholic, men only, instruction in French), St. John's College (Anglican), St. Paul's College (Roman Catholic) and United College (United Church).

CALENDAR ... Mid-September to early May. A summer session is held from early July to mid-August.

COURSES OF STUDY ... The University of Manitoba has the following departments: Agriculture, Architecture, Arts and Sciences, Commerce, Dentistry, Education, Engineering, Fine Arts, Home Economics, Law, Medicine, Nursing Education, and Social Work.

TUITION ... Tuition fees per academic year, full time: (a) for First degree—Law, $250; Agriculture, Arts, Education (1st year), Fine Arts, Home Economics, Interior Design, Nursing Education, $250; Commerce, Science, Social Work, $300; Pharmacy, $350; Architecture, Engineering, $400; Dentistry, $425; Medicine, $500; (b) for Master's degree, $160–$300; (c) for Doctor's degree—each year $250; examination and degree $75.

ADMISSION REQUIREMENTS ... See the Admission Requirements section in the opening summary on Canada.

ACCOMMODATIONS ... The University maintains residence accommodations for some of the students and helps the others to find private room and board.

AVERAGE COSTS ... Residence rates per month, room and board, $55 (or about $440 per academic year); private room and board can be expected to be slightly higher.

STUDENT LIFE ... Cultural, social, recreational and sports events, including intercollegiate sports; special-interest clubs and activities.

McGILL UNIVERSITY, MONTREAL

Montreal is Canada's biggest city, and one of the most cosmopolitan and intriguing on the continent. Of the close to 2,109,500 residents of greater Montreal—there are 1,191,100 in the city itself—more than two-thirds are French-Canadian. With the French language predominant, Montreal is the second largest French-speaking community in the world. But a large proportion of the population speaks both French and English and on every hand you encounter the bilingual character of Montreal—in speech, in press, in street names and signs, in cuisine and entertainment.

The site of the city is a large island connected to the mainland by 13 bridges spanning the St. Lawrence and several other rivers. Dominating the city is a 500-acre park, located atop a high hill called Mount Royal, from which the city derives its name. Jacques Cartier sailed 1,000 miles up the St. Lawrence River from the Atlantic in 1535 to become the first European to land on the site of Montreal. Ocean ships, both liners and freighters, still navigate the wide river to make this the largest inland seaport in the world.

Throughout the centuries, shipping has combined with finance, commerce and industry to make Montreal a major center of culture and business. Historic sites abound throughout the area. St. Joseph's Oratory dedicated to Brother André attracts more than 3,000,000 visitors each year.

There is a wide variety of entertainment, cultural events and sports available throughout the year. Starlight concerts atop Mount Royal, a French-Canadian theater directed by Gratien Gelinas, the Montreal Museum of Fine Arts, Château de Ramezay are only a few of the attractions. Winter and summer sports both abound with professional baseball, hockey and football teams headquartered in the city. Numerous yacht clubs and excellent golf courses are found on the island. Within an hour's drive north of the city are the Laurentian Mountains, one of the finest skiing areas in North America, and a major factor in making the Montreal area a year-round rendezvous for both spectator events and personal recreation.

McGill was founded under the bequest of the Hon. James McGill, a prosperous Montreal merchant who died in 1813. It was established as a university in 1821. It is non-denominational.

There are sixty-eight buildings on the main campus, a 65-acre area on the lower slopes of Mount Royal. These include teaching buildings, administration buildings, students' union, and residences. The University's extensive collections of general interest are housed in the Redpath Museum, the McCord National Museum, and the Ethnological Museum.

Among the distinctive programs at McGill, in addition to a full calendar of undergraduate and graduate courses, are Arctic studies, cellulose chemistry, community planning, cyclotron physics, international air law, Islamic studies, neurology, meteorology, parasitology, radiochemistry, international social work, and woodlot management.

SIZE ... About 9,000 full-time students, of whom 15.6 per cent are from outside Canada.

Constituent colleges are Macdonald College at Ste. Anne de Bellevue and Royal Victoria College, Montreal.

Affiliated are the Montreal Diocesan Theological College (Anglican, men only), the United Theological College of Montreal (United Church) and the Presbyterian College of Montreal (Presbyterian, men only).

CALENDAR ... Mid-September to early May. (June in Medicine and Dentistry and other professional schools.) Summer session from July to mid-August.

COURSES OF STUDY ... McGill University has the following departments: Agriculture, Architecture, Arts and Sciences, Commerce, Dentistry, Education, Engineering, Home Economics, Law, Library Science, Medicine, Music, Nursing, Physical Education, Physical and Occupational Therapy, Social Work, and Theology.

SUMMER COURSES ... French language, literature and civilization. French language conducted in French.

TUITION ... Fees per academic year, including tuition and miscellaneous fees: Architecture, $525; Arts, $425; Commerce, $425; Dentistry, $500; Divinity, $400; Education, $425; Engineering, $525; Graduate Studies, $425; International Air Law, $425 (1st, 2nd and 3rd years), $350 (4th year); Library School, $425; Medicine, $600; Music, $400–$550; Physical and Occupational Therapy, $400; Science, $475; Social Work, $425.

ADMISSION REQUIREMENTS ... See the Admission Requirements section in the opening summary on Canada.

ACCOMMODATIONS ... The University maintains residence halls for a portion of the students; for the others the University offers assistance in finding private room and board.

AVERAGE COSTS ... Residence rates per academic year, room and board, $675 to $835 for men, $725 to $910 for women. Private room and board are usually slightly higher.

STUDENT LIFE ... There is a diversity of activities for students, including cultural, recreational and social events; special-interest clubs and activities; and intercollegiate sports such as football, basketball, hockey, track and field.

McMASTER UNIVERSITY, HAMILTON

Hamilton is an industrial center of 274,000 at the western end of Lake Ontario, fronting on a fine harbor and backed by the steep rise of the Niagara Escarpment. In heavy industry, particularly steel, it ranks as a major contributor to the Canadian economy.

Parklands in many parts of the city—such as the vast Royal Botanical Gardens on the north and west outskirts—add beauty to the community. Football and other sports, concerts and light entertainment are among the attractions for visitors as well as residents.

McMaster University had its beginnings in the Canada Baptist College, founded in Montreal in 1836; Woodstock College, founded in Woodstock, Ontario, in 1857; and Toronto Baptist College, founded in Toronto in 1881. McMaster University was incorporated in 1887, under Baptist direction, and it was located in Toronto until 1930, when it moved to a new campus at Hamilton.

The University now is a non-denominational private institution. The traditional Baptist connection is continued through an affiliated theological college.

The large campus is in the west end of Hamilton, bordered by parkland of the Royal Botanical Gardens, in whose program the University co-operates. There are 20 permanent and 5 temporary buildings, including library, nuclear research building, research greenhouse, teaching and administration buildings and residences. McMaster University is unique in being the possessor of a nuclear reactor, the first on a university campus in the British Commonwealth.

Distinctive programs among the varied courses of study include nuclear and atomic research, biology, psychology and engineering, (particularly chemical, metallurgical, and engineering physics).

SIZE ... About 2,000 full-time students of whom 5 per cent are from outside Canada.

Constituent colleges are Hamilton College and University College. Affiliated are McMaster Divinity College (Baptist) and Women's Leadership Training School (Baptist, women only).

CALENDAR ... Late September to mid-May. A summer session is held from early July to mid-August.

McMaster University, Tower Building

COURSES OF STUDY ... McMaster University has the following departments: Arts and Sciences, Commerce, Engineering, Nursing, Physical Education, and Theology.

TUITION ... Tuition fees per academic year, full time: (a) Arts, $465; Engineering, $550; Nursing, $350; Science, $465; (b) for Master's degree—$325 for 1st year, $175 for 2nd year, $50 for subsequent years; (c) for Doctorate—$325 per year for two years, $50 per year for on-campus study thereafter, $10 per year for off-campus study thereafter. B.D. course, $87.50 per year.

ADMISSION REQUIREMENTS ... See the Admission Requirements section in the opening summary on Canada.

ACCOMMODATIONS ... The University maintains residences for a portion of the students, and it helps others to find private room and board.

AVERAGE COSTS ... Residence rates per academic year, room and board, $625. Private room and board are usually slightly higher.

STUDENT LIFE ... Cultural, social, recreational and sports events; special-interest clubs and activities.

MEMORIAL UNIVERSITY OF NEWFOUNDLAND, ST. JOHN'S

St. John's is a city of 63,600 on the eastern coast of Newfoundland, Canada's easternmost province. Built on hills overlooking a fine harbor, it is the capital of the province, the center of its commerce and industry and the base of its great fishing fleet. The history of the city goes back to the early 1500s. It was a naval base during the American Revolution and the War of 1812, and an army, naval and air force base during the Second World War. It is also the place where Marconi heard the first transatlantic wireless message (1901).

Memorial University of Newfoundland was founded in 1949, succeeding Memorial University College, which had been founded in 1925. It is the provincial university and is in the midst of a building program on a new 120-acre campus, with the first five buildings completed in the summer of 1961.

SIZE ... About 2,000 full-time students.

Affiliated are Queen's College (Anglican, men only) in St. John's, and St. Bride's College (Roman Catholic, women only) in Littledale, Newfoundland.

CALENDAR ... Mid-September to mid-May. A summer session is held from the end of June to early August.

COURSES OF STUDY ... Memorial University of Newfoundland has the following departments: Arts and Sciences, Commerce, Education, Engineering, Forestry, Physical Education.

TUITION ... Full-time tuition fees per year: (a) for First degree—Arts I and II, Education I and II, $235; Arts III and IV, Education III and IV, Science I and II, $240; Pre-Medical I, Science III and IV, Engineering I, $245; Pre-Medical II and III, Engineering II, Forestry I and II, $250; Engineering III, $255; (b) for Master's degree—$240.

ADMISSION REQUIREMENTS ... See the Admission Requirements section in the opening summary on Canada.

ACCOMMODATIONS ... There are two student residences and a dining hall. Private board and room are readily available as well.

AVERAGE COSTS ... Private room and board could be expected to be $500 to $650 per academic year.

STUDENT LIFE ... Cultural, recreational, sports and social events; special-interest clubs and activities.

UNIVERSITY OF MONTREAL

The University of Montreal is on a 125-acre campus on the slopes of Mount Royal in Montreal. (For information about Montreal, see McGill University.)

The University is one of Canada's largest, and it is the largest French-speaking university on the continent. Most of its faculties are housed in tall modern buildings on the main campus.

Teaching began in 1878, when the University was set up as part of Laval University. In 1920 it became independent with its present name and status. It is a private institution with both Roman Catholic and civil charters.

Special programs among the wide variety of courses include nuclear physics, microbiology and hygiene, psychology, simultaneous translation and interpretation, Slavic and Eastern European studies, experimental medicine and surgery, town planning, gerontology.

SIZE ... About 21,000 full-time students (including all affiliated institutions), of whom about 2 per cent are from outside Canada.

Connected with the University are 13 affiliated institutions, 25 colleges for male students, 6 colleges for female students, and 22 other institutions, including music and home economics schools.

CALENDAR ... Mid-September to the end of May. A summer session is held from the first of July to mid-August.

COURSES OF STUDY ... The University of Montreal has the following departments: Agriculture, Arts and Sciences, Dentistry, Commerce, Education, Health and Physical Education, Law, Medicine, Music, Nutrition, Optometry, Pharmacy, Social Work, Theology, Veterinary Medicine.

SUMMER COURSES ... French language and literature at various levels—conducted in French.

TUITION ... Tuition fees for full-time students per academic year: Hospital Administration, $500; Agriculture, $200; Arts, various; Dentistry, $475; Commerce, $240 (1st year); Law, Medieval Studies, Philosophy, Religious Sciences, Psychology,

University of Montreal

Rehabilitation, Social Sciences, Social Service, $375; Health, Physical and Recreational Education, $115 (per term); Engineering, $350 (1st year); Medicine, $525; Veterinary Medicine, various; Music, Dietetics and Nutrition, $360; Optometry, $400; Education, $150 to $375; Pharmacy, Science, $425; Theology, $200.

ADMISSION REQUIREMENTS ... See the Admission Requirements section in the opening summary on Canada.

LANGUAGE OF INSTRUCTION ... French.

ACCOMMODATIONS ... The University maintains on the campus a residence for male students. It can also provide lists of suitable living accommodations. Many students live in boarding-houses or privately operated hostels or students' homes.

AVERAGE COSTS ... Private room and board can be expected to cost $700 per academic year.

STUDENT LIFE ... The city of Montreal has many attractions for students. At the University itself there are sports, cultural, recreational and social events, along with special-interest clubs and activities.

MOUNT ALLISON UNIVERSITY, SACKVILLE

Mount Allison University, New Physics and Engineering Building

Sackville, a town of 3,000, is a few miles from the sea both to the north and south on the narrow isthmus linking New Brunswick and Nova Scotia. Mount Allison Wesleyan College was founded here in 1843 as an academy, and it became Mount Allison University in 1913.

The connection of the University is with the United Church of Canada, but it is conducted on non-sectarian principles. It is privately endowed.

Location of the University is on a hilltop in the center of the town, overlooking the Tantramar Marshes. There are eight teaching buildings on the 100-acre campus, and a library, administration facilities, rink and gymnasium.

Distinctive programs among the varied courses are music, fine arts, French, and institution management.

SIZE ... The University has about 1,200 full-time students, of whom 7 per cent are from outside Canada.

The Maritime School of Social Work is associated.

CALENDAR ... Mid-September to early May. A summer session is held from early July to mid-August.

COURSES OF STUDY ... Mount Allison University has the following departments: Arts and Sciences, Commerce, Education, Fine Arts, Home Economics, Music, Secretarial Studies.

TUITION ... Tuition and Incidental fees per academic year, full time: (a) for First degree—Arts, $460, Arts with Secretarial Certificate, $460; Commerce, $460; Education, $460; Fine Arts, $525; Home Economics, $475; Music, $500; pre-Medical and pre-Dental, $475; Science, $475; (b) postgraduate year, $300.

ADMISSION REQUIREMENTS ... See the Admission Requirements section in the opening summary on Canada.

ACCOMMODATIONS ... Mount Allison is basically a residential college, with three residences for women and four for men.

AVERAGE COSTS ... Residence fees per academic year, room and board, $590.

STUDENT LIFE ... Cultural, recreational, sports and social events; special-interest clubs and activities.

UNIVERSITY OF NEW BRUNSWICK, FREDERICTON

Fredericton, a city of 19,700, is the capital of New Brunswick and one of the main centers of trade and commerce in the province. Described as the "City of Stately Elms," Fredericton is situated on a graceful bend of the famed Saint John River. Of United Empire Loyalist beginnings, the city wears her traditions proudly and includes among her noted educational and cultural facilities one of the finest galleries in Canada, the Beaverbrook Art Gallery.

The hillside University, which affords a panoramic view of the city and surrounding slopes of the historic Saint John River Valley, also traces its beginnings to the United Empire Loyalists. It was they who brought the standards of Harvard and King's College, New York, to the New Brunswick wilderness and on December 13, 1785, petitioned the Governor-in-Council for a Provincial Academy of Liberal Arts and Sciences. In 1800 the Academy was transformed by Royal Charter into the College of New Brunswick, and through various legislative acts it has achieved its present name and status. The University is a provincial institution and is non-denominational.

On campus are seven classroom buildings, a library, creative arts center, students' center, administration buildings, including the oldest existing university building in Canada, a gymnasium and residences. A University forest tract of 7,000 acres is available for field work in forestry.

Distinctive programs in addition to the varied courses include forestry, mining and surveying engineering, nursing, education, and research in structural chemistry covering the whole field of aconite alkaloids.

SIZE ... About 2,200 full-time students, of whom 7 per cent are from outside Canada.

CALENDAR ... Mid-September to mid-May. A summer session is held from early July to mid-August.

COURSES OF STUDY ... The University of New Brunswick has the following departments: Arts and Sciences, Business Administration, Education, Engineering, Forestry, Nursing, Physical Education.

TUITION ... Tuition fees per year, full time: Nursing, $360; Education, $410; Physical Education, $410; Law, $400; Arts, Business Administration, $435; Science, $460; Forestry, $485; Engineering, $510 1st year, $535 all others.

ADMISSION REQUIREMENTS ... See the Admission Requirements section in the opening summary on Canada.

ACCOMMODATIONS ... The University maintains several residence halls for men and women; the Accommodations Office will assist those students requiring private lodgings.

AVERAGE COSTS ... Residence rates, room and board, $575 to $650; private room and board are usually slightly higher.

STUDENT LIFE ... Cultural, recreational, sports and social events; special-interest clubs and activities, including a closed-circuit radio station, campus literary magazine and Canada's oldest official student newspaper.

University of New Brunswick

University of Ottowa, Administration Building

UNIVERSITY OF OTTAWA

Ottawa is the capital of Canada and in many ways it is typical of the country. It is on the upper fringe of the commercial and financial area dominated by Montreal and Toronto. It is across the Ottawa River from the province of Quebec, and English and French languages and cultures are side by side and intermingled. One of Canada's great primary industries, lumbering, was important in its early growth and still plays a significant role in Ottawa's economy. Less than a century removed from pioneer days, the city combines the vitality of youth with the dignity and confidence of maturity.

In the early days, beginning as a lumber camp, it was a settlement called Bytown. Its selection as the capital in the mid-nineteenth century gave impetus to steady growth and propelled the city to international prominence.

The population of Ottawa is 268,200 and its biggest single industry and interest is government. Here are the stately parliament buildings, overlooking the river from a 35-acre park; the residence of the Governor-General; the ceremonies and functions that carry on the traditions accompanying Canada's democratic government; the office buildings where thousands of men and women perform the detailed daily tasks of federal departments and commissions; the embassies of other nations throughout the world; and such accessories to a capital as the National Gallery, the National Museum, the Supreme Court and the Public Archives.

The Capital District Commission is in the midst of a program to further plan and beautify the city and surrounding area. Professional sports (especially football), a symphony orchestra and an active amateur theater are examples of the varied attractions for visitors. The Tulip Festival in May is renowned for its spectacular beauty. Nearby are the Laurentian Mountains, one of the finest skiing areas on the continent.

The University of Ottawa was founded (as College Saint-Joseph) in 1848 and subsequently achieved its present name and status. It was granted a charter as a bilingual university in 1866, and it now offers most of its courses in both French and English. It is under Roman Catholic direction.

The campus at present covers an area of 39 acres in the Sandy Hill district of Ottawa and it will expand in future to extend over a distance of a mile along the left bank of the Rideau Canal. There are nine teaching buildings, six temporary buildings, six faculty and school libraries, the University of Ottawa Press, and residences.

Distinctive programs among its varied courses are psychiatry, radiology, and computer programming and operation as applied to accounting and management control.

SIZE ... About 4,000 full-time students, of whom 10 per cent are from outside Canada.

St. Patrick's College (Roman Catholic) is a constituent college. There are ten affiliated colleges, some of them in Western Canada.

CALENDAR ... Mid-September to the end of May. A summer session is held from about the first of July through the first week of August.

COURSES OF STUDY ... The University of Ottawa has the following departments: Arts and Sciences, Commerce, Education, Engineering, Law, Library Science, Medicine, Nursing, Social Work and Theology.

TUITION ... Tuition fees per academic year, full time: Nursing (diploma), $90 to $130; Science, $340 to $490; Arts, Commerce, Social Sciences, $340 to $485; Philosophy, $385; Theology, Canon Law, $315; Law, $405; Social Welfare, $350; Engineering, $340 to $530; Psychology, Education, Library Science, $415; Medicine, $480 to $590.

ADMISSION REQUIREMENTS ... See the Admission Requirements section in the opening summary on Canada.

LANGUAGES OF INSTRUCTION ... The University uses both French and English as languages of instruction. Most courses are available in either language.

ACCOMMODATIONS ... The University maintains residences for a small proportion of its students. Most find private room and board.

AVERAGE COSTS ... The cost of room and board can be expected to be $500 to $700 per academic year.

STUDENT LIFE ... Location in Canada's capital provides many areas of interest for students. At the University there are cultural, recreational, sports and social events, and special-interest clubs and activities.

QUEEN'S UNIVERSITY, KINGSTON

Kingston is a city of 53,500 on the northeast shore of Lake Ontario. It was prominent in Canada's early history and once was the capital. Here is the site of Fort Frontenac, built in 1673, rebuilt in 1675, of which only the foundations now remain; Fort Frederick, built during the American Revolution as a shore battery to protect nearby naval yards, of which the stone tower still stands; Old Fort Henry, built as a blockhouse during the War of 1812, now restored as an attraction for historians and tourists and patrolled by red-uniformed guards.

Kingston has been a garrison town, and the military, along with the University, still helps to shape the character of this commercial and industrial center. Just to the east is the Royal Military College (similar to West Point in the U. S.), one of Canada's three tri-service colleges.

Queen's University at Kingston was founded (as Queen's College at Kingston) in 1841 by the Presbyterian Church of Canada in connection with the Church of Scotland. By successive legislation it became non-denominational and achieved its present name and status under its own independent directorate.

The University is near the heart of Kingston. It has 25 teaching buildings, an administration building, two libraries, laboratories (including a synchroton laboratory and a foreign language laboratory), an experimental station, residence and dining accommodations, an art center, music room and gymnasium. Queen's has its own radio station, operated by the Student Radio Club.

Distinctive programs among the varied courses include local government, the summer institute of economic research, geophysics, radio astronomy and nuclear physics.

SIZE ... About 3,500 full-time students, of whom 5 per cent are from outside Canada.

Queen's Theological College (United Church, co-educational) is affiliated.

Queen's University, Grant Hall

CALENDAR ... Mid-September to mid-May. A summer session is held from early July to mid-August.

COURSES OF STUDY ... Queen's University at Kingston has the following departments: Arts and Science, Business Administration, Commerce, Education, Engineering, Law, Medicine, Nursing, Physical and Health Education.

TUITION ... Tuition fees per year, full time: (a) for First degree—Arts and Science, Commerce, Law, Nursing, $410; Medicine (pre-Medical years), $425; Physical Health and Education, $425; Engineering (1st and 2nd years), $500; Medicine (medical years), $550; Engineering (3rd and 4th years), $550; (b) for Master's degree—Arts, Science, $325; Business Administration, $425; (c) for doctorate—$325; (d) for graduate diplomas—Engineering, Medical Radiology, Diagnosis, Therapy, $325; Business Administration, $425.

ADMISSION REQUIREMENTS ... See the Admission Requirements section in the opening summary on Canada.

ACCOMMODATIONS ... The University has residence accommodations for nearly half the students. Others find private lodgings in the city.

AVERAGE COSTS ... Residence rates, board and lodging, $600 to $680 for the academic year. Private board and room are usually slightly higher.

STUDENT LIFE ... Cultural, recreational and social events; special-interest clubs and activities; intercollegiate sports, especially football and basketball.

ST. FRANCIS XAVIER UNIVERSITY, ANTIGONISH

Antigonish is a town of 4,300 on George Bay, which is off the Gulf of St. Lawrence on the north shore of Nova Scotia. The University was founded as a diocesan college in 1853 in Arichat, Nova Scotia, and transferred to Antigonish two years later.

The University has six teaching buildings, a library, chapel, gymnasium, rink, and residences. It is Roman Catholic and is widely known for its work in adult education.

SIZE ... About 1,600 full-time students, of whom 2.5 per cent are from outside Canada.

Xavier Junior College and the Coady International Institute are integral parts of St. Francis Xavier University.

The Maritime School of Social Work is an associated professional school. Affiliated are Mount St. Bernard College (Roman Catholic, women only) and St. Martha's School of Nursing (Roman Catholic).

CALENDAR ... Mid-September to mid-May. A summer session is held from early July to mid-August.

COURSES OF STUDY ... St. Francis Xavier University has the following departments: Arts and Science, Commerce, Education, Engineering, Nursing, Secretarial Studies.

TUITION ... Tuition fees per year, full time: Arts, $475; Science, $525.

ADMISSION REQUIREMENTS ... See the Admission Requirements section in the opening summary on Canada.

ACCOMMODATIONS ... Nearly all students are accommodated in the six men's and two women's residences.

AVERAGE COSTS ... Board and room per academic year, about $645.

STUDENT LIFE ... Cultural, recreational and social events; special-interest clubs and activities.

UNIVERSITY OF SASKATCHEWAN, SASKATOON AND REGINA

The act establishing the University of Saskatchewan was passed in 1907 but first classes were not held until the fall of 1909. The University is a provincial university, is non-denominational and grants all degrees in Saskatchewan except Theology, which is awarded by the following three affiliated institutions: Emmanuel College, St. Andrew's College and Luther Theological Seminary.

At Saskatoon (population 95,500), the University occupies a 2,600-acre site on the South Saskatchewan River. The campus covers 140 acres; the other acreage is set apart for the University's farm and experimental plots. There are 15 buildings on the campus in which classes are given regularly, a library, farm building, facilities for administration and student activities, residences, one federated arts college and two affiliated theological colleges.

Regina is the capital city of Saskatchewan with a population of 112,000. As enrollment demands and finances permit, the southeast skyline of Regina is undergoing dramatic alteration as the University of Saskatchewan, Regina Campus, slowly rises above the prairie on a 180-acre site.

The University operates a summer art school on a 128-acre site it owns at Emma Lake in northern Saskatchewan.

Among distinctive programs on the Saskatoon campus are agriculture, northern studies, upper atmospheric research, cancer research and community studies. In a few years a program involving use of one of the most powerful linear electron accelerators in the world will be under way.

SIZE ... About 6,500 degree and other day students, of whom 3 per cent are from outside Canada. In addition there is a large number of night class, correspondence and summer school students.

St. Thomas More College (Roman Catholic) is a federated arts college. Affiliated are Campion College (Roman Catholic), Emmanuel College (Anglican), Luther College (Lutheran), Luther Theological Seminary (Lutheran, men only), St. Andrew's College (United Church), St. Chad's College (Anglican), St. Peter's College (Roman Catholic, men only), and Saskatchewan Teachers College (provincial, non-denominational).

CALENDAR ... Late September to early May. Certain courses are offered in an intersession, May and June, and in a summer session, early July to mid-August.

COURSES OF STUDY ... The University of Saskatchewan has the following departments: Agriculture, Arts and Sciences, Commerce, Education, Engineering, Home Economics, Law, Medicine, Nursing, Pharmacy, and Physical Education.

TUITION ... Tuition fees per academic year; full time: (a) for First degree—Agriculture, Arts and Sciences, Education, Home Economics, Nursing, $200 to $225; Commerce, Law, Pharmacy, $225 to $250; Engineering, $275 to $350; Medicine, $425 to $475; (b) for Master's degree, $175; (c) for Doctor's Degree, 1st and 2nd years, $175; 3rd year, $125; examination $75.

ADMISSION REQUIREMENTS ... See the Admission Requirements section in the opening summary on Canada.

ACCOMMODATIONS ... The University maintains residences for a small number of students, and helps others to find private room and board.

AVERAGE COSTS ... Residence rates per month, room and board, $66–$73 (or about $495–$548 per academic year). Private room and board can be expected to be slightly higher.

STUDENT LIFE ... Cultural, social, recreational and sports events, including intercollegiate sports; special-interest clubs and activities.

University of Saskatchewan

University of Sherbrooke

UNIVERSITY OF SHERBROOKE

Sherbrooke is a commercial and industrial center (population 66,500) in the portion of Quebec Province that is south of the St. Lawrence River. Over three-quarters of the people are French-Canadian, and French is the predominant language. There is a sizable English-speaking group, too, and bilingualism is common.

The University was founded in 1954 as a Roman Catholic institution. Most of the buildings are on a 1,000-acre campus on the outskirts of the city, including the following teaching buildings: Sciences, Commerce, Law, Arts, University College, School of Education, Teachers College for Men, and Divinity School. Also on the campus are the Administration Building, chapel, cafeteria, library, students' social center and men's residence hall.

SIZE ... About 2,300 full-time students, while more than 3,000 attend affiliated colleges or are enrolled as part-time students.

CALENDAR ... Mid-September to mid-May.

COURSES OF STUDY ... The University of Sherbrooke has the following departments: Arts and Sciences, Commerce, Education, Home Economics and Law.

TUITION ... Tuition fees for full-time students per year: Science and Commerce $380; Law and School of Education $350; Arts $300.

ADMISSION REQUIREMENTS ... See the Admission Requirements section in the opening summary on Canada.

LANGUAGE OF INSTRUCTION ... French. In Science and Commerce, lectures are also given in English.

ACCOMMODATIONS ... Besides a residence for faculty members, four men's residence halls accommodate 500 students. The University helps students to find suitable private room and board.

AVERAGE COSTS ... The cost of private room and board can be expected to be from $450 to $700 per academic year.

STUDENT LIFE ... Cultural, recreational, sports and social events; special-interest clubs and activities.

UNIVERSITY OF TORONTO

Toronto is a bustling city on the north shore of Lake Ontario, capital of the province of Ontario and the main center of its commerce, finance and industry. This is Canada's second largest city with a population of 672,400, and it is the hub of a fast-growing, closely integrated metropolitan area with total population of more than a million and a half.

Entertainment and cultural attractions are diverse and numerous. There are professional sports (including hockey, football and baseball), amateur sports in abundance, active theater and concert groups, performances by leading artists and entertainers from New York, Hollywood and London, as well as from throughout Canada. The Royal Ontario Museum (which is within the framework of the University of Toronto) is the largest museum in the British Commonwealth outside London.

The University of Toronto was founded (as King's College at York) in 1827 as a state university in close connection with the Church of England. In 1849 it became the non-denominational University of Toronto. It has since grown into a federation of universities and colleges, centered on a campus about a mile square near the heart of the city. In all it has more than 100 buildings. It is the provincial university but draws direction and support from an alliance of government, business and the public.

Distinctive programs, in addition to the varied courses

University of Toronto, The Great Hall

available, include astronomy, medical research, hygiene, aeronautical research, child study, East Asiatic studies, Near Eastern studies, Slavic studies, nuclear engineering, forestry, medieval studies, art and archaeology, and anthropology.

SIZE ... About 15,000 full-time students, of whom 10.5 per cent are from outside Canada.

The University now is in the midst of a building program that is planned to handle an enrollment of 23,000 by 1968.

Many of the institutions within the University of Toronto framework have long and distinguished histories of their own, and independent reputations for scholarship.

Federated universities are the University of St. Michael's College (Roman Catholic), the University of Trinity College (Church of England) and Victoria University (United Church).

York University is affiliated. It was founded in 1959 and is scheduled to be affiliated only for four to eight years.

Federated colleges are Knox College (Presbyterian), Wycliffe College (Anglican), Emmanuel College of Victoria University (United Church) and Massey College.

Also affiliated are the Federated Colleges comprising Macdonald Institute, Ontario Agricultural College and Ontario Veterinary College, all of Guelph, Ontario.

CALENDAR ... Mid-September to early May. Certain courses are also offered in an intersession, May and June; and in a summer session, early July to mid-August.

COURSES OF STUDY ... The University of Toronto has the following departments: Agriculture, Architecture, Arts and Sciences, Commerce, Dentistry, Education, Engineering, Forestry, Home Economics, Law, Library Science, Medicine, Music, Nursing, Pharmacy, Physical and Health Education, Social Work, Veterinary Medicine, Theology.

TUITION ... Full-time academic fees per year: (a) for First degree—Applied Science and Engineering, $600; Architecture, $600; Art as applied to Medicine, $410; Artist and Licentiate Diplomas in Music, $410–$470; Arts and Sciences, $410; Certificate Courses for Nurses, $410; Certificate in Teaching Physical and Occupational Therapy, $300; Child Study, $300; Commerce, $440; Course for Graduate Nurses, $410; Dental Hygiene, $410; Dentistry, $600; Education, $200; Forestry, $440; General Music and Musical Education, $410; Household Science, $410; Law, $440; Library School, $250 (non-Ontario students, $310); Medicine, $650; Nursing (basic course), $340; Pharmacy, $440; Physical and Health Education, $440; Physical and Occupational Therapy, $425; pre-Medicine and pre-Dentistry, $410; Science of Dentistry, $250; Science of Medicine, $250; (b) for graduate courses—Graduate Studies, $375; Master of Surgery, $185; Social Work (Bachelor), $440; Diploma or Certificate Courses—Anaesthesia, $150–$200; Bacteriology, $575; Dental Public Health, $375; Hospital Administration (2 years), $650; Industrial Health, $575; Medical Radiology, $95–$210; Nutrition, $575; Public Health, $575; Psychiatric, $95–$140; Speech Pathology and Audiology, $400; Town and Regional Planning, $310; Veterinary, Public Health, $575.

ADMISSION REQUIREMENTS ... See the Admission Requirements section in the opening summary on Canada.

ACCOMMODATIONS ... Several residence halls are maintained by the University and its federated and affiliated institutions. Many students find private lodgings close to the campus.

AVERAGE COSTS ... Residence rates, board and room, $585 to $629. Private room and board are usually slightly higher.

STUDENT LIFE ... Cultural, recreational and social events; special-interest clubs and activities; a wide range of intercollegiate sports, including football and basketball.

UNIVERSITY OF WESTERN ONTARIO, LONDON

London is located in southwestern Ontario, the hub of a thriving area of agriculture, commerce and industry. It has a wide variety of attractions in the fields of sports, entertainment, culture and education.

The University was founded in 1878 as The Western University of London, Ontario. Various legislative acts have led it to the present title and status. Western is privately controlled but receives financial support from the City of London, the Province of Ontario and the federal government.

The main campus is a 300-acre area on the outskirts of the city. There are 13 teaching buildings, 2 libraries, an administration building and 2 medical research buildings.

In addition to the varied courses available, the University has two distinctive summer programs: a summer school in French Canada (at Trois-Pistoles, Quebec), and a summer school of Indian archaeology at Penetanguishine, Ontario.

SIZE ... About 5,000 full-time students, of whom 4.5 per cent are from outside Canada.

Constituent colleges are University College, Middlesex College and the College of Music.

Affiliated are Huron College (Anglican), St. Peter's College of Arts (Roman Catholic, men only), College of Christ the King (Roman Catholic, men only) and Ursuline College (Roman Catholic, women only).

CALENDAR ... Mid-September to mid-May. Certain courses are duplicated in a summer session from early July to mid-August.

COURSES OF STUDY ... The University of Western Ontario has the following departments: Arts and Sciences, Business Administration, Engineering, Law, Medicine, and Nursing.

TUITION ... Tuition and incidental fees per year, full time: (a) undergraduate—Medicine, $675; Engineering, $550; Law, $500; Business Administration, $465–$490; Arts and Sciences, $425–$465; all others, $465; (b) graduate studies—M.B.A., LL.M., $490; M.Sc.N., $465; M.Cl.Sc., $405; all others, $340; part time (per course), $70–$85.

ADMISSION REQUIREMENTS ... See the Admission Requirements section in the opening summary on Canada.

ACCOMMODATIONS ... Several residence halls are maintained by the University and its affiliated colleges. Some students find private lodgings, however, and a committee of the University will provide students with a list of suitable boardinghouses or student homes.

AVERAGE COSTS ... Residence rates, board and room, $600–$650 for 33 weeks. Private board and room are usually slightly higher.

STUDENT LIFE ... Cultural, recreational and social events; special-interest clubs and activities; intercollegiate sports, especially football and basketball.

University of Western Ontario

CHILE

★ SANTIAGO

CHILE

UNIVERSITIES OF CHILE ... There are several very fine universities in Chile which deserve to be mentioned. They are as follows:

The National University of Chile, one of the most important universities in Latin America, has its faculties, schools, and institutes located in both Santiago and Valparaiso; The Catholic University of Chile, in Santiago, is a pontifical university with a well-organized and highly competent faculty. Of all the Chilean universities, the University of Concepción, in Concepción, most nearly resembles an American university campus. In contrast with other Chilean institutions of higher learning, most of its staff is employed full time. The Technical University Federico Santa Maria situated in Valparaiso was created as a private foundation devoted to the instruction of industrial crafts and engineering. Its faculties are perhaps the best in the country and its staff has been recruited according to strict selection standards, mostly from Germany. In addition, there are the Technical State University in Santiago, the Catholic University in Valparaiso, the University Austral in Valdivia and the University of the North in Antofagasta.

CHILEAN UNIVERSITY SYSTEM ... Chilean universities are patterned after the European lecture system, which involves very little student participation in the classroom. Class attendance is often strictly controlled. Instead of the credit system used in the United States, students are automatically promoted to the next year after completing satisfactorily examinations given at the end of the academic year. They graduate after submitting a thesis and passing a final exam.

ADMISSION REQUIREMENTS ... It is generally required that those applying for admission to a university in Chile submit a letter stating their previous schooling, courses followed, and enclose a certified grade transcript approved by the Chilean Consul in the student's own country.

CREDIT TOWARD AN AMERICAN DEGREE ... Generally speaking, degrees issued by American universities are not recognized in Chile, nor are university studies in Chile accredited in the United States. Therefore, American graduate students should not expect to obtain credits during their stay in Chile. They may, however, enroll as *alumnos libres* and perhaps employ the result of their research and studies in writing a thesis or dissertation that may help them obtain an advanced degree in the United States. There are ample courses for U.S. graduate students and researchers in Hispanic-American literature, Spanish language, and arts of Chile and South America.

REGULATIONS ... For student visa and entrance procedure, see the For Further Information heading at the end of this section.

TUITION ... Tuition is generally very low at each university in Chile. In some cases it is based upon how much the student can afford to pay. The minimum established is $2. A student, however, must be prepared to pay for books and materials.

LIVING COSTS ... It is difficult to calculate the cost of living for a student, owing to the differences in personal tastes and needs. However, $150 has been established as an amount adequate for average monthly requirements.

COMMON COURTESIES AND LOCAL CUSTOMS ... The dinner hour is 9 o'clock or later in Chile. If invited for dinner to a Chilean home, ask your host the time you are expected, and you may correctly arrive about half an hour late. It should not be much more, since cocktails are usually served before dinner, and this will help you get more easily acquainted with your hosts and other guests. Time to leave depends mostly on how the party is going, keeping in mind, however, if the next day is a work day or a holiday. If asked to stay longer, you may, because this request is usually born out of enjoyment and not just mere politeness.

FOR FURTHER INFORMATION ... For complete information about a university and how to enroll write to the individual university. For information on the University of Chile write to UNIVERSIDAD DE CHILE, Alameda Bernardo O'Higgins, 1058 Casilla 10–D, Santiago, Chile.

For travel particulars and documentation, write to Educational Department, NHE, Pan American Airways, Pan Am Building, New York, N. Y. 10017.

HOW TO GET THERE ... By National, Pan American and Panagra without change of plane down the west coast of South America, 14 hours (elapsed time) from New York, 10¼ hours from Miami. Stopovers if you wish en route. By Pan American Jet Clipper down the east coast, 12½ hours to Buenos Aires from New York. Then, by Panagra, Santiago is 1¾ hours from Buenos Aires. From the United States West Coast, flights for South America connect at Miami or Panama City. By ship, about 18 days from New York to Valparaiso and about 30 days from the United States West Coast.

UNIVERSITY OF CHILE, SANTIAGO

The University of Chile, founded in the year 1842, has been the country's main cultural center for a century. The University, with its numerous faculties, is located in the heart of Santiago, the capital of Chile.

SIZE ... Enrolled in the University's 12 faculties and 55 schools are approximately 14,500 students.

CALENDAR ... The regular school year begins mid-March and continues until mid-December with a 2- or 3-week vacation in July and another week in September. The summer school is held during January and February. It is important to remember that their summer season is our winter. Santiago, however, is mild the year round. The climate is similar to that of Southern California.

COURSES OF STUDY ... The National University of Chile is composed of the following 12 faculties: Agronomy, Architecture, Musical Arts, Fine Arts, Economic Sciences, Juridical and Social Sciences, Animal Husbandry, Philosophy and Education, Medicine, Odontology, Chemistry and Pharmacy. In addition, there are 55 schools that report to these faculties, as well as several research institutes and graduate centers.

TUITION ... Tuition is dependent upon how much the student can afford to pay for his studies. It is recommended, however, that he pay not less than $2 a year. The actual matriculation fees are approximately $5 a year. Students must buy their own books which generally cost $20 a year. This fee varies with the student's particular field of study.

ADMISSION REQUIREMENTS ... The admission of North American students will be based on the letter written by the candidate requesting admission. This letter should contain the following information:

a) The material and/or courses the student wishes to study
b) A complete statement of previous schooling, giving names of schools, courses studied, etc.
c) Information considered pertinent by the student.

The request for admission will not be considered complete unless the student also sends a certified or photostatic copy of his credits. This certified grade transcript *must be approved by a Chilean Consul in the United States.*

LANGUAGE OF INSTRUCTION ... All university courses are conducted in Spanish.

ACCOMMODATIONS ... Since there are no university dormitories, the University itself will provide students with a list of rooming houses or pensions where they can stay at reasonable rates. Students can also arrange to live with Chilean families.

University of Chile

AVERAGE COSTS ... A student may live reasonably well in Chile on an average of $150 a month.

STUDENT LIFE ... Organized campus life as we know it in the United States is uncommon in Chile. There is, however, an active Student Federation at the University. This organization plays an important role in forming University policy.

COLOMBIA

UNIVERSITIES OF COLOMBIA ... In the year 1844 three university districts were organized with centers in Popayán, Bogotá and Cartagena; colleges were established in many provinces, and normal schools were opened in all of them. Public elementary and university education were greatly broadened in scope by the law of 1867 which authorized the establishment of the National University of Bogotá. Today this university is the leading public institution in Colombia. It is located in a residential district of Bogotá and has a large campus offering housing facilities to its students. The University is well known for its fine Faculty of Medicine.

Twenty-two of Colombia's institutions of higher education are classified as universities, with eleven of them being located in Bogotá. In addition to the National University in Bogotá, there is the University of the Andes and the Javeriana University, a Jesuit university with its well-known Faculty of Architecture.

In Medellín, there are the University of Antioquia and the University of Medellín. The city of Cali maintains the University of Valle. Others to be mentioned are the University of the Atlantic in Barranquilla, and the Industrial University of Santander in Bucaramanga.

COLOMBIAN UNIVERSITY SYSTEM ... In Colombia, the direction and control of public instruction are vested by the Constitution in the President, who delegates authority and responsibility to his Minister of Education. The national officials work in close co-operation with the departmental directors of education appointed by the Minister. Secondary schools and universities are, in general, the responsibility of the national government, whereas public elementary schools are, for the most part, built and financed by the departments and municipalities.

Secondary schools offer a 6-year course following 5 years of elementary education. Completion of the secondary school course is marked by a diploma for the baccalaureate, which is required for admission to a university in Colombia.

The best fields of study on a university level in Colombia are: Colombian and Latin American literature, languages, history and research in anthropology.

Universities in Colombia are modeled after those in Europe, and French has traditionally been the second language studied at Colombian universities.

ADMISSION REQUIREMENTS ... In applying for admission to a Colombian university it is necessary that a student have two years of college and present a record of his grades for the last six years. He must take a medical exam and pass the entrance examination given by the university.

CREDIT TOWARD AN AMERICAN DEGREE ... In order for a U.S. student to receive credit for work done at a Colombian university, he must have his courses evaluated by the American university in which he is enrolled.

REGULATIONS ... For student visa and entrance procedure, see the For Further Information heading at the end of this section.

TUITION ... Tuition varies with each university in Colombia. For example, at the private University of the Andes a student pays approximately $200 a year, whereas at the National University tuition is dependent upon the family's income and how much they can afford to pay.

LIVING COSTS ... Students will find that they can live on approximately $150 a month. This, of course, will not include certain luxuries a student may desire.

COMMON COURTESIES AND LOCAL CUSTOMS ... The dinner hour can often be as late as 10:30 p.m. Night life in Colombia is generally rather formal, the Colombian people being home-loving and more interested in spending their free hours in small gatherings with their friends.

FOR FURTHER INFORMATION ... For complete information about a university and how to enroll, see the How to Enroll section at the end of each university listing.

For travel particulars and documentation, write to Educational Department, NHE, Pan American Airways, Pan Am Building, New York, N. Y. 10017.

HOW TO GET THERE ... By Pan American Jet 4½ hours from New York to Caracas, which in turn is 1½ hours from Bogotá. Miami–Barranquilla 4 hours. Panama to Bogotá nonstop 1¼ hours; Quito–Bogotá 1¼ hours; Panama–Barranquilla 1½ hours; Panama–Medellín 1½ hours; by Panagra, Panama–Cali 1¾ hours; Quito–Cali 1¼ hours.

JAVERIANA UNIVERSITY, BOGOTÁ

The Javeriana University, the oldest of the private universities of Colombia, was founded in 1623 by the Jesuit congregation. It is situated on a very modern campus located in a residential district of Bogotá. The governing body of the University is made up of the Rector assisted by two vice-rectors and the deans of all the faculties.

SIZE ... According to enrollment records there are over 7,000 students in the 21 faculties or approximately 25 per cent of the total number of students attending Colombian universities.

CALENDAR ... The school year begins in the first week of March and ends the second week of December.

COURSES OF STUDY ... The Javeriana University maintains the following schools: Architecture, Economics, Medicine, Philosophy and Letters, Odontology, Civil Engineering, Electronic Engineering, and Social Sciences. Within these schools, but autonomously organized, function the Departments of Bacteriology, Decoration and Art, Dietetics, Languages, Infirmary, and Journalism. Furthermore, there are University extension courses where part-time students can take a variety of single courses. For these courses a certificate of attendance is given.

TUITION ... Students at the Javeriana University pay an annual tuition fee of approximately $250.

ADMISSION REQUIREMENTS ... See column at left.

LANGUAGE OF INSTRUCTION ... All university courses are taught in Spanish.

ACCOMMODATIONS ... The University has a limited number of rooms (dormitory style) available. A deposit of $10 is required and the monthly rate is $5 for triple accommodation without meals.

AVERAGE COSTS ... The estimated minimum monthly allowance for an American student living in Bogotá is $150.

STUDENT LIFE ... Students at the Javeriana University participate in numerous sports events, publish several magazines and can take an active part in scientific and fine arts conferences.

HOW TO ENROLL ... For complete information on the Javeriana University, write to: UNIVERSIDAD PONTIFICIA JAVERIANA, Carrera 7a–#40–62, Bogotá, D.E., Colombia.

University of the Andes

UNIVERSITY OF THE ANDES, BOGOTÁ

The University of the Andes, founded in 1948 by a group of young Colombians, is a completely independent school. Overlooking the city, the University rests on a steep rocky slope of the beautiful Andean mountain chain that surrounds the plains of Bogotá. It is probably the only truly private university in Latin America. The University receives some of its financial support from individuals but more from domestic companies and international firms operating in Colombia. Unlike other universities in Latin America, the Andes has many full-time teachers.

SIZE ... There are approximately 1,000 students enrolled in the University. Of the total student body, 150 are girls.

CALENDAR... The school year begins the first week in February and continues until the second week of December.

The climate in Bogotá is cool throughout the year, similar to spring in the United States. Summer session is conducted from mid-June through July.

COURSES OF STUDY ... The University of the Andes maintains the following schools: Architecture, Economics, Engineering, Fine Arts, Philosophy and Letters, and Science. Within these schools, but autonomously organized, function the Departments of Bacteriology, Biology, Chemistry, English (which is required of all students), Humanities, Languages (other than English and Spanish), Mathematics, Physics, pre-Medical and Spanish. Furthermore, there are university extension courses where part-time students can take a variety of single courses. For these courses a certificate of attendance is given, whereas the full-time students enrolled in any of the schools receive a regular degree recognized by the Ministry of Education in Colombia.

The University of the Andes finances a study-abroad program by a rotating loan fund, which provides the amount which the student or his family cannot raise on their own. These loans are paid back by the student at an interest rate of 10 to 20 per cent of his monthly salary once he has finished his studies and is working in Colombia.

SUMMER COURSES ... The summer school at the Andes is conducted from mid-June through July. Since all instruction is in Spanish, admission is limited to students who have had one or two years of Spanish at the college level. The special course for undergraduates includes: Spanish (intermediate and advanced), Latin American Economics, Socio-political History, and Introduction to Ibero-American Literature.

Since the university has no dormitory facilities, it will arrange lodging for the students in private homes at the cost of $110 for the season.

Additional information on the summer school may be obtained by writing to the Secretario General de la Universidad de los Andes, Bogotá 1, D.E., Colombia.

TUITION ... Students at the University of the Andes pay an annual tuition fee of approximately $300.

ADMISSION REQUIREMENTS ... See page 61.

LANGUAGE OF INSTRUCTION ... All university courses are taught in Spanish.

ACCOMMODATIONS ... A student must provide for his own living quarters since the University does not as yet have student housing facilities.

AVERAGE COSTS ... The estimated minimum monthly allowance for an American student living in Bogotá is $140.

STUDENT LIFE ... Although social life is limited at the University, the students do hold occasional dances and gather for informal cookouts.

HOW TO ENROLL ... For complete information on the University of the Andes, write to the UNIVERSIDAD DE LOS ANDES, Calle 18A y Carrera 1 Este, Apartado Aereo 4076, Bogotá, D.E., Colombia.

NATIONAL UNIVERSITY OF COLOMBIA, BOGOTÁ

The National University of Colombia was founded in 1936 by incorporating several already existing faculties, institutions and schools. This autonomous university, situated on a beautiful campus, is located in a residential district of Bogotá called University City.

SIZE ... About 5,000 students enrolled in the 22 faculties, schools and institutes of the National University of Colombia. Co-educational.

CALENDAR ... The academic year at the University begins in March and continues through December. The climate at this time of year is cool, springlike.

ADMISSION REQUIREMENTS ... The National University of Colombia requires a student to present his secondary school certificate, a medical certificate, and take an entrance examination given by the Institute of Applied Psychology of the National University to test the student's knowledge and learning capacity upon applying for admission to the University. All applicants must be at least 16 years of age. Foreign students must have their secondary school certificates revalidated by the Ministry of Education.

REGULAR COURSES OF STUDY ... The National University of Colombia maintains the Faculties of Medicine, Law, Philosophy and Letters, Economics, Science, Dentistry, Veterinary Medicine, Pharmacy, Chemistry, Architecture, Engineering, Agriculture (Medellín), Agriculture (Palmira), Engineering (Manizales), Mining (Medellín), Conservatory of Music, School of Fine Arts, Institute of National Sciences, Radium Institute, Institute of Labor Legislation, Institute of Criminology and Institute of Psychology.

TUITION ... Tuition at the National University is dependent upon the income of the applicant's family and how much they can afford to pay.

LANGUAGE OF INSTRUCTION ... All classes are taught in Spanish. Theses and dissertations must be written in Spanish.

ACCOMMODATIONS ... There are university dormitories and dining facilities for about 300 students. The remaining students live in private homes.

AVERAGE COSTS ... An American student in Bogotá should plan on needing $150 or more a month for board, room and incidental expenses.

STUDENT LIFE ... Students at the National University participate in numerous sports events, publish their own student magazines, and take an active part in politics.

HOW TO ENROLL ... For complete information on the National University of Colombia, write to the UNIVERSIDAD NACIONAL DE COLOMBIA, Ciudad Universitaria, Bogotá, D.E., Colombia.

COSTA RICA

SAN JOSE

COSTA RICA

Costa Rica has one university, the University of Costa Rica, located in San José. In addition there are several private commercial schools, and a government-operated 4-year school of commerce. The Normal School of Costa Rica offers a 2-year course for students who have completed the regular 5-year secondary school program and wish to become elementary school teachers. The Inter-American Institute of Agricultural Sciences is a specialized organization of the Organization of American States. It is primarily a center for research, postgraduate instruction and agricultural extension work.

COSTA RICAN UNIVERSITY SYSTEM ... The University of Costa Rica, an autonomous institution, is governed by a University Rector, a University Assembly and a University Council. The highest authority is the Assembly, which is composed of the Minister of Public Education, who is the presiding officer; professors from the university schools; members of the University Council; members of boards of alumni associations; and student representatives from each school. The Assembly elects the Rector and the Secretary General of the University.

The University Council, made up of the Minister of Public Education, Rector, deans of schools, secretary of the university, and two student representatives, approves the annual budget, revalidates foreign studies and degrees, appoints faculty members, directors, etc.

The Rector of the University administers the University's finances and prepares and submits the annual budget to the Council.

ADMISSION REQUIREMENTS ... In order to be admitted to the University of Costa Rica, a foreign student must present a description of the courses he has taken in his home school so that the University can evaluate his studies and give the student his necessary credits upon entrance. The equivalent of two years of college is required.

CREDIT TOWARD AN AMERICAN DEGREE ... An American student wishing to obtain credit in an American university for studies in Costa Rica must present his transcript from the University of Costa Rica to the U.S. university. Credit toward an American university degree would depend entirely on the American university's evaluation of his work.

At present the University of Kansas and the University of Costa Rica exchange students and professors under a mutual plan whereby both groups receive credit for their studies completed.

REGULATIONS ... For student visa and entrance procedure, see the For Further Information heading at the end of this section.

COMMON COURTESIES AND LOCAL CUSTOMS ... The dinner hour, as in most Latin American countries, is quite late. The Costa Ricans are extremely sociable and do a good deal of entertaining in their homes or in one of the numerous clubs.

HOW TO GET THERE ... By Pan American Clipper direct from Houston via Mexico City and Guatemala in 6 hours, or from San Francisco, Miami or New Orleans via Guatemala. About 1 hour by Clipper from Managua, 1 hour from Panama.

FOR FURTHER INFORMATION ... For complete information about the university and how to enroll, write to the UNIVERSIDAD DE COSTA RICA, Ciudad Universitaria, San José, Costa Rica.

For travel particulars and documentation, write to Educational Department, NHE, Pan American Airways, Pan Am Building, New York, N. Y. 10017.

UNIVERSITY OF COSTA RICA, SAN JOSÉ

The University of Costa Rica was originally founded in 1814 as the Casa de Ensenanza de Santo Tomas. In 1843 it became the Universidad de Santo Tomas. The University closed in 1888 with only the Faculty of Law continuing. The following year the Congress ordered the entire university closed. On March 7, 1941, the University of Costa Rica opened officially. The only university in Costa Rica, it is an autonomous institution both economically and administratively independent of the state. It is governed by a University Rector, University Assembly, and a University Council.

SIZE ... There are approximately 5,600 students enrolled in the 11 schools of the University of Costa Rica. Co-educational.

CALENDAR ... The school year at the University of Costa Rica is held from the beginning of March through November. The climate is ideal at this time of year.

COURSES OF STUDY ... The University maintains the Schools of Agronomy, Fine Arts, Science and Letters, Conservatory of Music, Economic and Social Science, Law, Education, Pharmacy, Engineering, Medicine, Microbiology, and Dentistry.

TUITION ... The average registration fee at the University is $135 per year.

ADMISSION REQUIREMENTS ... See the Admission Requirements section in the opening summary on Costa Rica.

LANGUAGE OF INSTRUCTION ... All classes at the University are conducted in Spanish.

ACCOMMODATIONS ... There are no dormitory facilities at the University. Therefore, it is necessary for students to arrange to live in private homes or in boardinghouses.

AVERAGE COSTS ... A student can live in a boardinghouse for approximately $75 per month. Transportation is readily available and inexpensive.

STUDENT LIFE ... The University offers its students a theater, radio station and sports as a means of encouraging student participation along cultural lines. Conferences, expositions, recitals, etc., are arranged by the University administration.

University of Costa Rica

DENMARK

There is practically no illiteracy in Denmark, where schooling has been compulsory since 1814, and educational facilities are many and thorough. I believe it is not bragging to speak of Denmark as one of the most enlightened countries in the world.

Parents take an intense interest in the education of their children, from elementary school and on, and teachers are held in high esteem as leading personalities in their communities.

A significant feature of rural education has been the Danish Folk School movement started in 1844. In Denmark these schools are known as Folk High Schools but should not be confused with the high school as known in the United States, which in Denmark would correspond roughly to the gymnasium. The Folk High Schools are commonly identified with the names of Bishop N. F. S. Grundtvig, clergyman, poet, philosopher, historian, educator, who conceived the movement, and with Kristen Kold, who largely in the early Folk School carried out Grundtvig's idea. Offering short courses to farmers' boys and girls preferably after, at the age of 17–18, they had worked some time on the farm, they are not vocational schools but cultural, inspiring the young with a desire to serve their community and country. Many of these groups have in time found their places as national leaders and promoters of agricultural co-operation, with resultant great productivity and high quality production. There are today such Folk Schools also for workers.

Reference to the Danish Folk Schools appears in this book. After the war, and the lively student exchange, several of these schools have been centers for study by students representative of less developed countries.

There are over 400,000 Danish-Americans with close family ties to the homeland. We know that there are many students among this group and other Americans who will be vitally interested in knowing of the educational opportunities in our Danish school system and institutes of higher learning. Although space is quite limited, we know that qualified American students studying in Denmark will find our country a second homeland and they will be made to feel at home from the day they arrive.

C. H. W. Hasselriis
Counselor of Information
Danish Government Information Office

HIGHER EDUCATION IN DENMARK ... Denmark has two universities; the major one at Copenhagen is a state institution. The University of Aarhus in Jutland is a self-supporting institution whose constitution and regulations are approved by the Ministry of Education. Additional universities are to be established, including probably one in Odense on Fyn. The technical colleges of Denmark offer degrees in the following: Chemical, Mechanical, Civil and Electrical Engineering; Veterinary and Agricultural Science; Economics and Business Administration; Pharmacy; and Dentistry.

The Royal Danish Academy of Fine Arts includes a School of Painting and Sculpture and a School of Architecture. The Royal Danish Academy of Music, now a state institution, works in co-operation with the University of Copenhagen and with the Royal Danish Opera.

The Scandinavian Seminar was organized in 1949 as an educational experiment in living and learning built around the Danish Folk High School movement. During the years, it has become a recognized program for college undergraduates, graduates and other adults. Those interested in education as a profession find it a particularly rewarding experience.

DANISH UNIVERSITY SYSTEM ... The Danish university system is similar to that of other European universities. The number of university teachers is somewhat small in relation to the number of students, and, generally speaking, participation in university instruction is voluntary. The student may attend lectures, classes and seminars, and present himself for examination when he considers himself ready for it. All students who present themselves for a degree examination must have passed an examination in *Filosofikum* to provide a background for scientific research.

ADMISSION REQUIREMENTS ... Foreign students may be matriculated at Danish universities as transfer students or after special examinations. Certain reservations and restrictions may be made in these cases. The technical schools are generally very crowded but may make exceptions and accept foreign students; in other words, each case is decided on its merits.

A limited number of foreigners may be admitted to the Academy of Fine Arts as temporary students. The Academy of Music may admit foreign students on the recommendation of the Ministry of Education.

The Scandinavian Seminar is open to qualified college undergraduates (except freshmen), graduates and other adults. There are no specific educational prerequisites. Each applicant is considered on his merits. No knowledge of the Scandinavian languages is required prior to acceptancce. The student generally attains fluent knowledge of his Scandinavian language before the end of the Seminar year.

All university students should be reasonably proficient in Danish before the beginning of the school year. Special language courses are offered for this purpose.

CREDIT TOWARD AN AMERICAN DEGREE ... Students who are candidates for a degree in an American university must make arrangements with their dean regarding transfer of credits.

The Scandinavian Seminar gives a certificate of completion to each student who has satisfactorily completed the year's program. Upon the student's request, the Seminar will send to his college an evaluation of his work; and, when justified, will recommend that college credit be granted.

REGULATIONS ... Permission to stay in Denmark is obtained through the Ministry of Justice once you are there. Applications may be sent through a Danish Consulate. If a student speaks Danish, he may consider a job. He will require a working permit, application for which may be obtained through a Danish Consulate provided the student has been promised a job in advance.

TUITION ... University instruction in Denmark is free of charge but in some cases students pay moderate fees for some seminars and special courses of instruction.

The Scandinavian Seminar fee is $1,800, which covers tuition, room and board for the academic year, and transportation from New York to Scandinavia.

LIVING COSTS ... The cost of living in Denmark is considerably lower than in the United States, especially for food and rent. The minimum monthly cost of board and lodging would be $80, and an additional minimum of $20 to $30 for incidentals should be allowed. Membership in a health insurance society is compulsory for citizens and is recommended for foreigners—it covers hospitalization and doctors' services for very small fees. There is a 6-week waiting period before the insurance takes effect, therefore students are advised to join immediately on arrival.

The exchange rate is about 7 kroner to the dollar (1 krone is about 15 cents).

LOCAL CUSTOMS ... Denmark is one of the tidiest countries in Europe. Everything is bright and shining. The people are genial and gay, the food is wonderful and plentiful. "Thank you" (*tak*) is the most often heard phrase in Denmark. You shake hands when you meet people and when you say good-bye.

The Committee for the Propagation of Knowledge about Denmark Abroad offers holiday courses in elementary Danish and introductory lectures on various aspects of Danish life and culture, along with some excursions.

FOR FURTHER INFORMATION ... For complete information about a school and how to enroll, write to the Danish Information Office in New York at 588 Fifth Avenue. Those interested in the Scandinavian Seminar program should contact their office at 62 West 58th Street, New York, N. Y. 10019.

For travel particulars and documentation, write to Educational Department, NHE, Pan American Airways, Pan Am Building, New York, N. Y. 10017.

HOW TO GET THERE ... By Pan American Jet Clipper about 9 hours (elapsed time) from New York via London; or fly Pan Am nonstop to Oslo in 7 hours, then to Copenhagen in about 1½ hours. By ship, about 10 days.

UNIVERSITY OF COPENHAGEN AND UNIVERSITY OF AARHUS

The University of Copenhagen dates from 1479. It was founded by King Christian I, but it wasn't until the nineteenth century that it began to grow. Now it is made up of five departments or faculties: Theology, Law and Economics, Medicine, Arts, and Science.

The ordinary lectures held by the universities are given in Danish and are based on the special background of Danish students.

SIZE ... There are about 9,000, including 100 foreign, students matriculated at the University of Copenhagen; and about 3,000, including 170 foreign, at Aarhus.

Both universities are co-educational.

CALENDAR ... The beginning of September through May. There is a 3-week Christmas vacation and a week's holiday at Easter. There are summer courses of varying lengths from the first of July through August.

ADMISSION REQUIREMENTS ... Danish University students must have passed at least the *Artium* examination, which corresponds to completion of two years of study at an American college. See also the Admission Requirements section in the opening summary on Denmark.

LANGUAGE OF INSTRUCTION ... Danish.

ACCOMMODATIONS ... Several organizations are set up to help the student find a room in Denmark. The minimum monthly cost of board and lodging would be $65 to $75, and an additional $20 to $30 for incidentals should be allowed.

STUDENT LIFE ... In the summer, sightseeing tours and excursions are available, and festivals, celebrations, tournaments and concerts are given. Student organizations have scheduled

extracurricular activities and social occasions. The climate is like that of northern New England and seasonal activities are varied and numerous.

INTERNATIONAL PEOPLE'S COLLEGE, ELSINORE

The International People's College has, since its establishment in 1921, based its teaching on the traditions and methods of the Danish Folk High Schools: a liberal education aimed at giving the student a broader outlook and a deeper understanding of himself and the society and time in which he lives. Being international, the aim is also to create better understanding between students of different nationalities and races.

Languages are the bridges to understanding other nations. By having some subjects compulsory and others free, the College avoids being a language school exclusively and fulfills its aim of broad orientation toward human and international understanding. All students must therefore have a good working knowledge of Danish, English, German or French, but preferably Danish or English.

International Orientation, one hour's manual work per day, and at least one Folk High School subject are compulsory for regular students. The Folk High School subjects vary with the teaching staff each term.

CALENDAR ... A 5-month term, which begins in early November. The College is closed two weeks over Christmas. A 3-month term starts in late April. Short summer courses of two weeks are given from late July through August, for which special programs can be requested.

COURSES OF STUDY ... Students are accepted in the fields of education, Folk High Schools, rural development, Danish agriculture, the Co-operative Movement, social legislation, welfare state problems and related subjects. The length of stay can vary according to the time the student has at his disposal.

SUMMER COURSES ... Orientation on Denmark and International Problems—in English.

ADMISSION REQUIREMENTS ... Students must be under 19 years of age for admission to the regular program. During term time, the College accepts some special students, usually older, who come to Denmark to study definite aspects of life in Denmark. These special students are given an adviser among the staff and guidance about courses they should follow and persons and institutions to visit in order to get a full picture. See also the Admission Requirements section in the opening summary on Denmark.

LANGUAGE OF INSTRUCTION ... English, French, German and Danish.

ACCOMMODATIONS ... The College is residential and co-educational. Students live in rooms accommodating one, two, three or four. Most rooms are double rooms. The College provides bedding and bed linen. Students must pay for their own personal laundry and join the health insurance program. No application is valid until a deposit of $15 is received.

AVERAGE COSTS ... Fees cover board, lodging, tuition and excursions. Approximate fees for the two terms are: $280 for the winter term and $165 for the summer term. Special students pay about $65 for one month, $20 for one week and $4

University of Aarhus

for one day. Books cost approximately $7. A single room will probably cost $7 extra per month.

STUDENT LIFE ... A free school for adults requires few rules. Quiet after 10:30 p.m., men and women separated after 10:30 p.m., and respect for the work and consideration for others are the main rules. Violation of rules leads to expulsion. The Elsinore Music Society is under the direction of the College music teacher. Meals are a Babel of many languages and include many national dishes. Excursions with international groups are especially stimulating.

HOLIDAY COURSES FOR STUDENTS AND VISITORS FROM ABROAD

The Committee for the Propagation of Knowledge about Denmark Abroad has organized a holiday course for foreigners in Danish language, life, literature and thought to be held annually in Copenhagen during the month of August. Students of 62 different nationalities have attended the course. The course is open to all, whether members of a university or not; it has been arranged so as to provide students with an opportunity of gaining a knowledge of the language and life of Denmark, and also of the natural beauties of the country, in a way that is at once pleasant and inexpensive.

Instruction includes exercises in phonetics, grammatical exercises, conversation, the reading of Danish texts, and lectures, some in English, others in Danish. Classes meet three hours daily, except Saturday.

An excursion around Copenhagen includes all the tourist attractions as well as a motor tour around the city and a boat trip around Copenhagen Harbor. The Committee also arranges two all-day motor excursions into the fine country surrounding Copenhagen.

Certificates of attendance will be issued to students if so desired.

ACCOMMODATIONS ... Applications must be sent to Holiday Courses for Students and Visitors from Abroad, c/o DIS, Skt. Peders Straede 19, Copenhagen K. Participants who desire assistance in obtaining accommodations should communicate with the committee several months before the beginning of the course.

FEES ... The fee for the course is approximately $17.35, payable at the beginning of the course.

Board and lodging for the duration of the course, during the month of August, will amount to a minimum of about $87.

SHORT COURSES ... There are also five short courses of one week's duration during the months of July and August. These courses are identical and include English lectures about Denmark, sight-seeing and visits to various institutions.

The fee for each short course is approximately $7.25, payable at the beginning of the course.

SCANDINAVIAN SEMINAR

Scandinavian Seminar, located at 62 West 58th Street, New York, N. Y. 10019, provides a 9-month study program in Denmark, Finland, Norway, or Sweden (extending from early August until May). The Seminar program in the other Scandinavian countries closely corresponds to the following description of the year in Denmark.

Upon acceptance into the program, the student receives appropriate language materials from the Seminar, which he should study before leaving the United States.

For most of the year, the student is on his own, living his life with Scandinavians, studying at Folk High Schools (*Folke-højskoler*), and meeting a wide cross section of the population. While the Seminar is in contact with its students throughout the year, it brings them together only for its general courses. Besides serving to integrate the many aspects of the Seminar year for the student, these courses give the staff an opportunity to get to know the students well, so that, through careful planning, the needs and interests of each student can be considered in arranging his year's program.

The Seminar program starts with an orientation course introducing the students to their year in Scandinavia, followed by intensive language instruction. Two additional language courses (about 10–14 days each) are held prior to the student's entering the Folk High School.

Alternating with these courses, the student lives with two different families, about one month with each. Here he is treated not as a guest but as a member of the family, so that he gets a genuine understanding of Scandinavian family and community life, and an opportunity for intensive practical language experience. These visits not only accelerate language learning, but also help the student to adapt quickly to the new country.

Each participant in the Seminar is enrolled in a Folk High School from November until April. There are usually no more than two Seminar students at a school. The Scandinavian Folk High Schools are residential schools for young adults, 18 to 25 years of age. While some of the newer schools are urban, most are located in rural communities. They usually range in size from 50 to 100 students, thus allowing for a close relationship between teacher and student. Courses and examinations, in the American sense of the word, do not exist. Instruction takes the form of lectures, class recitations, study circles and discussions. History, literature, the Scandinavian language and the social sciences constitute the core curriculum. Many Folk High Schools have special reputations in such fields as gymnastics and crafts that express aspects of the national or regional culture, and which will enrich the experience of the Seminar year.

During the New Year vacation, the Seminar students from all the Scandinavian countries come together at a general course, usually held in Norway. This gives them a welcome chance to share the experiences of their first months of adaptation to Scandinavia. During this course, lectures and discussions centered around inter-Scandinavian topics give the student a sense of the differences and similarities among these countries. Also, it gives the Seminar staff an opportunity to hold personal interviews with the students, to examine their language proficiency and to discuss the progress of their project paper.

The final general course of the year takes place in May, and marks the formal conclusion of the Seminar year.

Each student participating in the Seminar program is responsible for completing successfully an independent project in a field of interest to him, and related to his Scandinavian experience. The project is planned in consultation with the Academic Adviser, members of the Seminar staff and other pertinent specialists. It is developed through reading, by cultivation of special skills and by direct observation involving field trips and personal interviews. The project culminates in an original paper, to be submitted to the Seminar for evaluation approximately two weeks before the concluding general session of the Seminar year.

ADMISSION REQUIREMENTS ... Scandinavian Seminar is open to qualified college undergraduates (except freshmen), graduates and other adults. See also the Admission Requirements section in the opening summary on Denmark.

CREDITS ... College undergraduates seeking credit for their Seminar program are urged to consult with their college study adviser so that their independent study project will be acceptable for credit according to the requirements of their college.

In order to assist the colleges and universities in evaluating the Seminar program in terms of American college credit, the Seminar suggests granting the following credit units for a successful completion of the year's work: 15 semester hours for language study; 15 semester hours for all course work and the independent study project. A summary from the Director and the Academic Adviser of the Seminar forms the basis for an evaluation of the student's performance, which will be sent to his college at his request. Every member of the Scandinavian Seminar who completes the year's program satisfactorily will receive a certificate of completion.

AVERAGE COSTS ... The Scandinavian Seminar fee is $1,800, which covers tuition, room and board for nine months (except vacations), transportation from New York to Scandinavia (one way), language materials and administrative expenses. Return transportation, travel in Scandinavia and other personal expenses are not included. Limited scholarship loans are available to students in need of financial assistance.

ECUADOR

UNIVERSITIES OF ECUADOR ... Ecuador maintains five state universities—the Central University of Ecuador in Quito, the University of Guayaquil in Guayaquil, the University of Cuenca in Cuenca, the University of Loja in Loja, and the Technical University of Manabi in Portoviejo. In addition, there is the private Catholic University in Quito. All these universities are autonomous, each electing its own governing council composed of professors and students.

The Central University is the largest in Ecuador. It is composed of nine faculties, whereas the other universities maintain only three or four faculties.

ECUADOREAN UNIVERSITY SYSTEM ... The Constitution of Ecuador today provides for "lay education, free of charge, and obligatory." Educational institutions, both public and private, are under the control of the national government. The Ministry of Public Education exercises administrative and supervisory control over all types of national, municipal and private schools.

ADMISSION REQUIREMENTS ... Students applying for admission to a university in Ecuador must be 18 years of age or over. They must have a minimum of two years of college, take a medical exam given by the university and pay the necessary registration fees.

CREDIT TOWARD AN AMERICAN DEGREE ... In order for a student to receive credit toward his degree in the United States, he must have the courses he plans to take in Ecuador approved by the American university in which he is enrolled.

REGULATIONS ... For student visa and entrance procedure, see the For Further Information heading at the end of this section.

TUITION ... Tuition fees at Ecuadorean universities are quite nominal, with the exception of the Central University, which charges $14 to $16 a year. However, this fee does include registration, medical and regular exams taken by the student, his diploma and side trips he might take.

LIVING COSTS ... Room and board in a pension will cost a student approximately $50 to $60 a month.

COMMON COURTESIES AND LOCAL CUSTOMS ... Unlike in the United States, it is not customary for women to wear slacks in the street. Afternoon tea is a ritual in Quito's social life. The dinner hour is between 8 and 10 p.m.

FOR FURTHER INFORMATION ... For complete information about a university and how to enroll, write to the individual university. For information on the Central University of Ecuador, write to UNIVERSIDAD CENTRAL DEL ECUADOR, Ciudad Universitaria, Quito, Ecuador.

For travel particulars and documentation, write to Educational Department, NHE, Pan American Airways, Pan Am Building, New York, N. Y. 10017.

HOW TO GET THERE ... On the interchange flight of National, Pan American and Panagra, New York to Quito is 15¼ hours, to Guayaquil 16½ hours. From Miami to Quito the time is 10¾ hours, 12¼ hours to Guayaquil. Flying time between Quito and Guayaquil is only 50 minutes. Inquire about latest schedules. By ship, about 9 days from New York to Guayaquil.

CENTRAL UNIVERSITY OF ECUADOR, QUITO

The Central University of Ecuador was officially established in 1836 by merging three already existing universities—the Seminary of San Luis, founded in 1594; the Pontifical University of San Gregorio Magno, created in 1622; and the University of Saint Thomas Aquinas, founded by the Dominicans in 1681.

The Central University, with its modern buildings and pavilions, is located in the northern part of the city of Quito called University City. This university has a beautiful campus with all its buildings located in University City.

SIZE ... The Central University of Ecuador is the largest in the country, with an approximate enrollment of 6,000 students and 400 professors. The University is composed of nine faculties and several institutes. When the University is completed, there will be a total of 24 pavilions. Co-educational.

CALENDAR ... Classes at the Central University are conducted from the first of October to the end of July. There are three terms—the first term runs from the beginning of October to late December, the second from the second week of January to the end of March, and the third from the first of April to the end of June. Regular exams are given at the end of each 3-month period with final exams administered during the month of July.

It is important to note that in the coastal region (Guayaquil), classes start the first of May and end January 31. Here the climate is tropical, whereas Quito is quite cool. There is a summer session from mid-August to mid-September.

COURSES OF STUDY ... The University of Ecuador maintains the Faculties of Law, Medical Science, Physics and Math, Educational Science, Veterinary Medicine and Agriculture, Natural and Chemical Sciences, Economics, Odontology, and Architecture and Urbanization. In addition there is a School of Fine Arts and the National Conservatory of Music.

SUMMER COURSES ... The summer school at the Central University of Ecuador is generally conducted from August to September. It is open to all high school graduates 18 years of age or over. Tuition for the session is $2 plus $3 per day for room and board in university dormitories. All the courses are given in Spanish and they include Art, Biology, Foreign Languages, History and Geography of Ecuador, Geology and Natural Resources of Ecuador, Education, Ecuadorean Folklore, Literature, Law, Philosophy, Psychology, Quechuan, and Sociology.

TUITION ... Tuition varies from $14 to $16 a year. This

fee includes registration, medical exam, regular exams, diploma and any side trips or excursions made by the student. An additional fee, however, is charged to those students who are late in registering or late in taking their exams.

ADMISSION REQUIREMENTS ... There are certain conditions a student must comply with in applying to the Central University of Ecuador. He must present first an application to the Rector of the University stating his name, year of birth, place of birth, nationality and school attended. He must also designate the faculty in which he wishes to enroll and the courses he plans to take. Along with this application, he should present a certificate from his former high school showing the courses taken, a certificate from the state in which his home university is located showing that it is an accredited university, and lastly he must submit documents proving his identity. See also the Admission Requirements section in the opening summary on Ecuador.

LANGUAGE OF INSTRUCTION ... All university courses are conducted in Spanish.

ACCOMMODATIONS ... A large dormitory on the University campus accommodates 500 students who enroll in the University.

AVERAGE COSTS ... Room and board in a pension will cost a student approximately $50 to $60 a month. The cost of room alone in the University dormitory will be about $12 a month.

STUDENT LIFE ... Student life at the University is very active. There are plays given in the University theater, sports events held in the outdoor arena, and national student outings and social activities given at the end of the year.

Central University of Ecuador

FINLAND

Finland can offer a unique experience to the American student. In Finland, he will be able to put himself in the place of a member of a nation of four million, which through its history has been a buffer between East and West. Although Finland has enjoyed complete independence only since 1917, she has behind her a long and interesting course of democratic development and a rich heritage of national culture worthy to learn about.

The Finnish universities have no special institutes for foreign students and they do not give instruction in any languages except Finnish and Swedish, but they extend a warm welcome to American students and are prepared to give them individual attention. It is hoped that the experience of living among the Finns, taking part in the active student life with traditions from the Seventeenth Century, and seeing the country's natural charm in her vast forests and thousands of lakes will be a reward valuable enough to recompense the possibly lesser achievements in the strictly academic field caused by the difficulty of the Finnish language.

The cultural exchange between Finland and the U. S. A. has always been warm and friendly though limited in numbers. The collaboration on the university level during past years has developed under the protection of Asla and Fulbright scholarships. I hope that the cultural exchange between our countries will continue to grow. I wish all the students arriving from the U.S.A. to our universities success in their studies.

Armi Hosia
Minister of Education

HIGHER EDUCATION IN FINLAND ... In Finland, general education ends with the matriculation examination which terminates the secondary school, and all university studies are professional or pre-professional. The first university to be established in Finland was founded in Turku, the old capital, in 1640. When the city was almost completely destroyed by fire in 1827, the university was moved to Helsinki, which had become the capital in 1812, after Finland was annexed by Russia. Two other universities were founded soon after Finland won her independence in 1917: The Academy of Turku (Swedish-speaking) and the Finnish-speaking University of Turku. The University of Oulu was established in 1959.

Other institutions of university rank include the Finland Institute of Technology; Schools of Economics at Helsinki and Turku, both Finnish and Swedish; the School of Social Sciences in Tampere; and teacher training institutes in Helsinki, Turku, Jyväskylä and Oulu.

Scandinavian Seminar offers a 9-month study program in Finland based on the Folk High Schools. It extends from early August until May. (For a more detailed description, see under Denmark.)

There is in addition the International College Folk Academy —"Viittakivi"—at Hauho. It is interesting to note that Finland has the highest percentage of literacy in the world.

FINNISH UNIVERSITY SYSTEM ... In Finland, the university system is similar to that of other European countries. Finland has nothing like the American credit-hour system, and class attendance will not be of major importance. The curricula are laid down in officially printed plans for the different studies, and a student may register for his comprehensive oral and written examinations when he feels that he is sufficiently well prepared. There is nothing corresponding to the Bachelor's degree in Finland—the first degree granted will be more or less the equivalent of the American Master's degree.

ADMISSION REQUIREMENTS ... All secondary school students who are in the highest grade take the matriculation examination which is held each year in April. This examination is the basic requirement for admission to the institutions of university standing.

In addition, some faculties of the universities, and especially the engineering and business schools, which are seriously overcrowded, conduct their own examinations or admit only those applicants who have the highest marks.

A student from the United States would be required to have a secondary school certificate and at least two years at an accredited college.

Scandinavian Seminar is open to qualified college undergraduates (except freshmen), graduates and other adults. There are no specific educational prerequisites. Each applicant is considered on his merits. No knowledge of a Scandinavian language is required prior to acceptance.

REGULATIONS ... For student visa and entrance procedure, see the For Further Information heading at the end of this section.

CREDIT TOWARD AN AMERICAN DEGREE ... Students who are candidates for a degree in an American university must make arrangements with their dean regarding transfer of credits before applying for admission at a university in Finland.

The Scandinavian Seminar gives a certificate of completion to each student who has satisfactorily completed the year's program. Upon the student's request, the Seminar will send to his college an evaluation of his work; and, when justified, will recommend that college credit be granted.

TUITION ... Fees each term are about $1.50; health insurance, $1.50; membership in students' union amounts to about $6. Charges for taking examinations and degrees range from $1.25 to $5; fees for the use of laboratories and institutes range from $3 to $18. The Scandinavian Seminar fee is $1,800, which covers tuition, room and board for the academic year and transportation from New York to Scandinavia.

LIVING COSTS ... It is estimated that it costs a student about $100 a month for room, board and tuition.

The students' union usually owns buildings where students may find reasonable accommodations.

The Student Service helps students find lodgings, makes travel arrangements, and operates an exchange system for on-the-job experience in professions and some occupations.

The exchange rate is 3.20 Finnmark to the dollar.

LOCAL CUSTOMS ... The *sauna*, the famous Finnish bath, is a must—there is one in almost every home and in most hotels.

Both men and women always shake hands on meeting. When you are introduced, mention your last name.

The people are vigorous and hospitable, and the country has a rugged and mystic quality which makes it unusually delightful.

FOR FURTHER INFORMATION ... For complete information about a university and how to enroll, write to the Consulate General of Finland, 200 East 42nd St., New York, N. Y. 10017. Those interested in the Scandinavian Seminar program should contact Scandinavian Seminar for Cultural Study, 62 West 58th Street, New York, N. Y. 10019.

For travel particulars and documentation, write to Educational Department, NHE, Pan American Airways, Pan Am Building, New York, N. Y. 10017.

HOW TO GET THERE ... By Pan American Jet Clipper from New York to Helsinki, about 10 hours (elapsed time) via Oslo and Stockholm. Or fly by Pan Am Jet to Copenhagen in 9 hours and make connections there for Helsinki. Helsinki is only 1 hour's flying time from Stockholm. By ship, about 10 days from New York to Helsinki.

UNIVERSITY OF HELSINKI

The city of Helsinki, beautifully situated on the shore of the Gulf of Finland, is over 400 years old, but most of its buildings date from the beginning of this century. This accounts for its predominantly modern architecture. The "White City of the North" is dotted with beautiful parks and squares where some of Finland's magnificent sculpture can be seen.

The University of Helsinki was actually founded in Turku in 1640 under the name of Royal Academy of Turku. During the Napoleonic Wars, Finland was annexed by the Russian Empire and became a largely self-governing grand duchy. In 1812, the capital was moved from Turku to Helsinki to be nearer to St. Petersburg. It was decided to move Finland's only university there as well after a great fire in 1827 almost destroyed the city of Turku.

SIZE ... About 16,000 students are enrolled at the University of Helsinki, of whom 100 are foreigners.

CALENDAR ... The academic year is divided into two semesters: early September to late December and mid-January to the end of May. The University of Helsinki has no summer session, but several other towns in Finland, most of them situated in places of great natural beauty, arrange summer courses every year.

COURSES OF STUDY ... The University has these faculties: Agriculture, Forestry, Law, Medicine (including Dentistry), Philosophy (divided into the Department of History and Languages and the Department of Mathematics and Natural Sciences), Social Sciences (including Journalism), Theology. It has also a Pharmaceutical Institute and an Institute of Physical Education.

ADMISSION REQUIREMENTS ... The Consistory can accept a foreign student to be matriculated at the University if he can present a certificate that he has been a student of a foreign university of the same academic standing as the University of Helsinki. See also the Admission Requirements section in the opening summary on Finland.

LANGUAGE OF INSTRUCTION ... Finnish and Swedish.

ACCOMMODATIONS ... The Student Service will help students to find rooms in student dormitories or in private homes.

The union also operates restaurants and cafeterias where the student will find good food at reasonable prices.

AVERAGE COSTS ... It is estimated that it costs a student about $100 a month for room, board and tuition.

STUDENT LIFE ... The Finns are a rugged, hospitable people who share the mystic quality of their lovely country. They have fought hard for their freedom and are unique in that they have been a buffer between East and West throughout their history.

There are a number of associations and clubs of all kinds to which students may belong.

One of the high points of the year is the annual Sibelius Festival during the first two weeks of June.

UNIVERSITY OF OULU

The newly founded university in Oulu (1958) began its academic life in 1959 with three faculties: Philosophy, Technology, and Medicine and, in addition, a Teachers Institute.

SIZE ... The student body, including the Teachers Institute, numbers over 1,000. There are over 200 members of the faculty.

ADMISSION REQUIREMENTS ... See the Admission Requirements section in the opening summary on Finland.

LANGUAGE OF INSTRUCTION ... Finnish.

UNIVERSITY OF TURKU

Turku, in Swedish "Abo," is the ancient capital of Finland. It was founded in the thirteenth century. During the twelfth and thirteenth centuries Christianity was introduced into Finland and a union with Sweden was formed, of which the mighty Castle and glorious Cathedral are monuments. At present, 91 per cent of the Finns are Finnish-speaking and less than 9 per cent are Swedish-speaking. The Royal Academy of Turku, founded in 1640, was moved to Helsinki at the time of the great fire which destroyed much of Turku in 1827. This became the University of Helsinki.

A new era in the history of Turku began when Finland was declared an independent republic on December 6, 1917. Shortly after this date, the University of Turku was founded by public endowments.

The University of Turku opened its doors on June 27, 1922. The funds were raised by a nation-wide campaign which reached as far as the Finnish settlers in North America. One of the reasons behind the foundation of the University was the fact that at the University of Helsinki during the period from 1910 to 1920, more than half the lectures were given in Swedish. At the University of Turku, lectures were to be given only in Finnish. Because it was difficult to raise the large sum required for buildings, the University began its work in an old building which served it for thirty years. At a ceremony held in May 1959 to celebrate the rebirth of the University, the President of the

University of Turku

University of Helsinki, Main Building

There are a number of associations and clubs of all kinds to which students may belong.

One of the high points of the year is the annual Sibelius Festival in Helsinki during the first two weeks of June.

SWEDISH UNIVERSITY OF ÅBO

The geographical position of Turku, "Åbo" in Swedish, partly explains its early prominence in the history of Finland. At the time when the country was a part of Sweden, Åbo, in a sheltered harbor, was the starting point of the quickest sea route to Sweden, ending at Stockholm and navigable even in the depths of winter. It is still the seat of the Archbishop of the Lutheran Church of Finland. From 1640 to 1827 it was also the seat of the Academy founded in 1640 by Count Per Brahe, the Swedish Governor-General. In 1827 this Academy was removed to the new capital, Helsingfors, where it still exists as the first State University. About the beginning of this century the new Åbo Akademi was established to make it possible for the Swedish-speaking minority of Finland (about 9 per cent of the population) to pursue advanced studies entirely in their own language. The University opened its doors in 1918. Its buildings are grouped around the thirteenth-century cathedral as were those of the old Academy. Åbo Akademi is maintained by a private foundation.

SIZE ... About 1,000 students enrolled at the Academy proper. In addition, 300 belong to the School of Business Administration at the Academy. About 200 students of the Turku University also attend courses and lectures at the Åbo Akademi.

CALENDAR ... The academic year is divided into two semesters: the beginning of September to late December and mid-January to the end of May.

COURSES OF STUDY ... The Swedish University began with three faculties: Humanities, Science, and Social Science. In 1920, a Faculty of Chemical Engineering was added, and in 1924, one of Theology.

There is an agreement with the University of Turku by which each university recognizes the other's courses and examinations.

The Sibelius Museum is part of the College of Humanities. It houses the School of Music together with the world's largest collection of Sibelius manuscripts, prints, editions and biographical source materials.

ADMISSION REQUIREMENTS ... See the Admission Requirements section in the opening summary on Finland.

LANGUAGE OF INSTRUCTION ... Swedish.

ACCOMMODATIONS ... The students of Åbo Akademi and of the School of Business Administration at the Åbo Akademi form the Student Corporation of Åbo Akademi. Since 1950, the Corporation has owned a student hostel housing about 120 students. The Corporation has its own building, which has a dining room and restaurant.

AVERAGE COSTS ... It is estimated that it costs a student about $100 a month for room, board and tuition.

STUDENT LIFE ... Åbo Akademi is supported by a small minority group, the 350,000 Swedish-speaking people of Finland. It serves all of Finland as well and works in close co-operation with Finland's other universities.

Republic dedicated the beautiful, modern buildings as "A Gift of a Free People for Free Learning."

SIZE ... About 4,000 students are enrolled in the University of Turku.

Summer courses are given to more than 1,700 students.

CALENDAR ... The academic year is divided into two terms: early September to late December and mid-January to the end of May.

The summer session is held for six weeks from July to mid-August.

COURSES OF STUDY ... The University of Turku has Faculties of Humanities, Mathematics and Natural Sciences, Medicine, and Law.

Every summer since 1936 except in wartime, the University of Turku has organized summer courses lasting about six weeks to help prepare students planning to attend the University in the fall.

The School Certificate is not required for admission to summer courses.

ADMISSION REQUIREMENTS ... See the Admission Requirements section in the opening summary on Finland.

LANGUAGE OF INSTRUCTION ... Finnish.

ACCOMMODATIONS ... Very close to the University the union owns a group of buildings which furnish accommodations for about 600 students. There is a restaurant here, a gym, a swimming pool and a small chapel. The Student Service will help students find lodgings elsewhere in the town if this is preferred, or if the existing accommodations in the union buildings are filled.

AVERAGE COSTS ... It is estimated that it costs a student about $80 to $100 a month for room, board, tuition.

STUDENT LIFE ... The Finns are a rugged, hospitable people who share the mystic quality of their lovely country. They have fought hard for their freedom and are unique in that they have been a buffer between East and West throughout their history.

FRANCE

The American student who goes to France to study has a chance to acquire more than the formal knowledge taught at the university. The museums and ancient landmarks offer students an opportunity to see some of the greatest treasures of Western civilization.

In our universities in France, a warm welcome awaits American students, both men and women. Besides the regular courses offered in French universities they will find elementary courses in the French language. They will return home enriched with new friendships and a broader understanding of the world we live in. They will long remember an exciting experience in education.

Edouard Morot-Sir
Cultural Counselor
Representative in the United States
of French Universities

UNIVERSITIES OF FRANCE ... France has 17 major universities, all administered by the state. The University of Paris and 16 state institutions located in the provinces make up this list which includes the Universities of Aix-Marseille, Algiers, Besançon, Bordeaux, Caen, Clermont-Ferrand, Dijon, Grenoble, Lille, Lyons, Montpellier, Nancy, Nantes, Orléans, Poitiers, Reims, Rennes, Strasbourg and Toulouse. There are also several private institutions administered by religious groups, technical schools, teacher-training schools and various other colleges, institutes and specialized schools to which students may apply for admission.

In addition to the regular courses, each of the 17 state universities has established an Institut pour Étudiants Étrangers (Institute for Foreign Students), which offers courses in the French language, literature, art, geography and history, and other courses designed for foreign students.

FRENCH UNIVERSITY SYSTEM ... The French university system differs considerably from that of the United States. A Ministry of National Education supervises all education—primary, secondary, and higher education. France is divided into 17 educational districts called *Académies* and each has one of the state universities, under the jurisdiction of the Ministry. The administrative structure and teaching methods are the same in all the universities, although some subjects may be emphasized in certain institutions. The same academic standard is met by all universities.

A notable difference exists between an American course and a French *cours*. The *cours* is the main teaching method used and is a formal lecture given once a week. A student attends those lectures in the field in which he will have to take an examination at the end of the academic year. Attendance at the *cours* and preparation of oral or written assignments are compulsory at the Institut pour Étudiants Étrangers. A student's work depends to a great extent on his own initiative and his own method of preparation for the final examination.

A French student receives his *baccalauréat* degree after 7 years of study at the *lycée* or *collège* (during the ages of about 10 or 11 to about 17 or 18) and he is then prepared for university study.

ADMISSION REQUIREMENTS ... Courses at the Institut pour Étudiants Étrangers at each university are generally open to all students over 17 years of age. The secondary school certificate (high school diploma) is accepted for admission. The Sorbonne is very popular and more crowded than other institutions, but it is neither the only university to consider nor the right university for every student. The universities outside Paris, on the other hand, have space available for several hundred American students each. Therefore an educational opportunity exists in France for as many as 2,000 American students. Although it has become a practice for American students to apply to several colleges for admission at the same time, students seeking enrollment in French universities should not apply to more than one French university for admission—in fact applying to more than one may complicate processing of applications by French authorities.

Instruction is in French at all universities and the entrance, or placement, examination required by some *instituts* at enrollment time will determine the level at which one should begin his studies. A foreign student who has already attained an excellent command of the French language and who holds a B.A. or a B.S. degree may enroll as a regular student in a French university.

CREDIT TOWARD AN AMERICAN DEGREE ... A student must make arrangements for receiving credit toward an American degree from his own university before he leaves the United States. Because of the variations in credit systems within American universities, it is impossible to generalize about the number of credit hours a student may receive. Each student should discuss with his own dean or guidance counselor the requirements for receiving credit and the number of credit hours toward his American degree that may be awarded for study abroad. Sometimes full credit may be given for the period of study in France if the student passes the French examinations. But each American university will make its own evaluation of the study at each French university. Certain diplomas and certificates can be earned from the French universities.

REGULATIONS ... A visa is necessary for a student who will spend more than three months in France and the French Cultural Services, 972 Fifth Avenue, New York, N. Y. 10021, can give information on how to obtain a student visa. Students should check also on customs regulations. Although certain items, such as radios and typewriters, may not be subject to customs duties, they may have to be declared upon arrival in France.

TUITION ... Costs vary; higher fees prevail in Paris at the Sorbonne. In the universities in the provinces the costs are lower. Tuition for the academic year ranges from $46 to $200 in the Instituts pour Étudiants Étrangers; this includes about $10 for medical, library and examination fees.

LIVING COSTS ... Most American students will find that $140 a month will be sufficient for living expenses, but it is well to allow a small additional sum for extra expenses during the first month of getting settled. Board can be arranged in private homes or pensions (boardinghouses) for $60 per month upward. American students should not plan to supplement their allowance by working. Because of strict employment regulations it is extremely difficult for any non-French person to work in France. It is suggested that a student have about $35 in francs with him upon his arrival. Part of this money should be in small denominations for tips and incidental expenses at the time of his arrival.

COMMON COURTESIES AND LOCAL CUSTOMS ... Tickets are collected when you arrive at the train station in France. All apartment houses have *concierges* who guard the door. Doors are locked at early hours each night. In small buildings the elevator will take you up but you are expected to walk down. It is customary to shake hands when you meet someone and when you say good-bye. Students will find that they are entitled to free admission to many museums and that they are given reduced rates for transportation in some cases. A help to foreign students, as well as French students, is the Office du Tourisme Universitaire (O.T.U. Travel Office for Universities) in Paris. A representative of O.T.U. is located at 972 Fifth Avenue, New York, N. Y. 10021. It organizes travel and helps students find accommodations; no charge for its service.

In France cycling is a student way of getting beyond the limits of everyday life for a look at something new. American students who hop on a bike and take off for a ride in the country will have no difficulties; it's a good way to meet a French family. It will not seem strange to these country dwellers that a healthy cycler stops by to ask for a drink of water, or just for a short rest, and begins a friendly conversation. And perhaps a friendship.

FOR FURTHER INFORMATION ... For complete information about a university and how to enroll, write to the French Cultural Service, 972 Fifth Avenue, New York, unless there is a different address given under the heading How to Enroll of a particular university in this section.

For travel particulars and documentation, write to Educational Department, NHE, Pan American Airways, Pan Am Building, New York, N. Y. 10017.

HOW TO GET THERE ... By Pan American Jet Clipper, nonstop to Paris, about 7 hours from New York and Boston, about 15¼ hours from Los Angeles via Jet connection in New York, 10½ hours from U.S. West Coast via polar route to London, then by easy connection to Paris. Through Jet Clipper service to Nice on the Riviera via Lisbon and Barcelona about 10¾ hours from New York. Connections at Lisbon for Paris (2¼ hours). By ship, 5 to 9 days.

ACADEMIC YEAR ABROAD

Academic Year Abroad (AYA) specializes in setting up full academic year, and also summer, study programs for college-age students at the University of Paris. Now in its fifth year of activity, AYA designs individual programs for each student, taking into consideration his or her aptitude, interests and degree of preparation. Thus AYA can accept students at varying levels of achievement and varying stages of their formal education. Individual programs are designed within four general categories: 1. college credit programs (usually junior year); 2. pre-college programs (between school and college); 3. interim programs (for personal development rather than credits); 4. postgraduate programs (a year, or two, or transition between school or college and career). Brochure available.

CALENDAR ... Mid-September to mid-June. Indoctrination, orientation, special drill in French for six weeks to opening of the University about the first of November. Two semesters; Christmas and Easter vacations. Summer courses are offered from late June to early August, mid-August, or mid-September (choice).

COURSES OF STUDY AND TUITION ... Students are officially enrolled in many courses—French, History, Philosophy, Government, Literature, International Affairs, Fine Arts, etc.—at one or more of the many divisions of the University of Paris (the Sorbonne, École du Louvre, Institut d'Études Politiques, L'Institut Britannique, etc.). Cost for full year is $2,910, and covers tuition, room and board with French families, excursions and trips, theater, concerts, etc. Single semester, approximately half.

ADMISSION REQUIREMENTS ... Minimum, secondary school diploma. The average AYA student has completed two years of college work. See also the Admission Requirements section in the opening summary on France.

LANGUAGE OF INSTRUCTION ... French (with the exception of some special work in English for some students).

ACCOMMODATIONS ... Living arrangements are in all cases with French families chosen for their standards of material comfort and, more importantly, for their sincere interest in helping foreign students achieve a full and successful benefit from life in France.

STUDENT LIFE...In addition to the academic program at the University of Paris and the enjoyment of life within a French family, AYA students take full advantage of the cultural resources of Paris—theater and ballet evenings, concerts, museums, excursions—and two foreign trips (one to Switzerland and one to London) are included within regular fees. All AYA students are members of the Center for Students and Artists. The European Director and his wife (both Americans) and a resident academic dean provide guidance and assistance throughout the year.

HOW TO ENROLL ... Write directly to Academic Year Abroad, 62, Boulevard Montparnasse, Paris 15, France; *or* 225 East 46th Street, New York, N. Y. 10017.

ALLIANCE FRANÇAISE, PARIS

The Practical School of the Alliance Française offers courses in many countries of the world; its home, however, is Paris.

CALENDAR ... The School is open the year round and students may enroll at any time. Examinations are given at the end of each month; if a student has improved he may move from his own language class to a more advanced class the following month. The school year is generally divided into two sessions of 5 months each: early September to late January and early February to late June; a 2-month summer session from the beginning of July to late August; and an Easter session of about 12 days.

COURSES OF STUDY AND FEES ... Courses in the French Language cover Grammar, Vocabulary, Essay Writing, Reading, and Conversation and are offered daily; students have a choice of hours for this course and the tuition fee varies according to the hour chosen from $5.05 to $7.08. The Introductory Course on French Civilization covers History, Geography, Classical and Modern Literature, and Elements of French Law. Fee is $9.60 per month. A course designed for French teachers is offered for $9.60 per month. Special conversation group courses cost about $2.45 per month; the Preparation Course for the Diploma of Interpreter in French costs $9.60 per month. Translation courses cost about $2.45 per month; the Course in Commercial French costs about $2.45 per month. Students of the language courses are admitted free of charge to certain lectures and courses; these include the Phonetics course, Higher Grammar course, General French Literature courses, lecturers on Modern Literature from Symbolism to Existentialism, and lectures on Technical and Economic Information.

SUMMER COURSES ... French Language courses, courses in French Culture, including Literature and Phonetics, lectures on Literature and Art, including Contemporary Literature, Cinema, and conducted tours, and special courses in French teaching methods, French Civilization (History and Geography), Translation classes, Conversation classes, and Commercial classes are offered. Tuition is about $13 per month during the session, which begins early July and ends late August.

ADMISSION REQUIREMENTS ... Both the regular session and the summer courses are open to high school graduates. At the time a student enters the school he will take an entrance test to determine which level of language class he should enter; there are 5 sections from elementary to advanced. Certain diplomas and certificates can be earned after attending classes and passing the examinations. See also the Admission Requirements section in the opening summary on France.

LANGUAGE OF INSTRUCTION ... French.

ACCOMMODATIONS ... The Alliance Française can accommodate 125 students at La Maison de l'Alliance Française; there is a restaurant in the same building where meals can be obtained for about 75 cents and up. The school has plans to build a dormitory to house 500 students in the near future.

STUDENT LIFE ... The Maison de l'Alliance Française has many recreational facilities as well as a schedule of entertainment. There are conducted tours through Paris. "Dramatic Mondays" at the Maison offer the latest in the French theater; there are also French films, folklore entertainments, singing clubs, and lectures on the history of art and literature of France.

UNIVERSITY OF BESANÇON

Since the days of the Romans, Besançon has been a military outpost, and ancient fortified ramparts can be seen today on the outskirts of the town. The city has many buildings from the sixteenth, seventeenth and eighteenth centuries and one of the best collections of fine arts and prehistoric antiquities of east central France. These are housed in the Fine Arts Museum, Archaeological Museum, Art Gallery and Collection of Drawings. Besançon is a center of the watchmaking industry in France and students may visit factories typical of those in France. During September an outstanding music festival is held in Besançon. Fishing, boating, mountain-climbing, hiking, camping and swimming are popular with students. There is also a spa. The university was founded in 1422 at Dôle but transferred to Besançon in 1691.

SIZE ... About 3,000 students, of whom nearly 300 are from foreign countries.

CALENDAR ... October to late June. Summer courses are offered in August.

COURSES OF STUDY ... Special courses for undergraduate foreign students: At the *Institut de Langue et de Civilisation Françaises:* The *Cours Pratiques de Langue et de Littérature Françaises* including Vocabulary, Conversation, Pronunciation and Composition for elementary, intermediate and advanced students; lecture courses in the French Language, French Literature, Philosophy, Geography of France, Modern History and the History of Art.

Regular courses, opportunities for graduate study: Students may apply for study in the Faculties of Science, Letters and Law, Schools of Medicine and Pharmacy and Chemistry, National Observatory, Institute of Chronometry and the Institute of Studies concerning Local History, Jurassic Geology, and Folklore.

SUMMER COURSES ... Summer courses in the French Language and culture are held in August.

TUITION ... Fee for the *Cours Pratiques* and Lecture Courses is $29 per semester. A library fee of $6 per year and an examination fee of $1.45 are also charged.

Fees for the summer courses range from $35.50 to $56.

ADMISSION REQUIREMENTS ... For undergraduate foreign students a secondary school certificate (high school diploma) is acceptable for some courses.

For graduate study, the regular courses of the University of Besançon are open to qualified foreign students. In general, this means students holding a B.A. or a B.S. degree who have a very good knowledge of the French language. See also the Admission Requirements section in the opening summary on France.

LANGUAGE OF INSTRUCTION ... French.

ACCOMMODATIONS ... The *Cité Universitaire* operated by the University has dormitory and dining facilities for students, but it is necessary to apply early to secure these lodgings. A committee of the University is set up to help students find living accommodations. Furnished rooms, hotels, or local families offer students lodgings. Room and board with a family may be approximately $82 per month.

AVERAGE COSTS ... Fees about $64 per year. Room and board $60 to $105 per month.

STUDENT LIFE ... Students interested in recreation can fish, go boating, hiking, mountain-climbing, camping and swimming. During the International Festival of Music there are ballet and concert programs, presentations of recent films, dramatic readings, folk dancing, French song fests, social dancing. There are also student-organized trips to La Franche-Comté, Le Jura, Alsace, Lorraine, and Burgundy. Foreign students will have an opportunity to meet French students in the student cafeterias.

HOW TO ENROLL ... Write directly to the University: Monsieur le Secrétaire, INSTITUT DE LANGUE ET CIVILISATION FRANÇAISES, 30, rue Megevand, Besançon (Doubs).

University of Besançon

University of Bordeaux

UNIVERSITY OF BORDEAUX

Although Bordeaux is 60 miles from the sea it is one of the chief ports of France and the center for export of Bordeaux wines. Situated on the left bank of the Garonne River, which empties into the Gironde estuary and provides a route to the Atlantic, Bordeaux is the economic center of southwestern France and the country's fifth city in size, 258,348 inhabitants. Interesting churches, museums and parks are sprinkled throughout the city, but the liveliest part of town is the line of quays along the river where beret-wearing stevedores can be seen at work on the wharves. The University of Bordeaux was founded in 1441, and in addition to regular sessions it holds a summer school at Pau in the foothills of the Pyrenees mountain range.

SIZE ... About 12,400 students, 400 from foreign countries.

CALENDAR ... October to early June. Summer courses also held in July and August at Pau.

COURSES OF STUDY ... Special courses for undergraduate foreign students: The Centre d'Études Françaises pour Étudiants Étrangers offers an intensive course (the *Cours Spéciaux*) in French Language, Grammar, Reading and Composition. The *Cours Normaux* includes regular lecture courses in Literature, Philology, Modern Languages, Philosophy, Social Sciences, History, Archaeology, History of Art, and Geography.

Regular courses, opportunities for graduate study: Students may apply for study in the Faculties of Law, Medicine, Science and Letters, Institutes of Political Science, Juridical and Economic Studies, Geology, Psychological and Psychosocial studies, Demographic Studies, Applied Human Sciences, Business Administration, Practical Studies in Law, Criminal Science, Economic Techniques, and Pines (industrial use of the pine and its resinous products); College of Oenology; College of Chemistry and the Southwest Regional Center of Economics.

SUMMER COURSES ... Language and culture courses are offered and there are lectures, films and seminars.

TUITION ... Fees for the *Cours Spéciaux* and the *Cours Normaux* are $6 per month registration, $2.60 for matriculation and 60 cents for examination and diploma. A library and medical fee of about $10 may also be charged.

Summer session costs, including tuition, room and board, books and supplies, range from about $82 to $115 for three weeks.

ADMISSION REQUIREMENTS ... For undergraduate foreign students a secondary school certificate (high school diploma) is acceptable for some courses. Prerequisites for the regular courses (the *Cours Normaux*) are a good knowledge of the French language and 18-year age minimum.

For graduate study, the regular courses of the University of Bordeaux are open to qualified foreign students. In general, this means students holding a B.A. or B.S. degree who have a very good knowledge of the French language. See also the Admission Requirements section in the opening summary on France.

LANGUAGE OF INSTRUCTION ... French.

ACCOMMODATIONS ... The University operates dormitories and dining halls. It is necessary to apply very early to secure a room at the University. A foreign students' committee will assist American students to find housing with families, in pensions, or in modestly priced hotels. Costs run higher outside the University residence halls.

AVERAGE COSTS ... Fees about $56. Room and board $70 to $140.

STUDENT LIFE ... Students can take advantage of bus trips to mountain resorts, to Biarritz on the seashore, to the colorful Basque country in the south. There are museums, busy markets and factories of interest. *Pelote basque* and bullfights can be seen, and there are swimming, cycling, football and concerts and folklore groups; there are also many student clubs which plan their own activities.

HOW TO ENROLL ... Write directly to the University: Monsieur le Secrétaire, Comité de Patronage, 20, Cours Pasteur, Bordeaux (Gironde).

UNIVERSITY OF CAEN

Not far from the city of Rouen, made famous by Joan of Arc, is Caen, a city of art, the haunt of writers, and an intellectual center called the "Athens of Normandy." It is surrounded by a vast plain rich with apple orchards and rolling pasture lands. A canal links the city with the English Channel and the sea. During World War II many battles were fought in this part of Normandy and permanent war memorials and shrines are found at the sites of Omaha and Utah Beaches. Caen has two famous Romanesque churches, the Abbaye-aux-Dames and the Abbaye-aux-Hommes built by Queen Mathilde and William the Conqueror, respectively, and the beautiful Gothic Church of St. Pierre. The seaside resorts of Deauville, Trouville and Honfleur, preferred by artists, are very near Caen, Mont-St.-Michel, eighth-century sanctuary built on an island of granite at the junction of Normandy and Brittany, is within easy reach of Caen. Henry VI of England laid the cornerstone for the University of Caen in 1432.

SIZE ... About 7,000 students; about 150 are from foreign countries.

CALENDAR ... October to mid-June. There is a summer session in July.

COURSES OF STUDY ... Special courses for undergraduate foreign students are as follows: At the Cours de Langue, Civilisation et Littérature Françaises, Destinées aux Étudiants Étrangers, there are offered *Niveau Pour Débutants,* from October to March, Basic French; *Niveau d'Initiation,* Introduction to Grammar of the French Language, Basic Vocabulary, Reading, Conversation and Phonetics. The *Niveau de Perfectionnement* offers advanced courses for undergraduate students of the French language in Composition, Civilization and Contemporary Literature.

Regular courses, opportunities for graduate study, are as follows: Students may apply for admission to the Faculties of Law and Economics, Science and Letters; the School of Medicine and Pharmacy; Department of French Studies (mainly for foreign students); Normandy Institute of Engineering; Demographic Institute; Institute of Chemistry; Business Training Center and the Applied Geography Center.

SUMMER COURSES ... French language courses are offered from beginning to advanced levels.

TUITION ... The courses at the *Cours de Langue, Civilisation et Littérature Françaises, Destinés aux Étudiants Étrangers* each cost $45 per year; this fee includes registration in the course, matriculation at the university library; practical exercises, examinations and a monthly excursion.

For the summer courses, tuition, room and board, lectures, films, recreation and excursions for the entire period are available at an all-inclusive fee of $127.

ADMISSION REQUIREMENTS ... For the *Niveau de Perfectionnement* at the Cours de Langue, Civilisation et Littérature Françaises, Destinées aux Étudiants Étrangers, a student must have a good knowledge of French and at least two years of college.

University of Caen

For graduate study, the regular courses of the University of Caen are open to qualified foreign students. In general, this means students holding a B.A. or a B.S. degree who have a very good knowledge of the French language.

See the Admission Requirements section in the opening summary on France.

LANGUAGE OF INSTRUCTION ... French.

ACCOMMODATIONS ... The Cité Universitaire operated by the University has inexpensive dormitory and dining facilities for a limited number of students. A committee of the University takes applications; those it cannot accommodate in university lodgings are assisted in finding boardinghouse, hotel or private residence quarters. A room with a family may run $20 to $30 per month.

AVERAGE COSTS ... Fees about $45 per year. Room and board about $85 to $105 per month. However, the Cultural Counselor in New York suggests that each student be provided with a minimum of $140 per month.

STUDENT LIFE ... Excursions to Rouen and to Mont-St.-Michel are arranged by students. Folk music, dancing, film showings, lectures, receptions, trips to the seaside and hiking are popular activities. Many University buildings were destroyed by bombing in 1944, and the University has new modern buildings including student cafeterias that have become social centers.

HOW TO ENROLL ... Write directly to the University: Secrétaire des Cours pour Étrangers, UNIVERSITÉ DE CAEN, Rue du Gaillon, Caen (Calvados).

UNIVERSITY OF CLERMONT-FERRAND

Because of its location in the center of France, the city of Clermont-Ferrand becomes a crossroad for tourists during the summer. The city is important industrially and it produces shoes, clothes, chemical products and rubber goods. The population is 110,000 inhabitants. In the old quarter of the city, outstanding examples of Renaissance art and architecture can be seen. A nearby suburb, Montferrand, also has some fine buildings from the 1500s. The University was founded in 1810, although the Faculty of Medicine of the University of Clermont-Ferrand can be traced back to 1681, through the College of Medicine.

SIZE ... About 5,200 students; 60 are from foreign countries.

CALENDAR ... October to late June. A summer session is held in July.

University of Clermont-Ferrand

COURSES OF STUDY ... Special courses for undergraduate foreign students: The Cours Spéciaux pour Étudiants Étrangers offers the *Cours de Langue Française* including Grammar, Vocabulary, Reading and Composition.

Regular courses, opportunities for graduate study: Students may apply for study of courses in the Faculties of Science, Letters and Law; the School of Medicine and Pharmacy; the Schools of Notarial Studies, Social Work, Nursing, Midwifery, Child Welfare and Physiotherapy; the Institutes of Industrial Chemistry and Technology, Regional Studies, and Applied Psychology and Mental Hygiene; the College of Commerce; the Observatory (Seismology, Gravity Measurement and Meteorology Studies); the Regional Pedagogical Center; Biological Station; School of Dentistry; and the Regional School of Fine and Applied Arts.

SUMMER COURSES ... Advance course in medicine and pharmacy is offered.

ADMISSION REQUIREMENTS ... For undergraduate foreign students a secondary school certificate (high school diploma) is acceptable.

For graduate study, the regular courses at the University of Clermont-Ferrand are open to qualified foreign students. In general, this means students who have a B.A. or B.S. degree and a very good knowledge of the French language.

See also the Admission Requirements section in the opening summary of France.

LANGUAGE OF INSTRUCTION ... French.

ACCOMMODATIONS ... Rooms with private families, pension or hotel accommodations are available to students. A committee of the University is set up to assist foreign students in finding lodgings. The student cafeteria serves lunch and dinner for about 75 cents each. A room alone may cost around $20 per month; room and board with a French family about $3.50 a day; pension accommodations cost slightly more.

LIVING COST ... Room and board from about $73 to $105 up per month.

STUDENT LIFE ... Clermont-Ferrand has an interesting Museum of Local History and Art contained in a sixteenth-century building that is a must for every new student to see. The "old town" in Clermont-Ferrand also offers interesting monuments and buildings. The city is the capital of the province of Auvergne in the center of France and near numerous spas as well as winter resorts which offer skiing and ice skating. Tennis and golf are also popular with students. A more sedentary activity of many students is solving philosophical problems by discussions in cafés near the campus.

HOW TO ENROLL ... Write directly to the University: Monsieur le Secrétaire, Faculté des Lettres, 34, Avenue Carnot, Clermont-Ferrand (Puy-de-Dôme).

UNIVERSITY OF DIJON

The world over, Burgundy is famous for its wine and its food and every November to celebrate this culinary excellence a gastronomical fair is held in Dijon. Throughout the city are found superb restaurants and pastry shops where a variety of delicacies are offered: snails, hams, gingerbread among them. The vineyards of Burgundy are some of the world's great wine producers. The capital of the province of Burgundy, Dijon, is one of France's "art cities" as well. The Museum of Fine Arts was founded in 1783 and houses remarkable collections of primitives, French works, medieval specimens of furniture and art and sculpture. The University of Dijon was founded in 1722.

SIZE ... About 4,400 students; 100 are from foreign countries.

CALENDAR ... October to early June. Summer session from early July to the first of September.

COURSES OF STUDY ... Special courses for undergraduate foreign students: The Cours de Français pour Étrangers offers the *Cours et Exercices Pratiques* including Grammar, Vocabulary, Diction, Composition and Phonetics of the French Language; the *Cours Spéciaux* offers courses in Language and in Contemporary French Theater, Philosophy, French Literature and Civilization.

Regular courses, opportunities for graduate study, are as follows: The Faculties of Law, Science, or Letters; School of

University of Dijon

Medicine and Pharmacy; Institute of Comparative Law; Institute of Regional Economics; Institute of Business Studies; Center for Legal Studies; School of Legal Studies; Center for Administrative Studies; Center for Burgundian Studies; Franco-American Institute; School of Midwifery; Viticultural Experimental Station and Marine Zoological Station.

SUMMER COURSES ... Language courses are offered at elementary to advanced levels and in addition there are courses in Theater, Poetry, History and Philosophy.

TUITION ... Tuition for the Cours de Français pour Étrangers is $16 per semester or $32 per academic year. A library and medical fee of about $10 may also be charged.

For summer courses tuition ranges from $21 for four weeks to $38 for eight weeks.

ADMISSION REQUIREMENTS ... For the Cours de Français pour Étrangers a secondary school certificate (high school diploma) is acceptable for some courses; an admission examination may be given.

The regular courses of the University are open to qualified foreign students. In general, this means students holding a B.A. or B.S. degree who have a very good knowledge of the French language.

See also the Admission Requirements section in the opening summary on France.

LANGUAGE OF INSTRUCTION ... French.

ACCOMMODATIONS ... Student hostels and the Cité Universitaire operated by the University offer a limited number of students inexpensive accommodations. Many students live in modestly priced hotel rooms, boardinghouses or with private families. A room costs from $16 to $30 per month; meals are about 75 cents each at the student cafeteria.

AVERAGE COSTS ... Fees about $30 per academic year. Room and board about $40 to $105 per month. However, the Cultural Counselor in New York suggests that each student be provided with a minimum of $140 per month.

STUDENT LIFE ... Student dances, receptions, group trips to towns and cities of interest in Burgundy are planned by students. In the summer there are festivals and fairs including the Burgundy night *fêtes.*

HOW TO ENROLL ... Write directly to the University: Monsieur le Secrétaire, Cours Spéciaux pour Étudiants Étrangers, 36, rue Chabot-Charny, Dijon (Côte-d'Or).

THE EUROPEAN INSTITUTE OF BUSINESS ADMINISTRATION, PARIS

The European Institute of Business Administration has been established in Paris on the initiative of the Paris Chamber of Commerce and with the technical assistance of the Harvard Graduate School of Business Administration. Assistance has also been given by the Management Education Center of the Paris Chamber of Commerce and by major industrial organizations. The Institute is under the patronage of the European Productivity Agency, the International Chamber of Commerce and the European League for Economic Cooperation.

The purpose of the Institute is to train graduates from European universities as potential executives of banking, manufacturing or commercial enterprises in Europe.

The head office of the Institute is at 27 Avenue de Friedland, Paris 8e. The Direction and the program are located at the Palais de Fontainebleau and nearby, at Avon-House, which are about 40 miles south of Paris.

SIZE . . . The Institute can accommodate 80 or 90 students. No more than one-third may come from any one country.

CALENDAR . . . The Course of Study lasts for one academic year, from mid-September to late June. This period includes a study trip.

COURSES OF STUDY . . . The curriculum includes Marketing, Production, Finance, Control and Accounting, Human Relations, Business Policy, Economic, Social and Institutional Framework of Europe. Each subject is studied in relation to various countries with special emphasis on problems arising from the European integration. The Case Study Method is used in teaching, and practical problems of business life are handled. The Institute is organized on a basis of individual and group study.

TUITION . . . Tuition and fees are $1,800. This amount includes teaching material and board and lodging in the Institute premises during the whole academic year. As no financial consideration must prevent a good candidate from being admitted, loans and scholarships can be obtained on request and after a decision of the financial aid committee.

ADMISSION REQUIREMENTS . . . Applicants are required to have a Bachelor's degree or a Master's degree, or a diploma from an accredited technical college of university standard in the fields of engineering, economics, law, commerce, etc. The normal age of students is 22 to 29 years, the average being around 25. Applications must be submitted before the end of April. Selection of students is made on the basis of interviews and tests.

LANGUAGE OF INSTRUCTION . . . English, French and German. Students are required to be fluent in two and have a working knowledge of the third.

ACCOMMODATIONS . . . Students live in three different residences operated by the Institute: Hotel d'Albe, Résidence St. Honoré and Avon-House.

STUDENT LIFE . . . The student will find that the variety of national points of view and experience will be of great interest and benefit to him, both in his studies and in his extracurricular activities. Of course, he will find an unfailing source of entertainment and education in and around Paris. The Office de Tourisme Universitaire will provide information of all types on student excursions.

UNIVERSITY OF GRENOBLE

Snow-capped peaks of the French Alps form a spectacular backdrop for the city of Grenoble. Besides being a university center, it has long been a take-off point for Alpine excursions. Grenoble has a population of 100,000 inhabitants and is one of few large cities situated so romantically at the foot of picturesque mountains, on the banks of the river Isère. Swimming, hiking and fishing are easily available and the town itself is not far from the French Riviera to the south. The city is important in the manufacture of gloves and skis, and it has made much progress in the use of water power. The Museum contains a rich collection of paintings from the French, modern French, and Spanish schools. The University of Grenoble was founded in 1339.

SIZE . . . About 9,400 students, of whom 1,500 are from foreign countries.

CALENDAR . . . October to mid-June. There are summer sessions from the first of July through September.

COURSES OF STUDY . . . Special courses for undergraduate foreign students are as follows: *Cours Intensif Gradué* including French Language, Practical French Vocabulary, Diction, Composition, Reading and Dictation; *Exercices Pratiques* including Pronunciation and Conversation; and the *Cours Normal* including Phonetics, Grammar, Basic Vocabulary, Semantics, Composition in the French Language; and Business Correspondence, Translation into the French Language, French Civilization, Geography of France, Contemporary France, French Literature, Literary Actualities and Philosophy.

Regular courses, opportunities for graduate study, are as follows: Faculties of Law and Economics, Science and Letters; the National School of Medicine and Pharmacy; the National College of Electro-Technical Hydraulic and Radio-Electrical Engineering; the National College of Electro-Chemical and Electro-Metallurgical Engineering; School of Paper Manufacturing; School of Electrical Engineering; Center of Preparatory Studies in Science and Letters and Institutes of Political Studies, Law and Economics of Energy, Commercial Studies and Business Administration, and Radioactive Isotopes (Medical Applications and Biological Research).

SUMMER COURSES . . . Summer courses in French Language and Culture are given. There is also an advanced course in physics.

TUITION . . . Fees for the *Cours Intensif,* $32.20; *Cours Normal,* $26.50; *Exercices Pratiques,* $6.90; *registration and library,* $6.90; and examination, $2.50.

For summer courses, tuition is about $26.50 monthly, or for more intensive course, $32.20 monthly. Pronunciation and conversation exercises (3 hours per week) are offered for about $13.50 monthly, with a minimum registration of two weeks.

ADMISSION REQUIREMENTS . . . For undergraduate foreign students, a secondary school certificate (high school diploma) is acceptable for some courses; a *baccalauréat* or equivalent degree required for other courses.

For graduate study, the regular courses of the University are open to qualified foreign students. In general, this means students who have a B.A. or a B.S. degree and a very good knowledge of the French language.

See also the Admission Requirements section in the opening summary on France.

LANGUAGE OF INSTRUCTION . . . French.

ACCOMMODATIONS . . . Although the Cité Universitaire has residential facilities for some students it is difficult to obtain a room and application must be made very early. Many students live in boardinghouses or with families. A room alone may cost about $25 to $53 a month; room and board about $94 a month, meals about 85 cents each.

AVERAGE COSTS . . . Fees $30 to $35 per semester. Room and board $140 per month.

STUDENT LIFE . . . Because of its location in the mountains, Grenoble offers a wide variety of recreational opportunities to students. There are organized student excursions to the Roman Provence, the great glacier of Isère, and the Riviera. During the summer, a Folklore Festival is held at Megeve, a winter ski resort, and a Festival of Dramatic Art at Evian, a well-known spa. There are always hiking, swimming and tennis, and during summer weekend trips in the Alps, mountain-climbing and weekly receptions and dances. Plays are given in the Roman amphitheaters of Orange and Vienne. Ski weekends are popular in winter. Students often gather to recite poetry or listen to folk songs.

HOW TO ENROLL . . . Write directly to the University: Monsieur le Secrétaire, FACULTÉ DES LETTRES DE L'UNIVERSITÉ DE GRENOBLE, Place de Verdun, Grenoble (Isère).

University of Grenoble

University of Lille

University of Lyons

UNIVERSITY OF LILLE

Lille is an important industrial center located about 85 miles from Paris in the north of France. Out of its textile mills come linens, cottons and haberdashery for France and for export. It is the birthplace of General Charles de Gaulle and the ancient capital of French Flanders. The Museum houses a fine collection of paintings of the Flemish school as well as works from the Spanish, Italian, Dutch and French schools. One of the city's most interesting buildings is the ancient Bourse (Stock Exchange), a remarkable example of Flemish architecture of the 1600s. The building's inner courtyard, which is surrounded by galleries, once provided stalls for traders. The University of Lille was founded in 1560.

SIZE ... About 12,000 students, of whom 300 are from foreign countries.

CALENDAR ... October to mid-June. During July and August a summer session is held.

COURSES OF STUDY ... Special courses for undergraduate foreign students are as follows: The *Cours de Français* offers the *Cours Spéciaux* with courses in French Language, Literature, History, Geography, Art, Philosophy, Phonetics and Translation. The *Cours Pour Débutants* includes Vocabulary, Composition, Grammar and Phonetics. The *Enseignement Normal* is open to students who have had two years of college and whose academic background fits them for one of the regular courses.

Regular courses, opportunities for graduate study, are as follows: Faculties of Law, Medicine and Pharmacy, Science and Letters; Institutes of Economic Technics, Labor Studies, Criminology, Regional Economics, Business Training, School Hygiene, Physical Education, Forensic Medicine, Fluid Mechanics, Radio Technology, Applied Mathematics, and the Oil Institute; Workers Education Center; School of Notarial Studies; National College of Chemistry; Laboratory of Applied Geology; Electro-Mechanical Institute; Regional Seed Testing Institute; North of France Agricultural Institute; Industrial Research and Testing Bureau; and the Regional Laboratory of Applied Zoology.

SUMMER COURSES ... The summer session is held at Boulogne-sur-Mer on the English Channel from early July to late August. Elementary to advanced courses in French Language and Culture are offered.

TUITION ... Tuition for the summer session is about $3.50 per week.

ADMISSION REQUIREMENTS ... The *Enseignement Normal* is open to students who have had two years of college and whose academic background fits them for one of the regular courses.

For graduate study, the regular courses of the University are open to qualified students. In general, this means students who have a B.A. or a B.S. degree and a very good knowledge of the French language.

For summer courses students must be at least 18 years old.

See also the Admission Requirements section in the opening summary on France.

LANGUAGE OF INSTRUCTION ... French.

ACCOMMODATIONS ... The University operates one men's dormitory and one women's dormitory. Each has a dining room where inexpensive meals are served. Room and board with a private family cost about $105 a month; modest-priced hotel rooms and pension accommodations are also available and a committee of the University will assist foreign students to find these lodgings.

AVERAGE COSTS ... Fees about $28 per year. Room and board about $140 per month.

STUDENT LIFE ... Students organize their own tours to Paris from Lille. There are also excursions to Bruges, Belgium, to the forest of Boulogne and the Boulogne area itself and the

battlefields. Lille offers museums of fine arts, ceramics, archaeology, and sculpture. Seaside resorts are not far away and are popular with students during the season. Dances, receptions and parties on the campus offer students a full social life.

HOW TO ENROLL ... Write directly to the University: Monsieur le Directeur, Institut d'Expansion Universitaire, Office des Étudiants Étrangers, 9, rue August-Angellier, Lille (Nord).

UNIVERSITY OF LYONS

Lyons is situated in The Rhône Valley at the confluence of the Rhône and Saône rivers. The city is known for its silk industry and it was in Lyons that the Italians first introduced this craft to France in the fifteenth century. Because several of its streets traverse steep hills, a funicular railway, nicknamed the *Ficelle,* is in use in the city. The city's history goes back to 43 B.C. when a Roman colony was established where the modern city lies. In 1933 excavation began on the Roman theaters, which are now used for summer productions. There is an epigraphic museum of note as well as a fine arts museum with paintings, sculpture and furniture. The University of Lyons was founded in 1809.

SIZE ... About 13,000 of whom 500 are from foreign countries.

CALENDAR ... October to late June. There is a summer session during September and October.

COURSES OF STUDY ... Special courses for undergraduate foreign students are as follows: The Cours de Français pour Étrangers offers the *Cours Normal* including elementary, intermediate and advanced courses in French Language and Phonetics, French Literature and Civilization; the *Travaux Pratiques Supplémentaires* includes French Phonetics, Diction and Grammar.

Regular courses, opportunities for graduate study, are as follows: Students may apply for study in the Faculties of Sciences, Law and Economic Sciences, Letters and Human Sciences; the Institutes of Law Practices, Comparative Law, Law of Work and Social Security, Economic Studies, Administrative Sciences, Finance and Insurance, Political Studies, Study of the Population and International Relations, Applied Sciences, Chemistry, Geology, Meterology and Climatical Sciences, General Physics, National Antiquities, Classical Archaeology, Medieval and Modern Art, Egyptology, Geography and the Studies of the Rhône Valley; the Marine Biological Center, and the School of Practical Psychology and Pedagogics.

SUMMER COURSES ... French language, literature and civilization.

TUITION ... Tuition for the *Cours Normal* is $12 per month. For the *Travaux Pratiques Supplémentaires,* tuition is $6 per month. In addition, a library and medical fee of about $10 per academic year may be charged; a fee of $1 is charged for the *Certificat d'Études Françaises,* and a $2 fee for the diploma.

ADMISSION REQUIREMENTS ... For undergraduate foreign students, a secondary school certificate (high school diploma) is acceptable.

For graduate study, the regular courses of the University of Lyons are open to qualified foreign students. In general, this means students with a very good knowledge of the French language who have a B.A. or a B.S. degree.

See also the Admission Requirements section in the opening summary on France.

LANGUAGE OF INSTRUCTION ... French.

ACCOMMODATIONS ... The University operates dormitories and dining facilities, but application must be made very early to obtain these inexpensive accommodations. The University has a committee devoted to finding lodgings for foreign students with private families, in pensions, or in hotels. Costs vary, but a room alone may cost about $20 per month. Meals at the student cafeterias are about 75 cents each. Room and board with a family or in a pension runs about $3.50 per day, up.

AVERAGE COSTS ... Fees about $108 to $148 per academic year. Room and board about $140 per month.

STUDENT LIFE ... During the summer, students flock to the festival of music and drama held in Lyons from June 15 to July 4. Throughout the year there are offerings in the theaters of Lyons, ballet, grand opera, light opera and dramas. Students also organize walking tours of the city and visits to the museums. There are swimming, tennis and hiking, all popular with students. Students hold their own dances and discussions, equally attended.

HOW TO ENROLL ... Write directly to the University: Madame la Secrétaire, Cours aux Étudiants Étrangers, 18 Quai Claude Bernard, Lyons (Rhône).

UNIVERSITY OF AIX-MARSEILLES

As its name implies, the University of Aix-Marseilles has sections in both Aix-en-Provence and in Marseilles. Aix is but 18 miles north and inland from the historic Mediterranean port of Marseilles. Founded in 123 B.C., Aix-en-Provence was well liked by the Romans because of its hot springs. Considered one of the most beautiful art cities of France, Aix offers examples of art from medieval times to the Renaissance. There are fine arts, tapestry, and historical museums. Marseilles is the oldest city of France, having been founded about 600 B.C. by Greek navigators. Today its size is second only to that of Paris, 636,246 inhabitants; it is the country's leading port. Marseilles is a bustling, animated city, where traces of cultures from all over the world have met and mixed during a long history. The region of Provence has attracted Renoir, Van Gogh, Cézanne, Signac and Gauguin to paint its colorful scenes. The University was founded as Studium Generale by Louis II, King of Sicily, in 1409. The Faculties of Medicine and Pharmacy and of Science are at Marseilles; the Faculties of Law and Letters are at Aix.

SIZE ... About 15,000 students, of whom about 1,800 are from foreign countries.

CALENDAR ... October to early June. There are summer sessions held at Cannes and at Nice in August.

COURSES OF STUDY ... Special courses for undergraduate foreign students are as follows: The *Institut D'Études Françaises pour Étudiants Étrangers,* at Aix-en-Provence, offers practical exercises in the French Language including Reading, Diction, Phonetics, French Composition and Translation; and lecture courses in French Literature from the Middle Ages to the Twentieth Century, French Grammar, Philology and History of the French Language, History of French Thought in the Nineteenth and Twentieth Centuries, French Civilization and History of French Art. A prerequisite is two years of college.

The University of Aix-Marseilles has set up a center for foreign students at Nice, The Centre Universitaire Méditerranéen Cours de Français pour Étrangers, which offers the following courses: *Cours Préparatoire,* elementary courses in Grammar, Phonetics and Conversation in the French Language; *Cours Moyen,* intermediate courses in Grammar, Phonetics, Conversation in the French Language and French Civilization courses; *Cours Supérieur,* advanced courses in Grammar and Diction of the French Language; Introduction to French Literature, Art,

Music, Geography and Governmental Institutions; a prerequisite for this course is two years of college; *Cours de Langue et Civilisation Étrangères,* Arabic, Italian, German, Spanish and Russian languages; prerequisites are a good knowledge of French and two years of college; *Cours pour les Professeurs de Français à l'Étranger,* one year course in the French Language, Literature and Civilization, methods for students planning to teach; prerequisite is two years of college.

Regular courses, opportunities for graduate study, are as follows: Faculties of Law, Letters, Science, Medicine and Pharmacy; Institutes of Political Studies, Business Administration, Chinese Studies, Literature, Fluid Mechanics, and Criminology.

SUMMER COURSES ... Various summer courses in French are offered on "Contemporary France" including history, geography, political institutions, and economic, social, juridical, and cultural problems by the University in Nice.

TUITION ... At the Institut D'Études Françaises pour Étudiants Étrangers, fees for the first semester are $30, and $53 for two semesters. An examination fee of $1.45, diploma fee of $1.45, and medical and library fee of about $10 are also charged.

At the Centre Universitaire Méditeranéen Cours de Français pour Étrangers, The *Cours Préparatoire* costs $27 per semester; all others are $33 per semester. A medical and library fee of about $10 may be charged for the academic year.

For summer courses, tuition charges run from $12.30 for four weeks in Nice.

ADMISSION REQUIREMENTS ... For undergraduate foreign students, please refer to Courses of Study.

For graduate study, the regular courses of the University are open to qualified foreign students. In general, this means graduate students with a B.A. or B.S. degree and a very good knowledge of the French language.

See also the Admission Requirements section in the opening summary on France.

LANGUAGE OF INSTRUCTION ... French.

ACCOMMODATIONS ... Students may live with private families, in pensions or in hotels. A room with a family may cost about $20 to $30 per month; meals are available at the student restaurants for about 75 cents each. Room and board with a family or in a pension may cost about $3.50 and up per day. Prices are subject to change.

AVERAGE COSTS ... Fees about $66 to $74 per academic year. Room and board about $140 per month.

STUDENT LIFE ... The colorful region of Provence offers students a hundred byways to explore on foot or on bicycle. The range of sports popular with students is very wide including tennis, swimming and all kinds of water sports, volley ball, hiking, bicycle riding, golf and horseback riding. At Marseilles the beaches are convenient and popular with students. There are theaters, operas, concerts and, perhaps most interesting, the festivals. Aix-en-Provence is the setting for the annual *Festival de Musique,* an outstanding summer event in the South of France. Students new to the region will find their French counterparts willing to take them to see Provençal dancing, the *farandole,* done to the music of drum and fife. Certain cafés are centers of student activity in both university cities.

HOW TO ENROLL ... Write directly to the one school of your choice: Monsieur le Doyen, Institut d'Études Françaises pour Étudiants Étrangers, 23, rue Gaston-de-Saporta, Aix-en-Provence, Bouches-du-Rhône or Monsieur le Secrétaire, Centre Universitaire Méditerranéen, 65, Promenade des Anglais, Nice, Alpes-Maritimes.

University of Aix-Marseilles

UNIVERSITY OF MONTPELLIER

Montpellier has retained the character of a university city since the thirteenth century, when the Faculty of Medicine was established (1221). Monuments have been erected to three of the city's famous "students": Petrarch, Rabelais and Auguste Comte. But there is more than academic fare for the newcomer; the nearby mountains provide a vantage point for a panorama of southern France that stretches from the Pyrenees, to forests, vineyards, fishing villages and the Mediterranean Sea with its sandy beaches. All of these are within easy reach of Montpellier. Buildings occupied by the various university faculties are an attraction to many tourists as well as students. Some date from the fourteenth century.

SIZE ... About 11,500 students. Of these, about 1,500 are from foreign countries.

CALENDAR ... October to late June. A summer session is held from the beginning of September to mid-October.

COURSES OF STUDY ... Special courses for undergraduate foreign students are as follows: The *Cours Pratiques d'Initiation à la Langue Française* offers elementary and advanced sections in Conversation, Composition, Vocabulary, Pronunciation and Translation; *Cours Élémentaire*—Vocabulary, Phonetics, Composition, Elementary Grammar; *Cours Moyen* (intermediate and advanced)—Grammar, Diction, Phonetics, Translation, Text Analysis. The *Cours de Civilisation* offers History of France, French Literature, Music, Art, and Geography.

Regular courses, opportunities for graduate study, are as follows: Faculty of Law, the Institute of Business Training, Faculty of Sciences, Institute of Chemistry, Botanical Institute, the Faculty of Letters, Institute of Archaeology and the Institute of Mediterranean Studies.

SUMMER COURSES ... In a special September to October session the Institut des Étudiants Étrangers offers beginning, intermediate and advanced courses in the French Language and French Culture courses.

TUITION ... For the *Cours Pratiques d'Initiation à la Langue Française* and the *Cours de Civilisation*, fees are $25 per semester, including registration, library and examination fees.

For the summer session, tuition is $20 for two months.

ADMISSION REQUIREMENTS ... For undergraduate foreign students a secondary school certificate (high school diploma) is acceptable.

For graduate study, the regular courses of the University are open to qualified foreign students. In general, this means students with a very good knowledge of the French language, who have a B.A. or a B.S. degree.

See also the Admission Requirements section in the opening summary on France.

LANGUAGE OF INSTRUCTION ... French.

ACCOMMODATIONS ... The Cité Universitaire may have a limited number of inexpensive rooms available. Dining rooms are attached to these lodgings and meals cost about 50 to 75 cents each. A room with a family costs from $20 to $30 monthly; room and board with a family or in a pension costs about $3.50 a day; hotel accommodations are slightly higher. A committee of the university is set up to assist foreign students in getting settled into rooms.

AVERAGE COSTS ... Fees about $50 per year. Room and board about $140 per month.

STUDENT LIFE ... Today's students carry out a tradition begun in the days of Petrarch, once a student at Montpellier. Now, as then, discussions are of great length and moment and fundamental questions become the center of great debate. The big cafés on the Place de la Comédie are accustomed to an argumentative academic customer, and it is there that a conclusion, if there be one, is drawn to students' oral dissertations. For less sedentary activity, there is the nearby country of Provence, a region which attracts many artists to paint its blue skies and colorful countryside. There is the Roman amphitheater at Nîmes, the scene of a drama festival during July. Also in July is the artistic festival at Arles. Students organize their own trips to museums, landmarks, spots of geographical interest. In season, the sandy beach at Palavas-les-Flots, a picturesque fishing village on the Mediterranean, beckons students.

HOW TO ENROLL ... Write directly to the University: Monsieur le Secrétaire, Institut des Étudiants Étrangers, Montpellier (Hérault).

UNIVERSITY OF NANCY

In the twelfth century Nancy was the capital of the Duchy of Lorraine, part of the Holy Roman Empire. Since that time four towns have sprung up and grown together as Nancy: the Old Town, the New Town, the Eighteenth-Century Town, and the Modern Town, which includes the University, though it was founded in 1572. The Musée Lorrain, which is housed in a wing of the Ducal Palace in the Old Town, contains an outstanding collection of historical exhibits of France and Europe, paintings, engravings, sculpture, tapestries and furniture. The city has a fine collection of buildings of the eighteenth century. Now an important commercial and industrial center, Nancy utilizes the iron deposits of Lorraine which make France the third largest iron ore producer in the world. Nancy has retained an old world look, however, in spite of its industry.

SIZE ... About 7,900 students of whom about 350 are from foreign countries.

CALENDAR ... October to June. A summer session is held from July through August.

COURSES OF STUDY ... Special courses for undergraduate foreign students are as follows: The Cours de Français pour Étrangers offers *Degré Moyen* and *Degré Supérieure* in intermediate and advanced sections with classes in Grammar, Vocabulary, Phonetics and Pronunciation, Contemporary French Literature, Civilization, Geography, History, Economics, Art and other lecture courses.

Regular courses, opportunities for graduate study, are as follows: Faculty of Law and Economic Sciences, which embraces the Center of Business Training and Administration, the Commercial Institute, Institute of Criminology, Center of History of Lorrainese Law, Center for Economic Research and Documentation, University Center for Economic and Social Co-operation and the University Center of Political Studies; the Faculty of Sciences, which includes the Institute of Automatic Calculus and the Elie Cartan Institute of Mathematics; and the Faculty of Letters and Human Sciences, including the Institute of Demography, the Institute of Lorraine Studies and the European University Center.

University of Montpellier

University of Nancy

SUMMER COURSES . . . French Language, and Culture for Advanced Students.

TUITION . . . For the Cours de Français pour Étrangers, fees for registration, practical exercises and library are $26 per semester.

ADMISSION REQUIREMENTS . . . For undergraduate foreign students a secondary school certificate (high school diploma) is acceptable.

For graduate study, the regular courses of the University are open to qualified foreign students. In general, this means students with a B.A. or B.S. degree and a very good knowledge of the French language.

See also the Admission Requirements section in the opening summary on France.

LANGUAGE OF INSTRUCTION . . . French.

ACCOMMODATIONS . . . A committee of the university is set up to help students find rooms. The Cité Universitaire offers inexpensive lodgings, but application must be made early to secure these accommodations. The university operates student cafeterias where meals are available for 50 to 75 cents each. Many students eat at the cafeterias and take a room with a French family; such a room costs from $20 to $30 per month. Pension accommodations may cost about $3.50 up per day. A list of modest-priced hotels is also available from the University.

AVERAGE COSTS . . . Fees about $32 per year. Room and board from about $140 per month.

STUDENT LIFE . . . The city of Nancy and its countryside offer students countless corners to explore: there is the palace where Joan of Arc was received by Duke Charles II; there are museums, monuments, buildings and even a glassworks to visit. Tennis, golf, swimming, hiking and bicycling are popular. Many festivals—harvest festivals, folklore, wine, flower festivals—in the east of France attract students. In season, there are skiing, horse racing, polo, motor racing, music and drama.

HOW TO ENROLL . . . Write directly to the University: Monsieur le Secrétaire, Cours de Français pour les Étrangers, Faculté des Lettres, Nancy.

UNIVERSITY OF PARIS (LA SORBONNE)

Paris is home to the student. The Left Bank of the Seine truly belongs to him and has for hundreds of years. Cafés where clusters of students spend hour upon hour are found throughout the Latin Quarter, surrounding the Sorbonne, which is part of the University of Paris, founded in 1257 by Robert de Sorbon. In those days the students spoke Latin and the district came to be called the Latin Quarter.

SIZE . . . About 80,000 students at the University of Paris, of whom about 10,000 are from foreign countries.

CALENDAR . . . October to mid-June. The academic year of the Cours de Français pour Étrangers is divided into semesters. Summer courses for foreign students are offered during the period from early July to mid-August.

COURSES OF STUDY . . . Special courses for undergraduate foreign students are as follows: The *Cours de Civilisation Française pour Étrangers* offers the *Degré Préparatoire* for beginners in the French language (25 hours weekly); *Cours Pratique de Langue Française* including Grammar, Composition, and Diction (6 hours weekly); *Conférences de Civilisation Française* including French Economics, Political Science, Literature and Civilization; *Cours de Phonétique* including French Pronunciation and Diction; *Cours de Traduction* including Literary, Scientific and Technical Translation.

Information on the regular courses and opportunities for graduate study at the University may be obtained from the French Cultural Services of the French Embassy.

SUMMER COURSES . . . From July to mid-August various courses in French Language and Culture are held at the University of Paris, including the American Summer Course and the *Cours de Civilisation Française* (Sorbonne) and the École de L'Alliance Française.

TUITION . . . For special courses for undergraduate foreign students: *Degré Préparatoire,* $120 per semester; *Cours Pratique de Langue Française,* $28 per semester; *Conférences de Civilisa-*

tion Française, $26 per semester; *Cours de Phonétique,* $7 per 10 class hours; *Cours de Traduction,* $26 per semester; *Cours Pratique de Langue Française* and *Conférence de Civilisation Française* taken together are $32 per semester. In addition there is an examination fee of $2 and there may be a library and medical fee amounting to about $10 per year.

Fees for summer courses range from $11 to $96 per month.

ADMISSION REQUIREMENTS . . . For undergraduate foreign students a secondary school certificate (high school diploma) is acceptable.

For graduate study, regular courses at the University are open to students holding a B.A. or B.S. degree who have a good command of spoken French and an excellent reading knowledge of the language.

For summer courses, a high school diploma is required for admission.

See also the Admission Requirements section in the opening summary on France.

LANGUAGE OF INSTRUCTION . . . French (and also English for the American Summer Course).

ACCOMMODATIONS . . . Several organizations are set up to help the student to find a room once he arrives in Paris. Prices for single and double rooms range $30 to $50 per month. Lunch or dinner at the student cafeteria of the International House costs about 80 cents. The University will provide the student with a list of modestly priced hotels and pensions upon request.

AVERAGE COSTS . . . Fees $30 to $100 per semester. Room and board $140 per month.

STUDENT LIFE . . . Browsing in the bookstalls along the Seine can cost nothing and is an activity that fits well into many student budgets. So does sitting under the trees in the Luxembourg Gardens. No student need be without extracurricular activities in Paris and there are student-organized tours to cultural and artistic highlights of the French capital. But many students will find the center of activity is a café where a lively discussion can go on and on over a single cup of coffee. The Office du Tourisme Universitaire in Paris can provide information of all types on student excursions. Generally, Paris gets neither very hot nor very cold and walking is a popular pastime summer, winter, spring and fall.

HOW TO ENROLL . . . Write directly to the University: Monsieur le Secrétaire, Cours de Civilisation Française à la Sorbonne, 47, Rue des Écoles, Paris 5e.

UNIVERSITY OF POITIERS

In the heart of the château country on the Loire River lies the city of Tours, where the Institute of French Studies of Touraine, part of the University of Poitiers, holds its classes. Tours is the capital of the historical region of Touraine, an area whose lush flowers and vines have given it the name "The Garden of France." The magnificent châteaux in the Valley of the Loire were once country estates of kings and noblemen, and many of these castles are well preserved and can be visited the year round. Some contain historical relics and treasures; others are of architectural importance. Situated about three hours from Paris, Tours is the center for trips to many of these famous châteaux—Blois, Amboise, Chaumont, Chenonceaux, Chambord, Villandry, Azay-le-Rideau. During the summer, spectacular programs of "sound and light" can be seen at night; the castles are illuminated and dialogue dramas recalling scenes from the castle's history are presented. Night trips can be arranged from Tours. The University of Poitiers was founded in 1431 and has branches at Limoges and at La Rochelle as well as at Tours.

SIZE . . . About 7,500 students, of whom about 500 are from foreign countries.

CALENDAR . . . October to late June. An Easter session is held during March and April. A summer session is held from early July to the first of October.

COURSES OF STUDY . . . Special courses for undergraduate foreign students are as follows: Held at the Institute of French Studies of Touraine at Tours are the *Cours Intensif Gradué* including Grammar, Vocabulary and Pronunciation of the French Language; *Cours Moyen* including French Phonetics, Reading, Conversation and Composition; and the *Cours Supérieur* including lecture courses on French Civilization, Semantics,

Literature, History and Geography.

Regular courses, opportunities for graduate study, are as follows: Faculties of Law, Science, Letters; School of Medicine and Pharmacy; Institute of Business Training; Institute of Regional Studies; Institute of Pre-History; Center of Rural Law; Center of Renaissance Studies; Thermodynamic Center; Center of Fluid Mechanics; Research Station for Plant Biology, or Physiological Laboratory.

SUMMER COURSES ... During the summer period at Tours and at La Rochelle, courses are given for beginning, intermediate and advanced students in the French language and culture. The courses last from two weeks to three months.

TUITION ... Tuition at the Institute of French Studies of Touraine at Tours is $18 for each course for the academic year. A library and medical fee of about $10 may also be charged for the academic year.

For summer courses, tuition ranges from $16 to $64.

ADMISSION REQUIREMENTS ... For undergraduate foreign students a secondary school certificate (high school diploma) is acceptable.

For graduate study, the regular courses at the University of Poitiers are open to qualified foreign students. In general this means students with a B.A. or a B.S. degree who have a very good knowledge of the French language.

See also the Admission Requirements section in the opening summary on France.

LANGUAGE OF INSTRUCTION ... French.

ACCOMMODATIONS ... Many students take a room with a private family, but eat their lunch and dinner at the student cafeteria. Meals cost about 75 cents. A special committee of the University is set up to help students find lodgings; with a French family room and board may cost about $3.50 per day; a room only about $20 and up per month; in a pension from about $3.50 up per day. Prices are subject to change.

AVERAGE COSTS ... Fees about $28 per year. Room and board from about $140 per month.

STUDENT LIFE ... The student cafeteria is a center of student life which gives foreign students an opportunity to meet and mix freely with French and other foreign students. It is there that students often "solve the problems of the world." Sports popular with students in Tours are tennis, football, canoeing, swimming, golf and fencing. There are also theater, concerts, dances and student-organized excursions to the châteaux of the Loire Valley, Chartres, Mont-St.-Michel, Poitiers and Bourges. A

University of Poitiers

summer event of the Loire region is the festival of dramatic arts at Angers, June 20 to 29.

HOW TO ENROLL ... Write directly to the Institute of French Studies of Touraine at Tours: Monsieur le Secrétaire, Institut d'Études Françaises de Touraine pour les Étrangers, 1, rue de la Grandière, Tours (Indre-et-Loire).

UNIVERSITY OF RENNES

The intellectual center of Brittany, Rennes was once the capital as well. It has outstanding botanical gardens, museums of fine arts and archaeology and the Palais de Justice, the Law Courts, built between 1618 and 1654. The Courts originally housed the Breton Parliament and are outstanding for their remarkable interior decoration of gilt woodwork, carved ceilings and fine tapestries. Around the Cathedral is found the only area of the city which was not destroyed by fire in 1720; it stands as an antique reminder of old Rennes. The University was founded in 1461 as the University of Nantes by the Duke of Brittany; later it was transferred to Rennes, and today both cities have branches of the University.

SIZE ... About 12,000 students. Of these, about 800 are from foreign countries.

CALENDAR ... October to late June. A summer course is also offered from mid-July to late August.

COURSES OF STUDY ... Special courses for undergraduate foreign students are as follows: The Cours de Français pour Étrangers offers the *Cours de Langue* including classes in Grammar, Vocabulary, Conversation, Pronunciation and Composition; there are lecture courses in French Literature, Philosophy, Geography, History and the History of Art.

Regular courses, opportunities for graduate study, are as follows: Faculty of Law and Economic Sciences, embracing the Institute of Business Administration, Institute of Higher Administrative and Social Studies, Institute of Comparative Law, and the Institute of Law of Nantes (located in Nantes); Center for Prehistoric Ethnographic Studies and General Anthropology and the Institute for Advanced Studies of the Natural Sciences; and the Faculty of Letters, including the Institute of Historical, Economic and Social Research, the Center of Psychotechnical Studies and the Institute of Letters of Nantes (located in Nantes).

SUMMER COURSES ... The University holds its summer session at Saint-Malo on the English Channel. Elementary to advanced courses are offered in Language and Culture.

TUITION ... Tuition for the *Cours de Langue* for undergraduate foreign students is free: there may be a charge of about $10 per year for medical and library fees; the diploma may cost $5 to $6.

For the summer courses, tuition costs about $14.30 for 2 weeks to about $33 for 6 weeks.

ADMISSION REQUIREMENTS ... For the Cours de Français pour Étrangers a secondary school certificate (high school diploma) is acceptable.

For graduate study, the regular courses at the University of Rennes are open to qualified foreign students. In general, this means students with a very good knowledge of the French language who hold a B.A. or B.S. degree.

LANGUAGE OF INSTRUCTION ... French.

ACCOMMODATIONS ... A committee on lodgings will assist students to find suitable accommodations. The University maintains some residential facilities for students but the demand exceeds the supply so it is necessary to apply early. It is possible to get a room with a French family for about $20 per month; room and board with a family costs about $105 per month; meals at student cafeterias are 50 to 75 cents each. Pensions and hotels also offer student lodgings.

University of Rennes

AVERAGE COSTS ... Fees about $15 per year. Room and board about $140 per month.

STUDENT LIFE ... The picturesque region of Brittany beckons students as it does tourists to its colorful countryside. Breton tradition observes several religious celebrations or pilgrimages called *pardons* each year, throughout the year, and students congregate to see the festive dress worn by the participants. Students organize their own excursions to the coast, to Mont-St.-Michel, to the beaches, to fishing villages and to see the lighthouses which dot the coast of Brittany. For outdoor types there is salmon and trout fishing in the streams and rivers. Shellfish are plentiful along the coast. Popular with students are tennis, hiking and swimming.

HOW TO ENROLL ... Write directly to the University: M. le Secrétaire de la Faculté des Lettres et Sciences Humaines, 7, Place Hoche, Rennes (Ille-et-Vilaine).

UNIVERSITY OF STRASBOURG

Alsace has been called a corridor between Mediterranean and Northern culture, and Strasbourg, its capital, sits astride this crossroad. The city is situated on the Ill River near the Rhine. The Ill divides, encircles the city, and provides the most important river port of Alsace. Strasbourg has a population of 200,000 inhabitants and is an important economic center. Wood-processing, cellulose production, tanning, breweries, flour milling, food processing and metallurgy are important industries. During June, Strasbourg is the scene of the International Music Festival, the first French festival of its kind. More than half a dozen museums display the city's or Alsatian treasures: the Archaeological Museum, Museum of the Oeuvre Notre-Dame, Museum of Fine Arts, Museum of Decorative Arts, Historical Museum, Alsatian Museum and the Apartments of the Château des Rohan. Strasbourg's Gothic Cathedral of red sandstone is a remarkable building dating back to the eleventh century. The University of Strasbourg, founded in 1538 as the Academy of Strasbourg, became the university in 1621. The city has long been noted as a center of learning and it was here that Gutenberg perfected his printing press and that Rouget de Lisle first sang "The Marseillaise."

SIZE ... About 9,000 students, of whom about 800 are from foreign countries.

CALENDAR ... October to late June. There is also a summer session from early July to mid-September.

COURSES OF STUDY ... Special courses for undergraduate foreign students are as follows: The Cours de Français pour Étrangers offers two sections: Section I, the *Cours de Langue, Littérature et Civilisation Française* includes French Grammar, Phonetics, Vocabulary and Literature. Section II, the *Cours Théoriques* includes Civilization, Geography, History, Economics, Political Science, Art and other lectures; and the *Cours Pratiques* includes Translation, Pronunciation, Diction, Grammar, Composition, Readings and Civilization.

Regular courses, opportunities for graduate study, are as follows: Faculty of Law and Economic and Political Sciences embracing the Institute of Higher Commercial Studies, Institute of Business Management, Institute of Law and Comparative Economics, International Center of Higher Journalism, Institute of Labor, Institute of Crime and Punishments, Institute of

Political Studies, and the University Center of Higher European Studies; the Faculty of Sciences, embracing the Institutes of Botany, Chemistry, Geological Sciences, Mathematics, Nuclear Research, Physics, Zoology, and General Biology and Global Physics; and the Faculty of Letters and Social Sciences, embracing the Institutes of French Language and Literature, Modern French Studies, Modern Comparative Literature, German, English, Greek, Latin, Languages of Southern Europe, Dutch Language and Literature, General Linguistics and Orientalism, Scandinavian Languages and Literatures, Slavic Languages and Literatures, Rhenish and National Antiquities, Classical Archaeology, Archaeology and the History of Art of Eastern Europe, History of Art, Egyptology, History of Music, Geography, History of Alsace, Higher Alsatian Studies, Ancient History, Contemporary History, Modern History, History of the Middle Ages, History of Religions, Classical Philology, Roman Philology, Philosophy, Phonetics and Psychology and the Center of German Studies; and the Theology Department, including the Faculty of Catholic Theology, the Faculty of Protestant Theology, Institute of Canon Law, and the Institute of Dogmatic Theology.

SUMMER COURSES ... A German language course is offered as well as French Language, and Culture.

TUITION ... For the Cours de Français pour Étrangers tuition fees are $22 per year. A $10 medical and library fee may also be charged.

For summer courses, fees range from $8 a week for classes only, to $17.50 a week for classes and room and board.

ADMISSION REQUIREMENTS ... For Section I of the Cours de Français pour Étrangers a secondary school certificate (high school diploma) is acceptable. For Section II, either course, a prerequisite is two years of college.

For graduate study, the regular courses of the University are open to qualified foreign students. In general, this means students who hold a B.A. or a B.S. degree and have a very good knowledge of the French language.

See also the Admission Requirements section in the opening summary on France.

LANGUAGE OF INSTRUCTION ... French.

ACCOMMODATIONS ... Although the University operates dormitory and dining facilities, these are usually secured by French students. A committee of the University is set up to help foreign students find suitable lodgings. Some may want to live with French families and take their meals in a student cafeteria; lunch or dinner costs about 50 to 75 cents; a room alone may be $20 to $30 with a family. In a pension, room and board costs from $3.50 up per day. A few hotels also offer inexpensive rooms.

AVERAGE COSTS ... Fees about $28 per year. Room and board about $140 per month.

STUDENT LIFE ... As everywhere in France, in Strasbourg discussions and debates are popular pastimes of students. But tennis, canoeing, swimming, dances, concerts, the theater, walking and museum visits are also popular. Students organize their own excursions to the nearby Vosges Mountains and to interesting villages and towns in Alsace and Lorraine. Guided tours of the Strasbourg Cathedral and some museums are arranged. In September there is a fair.

HOW TO ENROLL ... Write directly to the University: Monsieur le Secrétaire, Institut d'Études Françaises Modernes, Cours pour Étrangers, Faculté des Lettres, UNIVERSITÉ DE STRASBOURG, Strasbourg (Bas-Rhin).

UNIVERSITY OF TOULOUSE

Because of its numerous red brick buildings, Toulouse has been called a rose-red city. It is the fourth city in size in France and the metropolis of the southwest, lively with commerce and industry. Still it remains an important art city and its brick buildings give it a special atmosphere. During the Middle Ages, Toulouse was the residence of the sovereign Counts of Toulouse and it boasted the most civilized court in France. This glorious history is recalled in the Musée des Toulousains de Toulouse, one of seven important museums in the city. A former Augustinian Monastery, now the Musée des Augustins, houses a remarkable collection of Romanesque sculpture. Less than fifty miles from Toulouse is the picturesque town of Albi, birthplace of Henri de

University of Strasbourg

Toulouse-Lautrec, and the site of a museum displaying a great part of that artist's works. The University of Toulouse was founded in 1229.

SIZE . . . About 13,500 students, of whom about 1,000 are foreign students.

CALENDAR . . . October to June. A summer session is also held from mid-July to late August.

COURSES OF STUDY . . . Special courses for undergraduate foreign students are as follows: The *Institut Normal d'Études Françaises* offers courses in the French language including Phonetics, Grammar, Vocabulary and Reading and lecture courses in History, Geography, Philosophy, Art and the Civilization of France.

Regular courses, opportunities for graduate study, are as follows: Students may apply for study in the Faculty of Law, which embraces the Institutes of Business Training, Criminology and Penal Studies, Applied Law, Comparative Law of Latin Countries, Applied Economics, Rural Management and Legislation, and of Political Studies; the Faculty of Sciences, including the Institute of Chemical Engineering and the Institute of Fluid Mechanics and the Faculty of Letters, including the Institute of Southern European Studies.

SUMMER COURSES . . . Various summer courses are offered by the Universities of Toulouse and Bordeaux at Pau near the Basque country. Elementary to advanced courses in the French language, lectures in culture and seminars are offered.

TUITION . . . For the Institut Normal d'Études Françaises a medical and library fee of about $10 may be charged for the academic year, but tuition is free.

For the summer courses, fees range from about $82 for 3 weeks, including room and board, books, registration and supplies, to $192 for 6 weeks.

ADMISSION REQUIREMENTS . . . For the Institut Normal d'Études Françaises a secondary school certificate (high school diploma) is acceptable.

For graduate study, the regular courses of the University are open to qualified foreign students. In general, this means students with a very good knowledge of the French language who have a B.A. or B.S. degree.

See also the Admission Requirements section in the opening summary on France.

LANGUAGE OF INSTRUCTION . . . French.

ACCOMMODATIONS . . . Some residential facilities are offered by the University. Other students live with families or in pensions or hotels. A room alone with a family may cost $20 to $30 per month; room and board about $3.50 up per day. For 50 to 75 cents lunch or dinner is available at the student cafeteria.

AVERAGE COSTS . . . Room and board from about $140 per month.

STUDENT LIFE . . . Opera, musical comedies, and concerts are to be enjoyed in Toulouse. Students often form theater parties for these events. Excursions to monuments and historic areas farther away are also organized by student groups. There are tennis, hiking, swimming, debating and cycling.

HOW TO ENROLL . . . Write directly to the University: Monsieur le Secrétaire, Institut Normal d'Études Françaises, Faculté des Lettres, 56, rue du Taur, Toulouse (Haute-Garonne).

VICHY, INSTITUT CULTUREL INTERNATIONAL (SUMMER COURSES)

Vichy is the thermal capital of the world. The parks bordering the town on the west form a magnificent belt of greenery and flowers. Most water sports are possible on the Allier River.

CALENDAR . . . The summer school runs from early July to late August.

COURSES OF STUDY . . . There are three possible courses of study:

1. *Études Théorique et Pratique de la Langue Française*— Translation and Conversation.

2. *Problèmes de la France Contemporaine:* Panorama of the Modern Theater, Adventures in Modern Poetry, Thought and Political Parties, Contemporary French Art, France Today.

3. *Littérature.*

TUITION . . . There is a charge of $8.50 for two weeks, $13 for three weeks, $15 for four weeks, $21 for seven weeks.

ADMISSION REQUIREMENTS . . . See the Admission Requirements section in the opening summary on France.

ACCOMMODATIONS . . . Complete room with board, from $4 per day. For further information write to the address below.

STUDENT LIFE . . . There are facilities for swimming, water sports and tennis. Excursions are possible to the Bourbonnais and to Auvergne.

HOW TO ENROLL . . . Write to: Monsieur le Professeur Perronin, 8, rue Voltaire, Vichy (Allier).

University of Toulouse

FEDERAL REPUBLIC OF GERMANY

Through technical developments the world has become smaller in many respects. It is, therefore, essential that the free people of the world learn to know one another. In these times, it can be decisive that the free world builds an impregnable front line of intellect and spirit. If we exert our intellectual and spiritual powers, we can live in hope to survive the so-called atomic age. And how can this be better and easier achieved than by the exchange of students, by studying abroad.

Germany has regained its place in Europe in the field of studies, and welcomes students from foreign countries.

Dr. Hanns-Erich Haack, *Counselor of Embassy (in charge of Educational and Cultural Affairs) German Embassy, Washington, D. C.*

Nothing has changed the basic beauty of Germany: its glorious scenery, art treasures, music, festivals and ancient customs survive. The tremendous progress the country has made toward reconstruction since 1945 is really remarkable. In 1949, the Constitution of the German Federal Republic proclaimed once more the principle of freedom of teaching and research.

UNIVERSITIES IN GERMANY . . . Germany's universities have customarily accepted some students from overseas, but the number of such vacancies is generally very limited because of heavy demand for admission from German students.

There are 28 universities in the Federal Republic and Berlin (West), some to be described in later pages and all listed herewith: Free University of Berlin, Universities of Bonn, Cologne, Erlangen-Nuremberg, Frankfurt, Freiburg, Giessen, Göttingen, Hamburg, Heidelberg, Kiel, Mainz, Marburg, Munich, Münster, Saarbrücken, Tübingen, Würzburg; Institutes of Technology at Aachen, in Berlin, Brunswick, Darmstadt, Hanover, Karlsruhe, Munich and Stuttgart; three additional universities are being planned at Bremen, Bochum and Konstanz; other schools of university status are the School of Mining and Metallurgy at Clausthal-Zellerfeld, the School of Medicine and Dental Surgery at Düsseldorf, the School of Veterinary Science at Hanover, the School of Industrial Management at Mannheim, the School of Agriculture at Stuttgart-Hohenheim. In addition there are various schools for training in fine arts, music, drama and dance.

GERMAN UNIVERSITY SYSTEM . . . German institutions of higher learning (*Hochschulen*) are supervised by the ministries of education of the states (*Länder*) in which they are located, and a considerable degree of local control and development is generally permitted. Instruction is divided into lectures, exercises, seminars and practical work in laboratories or clinics. The American student must recognize the need for self-discipline in the German concept of academic freedom, where there is little supervision of studies and few examinations. The academic atmosphere and level of work correspond to graduate study in the United States.

ADMISSION REQUIREMENTS . . . It is very difficult to gain admission to German universities and *Technische Hochschulen*. American students must have a minimum of two years of successful study at an accredited college in the United States. Holders of the Bachelor's degree are of course considered better prepared for study in German universities. Application for admission must be made directly to the rector of the selected university, three months before the beginning of the semester. It must include a complete résumé, an official transcript of work with German translations, and proof of proficiency in German. Even after acceptance by the university, a difficult language exam must be passed *after arrival in Germany*. It is advisable to apply for a residence permit at the local police office in the town where the university is located. The application must be in German and give date of birth, citizenship and home address of applicant.

CREDIT TOWARD AN AMERICAN DEGREE . . . Students who are candidates for a degree in an American university must make arrangements with their dean regarding transfer of credits before applying for admission to a German university. The final academic examinations can be taken by foreign students without restrictions.

TUITION . . . The foreign student pays the same fees as the German student. There is a single registration fee, about $7 each year. There are also fees paid each semester which vary slightly: the liberal arts, approximately $42; natural sciences and technological subjects, approximately $48 to $55; medicine, dentistry and veterinary science, pre-clinical semesters, approximately $60, clinical semesters, approximately $72. Books and study materials will range from about $25 to $50 per semester depending on the course. Examination fees are from $10 to $50.

LIVING COSTS . . . In a small or medium-sized university town, a private room costs from $15 to $30 per month—in a city it will be $20 to $35. Prices of food don't vary much; student dining halls, or *Mensas,* serve meals for from 20 to 30 cents each, with reductions for season tickets. Board and room in a university town will run from $100 depending on the location and quality of room and food. It is wise to allow about $90 per month for living expenses, and a student should make arrangements with the Academic Lodging Office well in advance. Students may also find accommodations in student homes. Most of these provide full board, and the total charge will be about $30 to $40 per month.

COMMON COURTESIES AND LOCAL CUSTOMS . . . The German academic atmosphere is much more formal than in the United States, and Latin terms are used extensively. Lectures and most academic events usually begin at a quarter after the hour (the Academic Quarter) and continue until the next hour. Professors are addressed by their full titles, and the Rector of the University is addressed as *Eure Magnifizenz* (Your Magnificence).

FOR FURTHER INFORMATION . . . For complete information about a university and how to enroll, write directly to the university selected. An American student should start inquiries at least a year in advance of intended studies.

For travel particulars and documentation, write to Educational Department, NHE, Pan American Airways, Pan Am Building, New York, N. Y. 10017.

HOW TO GET THERE . . . By Pan American Jet Clipper, New York to Munich, 10¾ hours; to Düsseldorf, 8¼ hours; Hamburg, 8½ hours; Frankfurt, 7½ hours; Berlin, 9 hours. Frankfurt is 10 hours from Chicago and 16 hours from the U.S. West Coast via polar route. Also through service from Dallas, Houston, Atlanta and New Orleans. Frequent local service via Pan Am between Berlin and Hamburg, Frankfurt, Nuremberg, Stuttgart, Hanover, Cologne, Düsseldorf, Munich. By ship, about 9 days from New York to Hamburg or Bremen.

Free University of Berlin, Library

FREE UNIVERSITY OF BERLIN

Since 1945, Berlin has been divided into four sectors: the three Western sectors are the American, British, and French; East Berlin is the Soviet sector. Berlin is no longer the capital of the German Republic, but situated as it is, it is a focal point in world politics. The great Friedrich-Wilhelms-Universität is now in the Soviet sector and is known as the Humboldt Universität Unter den Linden.

The Freie Universität Berlin, Germany's second youngest university, was founded on December 4, 1948. Its foundation was the reply of freedom-loving students, professors and citizens in West Berlin to the violations of academic freedom in the Soviet sector, notably at the Humboldt University. Student initiative was largely responsible for the foundation of this university.

SIZE ... About 14,250 students, of whom about 800 are foreigners.

CALENDAR ... The winter semester runs from the end of October to the beginning of March; the summer semester from the end of April to the beginning of August.

COURSES OF STUDY ... The Free University of Berlin has six faculties: Medicine, Veterinary Science, Law, Economics and Social Sciences, Arts, Mathematics and Natural Sciences.

Foreign students may attend the University as guest students and should write to the dean of the faculty concerned for an application form.

German courses for foreigners are held each semester under the auspices of the Faculty of Arts.

TUITION ... Registration and matriculation fees amount to about $7.20 with an additional $2.50 for registration in a second faculty.

Semester fees amount to $50 to $60 per semester for matriculated students depending on the number of lectures required. Guest students pay about $7.20 per semester for five or more hours per week, plus about $7.20 in addition for lecture fees and departmental fee.

ADMISSION REQUIREMENTS ... See the Admission Requirements section in the opening summary on Germany.

LANGUAGE OF INSTRUCTION ... German.

ACCOMMODATIONS ... There are only enough hostels to accommodate a small percentage of the students who apply, and German students usually find a room in town. Foreign students are advised to inquire at the University Lodgings Office. Cost of heating is not usually included in the rent of furnished rooms and there is often an extra charge for electricity. Students may get meals at the University refectory (*Mensa*). Most German students get one warm meal a day here and prepare breakfast and supper in their rooms.

AVERAGE COSTS ... Rent for a furnished room will be between $20 and $30 per month. The charge for central heating in the winter months may be an additional $2.50 to $5 per month. Electricity will cost an extra 50 cents to $1.25 per month in some cases.

Meals in the *Mensa* cost 25 cents to 30 cents—in a restaurant they range from 60 cents to $1.

A student will be able to manage on $90 per month, although a little extra may be needed in the first few months. In addition, tuition of $50 to $60 per month will be needed plus money for books.

STUDENT LIFE ... There are many student organizations and associations at the University. All of these arrange lectures, social evenings, dances, and excursions for their members. The Student Club House in Berlin, Zehlendorf, is open to all students.

UNIVERSITY OF BONN

The University of Bonn is located in what is now the provisional capital city of the Federal Republic of Germany—*Bundesrepublik Deutschland*. This once quiet old city on the west bank of the Rhine has been rebuilt and expanded in the last decade. It lies at the northern end of the romantic Rhineland with its legendary castles and vineyards and was the birthplace of the great Ludwig von Beethoven. It lies among the hills in beautiful country along the river. Steamers make excursions north toward Cologne and on to the industrial areas around Düsseldorf and Essen or south past Bingen, the Lorelei and Koblenz.

The University was founded in 1818 and has the usual Liberal Arts departments as well as departments of Catholic and Protestant Theology, a Medical School and an Agricultural School.

SIZE ... About 13,000 students enrolled at Bonn University, of whom about 1,230 are foreigners.

CALENDAR ... The academic year at German universities is divided into two semesters. The winter semester lectures usually begin at the end of October and end in March. The summer semester begins at the end of April and runs through July. Summer courses are given from July to September.

COURSES OF STUDY ... Most regular courses of study are open to U.S. students who have fulfilled all admissions requirements and, in addition, have passed a difficult language exam. Foreign students of medicine, dentistry and veterinary science receive a diploma which does not allow them to practice in Germany.

SUMMER COURSES ... Summer courses are given from July to September on Germany Today and German Language and Literature.

TUITION ... There is a registration fee of about $7 per year, and also fees paid each semester which vary slightly for the different departments: Liberal Arts, $42; Natural Sciences and technical subjects, $48–55; Medicine, $60–72.

ADMISSION REQUIREMENTS ... See the Admission Requirements section in the opening summary on Germany.

LANGUAGE OF INSTRUCTION ... German.

ACCOMMODATIONS ... Many students take a room with a private family and eat in student dining halls, known as *Mensas*. Every *Hochschule* in Germany has several student homes which accept a limited number of foreign students.

The Academic Lodging Office will help students find suitable quarters.

AVERAGE COSTS ... Fees about $150 per year. Room and board about $100 per month.

STUDENT LIFE ... The student dining hall is a center of social life. There are many student organizations in which the foreign student is welcome. There are still some survivals of the former romantic fraternity life in spite of their reorganization, and torchlight parades celebrate important university events.

Hiking in the surrounding countryside and paddling a *Faltboot* are popular pastimes.

UNIVERSITY OF COLOGNE

Cologne is the third largest city of the Federal Republic and dates from about 50 B.C., when it was a Germanic settlement which later became a Roman veterans' colony. In the Middle Ages it was a Hanseatic Town of considerable importance, situated as it was on the main routes of commerce. The city suffered considerable damage during World War II, but reconstruction is proceeding rapidly.

The University of Cologne was founded in 1388 by the citizens of the town. In 1798, as a result of the political after-effects of the French Revolution, it was suspended. It wasn't until 1919 that a university was established once more in Cologne through the amalgamation of the Commercial College (founded in 1901), the Academy of Practical Medicine (founded in 1904), and the College of Commercial and Social Administration (founded in 1912). The new University building opened in 1935.

SIZE ... About 17,800 students enrolled, of whom about 1,125 are foreigners.

CALENDAR ... The winter semester runs from the end of October to the beginning of March; the summer semester from the end of April to the beginning of August. A summer session is held from September through October.

COURSES OF STUDY ... The University of Cologne has five faculties: Economics and Social Sciences, Law, Medicine, Arts, Mathematics and Natural Sciences.

German language courses for beginners and advanced students are held throughout each semester.

SUMMER COURSES ... Courses are given in music, and German language.

The University organizes a 4-week international vacation course in August each year. This course includes German language and literature classes and also lectures on general cultural subjects and excursions to surrounding areas.

TUITION ... Registration and matriculation fees amount to about $7.20 with an additional $2.50 for registration in a second faculty.

Semester fees amount to $50 to $60 per semester for matriculated students depending on the number of lectures required. Guest students pay about $7.20 per semester for five or more hours per week, plus about $7.20 in addition for lecture fees and departmental fee.

ADMISSION REQUIREMENTS ... See the Admission Requirements section in the opening summary on Germany.

LANGUAGE OF INSTRUCTION ... German.

ACCOMMODATIONS ... There are only enough hostels to accommodate a small percentage of the students who apply, and German students usually find a room in town. Foreign students are advised to inquire at the University Lodgings Office. Cost of heating is not usually included in the rent of furnished rooms and there is often an extra charge for electricity.

Students may get meals at the University refectory (*Mensa*). Most German students get one warm meal a day here and prepare breakfast and supper in their rooms. It is well to bear in mind that because of the heavy damage Cologne suffered during the war, accommodations may be scarce, and a prospective student should make arrangements as early as possible.

AVERAGE COSTS ... Rent for furnished rooms will be between $20 and $35 per month. The charge for central heating in the winter months may be an additional $2.50 to $5 per month. Electricity will cost an extra 50 cents to $1.25 per month in some cases.

Meals in the *Mensa Academica* cost about 25 cents—in a restaurant they range from 60 cents to $1.

A student will be able to manage on $90 per month although a little extra may be needed in the first few months. In addition, tuition of $50 to $60 per month will be needed, plus money for books.

STUDENT LIFE ... There are many student organizations and associations at the University. All of these arrange lectures, social evenings, dances, and excursions for their members. Special student tickets at reduced rates are available for performances given by the Municipal Theater Company.

UNIVERSITY OF FREIBURG

Freiburg im Breisgau is an ancient city in the Black Forest region of southwestern Germany. The Black Forest is famous in legends and fairy tales and gets its name from the great stands of black fir which cover the mountains. Freiburg is set among these peaks which are within easy reach for hiking in the summer and for skiing in winter.

The University was heavily damaged by bombing, as was much of the city. The Cathedral, however, was virtually untouched. The reconstruction has been remarkable, and the University is again the center of life in this old town as it has always been. It is noted for its Department of Catholic Theology, and has all the Liberal Arts departments, Philosophy, Law and Political Science, Mathematics and the Natural Sciences, as well as a Medical School and an Academy of Music.

SIZE ... About 11,600 students of whom 900 are foreigners.

CALENDAR ... The academic year at German universities is divided into two semesters. The winter semester lectures usually begin at the end of October and end in March. The summer semester begins at the end of April and runs through July. A summer session runs from August through September.

COURSES OF STUDY ... Most regular courses of study are open to U.S. students who have fulfilled all admission requirements and, in addition, have passed a difficult language exam. Foreign students of medicine, dentistry and veterinary science receive a diploma which does not allow them to practice in Germany.

SUMMER COURSES ... Summer courses are given in German language and culture at the advanced level.

TUITION ... There is a registration fee of about $7 per year, and also fees paid each semester which vary slightly for the different departments: Liberal Arts, $42; Natural Sciences and technical subjects, $48–$55; Medicine, $60–$72.

ADMISSION REQUIREMENTS ... See the Admission Requirements section in the opening summary on Germany.

LANGUAGE OF INSTRUCTION ... German.

ACCOMMODATIONS ... Many students take rooms with private families and eat in student dining halls, known as *Mensas*. Every *Hochschule* in Germany has several student homes which accept a limited number of foreign students.

The Academic Lodging Office will help students find suitable quarters.

AVERAGE COSTS ... Fees about $150 per year. Room and board about $90 per month.

STUDENT LIFE ... The student dining hall is a center of social life. There are many student organizations in which the foreign student is welcome. There are still some survivals of the former romantic fraternity life in spite of their reorganization, and torchlight parades celebrate important university events.

Hiking and climbing in the Black Forest are favorite pastimes, and in winter snow conditions usually permit excellent skiing. The area is noted for its hand-carved wooden toys and other articles.

University of Freiburg

GOETHE-INSTITUTE, MUNICH

The Goethe-Institute, whose headquarters are in Munich, has branches throughout West Germany and holds courses in places where lovely scenery and an atmosphere of human friendship are to be found. The Institute is of particular value to foreign students who are yet unacquainted with the German way of life, and who wish to learn as much about Germany as about the German language.

The main purpose of the Institute is to give foreigners the opportunity to acquire a good working knowledge of German within the shortest possible time. Eight-week introductory and advanced courses are offered.

CALENDAR ... Every two months, year round.

ADMISSION REQUIREMENTS ... The students must be at least 18 years of age. Applications should be made five months in advance (summer—seven months) to: The Goethe-Institute, Abt. Unterrichtsstätten, München 2, Lenbachplatz 3/I.

LANGUAGE OF INSTRUCTION ... German.

TUITION ... $250 payable not less than one month in advance.

ACCOMMODATIONS ... Room and board (usually in double rooms) is included in the cost of tuition. Sunday and holiday meals are not included. There is also a $9 monthly charge for heating from October to April.

UNIVERSITY OF HAMBURG

Hamburg has been a valuable port and trading center for more than 1,000 years. In 1188, the "New Town" was founded and a regular harbor was constructed. After the German Empire was established in 1871, Hamburg became a port of international importance. It was a center of shipbuilding as well. Although air raids during the Second World War caused heavy damage, Hamburg has carried out a vigorous program of reconstruction, and is now the largest city in West Germany and one of the ten *Länder* in the Federal Republic.

The University of Hamburg, one of the most recent in Germany, was founded in 1919 as a result of the amalgamation of a number of academic institutes of long standing and tradition.

Because of Hamburg's position as a port of world-wide importance, tradition has developed a particular emphasis on those branches of learning which are concerned with trade, navigation, languages, and world cultures.

SIZE ... About 17,000 students of whom about 1,200 are foreigners.

CALENDAR ... The winter semester runs from the end of October to the beginning of March; the summer semester from the end of April to the beginning of August. There is a summer session in August.

A University Vacation Course—Medical—is offered in August.

University of Hamburg

COURSES OF STUDY ... The University of Hamburg has six faculties: Protestant Theology, Law, Economics and Social Sciences, Medicine, Arts, Mathematics and Natural Sciences. In addition, there is a Teacher Training Institute.

SUMMER COURSES ... Courses are given in German language, literature, phonetics, teaching methods and political science.

University Vacation Courses are held during the first three weeks of July, in Tropical Medicine and in Internal Medicine. Enrollment is limited.

TUITION ... Registration and matriculation fees amount to about $7.20 with an additional $2.50 for registration in a second faculty.

Semester fees amount to $50 to $60 per semester for matriculated students, depending on the number of lectures required. Guest students pay about $7.20 per semester for five or more hours per week, plus about $7.20 in addition for lecture fees and departmental fee.

Foreign students may attend the University as guest students and should apply to the dean of the faculty concerned for an application form.

ADMISSION REQUIREMENTS ... See the Admission Requirements section in the opening summary on Germany.

LANGUAGE OF INSTRUCTION ... German.

ACCOMMODATIONS ... There are only enough hostels to accommodate a small percentage of the students who apply, and German students usually find a room in town. Foreign students are advised to inquire at the University Lodgings Office. Cost of heating is not usually included in the rent of furnished rooms and there is often an extra charge for electricity. Students may get meals at the University refectory (*Mensa*). Most German students get one warm meal a day here and prepare breakfast and supper in their rooms. It is well to bear in mind that because of the heavy damage Hamburg suffered during the war, accommodations may be scarce, and a prospective student should make arrangements as early as possible.

AVERAGE COSTS ... Rent for furnished single rooms ranges $25 to $40 per month. The student hostels have very limited accommodations, especially for foreign students. The rent at these hostels is about $12 per person per month, plus a monthly fee of about 75 cents for light and telephone. No meals are served at the hostels, but students may prepare their own in the hostel kitchens. Meals at the *Mensa* cost from about 25 cents to 50 cents.

A student will be able to manage on $60 to $90 per month for room and board, although a little extra may be needed in the first few months. In addition, tuition fees and money for books must be included.

STUDENT LIFE ... There are many student organizations and associations at the University. All of these arrange lectures, social evenings, dances, and excursions for their members.

Special student rates are available for the subway, for theaters and concerts. The *Studentenhaus*, which opened in 1956, is the focal point of student life at the University. Facilities for many sports are readily available, including gliding, sailing, and swimming.

UNIVERSITY OF HEIDELBERG

Heidelberg is the oldest university town in Germany. It lies in beautiful country where the Neckar River flows into the Rhine plain. The town is surrounded by the mountains of the Odenwald which provide it with a very mild climate. Mountains, forests, and the lovely Neckar valley make this one of the most enchanting regions of Germany.

The University of Heidelberg was founded in 1386 on the same plan as the Sorbonne. It is famous for the great scholars who have been associated with it in all periods of its history. It was reorganized in 1803, and in 1930–1931 the "New" University was built beside the "Old," with funds made available by the American Shurman Foundation.

SIZE ... About 10,000 students, of whom about 1,600 are foreigners.

CALENDAR ... The winter semester runs from the end of

October to the beginning of March; the summer semester from the end of April to the beginning of August. A summer session is held in August.

COURSES OF STUDY ... The University of Heidelberg has six faculties: Theology, Law, Medicine, Arts, Interpreters' School, Mathematics and Natural Sciences. There is a special department within the Interpreters' School which teaches German to foreign students. Two such courses are given, each lasting two semesters. In addition to the language classes, lectures are held on German history, geography, literature, and culture. Foreign students may attend the University as guest students and should apply to the Rector informally.

SUMMER COURSES ... Courses are given in German language and contemporary German literature. There is also a course for teachers of German.

TUITION ... Registration and matriculation fees amount to about $7.20 with an additional $2.50 for registration in a second faculty.

Semester fees amount to $50 to $60 per semester for matriculated students, depending on the number of lectures required. Guest students pay about $7.20 per semester for five or more hours per week, plus about $7.20 in addition for lecture fees and departmental fee.

ADMISSION REQUIREMENTS ... See the Admission Requirements section in the opening summary on Germany.

LANGUAGE OF INSTRUCTION ... German.

ACCOMMODATIONS ... There are only enough hostels to accommodate a small percentage of the students who apply, and German students usually find a room in the town. Foreign students are advised to inquire at the University Lodgings Office. Cost of heating is not usually included in the rent of furnished rooms and there is often an extra charge for electricity. Students may get meals at the University refectory (*Mensa*). Most German students get one warm meal a day here and prepare breakfast and supper in their rooms.

AVERAGE COSTS ... Rent for a furnished room will be between $20 and $35 per month. The charge for central heating in the winter months may be an additional $2.50 to $5 per month. Electricity will cost an extra 50 cents to $1.25 per month in some cases. Meals in the *Mensa* cost 50 cents to 90 cents—in a restaurant they range from 85 cents to $1.75.

A student will be able to manage on $85 per month for room and board, although a little extra may be needed in the first few months. In addition, allowances should be made for tuition fees and books.

STUDENT LIFE ... There are many student organizations and associations at the University. All of these arrange lectures, social evenings, dances, and excursions for their members. Special student rates are available for theaters and concerts. The *Studentenhaus* is the focal point of student life at the University. Facilities for many sports are readily available, including gliding, sailing, and swimming.

UNIVERSITY OF MUNICH

Munich, the capital of Bavaria, was founded by Henry the Lion in 1158. In the course of the following centuries it became the scholarly and cultural center of southern Germany.

During the last war, large sections of the city were destroyed, but since 1951 reconstruction has been progressing rapidly. Munich is famous for its art galleries and museums. It is the gateway to the Bavarian and Austrian Alps.

The Ludwig-Maximilian University now the University of Munich was founded in 1472 by Ludwig the Rich in Ingolstadt. In 1800 it was transferred to Landshut by King Max-Joseph, and in 1826 King Ludwig I transferred it finally to the capital of the kingdom.

SIZE ... About 21,500 students, of whom about 2,000 are foreigners.

CALENDAR ... The winter semester runs from the end of October to the beginning of March; the summer semester from the end of April to the beginning of August. A special summer course is held during August.

COURSES OF STUDY ... The University of Munich has eight faculties: Theology, Law, Political Economy, Medicine, Veterinary Science, Arts, Natural Science and Mathematics, and the Institute of American Studies. German language courses for foreign students are held throughout each semester.

SUMMER COURSES ... There are courses given on Germany Today, Germany in the Twentieth Century, language, literature and culture.

TUITION ... Registration and matriculation fees amount to about $7.20 with an additional $2.50 for registration in a second faculty.

Semester fees amount to $50 to $60 per semester for matriculated students, depending on the number of lectures required. Guest students pay about $7.20 per semester for five or more hours per week, plus about $7.20 in addition for lecture fees and departmental fee.

ADMISSION REQUIREMENTS ... See the Admission Requirements section in the opening summary on Germany.

LANGUAGE OF INSTRUCTION ... German.

ACCOMMODATIONS ... It is still difficult to find moderately priced private accommodations in Munich. There are only enough hostels to accommodate a small percentage of the students who apply. Foreign students are advised to inquire at the University Lodgings Office. Students may get meals at the University refectory (*Mensa*). Most German students get one warm meal here and prepare breakfast and supper in their rooms.

AVERAGE COSTS ... Rent for a furnished room will be between $25 and $40 per month. The charge for central heating in the winter months may be an additional $2.50 to $5 per month. Electricity will cost an extra 50 cents to $1.25 per month in some cases.

University of Heidelberg

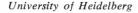

Meals in the *Mensa* cost 25 cents to 30 cents—in a restaurant they range from 55 cents to $1.

A student will be able to manage on $90 per month for room and board, although a little extra may be needed in the first few months. In addition, tuition fees and money for books must be considered.

STUDENT LIFE ... There are many student organizations and associations at the University. All of these arrange lectures, social evenings, dances, and excursions for their members.

Facilities for many sports are available in Munich. Schwabing, the Montmartre of Munich, is a favorite haunt of students.

STUTTGART TECHNICAL UNIVERSITY

The city of Stuttgart is the ancient capital of Württemberg and is famous for its beautiful setting. It is located about 120 miles south of Frankfurt and is surrounded by mountains whose slopes are covered with orchards and vineyards.

The Stuttgart Technical University was founded in 1829 as a technical school. In 1840, it was renamed Polytechnische Schule, but it wasn't until 1890 that it was designated as a Technical University. In 1900 it was granted the right to award the academic degree of Diploma—Engineer and also doctorates in its technical departments.

In the last war, a large proportion of the university buildings were destroyed and reconstruction is in progress.

SIZE ... About 7,000 students, of whom about 875 are foreigners.

CALENDAR ... The winter semester runs from the end of October to the beginning of March; the summer semester from the end of April to the beginning of August. A summer session is held during June.

COURSES OF STUDY ... The Stuttgart Technical University has three main faculties: Natural Sciences (including Mathematics) and Arts, Civil Engineering (including Architecture), Engineering (including Electrical and Aeronautical Engineering).

SUMMER COURSES ... A university vacation course is held each year during July. Courses are given in natural science, technology and architecture, economics, philosophy and literature; also German language.

TUITION ... Registration and matriculation fees amount to about $7.20 with an additional $2.50 for registration in a second faculty.

Semester fees amount to $50 to $60 per semester for matriculated students, depending on the number of lectures required. Guest students pay about $7.20 per semester for five or more hours per week, plus about $7.20 in addition for lecture fees and departmental fee.

ADMISSION REQUIREMENTS ... Students will be required to submit evidence of having completed prerequisites for certain courses. See also the Admission Requirements section in the opening summary on Germany.

LANGUAGE OF INSTRUCTION ... German.

ACCOMMODATIONS ... There are only enough hostels to accommodate a small percentage of the students who apply, and German students usually find a room in the town. Foreign students are advised to inquire at the University Lodgings Office. Cost of heating is not usually included in the rent of furnished rooms and there is often an extra charge for electricity. Students may get meals at the University refectory (*Mensa*). Most German students get one warm meal a day here and prepare breakfast and supper in their rooms.

AVERAGE COSTS ... Rent for a furnished room will be between $20 and $30 per month. The charge for central heating in the winter months may be an additional $2.50 to $5 per month. Electricity will cost an extra 50 cents to $1.25 per month in some cases.

Meals in the *Mensa* cost 25 cents to 30 cents—in a restaurant they range from 50 cents to $1. A student will be able to manage on $85 per month, although a little extra may be needed in the first few months.

In addition, tuition fees will be needed, plus money for books.

STUDENT LIFE ... There are many student organizations and associations at the University. All of these arrange lectures, social evenings, dances, and excursions for their members.

Special student rates are available for theaters and concerts. Facilities are available for all kinds of sports.

GREECE

It is an instinct of all human beings to go back and seek out their beginnings. Naturally enough, therefore, many educated men and women feel the lure of Greece, the corner of Europe wherein was lit the beacon which spread the light of civilization to the rest of the Western world.

Modern air transportation has minimized distance. Greece today extends her warm welcome to young people from abroad who wish to enjoy and study her great history and culture. American students coming to her shores will find her schools and universities hospitable and will enjoy a rewarding and enriching experience amid surroundings of incomparable beauty.

Alexis S. Liatis
Former Ambassador of Greece to the United States

GREEK UNIVERSITY SYSTEM ... In Greece most of the universities are subsidized by the state. The Ministry of Religion and National Education exercises nominal control, but actually the Faculty Senate governs. The curriculum is patterned after the old North German universities and is theoretical and academic in character. In common with most other European university systems, the Greek universities offer instruction to the students who present themselves for examination for each academic year and for final examination when they feel qualified.

UNIVERSITIES OF GREECE ... There are two major universities in Greece: Athens and Salonika (Thessaloniki). There are also the National Technical University of Athens and three schools of higher education for political, agricultural, economical and commercial studies, also academies and teachers colleges.

The Greek educational system is in the process of reorganization, and reforms are being made at the present time, resulting in an increase of faculties, an increase of university departments, and the prospect of the foundation of a third university in Greece. There is an increasing desire to bring the old academic curriculum more into line with present-day problems. The last half-century has brought turbulence, disaster and regeneration to Greece, and these changes are reflected in the educational picture.

ADMISSION REQUIREMENTS ... Foreign students are not required to take these examinations, but in order to attain an equivalent level, the United States student should have at least two years at an accredited college and a good understanding of modern Greek.

TUITION ... Tuition for the academic year ranges from $50 to $100 (including the course fees and laboratory fees) depending on the faculty.

There are also examination fees.

LIVING COSTS ... Greece is a very inexpensive country for tourists and foreign students. The drachma is the monetary unit, and the exchange rate is 30 drachmas to the dollar. A student will need $700 to $1,000 per year for moderately priced room and board.

COMMON COURTESIES AND LOCAL CUSTOMS ... Shaking hands is the normal practice in Greece when meeting or leaving someone.

The summer siesta is an institution (2:00 p.m. to 5:00 p.m.) in the hot summer months.

The Greeks are a vital people, passionately interested in the drama of life. They are probably the most talkative people in Europe, the most social, the most hospitable.

The "Cradle of Civilization" is a land of great natural beauty in addition to being a storehouse of the past.

REGULATIONS ... No visa is required. A sojourn and exit permit are needed after a 2-month stay. Typewriters, radios, cameras and film are registered on the passport and can be taken out again without trouble.

CREDIT TOWARD AN AMERICAN DEGREE ... It is important for the student to make arrangements for receiving credit toward an American degree from his own university before he leaves the United States. There is nothing to correspond to the credit-hour system at Greek universities, and each student should discuss with his dean the basis on which his work should be evaluated.

FOR FURTHER INFORMATION ... For complete information about a university and how to enroll, write to the Greek Information Service, 69 East 79th Street, New York, N. Y. 10021.

For travel particulars and documentation, write to Educational Department, NHE, Pan American Airways, Pan Am Building, New York, N. Y. 10017.

HOW TO GET THERE ... By Pan American Jet Clipper to Rome, 8 hours, then by Olympic Airways, only 1¾ hours to Athens; or 3 hours from Beirut via Middle East-Air Liban. By ship from New York, 15 to 18 days.

UNIVERSITY OF ATHENS

The early glory of Greece lives on today as the foundation of the civilization of the Western world. The heart of ancient Athens, the goal of scholars of the world, is the Acropolis, crowning the modern city. Its surviving monuments are easily accessible, and are part of the daily life of Greece.

The University of Athens was founded in 1837 by King Otho for whom it was named. However, King Otho was exiled, and the University was renamed National University and merged with the Capodistrian College, which had been named for the first ruler of liberated Greece. The administration is in the hands of the Faculty Senate.

University of Athens

SIZE ... About 9,000 students are enrolled at the University of Athens, of whom about 200 are foreigners.

CALENDAR ... The academic year runs from the beginning of October to mid-June.

COURSES OF STUDY ... The National University of Athens has Faculties of Theology, Law, Medicine, Letters and Science. The Faculty of Medicine has a School of Dentistry; the Faculty of Letters (Philosophy) has divisions of English and French Literature; the Faculty of Sciences includes Natural Sciences and Mathematics.

TUITION ... Tuition for the academic year ranges from $50 to $100 including course fees and laboratory fees, depending on the faculty. There are also fees for examinations.

ADMISSION REQUIREMENTS ... See the Admission Requirements section in the opening summary on Greece.

LANGUAGE OF INSTRUCTION ... Greek.

It is essential that the foreign student have a good understanding of modern Greek. French is useful for conversational purposes but English is widely understood.

ACCOMMODATIONS ... The student will have to find his own lodgings in the city, since there are no student dormitories or hostels.

AVERAGE COSTS ... Greece is a very inexpensive country for tourists and foreign students. The drachma is the monetary unit and the exchange is 30 drachmas to the dollar. A student will need $700 to $1,000 per year for moderately priced room and board.

STUDENT LIFE ... The Greeks are a very hospitable people—very talkative and passionately interested in everything under the sun. The Kafenion is the center of activity, and discussion goes on unceasingly.

UNIVERSITY OF THESSALONIKI

Thessaloniki (Salonika) is in the province of Macedonia, the home of Alexander the Great. It is a thriving port city which has a Byzantine flavor due to its proximity to ancient Byzantium. Until 1912 Salonika was a Turkish city. The white houses surrounded by white walls and the Moslem mosques are reminders of Turkish rule. The broad streets are paved with lava.

The University of Thessaloniki was founded in 1925. It is housed in a large building erected by the Turks as a college. The University is surrounded by extensive grounds and beautiful gardens, and new buildings are being completed.

SIZE ... About 9,000 students, of whom very few are foreigners.

CALENDAR ... The academic year runs from the beginning of October to mid-June.

COURSES OF STUDY ... The University of Thessaloniki has the following faculties: Theology, Philosophy and Letters, Science, Law and Economics, Agriculture and Forestry, Medicine. A Faculty of Veterinary Medicine was established in 1951.

TUITION ... Tuition for the academic year ranges from $50 to $100 depending on the faculty.

ADMISSION REQUIREMENTS ... See the Admission Requirements section in the opening summary on Greece.

LANGUAGE OF INSTRUCTION ... Greek.

It is necessary for students to have proficiency in modern Greek in order to be able to follow lectures and instruction.

ACCOMMODATIONS ... The University operates dormitory and dining facilities for "indigent or bandit-stricken" students.

Other students must find their own lodgings in the city.

AVERAGE COSTS ... Greece is a very inexpensive country for tourists and foreign students. The drachma is the monetary unit, and the exchange rate is 30 drachmas to the dollar. A student will need $700 to $1,000 per year for moderately priced room and board.

STUDENT LIFE ... The Greeks are a very hospitable people—very talkative and passionately interested in everything under the sun. The Kafenion is the center of activities, and discussion goes on unceasingly.

AMERICAN SCHOOL OF CLASSICAL STUDIES, ATHENS

The American School of Classical Studies in Athens was founded in 1881 as a postgraduate school for students of Greek literature and history and classical archaeology. It is controlled by a committee representing seventy American universities.

The main school building, erected in 1888, contains directors' quarters, the school library, administrative offices, and rooms for students or visitors. Loring Hall, completed in 1930, is a residence for students and professors, and has dining and recreation rooms. The School's library, the Gennadeion, is devoted to works on Greece, the Near East, the Balkans, and travel accounts. It is open to scholars of all countries and to Greek university students. The original collection was given by Joannes Gennadius to the American School of Classical Studies at Athens in 1922.

The School's principal excavations have been at Corinth and the Agora of ancient Athens.

CALENDAR ... The regular academic year runs from mid-September to the end of May. The summer session starts at the beginning of July and ends in mid-August.

COURSES OF STUDY ... Students entering immediately after graduation from a university or college spend the fall and winter receiving regular instruction in archaeology, sometimes in Greek literature and history. They go on conducted tours to the major archaeological sites of Greece, for which preparation is expected. In the spring, some students are allowed to go to the School's excavations at Corinth for training. Besides the new students, each year some advanced archaeologists with special projects arrive to work independently. Each year two or three students are taken on at the Agora to learn the techniques of excavating and to help with the work of keeping records.

The School issues a certificate showing the length of time spent and the work done by the student.

SUMMER COURSES ... Classical Civilization—for advanced students of the classics and related subjects.

ADMISSION REQUIREMENTS ... Candidates must be graduates of an American college or university and furnish credentials showing definite and serious purpose in studying at Athens and that the candidate would profit from such study by reason of previous preparation.

LANGUAGE OF INSTRUCTION ... English.

ACCOMMODATIONS ... The School operates dormitory and dining facilities for the students. Foreign students usually live at the School.

AVERAGE COSTS ... The average cost of lodging is $700 to $1,000 a year.

University of Thessaloniki

GUATEMALA

UNIVERSITIES OF GUATEMALA ... Guatemala has only one main institution of higher learning, the University of San Carlos, located in Guatemala City. There is, however, the Universidad Popular (People's University) also in Guatemala City. This University, supported by contributions and donations, offers short courses and lectures to anyone 16 years of age or over who is able to read and write. There are no fees and all textbooks and materials are furnished without charge. Courses include Journalism, Literature, Engineering and Law. At the completion of a 3-year course, a student receives a diploma as a "graduate of the People's University."

GUATEMALAN UNIVERSITY SYSTEM ... The University of San Carlos, an autonomous institution, is governed by a Superior Council. This Council is composed of equal representation from the faculty, the student body, and the professional alumni. Each school is governed by a board of directors with the same proportional representation as the Superior Council. The Rector of the University is elected for a period of four years as are the deans of the respective faculties. Classes are generally held from 7:00–9:00 in the morning or from 5:00–9:00 in the evening, depending on the individual faculty. Some faculties are conducted on a semester system while others function on an annual basis.

ADMISSION REQUIREMENTS ... There are several steps to be taken in applying for admission to the University of San Carlos. These are as follows:

a) Present a written request giving full name, age, civil status, nationality, address and whether or not you wish to enroll as a regular student or as an auditor.

b) Present certification of good health on a form provided by the University.

c) Have a diploma of secondary education or college transcript of credit (notarized in the U.S.A., inspected at the nearest Guatemalan Consulate, and translated by the Ministry of Foreign Affairs) which meets the requirements of each faculty and the Superior Council.

d) Pay the registration fees.

TUITION ... Tuition is free at the University. There is, however, an annual registration fee of approximately $30. This fee varies with each faculty.

LIVING COSTS ... Room and board in Guatemala vary from $75 to $150 monthly. To cover all minimum expenses a student should provide himself with no less than $175 a month.

COMMON COURTESIES AND LOCAL CUSTOMS ... Since Guatemalans are quiet spoken and well bred, loudness in speech and manners and exaggerated dress are frowned upon. It is customary for a man to wear a jacket in restaurants and clubs.

FOR FURTHER INFORMATION ... For complete information about the University and how to enroll, write to the UNIVERSIDAD DE SAN CARLOS NACIONAL Y AUTONOMA, 2a Avenida 12–40, Zona 1, Guatemala City, Guatemala.

University of San Carlos

For travel particulars and documentation, write to Educational Department, NHE, Pan American Airways, Pan Am Building, New York, N. Y. 10017.

HOW TO GET THERE ... By Pan American Jet Clipper, 3 hours from New Orleans; 2½ hours from Miami; 1½ hours from Mexico City; 4½ hours from Los Angeles. By ship, 3 days from New Orleans to Puerto Barrios.

UNIVERSITY OF SAN CARLOS, GUATEMALA CITY

The University of San Carlos, founded in Antigua in 1676, was moved to Guatemala City in 1777. It is Guatemala's only university and is one of the oldest seats of learning in the hemisphere.

SIZE ... The University consists of 10 faculties and 6 schools with 500 professors and an enrollment of 4,200 students. The University is co-educational.

CALENDAR ... The regular school term at the University of San Carlos begins in January and ends in October. The Summer School is conducted in July and August. The climate in Guatemala is almost always balmy and pleasant with an average temperature in Guatemala City of about 65 degrees.

COURSES OF STUDY ... The University includes the Faculties of Architecture, Agriculture, Economics, Dentistry, Engineering, Law, Humanities, Medicine, Veterinary Medicine and Pharmacy-Chemistry. There are also the Schools of Law, Economics, Humanities and Rural Social Service which are actually dependencies of the faculties and located in Quezaltenango, Guatemala. The Schools of Journalism and Fine Arts are in Guatemala City. There are no organized graduate studies as such. Only Humanities and Law offer a Doctorate.

SUMMER COURSES ... The University maintains a summer school for foreign students beginning in early July and continuing through mid-August. The program is designed to accommodate two basic groups of students: (1) those who do not have a solid grounding in Spanish and (2) those who have an adequate knowledge of Spanish and who wish to take courses at the high undergraduate level. There are two general areas of specialization: Literature and Language, and Archaeology and Anthropology. Information may be obtained by writing to the Secretary of the Summer School, Faculty of Humanities, 9 Avenida 13–39, Zona 1, Guatemala City, Guatemala.

TUITION ... The faculties of the University, except for summer courses, are tuition free. There is only an annual registration fee of $30 and this varies with each faculty.

ADMISSION REQUIREMENTS ... See the Admission Requirements section in the opening summary on Guatemala.

LANGUAGE OF INSTRUCTION ... All courses are taught in Spanish.

ACCOMMODATIONS ... There are no dormitories at the University of San Carlos. Therefore, the University provides a housing list for students so that they can arrange to stay with Guatemalan families or in pensions.

AVERAGE COSTS ... Room and board vary from about $75 to $150 a month. To cover all minimum expenses, a student should provide himself with a minimum of $175 monthly.

STUDENT LIFE ... As in other universities throughout Latin America, student social activities at the University of San Carlos are uncommon. The summer school, however, differs in this respect. Excursions and trips to places of interest in the interior can be arranged by the office of the summer school.

HAWAII

OAHU

HONOLULU

Note: Even though this book is concerned primarily with foreign universities, we have included schools in Alaska, Hawaii and Puerto Rico, since they are "abroad" in the sense of being outside the continental United States. In these schools entry requirements, transfers of credits, curriculums and methods of study are similar to those of all U.S. universities.

HOW TO GET THERE ... By Pan American Jet Clipper from San Francisco, Los Angeles, Portland or Seattle. Flying time from San Francisco, 4¾ hours. By ship from San Francisco, 4½ days.

UNIVERSITY OF HAWAII, HONOLULU

Honolulu is the capital of Hawaii as well as the home of the University of Hawaii, which was founded as a land-grant college in 1907. Supported by state as well as by federal funds, the University reflects the needs, racial composition, and geographical location of the Islands. Thus its instructional and research programs emphasize tropical agriculture, marine biology, geophysics, race relations, and East-West cultural exchange.

The University of Hawaii Agricultural Experiment Station works closely with the research institutions of Hawaii's basic sugar and pineapple industries, as does the University's Marine Laboratory with the U.S. Fish and Wildlife Service and the tuna fisheries of the state. The University's Social Science Research Institute conducts studies in sociology and race relations in the living laboratory provided by the state's unique ethnic composition. The United States Congress has backed the establishment of a multimillion-dollar Institute of Geophysics to further work now being conducted in meteorology, volcanology, and other aspects of geophysics, as well as an East-West Cultural and Technical Center, which will consolidate and augment work in which the University and the State of Hawaii as a whole have conducted distinguished programs in past decades.

The Honolulu campus is situated in green Manoa Valley against the backdrop of the picturesque Koolau Mountains, three miles from the center of the city and two miles from famous Waikiki Beach. The Hilo campus is located on the outskirts of Hilo on the island of Hawaii. The Agricultural Experiment Station has branches on three islands and the Agricultural Extension Service has resident farm and home demonstration agents in each of the counties.

The Gregg M. Sinclair Library contains nearly 390,000 bound volumes and strong collections on Hawaii, the other islands of the Pacific and the countries of Asia, as well as 835,000 unbound parts and pamphlets.

SIZE ... About 14,000 students, representing the racial diversity of the state. There are about 1,000 from the mainland, and 680 from some 50 foreign countries. About 600 foreign students are East-West Center scholars.

CALENDAR ... The year is divided into two 18-week semesters and a summer session of 6 weeks beginning the end of June. There is also a "post session" during August, plus two 5-week terms conducted concurrently with the regular 6-week session.

COURSES OF STUDY ... The University of Hawaii consists of the following colleges: College of Arts and Sciences, College of Engineering, College of Nursing, College of Education, College of Tropical Agriculture, College of Business Administration, the College of General Studies, which offers credit and non-credit afternoon and evening courses on campus as well as at off-campus centers, and the Graduate School, offering Masters' and Doctors' degrees in many fields. There is also a School of Social Work.

SUMMER COURSES ... Courses of study vary in length from three to six weeks and are offered from June to August. Over 370 courses in 70 fields of study are offered, including 5 institutes, 12 seminars, 4 study tours, over 30 Asian and Far-Eastern courses, and 14 "regional" courses. The Hilo campus of the University offers limited courses.

TUITION ... Each semester, students carrying twelve hours or more per semester are subject to a tuition fee of $85, a registration fee of $10, student health fee of 75 cents, and student activities fee of $13.25. Certain laboratory and other courses may have extra fees. Over 600 scholarships and grants are available.

Summer session fees are about $10 per credit hour plus a registration fee of $10; an activities fee of $2 is collected.

ADMISSION REQUIREMENTS ... A high school graduate must have completed a specified number of study units, as defined by the University, and must meet scholastic standards set forth by the University to enter as a freshman student. The Director of the Office of Admissions and Records can supply full and specific details of admission requirements; these are also set forth in the University catalogue. Undergraduate students enter as either regular students or as unclassified students; the latter term usually designates those not immediately working toward a degree at the University of Hawaii. All applicants must take college aptitude tests during their final year of secondary school; mainland candidates submit scores on the College Entrance Examination Board Scholastic Aptitude Test. Certain programs of study have special entrance requirements; these details are available from the departments concerned. The University of Hawaii is accredited by the Western Association of Schools and Colleges (WASC). Its students may transfer to other American and to foreign universities on the same basis as students of other American universities.

LANGUAGE OF INSTRUCTION ... English.

ACCOMMODATIONS ... Three dormitories are maintained by the University. Mary Dillingham Frear Hall offers double rooms to women for about $310 per semester, covering room and board expenses. Fee for the summer session is about $80. Hale Kahawai has double rooms for 140 women at about $310 per semester. Gateway House, a co-ed hall, has double rooms for 104 women and 104 men in separate twin towers. Cost is about $335 per semester. All hall residents are participants in a meal plan. John A. Johnson Halls have double rooms to house 192 men for about $310 per semester. Rates are subject to change without notice. The University has no accommodations for married couples. Priority is given to rural Oahu and neighbor island students. The Office of Student Housing maintains an

University of Hawaii

information file on rooming houses, single rooms in private homes and a few apartments. Because of rapid turnover in a tight housing market, the names of landlords cannot be sent through the mail. Three meals a day are served from Monday through Saturday at the University cafeteria. The cafeteria is located in Hemenway Hall, the student center.

AVERAGE COST ... Tuition is about $240 per academic year. Room and board and books can cost as much as $1,350 to $1,975 per year. The minimum average expenses per year run about $1,500, but this does not include laundry, clothing and personal items. Part-time employment opportunities are limited; the prevailing wage is $1.25 per hour. Students should have funds for all expenses for at least a semester, preferably a year. Jobs on the campus are generally held by students enrolled throughout the regular school year and summer session.

STUDENT LIFE ... Waikiki Beach is only two miles from the campus of the University and Hawaii's year-round shirt-sleeve weather lures students after classes to the famed sands for swimming, surf-board riding, sunning. From the first *aloha* to the last, students will enjoy the friendliness and atmosphere of mutual respect which prevails among the members of Hawaii's melting-pot—a unique feature of which Islanders are justly proud. The student will have an opportunity to become acquainted with the primitive culture of the indigenous Hawaiians and with the cultures of the Asians who have made Hawaii their home.

The Associated Students of the University of Hawaii has an activity program that offers drama, debates and athletics; it operates a weekly newspaper and a yearbook, and has an *a cappella* choir, chorus, band, orchestra, the University Theater Group and some eighty scholastic, honorary, professional, social or religious groups. The University Theater presents six plays a year, ranging from Shakespeare to Ibsen to the Japanese Noh play, *Kanton*. Students organize their own tours of various islands in the Hawaiian group. There are 30 major buildings and building complexes on campus with more under construction. At Hemenway Hall, the general social center for students, there are rooms for student organization offices, recreation rooms, cafeteria and lounges. The University uses Cooke Field and the Lower Campus (quarry) for football, baseball and track, and Honolulu Stadium for big inter-university contests. No student will consider his stay complete without visits to two independent but closely affiliated institutions: the Honolulu Academy of Arts, which features fine exhibits of European, American and Asian art, and the Bernice P. Bishop Museum of Anthropology, which includes a herbarium containing the most complete collection of Hawaiian plants in the world, some specimens of which are otherwise extinct.

FOR FURTHER INFORMATION ... For complete information about the University and how to enroll, write to the UNIVERSITY OF HAWAII, Honolulu.

For travel particulars and documentation, write to Educational Department, NHE, Pan American Airways, Pan Am Building, New York, N. Y. 10017.

HONG KONG

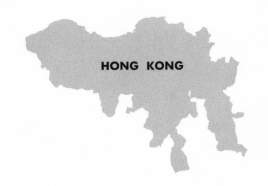

HONG KONG

UNIVERSITY OF HONG KONG

Hong Kong means "fragrant harbor" in Chinese, and that exotic appellation is well chosen, for there is excitement for the Westerner at every turn in this gateway between the East and the West. Hong Kong is a British Crown Colony, and the official language is English, but the Cantonese dialect is most commonly heard in the streets of this city populated almost entirely by Chinese. The Chinese New Year, celebrated sometime between the middle of January and the middle of February, is a colorful spectacle to see; so are other festivals observed around the calendar. Typical Chinese markets can be seen along either side of the narrow lanes with steep flights of stairs—the "ladder streets" of Hong Kong. The University of Hong Kong was founded in 1911; it has as its patron Her Majesty the Queen.

SIZE ... There are now 1,750 full-time students attending the University; about 150 of these are from foreign countries. In addition 4,400 students attend courses conducted by the University Department of Extra-Mural Studies. The University operates on the British pattern.

BUILDINGS ... The University is set in an estate of about fifty acres, between 160 and 460 feet above sea level, with a fine view of the harbor. The buildings include modrn laboratories, a museum and a new library (which now has 121,650 books and pamphlets in Western languages and 127,550 in Chinese). There is a new students' union building, a sports center, and staff quarters.

CALENDAR ... September–June. There are three terms of twelve, nine and nine weeks each, respectively.

COURSES OF STUDY ... The University has a Faculty of Engineering and Architecture, Faculty of Arts, Faculty of Medicine and Faculty of Science. Courses, which are conducted in English, are offered under the general headings of anatomy, architecture, botany, chemistry, Chinese, engineering, economics, education, English, geography, geology, history, mathematics, medicine, modern languages, political science, philosophy, physics, physiology, pathology, obstetrics and gynecology, social and preventive medicine, surgery and zoology. There is the well-known Institute of Oriental Studies, which is a Research Institute in Far East Studies generally and includes a language school for intensive tuition in the Cantonese and Mandarin languages. There is also a Department of Extra-Mural Studies that offers courses in subjects ranging widely from oriental drama to business administration.

POSTGRADUATE OPPORTUNITIES ... The University, in addition to the higher degrees of M.A. and M.Sc., offers excellent opportunities for proceeding to the degree of Ph.D., in particular in economic and cultural studies connected with China and matters Chinese. A postgraduate hall of residence is about to be built.

TUITION ... The minimum matriculation examination entry fee is $8.77; application for admission fee, $4.38; the deposit is $16.67; composition fee (including registration, tuition, laboratory or workshop, examination and student health) is charged according to the courses a student undertakes, and averages about $220 per year.

ADMISSION REQUIREMENTS ... Students reading for a degree must be at least 17 years of age, pass a medical fitness examination, the University of Hong Kong Matriculation Examination or a recognized equivalent examination such as the London G.C.E. in at least five subjects, which must include

English language, a second language, a science and two subjects at advanced level. Students who have completed two successful years in an American college or university of recognized academic standing may be exempted from Matriculation Examination.

It is possible for non-matriculated students to be admitted as external ("auditing") students not reading for a degree but attending lectures in the degree courses. The fee for this is about $45 per course per annum.

REGULATIONS ... For student visa and entrance procedure, see the For Further Information heading at the end of this section.

LANGUAGE OF INSTRUCTION ... English, except in Chinese literature, history and philosophy courses in the Department of Chinese. Students without a high proficiency in the Chinese language may not attend degree courses in the Chinese Department except in Chinese art and archaeology and a special course in Buddhism, both of which are taught in English.

ACCOMMODATIONS ... Some halls and colleges of residence are maintained by the University for men and women students. The cost of room and board per month at a men's hall is about $40; at a women's hall about $55. Not all students can be accommodated in these residences, which are on or near the University estate, but the University authorities endeavor when possible to house overseas students reading for a degree. External students are not normally accommodated.

STUDENT LIFE ... Many sports are popular—cricket, football, hockey, swimming, tennis, basketball, badminton. The Students' Union is the organization of the student body which undergraduate students are obliged to join. The Union maintains its own library, publishes the *Union Magazine,* and the *Undergrad,* the newspaper, which keeps students informed of campus activities, which include, in addition to sports, music, drama, astronomy, archaeology, painting. A new Union building has just been completed.

FOR FURTHER INFORMATION ... For complete information about the University and how to enroll, write to the Registrar, UNIVERSITY OF HONG KONG.

For travel particulars and documentation, write to Educational Department, NHE, Pan American Airways, Pan Am Building, New York, N. Y. 10017.

HOW TO GET THERE ... By Pan American Jet Clipper from the United States West Coast, about 15 hours (elapsed time) via Honolulu and Tokyo; about 2 hours from Manila, 2½ hours from Bangkok, 3½ hours from Tokyo. Hong Kong is on Pan Am's Round-the-World routes. By ship, about 18 days from San Francisco.

University of Hong Kong

IRELAND

Ireland is famous for the great missionaries and teachers whom it sent throughout Europe from the sixth to the tenth centuries. It is not, perhaps, so generally known that during this period of the country's Golden Age great numbers of students from abroad flocked to its shores.

Writing early in the eighth century, the Venerable Bede says that in his own day "there were many English nobles and lesser folk in Ireland. . . . Some of these devoted themselves to the monastic life, while others preferred to travel, studying under various teachers in turn. The Irish welcomed them all kindly and, without asking for any payment, provided them with books and instructors."

Present-day circumstances, unfortunately, call for tuition fees and other expenditures, but I can assure all overseas students that the old kindliness is still there at our Irish universities. There is not only to be found the heritage of learning from earlier centuries but also an excellent curriculum in the modern sciences.

John O'Brien
Consul General, New York

Ireland has two important universities; both are based on state charters. The National University of Ireland was founded by the Universities Act of 1908, which dissolved the Royal University of Ireland and set up in its place the National University and also the Queen's University of Belfast, in Northern Ireland. The National University of Ireland comprises three colleges. They are University College in Dublin, University College in Cork and University College in Galway. The three colleges are co-educational. St. Patrick's College, a Catholic seminary and so admitting only clerical students, is a recognized college of the National University of Ireland. The other university is the University of Dublin, which was founded in 1591 by Queen Elizabeth; it was planned that this university would have colleges in several cities and the first, in Dublin, was named Trinity College; because it is still the only college established under the University of Dublin the two names have become synonymous for the University. Students from several associated colleges receive their degrees from the University of Dublin; these colleges are Magee University College in Derry, Northern Ireland, Church of Ireland Training College in Dublin, and Veterinary College of Ireland in Ballsbridge. Foreign students are accepted by the universities; applications for admission are considered individually and students are accepted when they meet the admission requirements and space is available. It is necessary to point out that the four colleges are very close to the point of being filled to capacity. Instruction is in English. Instruction in Irish is also provided in the Faculties of Arts, Commerce, Science and Engineering in University College, Galway.

IRISH UNIVERSITY SYSTEM ... Each of the universities of Ireland is composed of various faculties. The National University of Ireland conducts its teaching at the three University Colleges in Dublin, Cork, and Galway, and at the recognized College of St. Patrick, Maynooth. The University Colleges each have Faculties of Arts, Science, Law, Medicine, Engineering and Commerce. In addition to these faculties there are others at one or two of the University Colleges, e.g., Agriculture and Architecture at University College, Dublin, Dairy Science at University College, Cork. The University of Dublin also offers courses in its Faculties of Medicine, Science, Arts, Law, and Engineering, and other faculties. The lecture is an important part of the teaching method and students are expected to attend the lectures given in the courses for which they are registered. Unless students meet

attendance requirements they may not take the examinations for the course; examinations must be passed to receive credit for the course. Upon certain occasions students may be required to appear in academic costume as defined by the University's Academic Council. Some faculties inspect the preparatory work, the notes, for instance, which a student may be doing for the course. Most courses require at least three years of study for the Bachelor's degree; advanced degrees may require from one to three years' additional study. To enter an Irish university, a student must prove his ability to carry on advanced-level academic work by passing the matriculation examination in at least five subjects. Exemption may be granted to foreign students who submit evidence that they have passed an equivalent examination in certain subjects.

ADMISSION REQUIREMENTS ... Students must have attained the age of 17 years by the January 15th following their registration to be accepted as students. The College Registrar will send upon request full details needed in the letter of application. Some faculties of the University Colleges are very much overcrowded and admission of students from Ireland must come ahead of admission of foreign students. Many faculties require a knowledge of Latin for admission. Students who wish to attend the University of Dublin, Trinity College, should obtain from the University the booklet on admission requirements, which gives full and complete details. Students must submit proof of their academic suitability, evidence of good personal character, a satisfactory medical certificate, and proof of a satisfactory level of general education. For Americans a minimum of two years of college is required, although four years is preferable (Bachelor's degree). Instruction is in English at all universities. Some courses may be given in the Irish language, but a knowledge of this language is not required of foreign students.

CREDIT TOWARD AN AMERICAN DEGREE ... A student must make arrangements for receiving credit toward an American degree from his own university before he leaves the United States. Because of the variations in credit systems within American universities and colleges, it is impossible to generalize about the number of credit hours a student may receive. Each student should discuss with his own dean or guidance counselor the requirements for receiving credit and the number of credit hours toward his American degree that may be awarded for study abroad. Sometimes full credit may be given for the period of study in Ireland if the student passes the Irish examinations. But each American university or college will make its own evaluation of the study at each Irish university. Sometimes certificates of attendance can be earned from the Irish universities.

TUITION AND OTHER FEES ... These vary within the colleges and according to the faculty enrolled in and the class year of the student. Tuition charges for non-residents of Ireland are 50 per cent more than for students whose home country is Ireland, for the three University Colleges of the National University of Ireland and at the University of Dublin. Fees for nationals range from $143 at Galway, to $168 at Cork, to $210 at Dublin for the year in the Arts Faculty; from $202 at Galway, to $238 at Cork, to $294 at Dublin for the year in the Science Faculty. At Cork fees in other faculties vary from $168 for the year for the Faculties of Commerce, Law, or Music, to $273 for the Faculties of Medicine and Dentistry. At Galway the fees range from about $110 for Law, to $143 for Commerce, to $231 for Medicine for the year. At Dublin the fees range from $189 for Music, to $210 for the Faculties of Law and of Commerce, to $294 for the Faculties of Engineering, Architecture, and Agriculture, to $336 for the Faculties of Medicine or Dentistry for the year. There are class fees and other small charges at the colleges of the National University of Ireland. Foreign students at the University of Dublin, Trinity College, pay a matriculation fee of about $17, a college fee of $252, and a capitation fee of $14 for clubs and societies. If students receive laboratory instruction they must pay an additional $42 per term.

REGULATIONS ... A visa is not required of American citizens for entry into or stay in Ireland. Students from the United States must have a valid passport to enter Ireland. Students should inform themselves of the regulations concerning currency set up in Ireland.

LIVING COSTS ... The cost of living for American students is about $100 per month. The University of Dublin, Trinity College, has residential facilities available for a limited number of students. The National University of Ireland keeps lists of accommodations available at each of the University Colleges. Students live in hostels, boardinghouses, or sometimes with families. Some of the universities maintain restaurants where meals can be purchased inexpensively. Students are generally required to live in University-approved residences, and the lists of such residences can be obtained without charge from the University. American students should not plan to supplement their allowance by working as it is extremely difficult for foreign students to obtain work in Ireland.

COMMON COURTESIES AND LOCAL CUSTOMS ... The same courtesies prevail as in America with regard to sending and acknowledgment of gifts, invitations, etc. Christmas is the biggest religious and civic festival of the year; on March 17 the Shamrock is worn and sent to friends in other countries to commemorate the feast of Ireland's patron, Saint Patrick.

FOR FURTHER INFORMATION ... For complete information about a university and how to enroll, write to the President of the university college chosen.

For travel particulars and documentation, write to Educational Department, NHE, Pan American Airways, Pan Am Building, New York, N. Y. 10017.

HOW TO GET THERE ... By Pan American Jet Clipper to Shannon, about 6 hours from New York. Shuttle service from Shannon airport to Dublin. By ship, about 5 days.

DUBLIN

Dublin is the capital of Ireland and the country's chief city. It lies between the mountains and the sea on Ireland's eastern coast, and has been known as an important port since ancient times. The list of literary figures associated with Dublin includes not only native Irish, James Joyce, George Bernard Shaw, Jonathan Swift, Oscar Wilde, Oliver Goldsmith, but also the poet Shelley, who lived in Grafton Street. The Abbey Theatre, the National Library of Ireland, the Trinity College Library, which dates from 1601, the Royal Irish Academy Library, the annual Irish Music Festival, the National Gallery, the Municipal Gallery of Modern Art, the National Museum of Ireland, and various theaters and learned societies provide the city with a full cultural life. Dublin Castle, the old Parliament House (now the Bank of Ireland), St. Stephen's Green, and the refreshing parks and gardens give architectural and beauty interest to Dublin. The University of Dublin, or Trinity College, was founded in 1591 by Queen Elizabeth. The Provost's House on the College grounds is an attraction because of its impressive appearance and its history. University College, Dublin, is a constituent college of the National University of Ireland established by the Act of 1908. The College dates back to 1852, however, when its forerunner, the Catholic University of Ireland, was founded, with John Henry Newman as its first rector.

University College, Cork

NATIONAL UNIVERSITY OF IRELAND, UNIVERSITY COLLEGE, CORK

Cork, in south central Ireland, is in the country's largest county, of the same name. Its population of about 100,000 inhabitants makes it the third largest city in Ireland. Perhaps Cork is most famous for the Blarney Castle and its celebrated stone, which are about five miles from the city. The countryside surrounding Cork, with its river valleys, moors, fields of heather, and rock-strewn mountains, its coastline of sandy beaches and scattered cliffs, gives a constantly changing scene. Shandon Church with its famous bells is Cork's most interesting building. Important Gaelic festivals are held every year in Cork. The city has a good many literary, scientific, music, and historical societies; the Cork Ballet Group has attracted much interest in recent years. University College, Cork, first opened its doors to students in 1849, then as Queen's College. By virtue of the Universities Act of 1908, the name University College became effective and the Cork university became part of the National University of Ireland.

SIZE ... About 1,650 students, including about 25 students from outside Ireland.

CALENDAR ... The beginning of October to the end of June.

COURSES OF STUDY ... The College is composed of several faculties including the Faculty of Arts, Faculty of Celtic Studies, Faculty of Commerce, Faculty of Dairy Science, Faculty of Engineering, Faculty of Law, Faculty of Medicine, and the Faculty of Science. Among the courses offered in the Faculty of Arts are Ancient Classics, Archaeology, Economics, Education, English, French, German, Philosophy, Geography, History, History of Modern Irish Literature, Irish History, Language and Literature, Irish Music, Mathematics, Music, Psychology, Sociology, and Statistics. The Faculty of Celtic Studies offers Celtic Language and Philology. The Faculty of Commerce offers Accounting and Business Administration, Economics, Economic Theory, various Law courses, and other courses. The Faculty of Dairy Science offers courses in Agriculture, Dairy Accounting and Economics, Dairy and Food Microbiology, Dairy Chemistry, Engineering, and Technology. The range of courses offered by the Faculty of Science is from Anatomy and Agriculture to Zoology. The Engineering Faculty offers courses in Civil, Dairy, Electrical, Mechanical, and Municipal Engineering, and in Geology, and Mathematics.

TUITION ... Different fees are established for the different faculties; foreign students pay 50 per cent more than Irish students; these additional costs have been included in the amounts given here. Tuition charges for undergraduate foreign students for the academic year for the Faculty of Arts, Faculty of Commerce, Faculty of Law, or the study of Music are $189; for the Faculty of Engineering, Faculty of Science, Agricultural course, pre-Dental or pre-Medical course, $275; for the Faculty of Dairy Science, $255; for the first year in Dentistry or Medicine, $294. Fees for examinations cost from $5.60 to $14. Students in chemistry laboratory courses must deposit $5.60 with the Bursar. There may be additional incidental expenses, such as for field trips, in some courses.

ADMISSION REQUIREMENTS ... Foreign students must satisfy all the requirements for matriculation—passing the matriculation examination of the University in five subjects as set forth by the faculty the student wishes to enter—or submit an acceptable equivalent academic record and apply directly to the President of the College for admission. Students may obtain a pamphlet, *Matriculation Regulations and Courses,* which sets forth all regulations for matriculation at the University College. Some faculties, such as Engineering, have special additional requirements for entrance. Latin and Greek are subjects on which prospective entrants are examined by most faculties. There are special stipulations for non-matriculated students; these can be obtained from the University.

See also the Admission Requirements section in the opening summary on Ireland.

LANGUAGE OF INSTRUCTION ... English.

ACCOMMODATIONS ... Although the University College does not operate residence halls, the College requires all students to live in University-approved hostels or lodging houses, or with families. Room and full board cost from about $250 to $325 per thirty weeks in a residence hostel. The College restaurant serves inexpensive meals as well as tea and coffee during the morning and afternoon. The College will help students to find suitable lodgings.

AVERAGE COSTS ... Fees about $175 and up per academic year. Room and board around $100 per month.

STUDENT LIFE ... A large number of clubs and societies have been set up at the University College. Among the recreational groups which are organized into clubs are the Association Football Club, Athletic and Cycling Club, Basketball Club, Boxing Club, Golf Club, Lawn Tennis Club, Rowing Club, Rugby Football Club, Swimming Club, and Women's Hockey Club. There are the Art, Biological, Chemical and Physical, Choral, Commerce, Dairy Science, Dental, Dramatic, Engineering, English Literature, Historical, Law, Medical, Philosophical, Psychological, Spanish, and French Societies. There is also a Chess Club. Students will have an opportunity to learn the Irish language in a course, if they choose, or informally from students. Students have cycling trips and hikes on which foreign students are welcome.

University College, Dublin

NATIONAL UNIVERSITY OF IRELAND, UNIVERSITY COLLEGE, DUBLIN

SIZE ... About 6,000 students of whom about 200 are from outside Ireland.

CALENDAR ... October to June. The Faculty of Medicine third (Trinity) term continues until July. There is a summer session in July.

COURSES OF STUDY ... The following faculties make up the University College: Faculty of Arts, Faculty of Science, Faculty of Medicine, Faculty of Dentistry, Faculty of Engineering, Faculty of Architecture, Faculty of Law, Faculty of Agriculture, Faculty of Commerce, Faculty of Veterinary Medicine, Faculty of Philosophy and Sociology, and Faculty of Celtic Studies. Students may also pursue studies leading to diplomas or degrees in Education, Library Training, Social Science, Public Administration, Child Care, Psychology, Teaching of the Deaf, Gaelic, Public Health, Psychological Medicine, and Physiotherapy.

SUMMER COURSES ... There is a course on Ireland: The Past and Present.

TUITION ... Foreign students pay 50 per cent additional tuition fees for the classes they attend. This additional amount is included here. Undergraduate foreign students enrolling in the Faculty of Arts, Faculty of Commerce, or the Faculty of Law pay $215 per college session; in the Faculty of Science, Faculty of Engineering, Faculty of Architecture, or the Faculty of Agriculture, $385 per college session; in the Music course $255 per session; $420 for the Faculty of Medicine or Dentistry. In addition there may be fees for college societies or student clubs, laboratory courses, and for the National University examinations.

ADMISSION REQUIREMENTS ... Foreign students who wish to become matriculated students (i.e., work for a degree or a diploma from the College) must meet all the matriculation requirements—pass the entrance examination in at least five subjects or have an acceptable equivalent academic record, as required by the faculty he wishes to enter—and satisfy specified

language requirements. Some faculties require a knowledge of Latin or Greek. There are special stipulations for non-matriculated students; these can be obtained from the University.

See also the Admission Requirements section in the opening summary on Ireland.

LANGUAGE OF INSTRUCTION ... English.

ACCOMMODATIONS ... Students must live in houses of residence approved by the College although not operated by the College. Several hostels are operated by religious organizations and students may obtain both room and board in such houses. Some students live with Irish families. American students will find that $100 per month will easily cover room and board.

AVERAGE COSTS ... Fees about $215 and up per college session. Room and board around $100 per month.

STUDENT LIFE ... Students may join groups devoted to cultural, social, religious, or intellectual activities. There are various learned societies of the city of Dublin which have lectures open to students. The city itself offers students many recreational activities; there are golf, tennis, swimming, cycling, hiking, boating; there are libraries to visit, museums to see, open-air bookstalls on the quays where students mix with old-timers to browse. Festivals, theaters, concerts, yachting, fishing, strolling are other diversions.

NATIONAL UNIVERSITY OF IRELAND, UNIVERSITY COLLEGE, GALWAY

Galway sits on the northern shore of Galway Bay in western Ireland. Its position makes it the ideal starting point for sightseeing in all of western Ireland and the Aran Islands, where only Gaelic is spoken and traditional customs of Ireland are preserved and practiced. Its location so near the Atlantic Ocean has made Galway an important port for centuries, and fishing is an important activity. Connemara, the Western part of Galway County, has fine scenic attractions. As early as the sixteenth century Galway was known as an educational center and had the country's best-known classical school. Opened as Queen's College in 1849, University College, Galway, was set up by the Irish Universities Act of 1908, which dissolved Queen's and made the Galway campus one of the constituent colleges of the National University of Ireland.

SIZE ... Almost 1,300 students, including about 20 students from outside Ireland.

CALENDAR ... October to June.

COURSES OF STUDY ... The College is composed of the Faculty of Arts, Philosophy and Celtic Studies, the Faculty of Science, the Faculty of Law, the Faculty of Medicine, the Faculty of Engineering and the Faculty of Commerce. Among the courses offered by the Faculty of Arts are Greek, Latin, English Language and Literature, Modern History, Celtic Archaeology, Philosophy, Logic, Psychology, Epistemology, Ontology, Ethics, Politics, Sociology, Education, French, German; Italian, Spanish and Economics; the Faculty of Science offers courses in Mathematics, Mathematical Physics, Experimental Physics, Chemistry, Physical Geography, Geology, Zoology, Bi-

University College, Galway

ology, Anatomy, Physiology, Bacteriology, Botany and Agricultural Science. The Engineering Faculty offers courses in Mathematics, Civil Engineering, Physics, Chemistry and Geology; the Faculty of Commerce offers courses in Economics, Romance Languages, Accounting, Banking, Commerce, Irish, English, French, Geography, German, History, Law and Statistics.

TUITION ... Each faculty has its own set of fees called the Class Fees, and foreign students pay 50 per cent additional to the set amount. The following fees include the additional charge. Undergraduate foreign students pay per college session: $177 for courses in either the Arts or the Commerce Faculties; about $110 for courses in the Faculty of Law; $255 for courses in Engineering, Science and Agriculture Faculties and for the pre-Medical and the pre-Dental courses. The Class Fees include a College Fee of $14 payable each year. The College Fee gives students membership in various student societies and clubs. Additional fees are charged for laboratory courses. Students who are not working for a degree pay the College Fee of $14 and about $17 per course.

ADMISSION REQUIREMENTS ... Requirements differ for non-matriculated and matriculated students, those working for a degree or diploma. The applicant must satisfy all the requirements for matriculation or have an acceptable equivalent academic record if he wishes to be a matriculated student working for a degree. Non-matriculated students may not be required to take the entrance examinations which regular students must pass.

See also the Admission Requirements section in the opening summary on Ireland.

LANGUAGE OF INSTRUCTION ... English. Some courses are given in the Irish language and attention is called to the fact that it is the aim of University College, Galway, ultimately to use the Irish language generally in its academic and official life.

ACCOMMODATIONS ... The College does not maintain dormitories for students. It does, however, keep a list of approved residences and hostels where students can take a room or room and board. The cost of living for American students is about $100 per month. Upon request the University Registrar will send students free a copy of the lodging-houses list.

AVERAGE COSTS ... Fees about $150 and up per college session. Room and board around $100 per month.

STUDENT LIFE ... The College Union is the student body organization which carries out an extensive program of activities. For students interested in rowing, boating, debating, natural history and science there are separate clubs or societies. There are also the literary society and the Athletic Union. Golf and tennis are available to students, and for those who like to fish, there are inviting streams, lakes, the River Corrib and Galway Bay. Galway has a sandy beach and a fine swimming area. Students frequently take cycling trips about the county or make excursions to the Aran Islands.

UNIVERSITY OF DUBLIN, TRINITY COLLEGE

SIZE ... There are about 2,850 students, including up to 1,300 from outside Ireland.

CALENDAR ... From October to July. A summer session is held in July.

COURSES OF STUDY ... The University is composed of the Faculty of Arts, Faculty of Sciences, Faculty of Engineering, Faculty of Medicine, Faculty of Commerce, Faculty of Law, Faculty of Dentistry, Faculty of Agriculture and Forestry, Faculty of Music, Faculty of Education, Faculty of Social Science, and the Faculty of Divinity. Among the courses in the General Studies program are French, German, Greek, Latin, English, Irish, Hebrew, Spanish, Pure Mathematics, Applied Mathematics, Mental and Moral Science, Experimental Psychology, Geography, and Economics.

SUMMER COURSES ... In July each year the University of Dublin conducts a summer school for foreign students on subjects of Irish interest. A course entitled Irish Heritage is given.

TUITION ... Foreign students entering the University pay a matriculation fee of about $22, a College Fee of $295 and a capitation fee of $14 for clubs and societies. An additional $136 per term is required for laboratory courses.

ADMISSION REQUIREMENTS ... American students who wish to enter the University of Dublin should take the College Entrance Board Examination and should apply directly to the Provost of the University of Dublin, sending a statement of their academic record, a letter of recommendation from their own college or former school head, a certificate of medical fitness, and some evidence of good personal character.

See also the Admission Requirements section in the opening summary on Ireland.

ACCOMMODATIONS ... Some residential facilities are operated by the University but there are not enough for all students. Accommodations can be found with families, in hostels, or in lodging houses. The University keeps a list of accommodations and assists students to find suitable places to live and eat. Not more than $100 per month is sufficient for room and board in Dublin.

AVERAGE COSTS ... Fees about $300 per academic year, room and board about $100 per month.

STUDENT LIFE ... The spacious parks—Phoenix Park with 1,760 acres is the largest city park in the world—the book-stalls, the zoo, the libraries, the museums, the art galleries all offer stimulating or relaxing spare-time activity for students. There are various clubs and groups within the University, each devoted to a special interest whether artistic, social, intellectual, or recreational.

Trinity College, Dublin

ISRAEL

Israel is the land of the Bible, the cradle of the world's three monotheistic faiths, the birthplace of the Jewish people. A land that within a decade and a half has seen the return to its borders of more than a million of its sons and daughters from some eighty countries the world over, a land in which the book and the school stand high in the scale of people's values, Israel offers the visiting student an unparalleled opportunity not only to study but, at the same time, to observe at first hand the practical aspects of his studies.

While the state itself, as a modern political unit, is only 17 years old, its leading institutions of higher learning were founded several decades ago and have established a name for themselves in the academic world. Increasingly, over the years, institutions such as the Hebrew University of Jerusalem, the Haifa Institute of Technology, the Weizmann Institute of Science, Bar-Ilan University and the University of Tel Aviv have attracted students, as well as outstanding professors and scientists, from abroad. The University's faculty includes some of the top men in their respective fields, recruited both locally and abroad.

It has been said, and rightly so, that Israel is a land of contrasts. But it is more than that: the Israel of today is a land seeking a wholesome balance between many of these contrasts, between the old and the new; between the nation's spiritual and its material needs; between the vastly divergent groups and communities that have gathered in this land, drawn by a spiritual bond that unites them all; between the call of humanism and the demands of a growingly technological and specialized world.

Perhaps it is the opportunity to witness this living process of nation-building, or indeed to take an active part in it, that has drawn so many students, visitors and immigrants to Israel's shores.

Ambassador Katriel Katz
Consul-General of Israel in New York

UNIVERSITIES OF ISRAEL . . . The University Bar-Ilan in Ramat Gan, founded in 1955, offers courses in Jewish Studies, Languages and Literature, Social Sciences, Mathematics and Natural Sciences. The Hebrew University of Jerusalem officially opened in 1925 and, because of its location, is Israel's major cultural and intellectual center. Special courses are offered in Jewish Studies and related subjects as well as the Humanities, Social Studies and Science. Technion, Israel Institute of Technology, founded in 1924 near Haifa, offers courses covering the entire range of engineering. Tel Aviv University, founded in 1953, offers courses in Humanities, Sciences and Medicine. Weizmann Institute of Science, founded near Rehovoth in 1934, is one of the world's great centers of science, offering advanced degrees in almost any scientific field imaginable.

ISRAEL UNIVERSITY SYSTEM . . . As in all rapidly developing new nations, the evolution of higher education in Israel reflects a constantly growing and changing cultural pattern. Institutions of higher education in Israel were originally patterned after European institutions, particularly those of Germany and England, but have in more recent years adopted certain educational concepts and practices from the United States. As in Europe, an academic tradition exists which emphasizes independent study and reading, and seminars. Attendance at classes is generally more mandatory than in Europe, but less so than in the United States. The credit-hour system familiar to American students is used only at Bar-Ilan University. It is generally considered that the level of Israeli students beginning studies at institutions of higher education corresponds to that of an American student who has completed one year of college.

ADMISSION REQUIREMENTS . . . A student must have a working knowledge of the Hebrew language and must be a high school graduate.

CREDIT TOWARD AN AMERICAN DEGREE . . . A student should consult his adviser with respect to receiving credit toward an American degree.

REGULATIONS . . . A valid American passport is required. A student visa (temporary residence visa) is also required. This visa will be issued by the consulate: upon receipt of the letter of acceptance by the university, a statement showing "evidence of means" or ability to meet all expenses, and passing a physical exam by a consulate-approved physician. A smallpox vaccination certificate is needed to reenter the United States.

TUITION . . . The average cost is approximately $250 per year at all the universities with the exception of the Weizmann Institute of Science for doctoral candidates, where no cost is involved.

LIVING COSTS . . . The average cost is about $100 to $125 a month.

COMMON COURTESIES AND LOCAL CUSTOMS . . . Israelis are pleased if they hear you speak even one word of Hebrew. The most used word is *shalom*, meaning "peace," an all-purpose greeting.

FOR FURTHER INFORMATION . . . For complete information about all the universities and how to enroll, write to Miss Ruth Routenberg, American Friends of the Hebrew University, 11 East 69th Street, New York, N. Y. 10021.

For travel particulars and documentation, write to Educational Department, NHE, Pan American Airways, Pan Am Building, New York, N. Y. 10017.

HOW TO GET THERE . . . By Pan American Jet Clipper to London, Paris, Rome, Vienna, Istanbul; then by connection. Elapsed time from New York to Tel Aviv via Rome, 12¼ hours. By ship, about 15 days.

UNIVERSITY BAR-ILAN, TEL AVIV

The University Bar-Ilan, the American University in Israel at Ramat Gan, was founded in 1955 by Dr. Pinkhos Churgin, with the support of the Mizrachi Organization. The University is governed by an Academic Senate in Israel and a Board of Governors in New York. It is presently an autonomous, co-educational institution offering courses in the various fields of human knowledge as well as in all branches of Judaica. The University has a religious orientation and aspires to train men and women to integrate Torah wisdom with modern knowledge in the secular fields.

The University extends over an area of some 12 acres in Ramat Gan, a suburb of Tel Aviv, and consists of a complex of administration buildings, lecture halls, classrooms, libraries and laboratory buildings; dining halls, recreation center and men's and women's dormitories; also a synagogue.

SIZE . . . About 1,200 students.

CALENDAR . . . Each semester of the academic year comprises 15 weeks of instruction, exclusive of the weeks devoted to final examinations. Sessions extend from October through June.

COURSES OF STUDY . . . The courses, leading to Bachelor of Arts (B.A.), Bachelor of Science (B.S.), Master of Arts (M.A.), and Master of Science (M.S.) are given within the framework of four divisions.

a) Division of Jewish Studies includes Bible, Talmud, Jewish History and Jewish Philosophy.

b) Division of Languages and Literature includes Hebrew, French, Arabic, English, German, Latin, Greek, Ancient Semitic Languages, Hebrew and World Literature.

c) Division of Social Sciences includes History, Philosophy, Psychology, Sociology, Economics, Education and Music.

d) Division of Mathematics and the Natural Sciences includes General Biology, Botany, Microbiology, Biochemistry, Physics and Mathematics.

TUITION ... The annual tuition fee is $910, American currency, payable two weeks prior to student's departure for Israel. This fee includes tuition, registration, dormitory room and board. Scholarships are awarded on the basis of need and merit upon selection by the Academic Committee.

ADMISSION REQUIREMENTS ... Include an Israeli Matriculation Certificate or corresponding qualifications of students from other countries. A working knowledge of Hebrew and a minimal knowledge of the Talmud are required of all students. Non-Jewish students who are accepted for study at Bar-Ilan University will not be held to the requirement of a knowledge of the Talmud, nor will they be bound by regulations governing required courses in Judaica.

Students from abroad wishing to enroll for one year of resident study may apply for admission. Such students will not be held to the normal curriculum requirement.

Candidates from the United States, Canada or Great Britain will be interviewed by Bar-Ilan University committees in those countries.

NOTE ... For further information, write American Committee for Bar-Ilan University, 10 East 40th Street, New York, N. Y. 10016.

HEBREW UNIVERSITY OF JERUSALEM

Jerusalem is a city holy to Judaism, Christianity and Islam, and is the modern capital of the State of Israel. Located high in the Hills of Judea, it enjoys a dry climate for eight months of the year—warm during the day, cool in the evenings. Among its memorable historic sites are Mount Zion, with the tomb of King David, and the nearby hill village of Ein Kerem, birthplace of John the Baptist. Rising in the western suburbs, on rolling hills, is the new complex of national and cultural institutions, including the Knesset (Parliament), the Bezalel National Museum, the central campus of the Hebrew University and the Shrine of the Book, housing the Dead Sea Scrolls.

The Hebrew University of Jerusalem was officially opened in 1925 on Mount Scopus. Its first campus became inaccessible as an aftermath of Israel's War of Independence in 1948. For the next six years the University functioned in makeshift premises scattered throughout the city, and in 1954, construction of a new central campus was begun at Givat Ram in western Jerusalem. Today, the major portion of the University's work is carried on at this campus, which is Israel's major cultural and intellectual center.

SIZE ... 9,000 students, including some 300 foreign students, mainly from the U. S. A., but many from Asia, Africa and Europe. The faculty numbers 1,000.

CALENDAR ... October to June; exams in July and September, and students may divide their exams between the two periods. There is a trimester system, but with the exception of the Faculty of Science, nearly all courses run for the full academic year and students must enroll for a full year. There are summer courses from mid-July to mid-August.

COURSES OF STUDY ... Special Course for American Students: The program lasts for a full year, beginning early in July with a 3½-month intensive Hebrew language course (*Ulpan*), which is given on five graded levels. During the University's regular academic year, students are offered a wide selection of special courses in Jewish Studies and related subjects, as well as courses from the curricula of the Faculties of Humanities, Social Sciences and Science. Program participants reside in student hostels throughout the year. The program includes guided tours of Israel and lectures on all phases of Israeli life. Credit for the year of study is determined by the student's own college in the U. S. A.

Regular Courses: The University has Faculties of Humanities, Social Sciences, Law, Medicine, Science, and Agriculture, including the following associated departments: Institute of Jewish Studies, Institute of Asian and African Studies, School of Education, Graduate Library School, School of Social Work, School of Pharmacy and School of Dentistry. Studies for the Bachelor's degree extend over three years; studies for the Master's degree require two years.

SUMMER COURSES ... Jewish and Middle East Studies are offered in July and August.

TUITION ... For the American Student Program the fee is about $1,700, covering round-trip transportation, tuition for the entire year, room for the year, meals for the period of the *Ulpan*, student medical and dental services and guided tours. Students need an additional sum of at least $500 to cover meals during the academic year and miscellaneous expenses. Some partial scholarships are available, and a scholarship application may be requested with the application for admission.

ADMISSION REQUIREMENTS ... The American Student Program is open to students who have completed at least two years of college, and to recent graduates. Participants are selected on the basis of academic achievement, character and seriousness of purpose. Some elementary knowledge of Hebrew is required, and applicants must show evidence of current Hebrew study.

Admission requirements for the regular courses, for Americans, one year of college is required for full matriculation. Students wishing to enter directly from an American high school may be admitted but will spend one year in special supplementary studies. Admission to the Faculty of Medicine is on the basis of a competitive examination, given in Hebrew, in Jerusalem. The Psychology and Geography Departments require special entrance examinations; students wishing to major in Science may also be required to sit for special examinations.

LANGUAGE OF INSTRUCTION ... Hebrew. In order to receive a degree, foreigners must pass an examination in Hebrew language, literature and the Bible. Hebrew instruction is offered —up to five hours a week—but these classes presume at least a basic knowledge of the language. Intensive Hebrew studies are offered prior to the start of the academic year only to participants in the American Student Program (see above).

ACCOMMODATIONS ... The number of student hostels is limited. Most students rent rooms in private apartments, generally with kitchen privileges. Minimum rental is about $20 a month. The Students' Organization has a housing service that provides information about available rooms and apartments.

AVERAGE COSTS ... Fees are about $225 per year, and living expenses average $100 to $125 a month. The students' cafeteria on campus offers inexpensive meals, and student hostels have kitchen facilities.

STUDENT LIFE ... The Students' Organization sponsors a dance troupe and a fortnightly cinema club. There are a University orchestra and drama group; also frequent public lectures at the campus and at Hillel House, in town. Movie-going and informal parties are the most popular social activities. During academic vacations, students often travel throughout the country, or take part in study expeditions of the Archaeology, Geology, Botany and other departments. Several repertory theaters and the Israel Philharmonic Orchestra pay regular visits to the city.

NOTE ... For further information, write to: Department of University Services, American Friends of the Hebrew University, 11 East 69th Street, New York, N. Y. 10021.

Hebrew University of Jerusalem

TECHNION, ISRAEL INSTITUTE OF TECHNOLOGY, HAIFA

Technion

The Technion, Israel Institute of Technology, is the oldest institution of higher learning in Israel, having opened its doors to an initial student body of 30 in 1924. The Technion is the only university in Israel devoted to the engineering sciences and has won an international reputation for its high academic and research standards. In addition to serving as a formal university, the Technion's workshops and laboratories carry on extensive research programs that are closely linked to the industrial development of Israel.

The idea of establishing a technical university in what was then Palestine was first broached in the early part of this century, and in fact construction of the original Technion campus in the heart of the city of Haifa began before World War I, when Palestine was under Turkish domination. The outbreak of war and the changeover from Turkish rule to British mandate status for Palestine delayed the formal inauguration of classes until 1924.

The early dreamers of a Jewish state reborn realized, a half century ago, that the age of science and technology was growing and that the need for engineers and applied scientists would increase. It was this need that spurred the creation of the Technion. Today, in a highly technical era, when the State of Israel changes each day more and more from an agricultural to an industrial economy, the impact of science and technology becomes greater, and the role of the Technion as the country's sole source of engineering manpower becomes sharper. Former Prime Minister David Ben-Gurion described the Technion as "a cornerstone of Israel's development."

The new Technion campus, occupying 300 acres on a slope of Mount Carmel some five miles from metropolitan Haifa, is one of the most beautiful campus sites in the world. The planners of the new campus have tried to retain the scenic beauty of the site while providing for an ever-expanding physical plant. The campus is still under construction, but there already are separate buildings housing such faculties as Electrical Engineering, Physics, Hydraulic Engineering, Industrial Engineering, Aeronautical Engineering, Agricultural Engineering, as well as similar structures devoted to building research, soil research, ceramics research. On a separate section of the campus are located eight dormitories that blend into the landscape and that provide housing for approximately 500 students.

SIZE ... The new Technion campus student body, including undergraduate and graduate students, consists of approximately 3,000 young men and women, while an additional 2,000 students still use the older facilities in Haifa proper.

CALENDAR ... The academic year begins in October and ends in July.

COURSES OF STUDY ... Courses lead to Bachelor's degree, as well as Master's and Ph.D. These courses cover the entire range of engineering, including agricultural, aeronautical, electrical, civil, mechanical, hydraulic, plus physics, mathematics and nuclear engineering.

TUITION ... Tuition is comparatively low, averaging approximately $250 per year while the average living costs for one year are estimated at $500.

ACCOMMODATIONS ... The vast majority of students live in or near Haifa since the limited number of dormitory accommodations are reserved for the large number of students from Asian and African countries attending Technion, as well as for newly arrived immigrants whose adjustment to life in Israel is facilitated by the pleasant environment of the dormitories.

Students at the Technion, including about 9 per cent girls, are a little older and therefore a little more serious than their counterparts in other sections of the world. The reason for this age differential is that most students, girls included, must complete their two or two and a half years of military service before being admitted to the Technion.

LANGUAGE OF INSTRUCTION ... The language of instruction is Hebrew, although most students are fluent in at least one other language.

STUDENT LIFE ... Although not extensive, there are expanding facilities for students interested in athletic activities, student folk dance groups, a student orchestra, a student publishing house and many other lesser activities.

NOTE ... For further information, write to American Technion Society, 1000 Fifth Avenue, New York, N. Y. 10028.

TEL AVIV UNIVERSITY

Tel Aviv University was founded in 1953 by the Tel Aviv Municipality and officially inaugurated in 1956. The original institute started with 17 students and the first academic year in 1956 saw an enrollment of 148. These figures rapidly increased, and for the 1962–63 year of studies there were more than 1,500 students. At present there are three faculties: Humanities, Sciences and Continuing Medical Education. The academic staff increased threefold from 1956 and now consists of approximately 200 professors, lecturers and assistants.

Up to the present, the Tel Aviv University has had to be content with the use of provisional quarters in Givat Herzl, in the southern suburbs of the city. Lecture halls, laboratories, library, and experimental zoological garden and botanical garden are all crowded together in a congested, poorly constructed site, which also houses the administrative block and the students' club and restaurant. Research institutions and other adjuncts are widely scattered throughout the city.

The Tel Aviv Municipality has set aside an area of 400 *dunams* (approximately 100 acres) north of the Yarkon River adjoining the Ramat-Aviv suburb, where the new university campus is now being erected. This area is on the slope of a hill, providing a magnificent view of the Mediterranean Sea. A beginning has already been made with the erection of a complex of buildings for Physics and Chemistry. The buildings contain up-to-date lecture halls and laboratories as well as classrooms and a reference library. Other buildings planned for the campus include the section for Humanities and Social Sciences (Jewish Studies, Education, Economics and History), further buildings in the Department of Natural Sciences (including Medical Research, Microbiology, Botany, Zoology and Climatology), a section devoted to Art (including Music, Architecture, Plastic Arts and Painting), the Administrative Main Block (which will include the faculty houses, main library, students' club, and restaurant) and the Dr. Nachum Goldman Center of Diaspora Studies, and finally a gymnasium, stadium and sports arena.

Since March 1962, the Tel Aviv University has been a public corporation sponsored mainly by the municipality and to some extent by the government. At its head are a Board of Governors and a Council. The academic authorities are headed by a Rector and the Senate.

SIZE ... About 1,500 students.

CALENDAR ... The academic year lasts from the beginning of November until the end of June. Lectures are offered in the late afternoon and evening.

COURSES OF STUDY ... Faculty of Humanities: toward the B.A.—Talmud, Bible, Hebrew Language, Hebrew Literature, General History, Jewish History, Middle East and African Studies, Ancient Middle Eastern Studies, Philosophy, Psychology, English Language and Literature, French Civilization, Classical Studies, Theatrical Arts. Toward the M.A.—to holders of the B.A.—Jewish History, Bible and Philosophy. The Institute for the Research of Zionism is included in the Faculty of Humanities. The University also has an Education Department which is mainly concerned with the training of teachers for secondary schools. Students of the Faculties of Humanities and Sciences who plan to become teachers get two years' professional training in this department, beginning from their third year of studies in the respective faculty. This department also accepts holders of B.A. and B.S. degrees from other universities toward a secondary school teacher's certificate. Faculty of Sciences: consists of the following departments—Botany, Zoology, Applied Mathematics, Experimental Biology (a department of the Tel Aviv University and the General Sick Fund, formerly the Rogov Institute), Microbiology, Physics, Chemistry. The following institutes are also included—Institute of Human Genetics of the Tel Aviv University and Tel-Hashomer Hospital, Institute of Physiological Hygiene of Tel Aviv University and Donolo Hospital. Studies in the Department of Microbiology last for four years, leading toward the M.Sc.; in Biology and Applied Mathematics toward the B.Sc. with M.Sc. offered in Botany and Zoology to holders of B.Sc. in Biology. Holders of B.Sc. in Physics are accepted for studies toward their M.Sc. The Faculty for Continuing Medical Education accepts holders of M.D. degrees. This faculty sees its tasks in the improvement of training of hospital residents and young specialists in the Greater Tel Aviv area in the various fields of medicine, who may later serve as specialists and teachers in their chosen fields in Israel or abroad, in compliance with the present trend of this country—the supply of medical aid to developing countries. Secondly, it is intended to contribute to the absorption of immigrant physicians by bringing up their standard to the one prevailing in this country. Teaching in the Faculty for Continuing Medical Education is organized in semestrial courses under the following sections: Opthalmology, Orthopedics, Diagnostic Radiology, Pathology, Anesthetics, Nose, Ear and Throat, Gynecology and Obstetrics, Dermatology, Neurology, Neurosurgery, Pediatrics, Internal Medicine, General Medicine, Psychiatrics, Basic Sciences.

TUITION ... The average cost is $180 per year (tuition, examination fees, loan fund, participation in study excursions).

ADMISSION REQUIREMENTS ... See Courses of Study.

ACCOMMODATIONS ... Owing to limited space, as mentioned above, there is no accommodation for living quarters for students.

STUDENT LIFE ... Students have a club and co-operative shop, but again, owing to crowded quarters and lack of space, common students' activities are very few.

WEIZMANN INSTITUTE OF SCIENCE, REHOVOTH

Sixteen miles southeast of Tel Aviv, on the busy highway to Beersheba and a mile beyond the city of Rehovoth, stands a low curving wall inscribed "Yad Chaim Weizmann." Here is the national memorial site dedicated to Israel's first President and founder of the Institute bearing his name. Here is the gateway to the Weizmann Institute of Science, whose modern buildings of gleaming white concrete and glass spread out on 200 acres of woodland and rolling green lawns.

The Institute is one of the world's great scientific centers. It began in 1934 in what was a little agricultural station in the desert. The Institute's campus is itself an oasis, transformed by Dr. Weizmann's vision into a landscape of matchless beauty by the executor of his legacy, Mr. Meyer W. Weisgal.

The visitor sees a main avenue laced with great Dalbergia trees; the long, low main library set in an expanse of rolling lawn and graced by silvery young olive trees; the auditorium framed by blue-blossomed jacaranda and orange trees, and beyond a grove of pines. An avenue of fig trees leads to the residential area, nestled in sparkling green lawns. The Institute has more than 60 acres of gardens, 25 acres of orange groves and a sea of flowers.

SIZE ... 200 students, including those from foreign countries.

CALENDAR ... End of October to mid-July.

COURSES OF STUDY ... In addition to being an oasis of science in the Middle East, with a staff of more than 1,000 scientists and technicians carrying out some 200 research projects in modern physics, biology and chemistry, the Weizmann Institute is also a great teaching center, increasingly attended by graduate students from Africa and Asia as well as Europe and the United States. The Weizmann Graduate School in the Natural Sciences offers courses leading to the M.Sc. and Ph.D. degrees. Doctoral students may take courses in General Relativity, Circuit Design of Digital Computers, Chemistry of Phosphorus Compounds, Tumor Pathology, Solid State Physics, Advanced Nuclear Physics, just to name a few of the courses available.

Major equipment at the Institute includes two high-speed electronic computers and a larger unit nearing completion; a heavy-water plant; two high-resolution magnetic resonance instruments; Van De Graaf and Heinemann Tandem Accelerators; a helium cryostat for low-temperature research; a large spectrometer-refractometer with an optical path of 200 meters, two electron microscopes.

Modern facilities in this self-contained City of Science include a liquid air plant, two high-precision instrumentation workshops, glass-blowing workshops, and animal breeding and isolation houses.

TUITION ... Scholarships (about $1,500) are available for Ph.D. students. Some financial support for M.Sc. students can be arranged. Opportunities for part-time work are also available. There are no tuition fees for doctoral candidates. For M.Sc. students, tuition fees average about $167 for the academic year.

ADMISSION REQUIREMENTS ... To study for a Master's degree, one must have a B.S. degree; for a Ph.D., a Master's is required. Admission is subject to the approval of the Admissions Board. Although courses are given in English as well as Hebrew, it is advisable to have a working knowledge of the native language.

LANGUAGE OF INSTRUCTION ... Knowledge of the Hebrew language is not a prerequisite for admission to the Graduate School, but some facility in its use is advised for foreign students.

ACCOMMODATIONS ... Dormitory housing is available for graduate students at low rates, and preference is given to foreign students. The faculty clubhouse includes a cafeteria and lounge.

ITALY

Italy is a country to which not only tourists but also students are going in great numbers.

The same traditional welcome reserved for tourists is given to students.

Italian universities organize courses ranging from the elementary to the most advanced levels. American students will acquire a university education as well as an understanding and penetration of the course of Italian civilization through the ages, from the Etruscans to present-day Italy. They will also acquire a valuable critical judgment of the fine arts, which only continuous familiarity with the great masterpieces can give.

Their return to America will be saddened by friendships left behind, but enriched with a greater sense of mutual understanding.

Professor Giuseppe Cardillo
Italian Cultural Attaché

UNIVERSITIES OF ITALY ... Italy has 24 state universities under the control of the Ministry of Education (*Ministero della Pubblica Istruzione*). These are the Universities of Bari, Bologna, Cagliari, Camerino, Catania, Ferrara, Florence, Genoa, Macerata, Messina, Milan, Modena, Naples, Padua, Palermo, Parma, Pavia, Perugia, Pisa, Rome, Sassari, Siena, Trieste and Turin. In addition there are two "free" (private) universities: the Catholic University of the Sacred Heart and the Luigi Bocconi Commercial University, both in Milan; also certain specialized institutes at university level: the Nautical University Institute and the Oriental University Institute, both in Naples. There are also many specialized schools including fine art academies, art institutes, music schools and private universities which meet the requirements set up by the Ministry of Public Instruction. These institutions also accept foreign students. The Italian University for Foreigners at Perugia and the Center of Culture for Foreign Students of the University of Florence are established solely for foreign students.

ITALIAN UNIVERSITY SYSTEM ... The Italian Ministry of Education (*Ministero della Pubblica Istruzione*), a part of the central government, supervises education at all levels throughout the country. Only institutions under Vatican control and those associated with the Ministry of Agriculture (commerce, forestry and agriculture schools) are excepted from this jurisdiction. The Ministry has a representative in each province of Italy who is responsible for all schools of that province. The Superior Council of the Ministry of Public Instruction sets standards which must be met by each university in Italy. Universities are organized according to one pattern and teaching methods are the same in each institution. Each university, however, has considerable autonomy as to internal affairs.

The year begins November 1 and ends the following October 31. Lectures continue from November to about the beginning of June. Examinations are given in February, June and October. Courses are of a year's duration or, sometimes, two or more years' duration. Subjects are either "compulsory" or "optional" and a certain number of subjects from each category must be taken by students working for a degree. An oral examination is given covering course work, and the final test, or thesis discussion, must also be passed for the Italian degree.

Lectures, given by the full professors, are the essential part of the teaching method, and students must attend. Generally three lectures are given each week for every course. Students must obtain the professor's signature to certify their attendance and the certification is necessary for admittance to the examination for the course.

REGULATIONS ... Students need a passport but are not required to have a visa for study in Italy. Declaration of residence must be made to local police authorities, however, within three days after arrival in Italy. In some cases, if a student is housed in an educational institution, the head of this institution will handle the declaration. Renewal of the residence permit is granted upon application by the student. Radios and personal effects can be taken into the country for temporary use. Students should inform themselves of custom regulations; the nearest Italian Consulate can provide this information.

COMMON COURTESIES AND LOCAL CUSTOMS ... Students greet each other and part with handshakes. Dinner hour is late and so are opera and theater performances. The siesta is popular with students; the universities observe the long lunch hour. This information varies very much from one region of Italy to another. When visiting churches, men wear coats; women should have a head covering, and wear dresses with sleeves. Never go to church in slacks. Students who attend the special courses of the University for Foreigners in Perugia and of the Dante Alighieri Society in Rome and Florence are given free passes to museums. Other students should apply, if in the United States, to the Instituto Italiano de Cultura, 686 Park Avenue, New York, N. Y. 10021, and if in Italy directly to the Ministero della Pubblica Istruzione, Officio Tessere, Viale Trastevere, Rome. Some theaters give cut-rate tickets to students. The Centro Italiano Viaggi Istruzione Studenti (C.I.V.I.S.) in Rome and the Centro Relazioni Universitarie con l'Estero (C.R.U.E.I.) office in every university help students find accommodations and offer information on student travel.

TUITION ... Costs vary considerably depending upon the course of study a student chooses and the university. In general fees for registration, examinations, enrollment, laboratories, library, and social assistance may average around $100 per year at an Italian university. Students enrolled in scientific faculties pay from $30 to $100 per year for laboratory fees. Fees for specialization courses range from $50 to $250 a year. Costs are much lower than in the United States, where the average is $800 to $1,000 for universities which charge tuition.

LIVING COSTS ... The cost of living varies from town to town in Italy, but in general it is low. American students will find that approximately $150 a month will see them through ordinary living expenses at the better known schools. Rome, Naples and other larger cities have residences for students, *Casa dello Studente,* although these are not operated by the university. Every university does operate a *mensa universitaria,* or student restaurant. Many students live with families, in small hotels, or in boardinghouses called *pensioni.* Full board (three meals a day) in a pension costs from $4 to $7.20 per day; a single room may cost from $1.50 to about $3 a day; a double room from about $3 to about $5 a day. Hotel rooms may begin at approximately the same prices, but cover a higher range, to about $4 a day for a single and about $5 daily for a double room. Hostels offer modest accommodations at lower prices, and some accept foreign students. It is very difficult for a foreign student to find employment in Italy and American students should not plan to supplement their funds by working. Students should have about $25 in lire with them at the time of arrival for tips and incidentals. Part of this money should be in small denominations.

CREDIT TOWARD AN AMERICAN DEGREE ... A student must make arrangements for receiving credit toward an American degree from his own university before he leaves the United States. Because of the variations in credit systems within American universities, it is impossible to generalize about the number of credit hours a student may receive. Each student should discuss with his own dean or guidance counselor the requirements for receiving credit and the number of credit hours toward his American degree that may be awarded for study abroad. Sometimes full credit may be given for the period of study in Italy if the student passes the Italian examinations. But each American university will make its own evaluation of the study at each Italian university. Certain diplomas and certificates of study can be earned from Italian universities.

ADMISSION REQUIREMENTS ... Institutions offering special courses for foreign students do not require a full presentation of previous academic records; the secondary school certificate (high school diploma) is acceptable. To be admitted to an Italian university as either a regular student or as an auditor or special student, American students must have completed two years of college work in the United States and have received sufficient marks to be admitted to the second biennial course. After getting their B.A.'s or B.S.'s, U.S. students are admitted by the Italian university authorities to the second or third year of a degree course according to the corresponding studies completed in the U. S. A. and those to be carried out in Italy. A regular student, one who carries a full academic program leading to a degree (*corsi di laurea*), must follow the same program as an Italian student. This program is prescribed by law and is the same for any one course of study in each of the universities. Auditors, or special students, who take only a few courses (*corsi singoli*) must also have completed two years of college work in the United States. In either case American students must apply through the nearest Italian Consulate. Several documents must be submitted and the Consulate will process these free of charge and forward them to the chosen Italian university. Instruction at all universities in Italy is in Italian and students will be given a language test in the form of an interview with the faculty dean or with a professor, usually at the beginning of the academic year. Italian universities, including the special courses for foreigners, have openings for as many as 2,500 American students.

FOR FURTHER INFORMATION ... Write to the Italian Government Information Center, 686 Park Avenue, New York, N. Y. 10021.

For travel particulars and documentation, write to Educational Department, NHE, Pan American Airways, Pan Am Building, New York, N. Y. 10017.

HOW TO GET THERE ... By Pan American Jet Clipper, only 8 hours direct from New York; service also via Paris, or via Lisbon, Barcelona and Nice. By ship to Venice, Naples or Genoa, 8 to 14 days.

UNIVERSITY OF BARI

On the eastern coast of southern Italy looking out at the blue waters of the Adriatic Sea from a promenade five and a half miles long stands the town of Bari, important commercial center and busy port for trade between East and West. Bari can trace its history back to 1500 B.C. and today there is the "Old Town" distinct from the "New Town" as a reminder of ancient glory. Streets lined with palm trees and greenery are a hint of the verdant gardens found throughout the city. Every year from the end of April until the beginning of June the traditional "Maggio di Bari" festival is held; a procession marches through the streets in historical costumes and a musical program is offered. In September Bari is host to one of Italy's two greatest yearly exhibitions, the International Fair of the Levant, a trade show lasting two weeks. The University of Bari was founded in 1924 although its School of Economics and Commerce dates back to 1887. Modern buildings, laboratories, restaurants, residences and a hospital make up a university city that is one of the largest and finest in Italy.

SIZE ... About 20,000 students attend the University.

CALENDAR ... Classes are held from the beginning of November to late May. There are no terms or semesters.

University of Bari

COURSES OF STUDY ... The University of Bari has Faculties of Agriculture, Economics and Commerce including a Department of Statistics, Law, Pharmacy, Engineering, Letters and Philosophy, Medicine and Surgery, Mathematics, Physics and Natural Sciences, and in addition, certain postgraduate and specialization courses and schools.

TUITION ... Registration fees are about $8, enrollment fee about $30, examination fees about $12. In addition there may be other fees for certain courses of study. Students who achieve exceptionally high marks may have their fees reduced.

ADMISSION REQUIREMENTS ... See the Admission Requirements section in the opening summary on Italy.

LANGUAGE OF INSTRUCTION ... Italian.

ACCOMMODATIONS ... Many Italian students live in pensions, where a single room costs about $1.50 to $2 a day; a double room costs from about $3 to about $3.50 a day; full board costs from about $4 to about $5 per day. Meals at the student restaurant cost about 50 cents each. The Provincial Tourist Organization (Ente Provinciale Turismo) in Bari will help foreign students find lodgings.

AVERAGE COSTS ... Fees add up to about $100 per year. Room and board about $75 per month, up.

STUDENT LIFE ... The festivals in Bari are important musts for newcomers to see; students organize their own groups to attend these festivities. Bari has a stadium which seats 40,000 persons and many student contests and events are held there. Bathing beaches, swimming, skin diving, boating and various water sports are popular with the university set. Volleyball and basketball are played indoors. Visits to the port, which is built on a large artificial dam, provide students a look at the international character of the city's trading.

UNIVERSITY OF BOLOGNA

Because Bologna presents a panorama of arcaded streets, serrated towers from medieval times, Gothic and Baroque, Romanesque and Renaissance churches, ancient palaces, uncommon museums, its atmosphere is individual among cities. The University of Bologna is the oldest of Europe, the University of Jurists dating from 1088, when it was the world's most famous center for the study of law. By the twelfth century it counted among its circle many foreign students. The University is now housed in several old palaces on the Via Zamboni, having moved there from the sixteenth-century Archiginnasio Palace, which is now the Public Library (worthy of a visit to see the coats of arms which decorate the rooms). The Civic Museum, Art Gallery, and Margherita and Montagnola Gardens invite notice. In March, a National Showing of Shoe Fashions is held; in May, an International Food Fair and a Samples Fair. The stadium in Bologna is one of the largest in Italy and offers athletic contests the year round.

SIZE ... During the regular academic year there are about 17,000 students, of whom 600 are from foreign countries.

CALENDAR ... The academic year runs from the first of November to the end of October; classes are held from November to June. There are no terms or semesters, but an examination session is held in June–July and again in October–November. A summer session for foreign students is held during August at Rimini.

COURSES OF STUDY ... The University of Bologna has Faculties of Law, Economics and Commerce with a Department of Statistics, Letters and Philosophy, Medicine and Surgery, Mathematics, Physics and Natural Sciences, Engineering, Pharmacy, Industrial Chemistry, Agriculture, Veterinary Medicine, and also postgraduate and specialization schools and courses.

University of Bologna

SUMMER COURSES ... During August, the University of Bologna offers a summer course of Italian language and culture for foreigners at Rimini on the Adriatic Sea. Courses in the Italian language, literature, culture, history and art are offered.

TUITION ... Registration fees are about $8, enrollment about $30, examination fees about $12. Certain courses may cost slightly more. Students who achieve exceptionally high marks may have their fees reduced somewhat.

For the summer course, enrollment fee is $27, and room and board are available to the earliest applicants for $100 for the period at the student residence, Casa Alberto Morvelli, via Cairoli 69, Rimini.

ADMISSION REQUIREMENTS ... A secondary school certificate (high school diploma) is acceptable for special courses for foreign students of the summer session. See also the Admission Requirements section in the opening summary on Italy.

LANGUAGE OF INSTRUCTION ... Italian.

ACCOMMODATIONS ... Boardinghouses, where many Italian students live, charge from about $2.50 to about $5 per day for room and board. A room only in the student hostel, *Casa dello Studente,* costs about $15 per month; meals at the student canteen cost about 50 cents each. Table d'hôte meals may be available in some restaurants for about $1. The Ente Provinciale Turismo in Bologna will assist students in finding accommodations.

AVERAGE COSTS ... Fees about $100 per academic year. Room and board from about $80 per month.

STUDENT LIFE ... Twentieth-century students carry on traditions nearly a thousand years old at the University of Bologna with discussions and debates outside the classrooms. In the nineteenth century the poet Carducci was for more than forty years Professor of Italian Literature at Bologna and he inspired long argumentations. Physical as well as mental exercise is popular; students have swimming pools, gymnasiums, and tennis courts. From November to February, the City Theater offers operas. Students organize trips to nearby towns and cities of interest. Within Bologna there are museums, monuments, palaces and churches to be visited. The festivals show students a part of Italy that is unforgettable.

UNIVERSITY OF CAGLIARI

Cagliari is the principal town of the island of Sardinia, so called by the ancients who inhabited it from its supposed shape of a sandal. On either side of Cagliari stands a large salt lagoon, behind it a mountain, before it the Mediterranean Sea. A Roman amphitheater is found not far from the center of the city; there is a museum, also a cathedral, but perhaps most attractive are the groves of orange, lemon and olive trees and the forests here and there about the island. Around Cagliari and along the coast palm trees grow at random. The University of Cagliari was founded in 1606.

SIZE ... About 4,000 students, including 32 from foreign countries.

CALENDAR ... The academic year runs from the first of November to the end of October. Classes are held from November to June. Examinations are given in the summer and again in the fall.

COURSES OF STUDY ... The University of Cagliari has a Faculty of Law, Faculty of Economics and Commerce, Faculty of Letters and Philosophy, Faculty of Medicine and Surgery, Faculty of Education, Faculty of Mathematics, Natural, Physical and Chemical Sciences, Faculty of Engineering, Faculty of Pharmacy, and certain postgraduate and specialization schools and courses.

TUITION ... Registration fees are about $8, enrollment about $30, examination fees about $12. Some courses cost an additional amount.

ADMISSION REQUIREMENTS ... See the Admission Requirements section in the opening summary on Italy.

LANGUAGE OF INSTRUCTION ... Italian.

ACCOMMODATIONS ... Average prices for room and board at boardinghouses in Cagliari are about $3.50 to $5 per day for full board; 90 cents to about $2.50 for a single room, or $2 to $2.30 for a double room, each per day. The *Mensa Universitaria* or students' restaurant serves meals for about 50 cents each. Many Italian students live with families, too, or in inexpensive hotels. The Ente Provinciale Turismo, tourist office, will assist students in finding accommodations.

AVERAGE COSTS ... Fees about $100 per academic year. Room and board about $75 per month and up.

STUDENT LIFE ... Students at the University of Cagliari have all the advantages of living in a seaport city; there are beaches, swimming, skin diving. But there are inland sports, too, and the hilly countryside of Sardinia provides many sights as destinations of walks or bicycle rides. Besides sight-seeing and debating—which consume much time on the schedule of many students—there is the Festival of St. Eficio, May 1st to 4th, when thousands of residents dress up in Sardinian costume, a gay and colorful celebration that should not be missed.

UNIVERSITY OF CAMERINO

A pleasant city in the Marches, Camerino has a very interesting collection of paintings.

SIZE ... About 1,000 students.

CALENDAR ... The academic year runs from the beginning of November to the end of October. Classes are held from November to the end of May and examinations follow.

COURSES OF STUDY ... The University has a Faculty of Law, Faculty of Mathematical and Natural Sciences and a Faculty of Pharmacy.

TUITION ... Fees are about $8 for registration, about $30 for enrollment and about $12 for examinations.

ADMISSION REQUIREMENTS ... See the Admission Requirements section in the opening summary on Italy.

LANGUAGE OF INSTRUCTION ... Italian.

ACCOMMODATIONS ... Many Italian students live in pensions where a single room costs about 90 cents to $1.50 a day; a double room costs about $2; full board costs about $2.50. Meals at the student restaurant cost about 50 cents each.

AVERAGE COSTS ... Fees add up to about $100 per year. Room and board about $75 per month and up.

UNIVERSITY OF CATANIA

The second most important city of the island of Sicily is Catania. Although it has been destroyed several times by the lava of Mount Etna or by earthquakes, it has today a population of nearly 350,000 inhabitants. Catania is the home of the eminent writer, Giovanni Verga, and of the Italian composer Bellini. The gardens named after Bellini are among the most restful spots of the city. Nearby is the Bellini Museum. Throughout the city there will be monuments, buildings, churches of interest, but one unusual sight to see is the Elephant Fountain, an elephant carved of lava with an ancient Egyptian obelisk on his back. The Via Etna and the Via Crociferi are streets which will provide a pleasant walk. The University Library is an attraction in itself; it is open to the public as well as to students of the University. The

University of Catania

University of Catania was founded in 1434 and is the oldest university in Sicily.

SIZE ... About 8,500 students attend the University; this number includes about 25 students from foreign countries.

CALENDAR ... The academic year opens in November; classes continue until May and are followed by examinations. The academic year ends in October.

COURSES OF STUDY AND FEES ... The University has a Faculty of Law, Faculty of Economics and Commerce, Faculty of Letters and Philosophy, Faculty of Medicine and Surgery, Faculty of Mathematics, Physics and Natural Sciences, Faculty of Pharmacy, Faculty of Engineering (2-year preparatory course), Faculty of Agriculture, and certain postgraduate and specialization schools and courses.

TUITION ... Registration fees are about $8, enrollment about $30 and examination fees about $12. Some courses may have additional charges.

ADMISSION REQUIREMENTS ... See the Admission Requirements section in the opening summary on Italy.

LANGUAGE OF INSTRUCTION ... Italian.

ACCOMMODATIONS ... Many Italian students live with their own families, with the families of relatives, or with other Italian families. Most foreign students find a room with a family or in a boardinghouse, where average prices range from about $1.30 to $2 a day for a single room, $2 to $3 a day for a double room, and about $3.50 to $5.50 per day for full board. The tourist organization in the city will help students find accommodations.

Students can also find accommodations at the *Casa dello Studente* (Student House), where they can obtain a single room, double room or room with three beds, for 15, 12 and 10 dollars, respectively, per month. The *Casa* operates an excellent dining room, where the students can have meals at low prices (50 cents per meal). Students living at the *Casa* have the benefit of recreational and cultural activities free of charge, such as lectures, practice in foreign languages, concerts, recitals, dances, etc.

AVERAGE COSTS ... Fees about $100 per academic year. Room and board about $80 and up per month.

STUDENT LIFE ... Broad stretches of sandy beaches provide a natural swimming place in Catania. With a motor scooter a student can ride through country roads where olive trees grow on either side—or lemons or oranges. There are hills to climb in summer or ski down in winter. Mount Etna provides a variety of winter resorts. A foreign student will find a hospitable welcome when he goes to Catania.

The American N.A.F. (Naval Air Force) and the U.S.I.S. (United States Information Service) are located at Catania, with a colony of U.S. personnel and their families.

UNIVERSITY OF FERRARA

The range of Renaissance palaces alone would make Ferrara a tourist attraction. But added to these, and there are at least four important ones, are the Este Castle, the Cathedral, monasteries, an abbey, City Art Gallery, Archaeological Museum, and the Civic Museum. Students will find the City Library, which frequently displays illuminated manuscripts and other rarities for bibliophiles, of special interest. It is open to students of the University. The countryside nearby is agricultural and very prosperous; a bicycle ride is well worth while to see some of Ferrara's surroundings. The University of Ferrara was founded in 1391 as a private university; it became a national university in 1942.

SIZE ... About 3,000 students attend the University.

CALENDAR ... The academic year runs from the first of November to the end of October. Classes end in May and examinations follow.

COURSES OF STUDY ... The University has a Faculty of Law, Faculty of Medicine and Surgery, Faculty of Pharmacy, Faculty of Mathematical, Physical and Natural Sciences, and postgraduate and specialization schools and courses.

TUITION ... Registration fees are about $8, enrollment fee about $30, examination fees about $12.

ADMISSION REQUIREMENTS ... See the Admission Requirements section in the opening summary on Italy.

University of Ferrara

LANGUAGE OF INSTRUCTION ... Italian.

ACCOMMODATIONS ... The student hostel is open throughout the year with the exception of August and September. Single rooms cost about $14 per month, double rooms about $9 per month, $6.50 per month for a room with three beds. Meals cost about 50 cents each. Hotel prices average about $2 to $4.50 per day for a double room; about $3.50 to $4.50 per day for full board. Meals are available at some restaurants for about $1. The tourist organization in the city will help foreign students find lodgings.

AVERAGE COSTS ... Fees about $100 per academic year. Room and board about $75 and up per month.

STUDENT LIFE ... Foreign students in Ferrara are treated with much friendliness and they will soon learn the favorite *caffès* and gathering places of students. There are sometimes excursions to other Italian cities; visitors are always welcome on such occasions. Ask an Italian student to tell the story of the Palazzina della Principessa Marfisa or Lodovico Ariosto, whose home is in Ferrara.

UNIVERSITY OF FLORENCE (INCLUDING THE CENTER OF CULTURE FOR FOREIGN STUDENTS)

Tuscany has been called the heart of Italy, and Florence is the heart of Tuscany. Its treasures of art objects and buildings make it the cultural rival of Rome. The Arno River divides the city, which is situated on softly rolling hills. The Piazza del Duomo, with the Cathedral and the Baptistery, is the center of the city. The Uffizi Gallery has one of the richest collections of paintings in the entire world and has been called the most important gallery of Italy. Pitti Palace Gallery offers another superb collection of art work. The majestic Palazzo Vecchio and the Ponte Vecchio, the oldest bridge in Florence, with jewelers' shops lining either side, are picturesque spots to see. Florence is a city whose history rings with the names of Michelangelo and Leonardo da Vinci, the Medicis, with art and beauty. The University of Florence was founded in 1321 by the Florentine Republic; its forerunner was the Studio Fiorentino.

SIZE ... More than 19,000 students attend the University of Florence, including 200 foreign students.

CALENDAR ... The Center of Culture for Foreign Students of the University of Florence holds four courses during the year as follows: winter courses, mid-November to early February; spring courses, early March to the end of May; summer courses, July and August; and autumn courses, mid-September to

University of Florence

early November. The University of Florence holds classes from November 1 until June, with the formal academic year running from November 1 until the following October 31. Examinations are given during June and July and again during October and November. A summer session is held from July until the end of October.

COURSES OF STUDY ... The Center of Culture for Foreign Students offers preparatory, intermediate and advanced courses in the Italian language; courses in Italian Culture Before 1870, including History and Structure of the Italian Language, Literature, History of Art, Lessons in the Main Art Centers of Tuscany and bordering regions; Lessons in Museums and Famous Buildings of Florence; Etruscan Civilization, History of Music, Political History; courses in Present Day Italy, including Literature, Fine Arts, Music, Politics and the Italian Society After 1870; and other special courses including Dante and the Civilization of the Middle Ages; Florentine Culture from Humanism to Galileo; and a Commercial Correspondence Course.

Regular Courses: The University of Florence has Faculties of Law, Political Science, Economics and Commerce, including a Department of Statistics, Letters and Philosophy, Medicine and Surgery, Mathematics, Physics and Natural Sciences, including a preliminary Engineering Course, Pharmacy, Architecture, Agriculture and Special Schools for Archivists and Paleographers.

SUMMER COURSES ... Italian language at all levels, literature, history, art, music, Dante, and Florentine culture.

TUITION ... At the Center of Culture for Foreign Students fees are approximately $38.50 for the winter and spring courses and about $31 for the summer and autumn courses. Students who wish to attend two language courses must pay about $10 additional during the winter and spring courses, and about $6.50 additional during the summer and autumn courses. A 20 per cent reduction is made in the fees charged to a student who enrolls in two consecutive courses (for example, winter, then spring). Certain certificates may cost about $1.50 or $2.

ADMISSION REQUIREMENTS ... The Center of Culture for Foreign Students does not require a diploma or certificate for admission. See also the Admission Requirements section in the opening summary on Italy.

LANGUAGE OF INSTRUCTION ... Italian is the language of instruction in *all* courses.

ACCOMMODATIONS ... Full board and room in a pension in Florence cost from about $3 and up per day. Meals at the student restaurant are 50 cents each. Many students take a room with an Italian family and eat in the student restaurants or small eating places. The Villa Fabricotti, a beautiful old Italian building, has been turned into an international house for students, known as the Casa Internazionale degli Universitari. Full board and room at the Villa costs about $2.50 daily. Board and room with a private family may cost about $150 per month. The Secretary of the Centro di Cultura per Stranieri has a list of pensions and families who offer accommodations to students.

AVERAGE COSTS ... Fees at the Center of Culture for Foreign Students, about $108 for three terms. Room and board about $100 to $150 per month.

STUDENT LIFE ... The wealth of Florence, historically and artistically, provides a constant temptation to inquiring students. The life of a student is not complete until he has participated in some of the spectacular events in the life of Florence. On Easter Sunday the "Explosion of the Cart" festival recalls the victorious return of the first Crusaders; in May and June the music festival is held, also a traditional football match; in January and July fashion shows are held; winter opera begins in December and lasts into February. There are Sunday football matches, golf, horse racing, car races, cycling, boating, skiing in winter, swimming and water sports in summer, fencing. Italian students are friendly and happy to introduce their fellow students from abroad to the customs of Tuscany and Italy.

UNIVERSITY OF GENOA

The name of Christopher Columbus is inseparable from the history of Genoa, and today "Christopher Columbus Celebrations" are held in Genoa from the 2nd to the 12th of October, Columbus' birthday, to commemorate the famous sea captain. The port of Genoa is the liveliest part of the city, and understandably, for it is Italy's chief port on the Mediterranean Sea. The city combines modern buildings with remnants of the Middle Ages, twentieth-century commerce with historic art treasures. It is also the gateway to the Italian Riviera and attracts tourists from all directions. The University of Genoa was founded in 1243.

SIZE ... About 10,000 students including 100 foreign students.

CALENDAR ... The academic year runs from the first of November to the end of October. Classes end in June and examinations are given in the summer and again in the fall. The University offers International Courses of Italian Studies from the middle of August to mid-September.

COURSES OF STUDY ... The University of Genoa has Faculties of Law, Economics and Commerce, Letters and Philosophy, Medicine and Surgery, Mathematics, Physics and Natural Sciences, Pharmacy, Education and Engineering, and also postgraduate and specialization schools and courses.

Special Courses: The International Courses of Italian Studies are held at Santa Margherita Ligure, a short distance south of Genoa on the Riviera di Levante. Courses are given in the Italian language, literature, art, folklore, music, philosophy, sciences, institutions and life, the cinema and the theater.

TUITION ... For the regular courses of study fees are about $8 for registration, about $30 for enrollment, about $12 for examinations.

For the International Courses of Italian Studies, enrollment for either of the 4-week courses is $20.

University of Genoa

ADMISSION REQUIREMENTS ... A secondary school certificate (high school diploma) is acceptable for admission to the International Courses of Italian Studies.

See also the Admission Requirements section in the opening summary on Italy.

LANGUAGE OF INSTRUCTION ... Italian. The International Courses of Italian Studies conducts its classes in Italian. However, these classes are divided according to native languages of the students and there are sections for beginners as well as more advanced students.

ACCOMMODATIONS ... Many students live in boarding-houses, where average prices are about $1.60 to $3 per day for a single room, $3 to $4.50 per day for a double room, full board from $3 to $5 per day. Meals at the student restaurant are about 50 cents each. Some rooms with private families are available for around $30 per month. Students may obtain a list of families, boardinghouses, and modestly priced hotels from the tourist office. In Santa Margherita Ligure a room with a private family costs about $1.50 a day; for three meals a day at a hotel the cost is about $3. A committee will help students locate appropriate lodgings.

AVERAGE COSTS ... Fees for special courses about $20 per session. Fees for regular courses about $100 for the academic year. Room and board about $100 per month.

STUDENT LIFE ... Sight-seeing excursions are arranged by student groups. Outdoor sports popular with students include swimming, tennis, golf, rowing, sailing, and cycling. There are debates, concerts, theater performances and, always, students eager for conversation. Art galleries, churches and historic places have rich treasures to show visitors; a student card entitles the holder to free admission to many of these institutions. One of the most popular activities of students is walking along Genoa's illustrious waterfront. A Genoese will willingly take along a fellow foreign student for this excursion.

INTERNATIONAL CENTER OF MEDITERRANEAN CULTURE, PONZA

The Island of Ponza lies off the coast of Italy in the Tyrrhenian Sea, west of Naples. The Interpreters' Colleges of Rome, Milan, Florence, and Naples have organized the International Center of Mediterranean Culture and have chosen the small island of Ponza as the proper setting for the teaching of courses in Italian language and culture.

SIZE ... The number of students varies from year to year, but no student is turned away from the summer courses.

CALENDAR ... Classes are held in July, August and September. Each period of work lasts two weeks and students may enter at the beginning of any 2-week period.

COURSES OF STUDY ... Courses in the Italian language are offered with practical exercises including study of grammar, conversation, phonetics, and reading. Lectures are given on Literature, History of Art, Civil and Political History of Italy, with special reference to the Mediterranean position; a course on the Italian Film from 1945 On is also offered. Many courses are illustrated with short films. A section also covers the History of Music, and these classes are assisted by the playing of records.

TUITION ... The fee for each 15-day period of language lectures is $6.50; the examination fee for a diploma or a certificate is 80 cents.

ADMISSION REQUIREMENTS ... There are no academic admission requirements. Students are divided into grades for the language courses, depending on their knowledge of the Italian language.

LANGUAGE OF INSTRUCTION ... Italian.

ACCOMMODATIONS ... The tourist office on the Island of Ponza will assist students to find accommodations; costs will not exceed prices on the mainland.

STUDENT LIFE ... Certain programs of entertainment are offered in the evenings during the summer school session. Opera is offered twice weekly, on Tuesdays and Fridays, via recordings at the school.

UNIVERSITY OF LECCE

A beautiful town in Apulia, Lecce is particularly known for its baroque buildings. It is, in fact, called the "Baroque Florence" or the "Athens of the Apulia."

SIZE ... About 900 students.

CALENDAR ... The academic year runs from the beginning of November to the end of October; classes end in May and examinations follow.

COURSES OF STUDY ... The University of Lecce has a Faculty of Law.

TUITION ... Fees are about $8 for registration, about $30 for enrollment, about $12 for examinations.

ADMISSION REQUIREMENTS ... See the Admission Requirements section in the opening summary on Italy.

ACCOMMODATIONS ... A single room in a boarding-house may cost from 30 cents to $2, a double room from $2 to $3.50; full board from $4 to $6. A room in a private house may be rented for approximately $25 a month.

UNIVERSITY OF MACERATA

Macerata, a modern city in the Marches, has an interesting collection of paintings and the richest, most important library of the region.

SIZE ... About 600 students.

CALENDAR ... The academic year runs from the beginning of November to the end of October; classes end in May and examinations follow.

COURSES OF STUDY ... The University has a Faculty of Law.

TUITION ... Fees are about $8 for registration, about $30 for enrollment, about $12 for examinations.

ADMISSION REQUIREMENTS ... See the Admission Requirements section in the opening summary on Italy.

ACCOMMODATIONS ... Average prices for room and board at boardinghouses in Macerata range from $1 to $1.30 per day for a single room, from $1.50 to $2.50 a day for a double room; full board from $2.20 to $2.50 a day. The *Mensa Universitaria,* or students' canteen, serves meals for about 50 cents each. The Ente Provinciale del Turismo, tourist office, will assist students in finding accommodations.

AVERAGE COSTS ... Fees are about $100 per academic year. Room and board about $75 and up per month.

UNIVERSITY OF MESSINA

Messina has been called "The Gate of Sicily" because of its location on the straits between the island and the mainland. Its port lies along the straits in a crescent on the lower fringes of the Peloritani Mountains. The city combines the greenery of its mountains with blue waters and white sands to attract visitors to its fine panorama. There are museums, cathedrals, and ruins, too, but these take a less important place than the natural beauty of this northeastern point of Sicily. Taormina, just south of Messina on the eastern coast of Sicily, is becoming more and more important as a beach resort; there are other historic and scenic spots near "The Gate of Sicily." The University of Messina was founded in 1548.

SIZE ... About 10,000 students, including 200 foreign students.

CALENDAR ... The academic year runs from the first of November to the end of October; classes end in May and examinations follow. The year is not divided into terms or semesters.

COURSES OF STUDY ... The University has a Faculty of Law, Faculty of Economics and Commerce, Faculty of Letters and Philosophy, Faculty of Medicine and Surgery, Faculty of Mathematics, Physics and Natural Sciences, Faculty of Pharmacy, Faculty of Education, Faculty of Engineering, Faculty of Veterinary Medicine, and postgraduate and specialization schools and courses.

University of Messina

University of Milan

TUITION ... Registration fees are about $8, enrollment about $30, examination fees about $12. In addition there may be other fees for certain courses.

ADMISSION REQUIREMENTS ... See the Admission Requirements section in the opening summary on Italy.

LANGUAGE OF INSTRUCTION ... Italian.

ACCOMMODATIONS ... Italian students live in the student hostel, in boardinghouses, or in inexpensive hotels if they cannot find an Italian family to live with. The tourist organization keeps lists of available accommodations and assists students in settling themselves into lodgings. Meals are available at the student hostel's canteen; the cost is about 50 cents per meal. Some religious institutions operate boardinghouses for students; average cost per day for full board is about $2. Average hotel prices per day for a single room run from about $1.10 to about $2.50; for a double room about $2 to $3.50 per day; and for full board from $3.50 to $5.50 per day. The student hostel is open the year round except for August and September; because there are not enough rooms to accommodate all students, applications must be made early in order to secure a room.

AVERAGE COSTS ... Fees about $100 per academic year. Room and board about $100 per month and up.

STUDENT LIFE ... Messina is just a ferryboat ride from the mainland of Italy and students find the trip an inexpensive and cool activity for summer and fall or late spring days. Up and down the coast of Sicily from Messina are panoramic views for the energetic bicycler who takes the short ride out from the city. There are sandy beaches, nearby Taormina with its remains of a Greek theater, and the tree-lined promenade along the sea—all popular haunts of students. The Messina Fair, held from August 4 to 19, presents folklore, sports, and entertainment events, and a procession and carnival; go with an Italian student to have the most fun.

UNIVERSITY OF MILAN

Opera lovers should not fail to visit Milan during the winter season, so that they can attend performances at La Scala. However, during the entire year there are musical, artistic, theatrical and sports activities in this city, which is the heart of Lombardy and the center of national and international communications.

The Duomo (Cathedral) is considered one of the greatest and most complete monuments of Gothic architecture in Italy. It is in Milan that one finds the "Last Supper" by Leonardo da Vinci. The Brera Gallery, the Poldi-Pezzoli Museum and the Castello Sforzesco contain noteworthy art collections. The University is outstanding among the many important buildings in Milan and Italy. Libraries and many collections are available to the students enrolled with the University of Milan. Although established in 1924, with a varied and complete curriculum, it existed for almost a century before that with a Faculty of Letters and Modern Languages, under the name of the Scientific Academy of Letters; also with a Faculty of Agriculture, a Faculty of Veterinary Studies, a Faculty of Medicine, as well as a Clinic Institute for postgraduate work and advanced training.

SIZE ... About 6,000 students are registered, including 130 foreign students.

CALENDAR ... The academic year runs from the first of November to the end of October; classes end in June and examinations follow. During the period from the first week in July to the end of August, summer courses are given at Gargnano on Lake Garda.

COURSES OF STUDY ... The University of Milan has a Faculty of Jurisprudence; Letters and Philosophy and Modern Languages; Medicine and Surgery; Mathematical, Physical and Natural Sciences, with seven postgraduate courses; also in Industrial Chemistry, Physics, Mathematics and Biology, Agriculture and Veterinary Medicine, in addition to specialization courses.

SUMMER COURSES ... During July the University has an elementary course in the Italian language and culture at Gargnano on Lake Garda; during August there is a second course in the Italian language and culture, including contemporary Italian history, art, music and the theater.

TUITION ... The registration fee is about $8, enrollment fee about $30 and examination fees about $12. The fees can be reduced by students who have a high standing in their studies.

For summer courses, the fee for each course is $25. Expense for lodgings and meals amounts to about $3 a day.

ADMISSION REQUIREMENTS ... The summer courses are open to all students who have a secondary school diploma (high school). For admission to the University of Milan as a regular student or as an auditor, in addition to the requirements given in the Admission Requirements section in the opening summary on Italy, an American student must have a diploma equivalent (or comparable) to the *licenza de maturità classica o scientifica* (diploma or certificate for completion of classical or scientific studies), in accordance with the Italian regulations.

LANGUAGE OF INSTRUCTION ... Italian.

ACCOMMODATIONS ... Average prices for complete pension (board and room) vary from $4.50 to $5.50 per day. Many students live at home or in pensions. Others find a room with a family and take their meals in the student dining room, where the prices are about 50 cents a meal. There are also possibilities of finding accommodations with various religious institutions at the price of about $3 per day. In Milan the Ente Provinciale del Turismo (Provincial Tourism Association) assists students to find suitable accommodations.

AVERAGE COSTS ... Fees about $100 per academic year. Room and board from $100 and up.

STUDENT LIFE ... The Italian students who love the opera and classical music advise their young American colleagues how to obtain tickets for performances at La Scala, or for the concerts which are held during the months of October and November, before the opening of the opera season, which starts in December. The season at La Scala lasts until May. Milan also offers excellent theater and continual shows (exhibits, displays) of industrial art, the decorative arts and modern architecture. The students organize excursions, walks and picnics, and student cards frequently make it possible to obtain free admission to the museums, libraries and art galleries. Many sports events—outdoor games, automobile races, horseback riding, cycling and football games—take place in Milan. There are also excellent opportunities for enjoying golf and tennis.

UNIVERSITY OF MODENA

Industry and agriculture rival each other for first importance economically in Modena. Located about 23 miles from Bologna on the road from Milan, Modena's Ghirlandina Tower, stretching nearly 300 feet into the air, can be seen for some miles as one approaches the city. The Cathedral is one of the important examples of Romanesque architecture of the tenth to thirteenth centuries. There are fine collections of art in the museums and libraries of the city. Modena has a good football stadium and an important flying school. The University of Modena was founded in the twelfth century, according to some authorities in 1175, as a school of law.

SIZE ... About 3,000 students, including 140 foreign students.

CALENDAR ... The academic year begins in November and ends the following October. Classes are held from November until May and examinations follow. The year is not divided into semesters or terms.

COURSES OF STUDY ... The University of Modena has a Faculty of Law, Faculty of Medicine and Surgery, Faculty of Mathematics, Physics, and Natural Sciences with degree courses in Mathematics and Physics, Chemistry, Natural Sciences, Biological Sciences and Preliminary Engineering course and of Pharmacy. Under the Faculty of Medicine and Surgery, there are the following specialization schools: Pediatrics, Infectious and Tropical Diseases, Gynecological Clinics, Radiology and Physical Therapy, Neuro-psychiatric Clinics, General Oncology, Gastrointestinal Diseases, General Surgery, Legal Medicine, Optical, Blood Diseases and Anesthesiology.

ADMISSION REQUIREMENTS ... See the Admission Requirements section in the opening summary on Italy.

LANGUAGE OF INSTRUCTION ... Italian.

ACCOMMODATIONS ... Many Italian students live with their families while going to the University; some from out of town find a room with another family. Many foreign students take a room with an Italian family and eat their meals at the students' canteen, the *Mensa Universitaria*. Average cost of a meal is about 50 cents. Some restaurants in Modena serve table d'hôte meals for $1 and up. Hotel rooms may be obtained for about $1 to $2 a day for a single room; a double room costs about $2 to $3 per day; full board at a hotel costs from $3 to $4.50 per day. Boardinghouses and homes run by religious institutions also have accommodations for students at slightly lower prices than hotels. The tourist office will assist students to find suitable lodgings. There is a *Casa dello Studente* (Student House) run by the University of Modena. A University College is being built.

AVERAGE COSTS ... Fees about $100 per academic year. Room and board about $70 and up per month.

STUDENT LIFE ... For racing enthusiasts there are car-racing and horse-racing contests to watch at Modena. Students who are skiers will find good slopes in the Apennines, ski jumps at Piandelagotti, near Modena, and good ski lifts there, too. There are chair lifts at Lizzano also not far away. The University has tennis courts and swimming pools. Italian students will welcome foreign students on their excursions to points of interest outside the town; they will introduce newcomers to the student haunts within the town.

University of Modena

University of Naples

UNIVERSITY OF NAPLES

Naples will not disappoint those who picture it as a gay, colorful, busy city where Neapolitan song and laughter mix with the day's work. Its population is slightly above the million mark and industry and commerce, the port and tourism are important to the economy. Its most important art collections are those of the National Museum of Classical Antiquities, the Museum and Galleries of Capodimonte and the San Martino National Museum. The environs of Naples—Sorrento, Capri, Amalfi, Pompeii, Herculaneum—have been celebrated in music and history. Pompeii, one of the most remarkable spots of Italy, founded in the sixth century B.C. and covered by Mount Vesuvius' eruption in A.D. 79, today is almost restored to its state of more than 1800 years ago. A southern city, Naples boasts fine year-round weather. On either side of the University's Main Building palm trees grow, adding splendor to the grounds. The University of Naples was founded in 1224 by Frederick II of Sweden.

SIZE ... About 31,000 students, including 200 foreign students.

CALENDAR ... The academic year runs from the beginning of November to the end of October. Classes begin in November and end in May and examinations follow.

COURSES OF STUDY ... The University of Naples has a Faculty of Law, Faculty of Economics and Commerce, Faculty of Letters and Philosophy, Faculty of Medicine and Surgery, Faculty of Mathematics, Physics and Natural Sciences, Faculty of Engineering, Faculty of Pharmacy, Faculty of Architecture, Faculty of Veterinary Medicine, Faculty of Agriculture, and some postgraduate and specialization schools and courses. There are also about one hundred institutes and schools of the various faculties.

TUITION ... Registration fees are about $8, enrollment about $30 and examination fees about $12. In addition some special charges may be made for certain courses and in some institutes of schools.

ADMISSION REQUIREMENTS ... See the Admission Requirements section in the opening summary on Italy.

LANGUAGE OF INSTRUCTION ... Italian.

ACCOMMODATIONS ... The *Casa dello Studente,* or students' hostel, of the University of Naples welcomes foreign students. Rooms are limited, however, and application must be made early to secure a room. The cost is about $75 a month. Meals are 50 cents each at the student restaurant, the *Mensa Universitaria*. Many students take a room with a family and eat their meals at the student restaurant; or they live in boardinghouses. Average prices there are about $1.75 to $2.50 per day for a single room, $3 to $5 per day for a double room, and about $4 to $4.50 a day for full board. Some religious institutions maintain lodgings for students at modest prices. The provincial tourist office keeps lists of accommodations available to students.

AVERAGE COSTS ... Fees about $100 per academic year. Room and board about $100 and up per month.

STUDENT LIFE ... Neapolitan students have pride in their city and American students will find them willing to serve as "guides" on walking tours about the town. The University Student Card will allow free admission to many of the museums and monuments and students will find ample places to spend leisure hours. There are student-organized tours to the area surrounding Naples; boat trips to Capri, drives to Sorrento and Amalfi, and visits to Pompeii. Swimming, cycling, volleyball, ping pong, and basketball are among the sports popular with the students.

University of Padua

UNIVERSITY OF PADUA

The history of Padua (Padova) is in large part the history of the University of Padua; in ancient times the city and the University, which was founded in 1222, attracted merchants and scholars; today there is thriving commerce in the traffic-crowded streets. The University keeps pace with the times with a group of modern buildings to accommodate many foreign as well as Italian students. Titus Livy, the historian, is among the city's famous names. Of special interest to students is the *Caffè Pedrocchi,* an elegant nineteenth-century building, which has long been a stopping place for artists and writers passing through Padua. An outstanding building in the university group is the Liviano, a sixteenth-century structure with frescoes by Campagnola which houses the Faculty of Letters. A second modern building adjoins the older one. Besides the astronomer Galileo, who taught there, the philosopher and mathematician Pietro d'Abano and the anatomist Giambattista Morgagni were once instructors at the University of Padua.

SIZE . . . About 13,000 students.

CALENDAR . . . The academic year runs from the first of November to the end of October; classes are held from November to June. During July and August a summer session for foreign students is held at Bressanone.

COURSES OF STUDY . . . The University of Padua has Faculties of Law, Political Science, Letters and Philosophy, Medicine and Surgery, Mathematics, Physics and Natural Sciences, Pharmacy, Engineering, Agriculture, Education, and postgraduate and specialization schools and courses.

SUMMER COURSES . . . Besides language courses designed for beginners as well as for advanced students, courses in Italian Culture are offered at Bressanone.

TUITION . . . Fees are about $8 for registration, $30 for enrollment and $12 for examinations.

ADMISSION REQUIREMENTS . . . A secondary school certificate (high school diploma) is acceptable for summer courses. See also the Admission Requirements section in the opening summary on Italy.

LANGUAGE OF INSTRUCTION . . . Italian.

ACCOMMODATIONS . . . Some rooms may be available to foreign students who apply early at the various student hostels. Single rooms are about $13.50 to $17.50 per month; double rooms may cost about $8.50 to $11.50 per month. At the *Mensa Universitaria* meals are about 50 cents each. Some restaurants offer full meals from $1 up. Average hotel prices are about $1.50 to $3 per day plus service charge for a single room; a double room is about $3 to $4.50 per day plus service charges. Full board at a hotel costs about $4.50 to $6.50 per day. Religious institutions also offer accommodations with prices ranging from $2 to $2.50 per day for full board. The Ente Provinciale Turismo will help students find lodgings from its list of boardinghouses, hotels and private homes.

AVERAGE COSTS . . . Fees about $100 per academic year. Room and board about $65 up per month.

STUDENT LIFE . . . Padua is on the road to Venice in gently hilly country that attracted Byron and Shelley and today attracts students as well as poets. A bicycle ride will take one to scenic spots not far from the town. Shopping in the arcades along the streets or walking in Padua's famous Botanical Gardens will provide relaxation. The Gardens were begun in 1545 and are considered the oldest in Europe. There is the Fair of St. Anthony of Padua which is a "must see," the first two weeks of June. Students organize excursions to the museums, galleries, and historic spots and to nearby Venice.

UNIVERSITY OF PALERMO

Palermo, the capital of Sicily, has been ruled during its long history by Carthaginians, Romans, Byzantine Emperors, Arabs, Normans, Bourbons and Italians. Today traces of art and history from every period are blended in the architecture and monuments of the city. Combined with the natural beauty of the setting in a cloister of mountains along the northern coast of Sicily, these attractions lure tourists from November to the end of May—in fact, the year round. The side streets with the *vucciria*—the market—are another picturesque bit of the city and a striking contrast to the modern tall buildings found along the main streets. Only a few miles outside the city are fine sandy beaches, fishing villages, and an ancient monastery, with scenic drives in between these spots. There are several youth hostels in Sicily including a very popular one at Sferracavallo, only a bicycle ride from Palermo. The Royal Academy, the forerunner of the University of Palermo, was founded in 1776; it became a university in September 1805.

SIZE . . . 13,000, including 200 foreign students.

CALENDAR . . . The academic year runs from the beginning of November to the end of October; classes begin in November and end in May. The year is not divided into terms or semesters. Examinations are given at the end of the period of classes and again in October.

COURSES OF STUDY . . . The University has a Faculty of Law, Faculty of Economics and Commerce, including a Department of Statistics, Faculty of Letters and Philosophy, Faculty of Medicine and Surgery, Faculty of Mathematics, Physics, and Natural Sciences, Faculty of Pharmacy, Faculty of Engineering, Faculty of Agriculture, Faculty of Architecture, Faculty of Education, and also postgraduate and specialization schools and courses.

ADMISSION REQUIREMENTS . . . See the Admission Requirements section in the opening summary on Italy.

LANGUAGE OF INSTRUCTION . . . Italian.

ACCOMMODATIONS . . . Many students live in boardinghouses, small hotels, or with Italian families. Average costs at a boardinghouse are about $1.25 to $2.50 a day for a single room, $2 to $4 a day for a double room, and $3 to $6.20 per day for full board. At boardinghouses maintained by religious groups the average costs are about $1.95 to about $2.90 for full board and room per day, and about $1.30 to $2.50 per day for bed, breakfast and one meal per day. A room only with an Italian family costs about $50 to $75 per month. The Ente Provinciale Turismo in Palermo will assist students to find suitable lodgings.

AVERAGE COSTS . . . Fees about $100 per academic year. Room and board about $70 and up per month.

STUDENT LIFE . . . Besides sun and sea bathing, which is almost year-round activity in Palermo, students enjoy cycling, camping, and skiing. It is possible to swim outdoors and ski all in the same day, in the environs of Palermo. The opera season lasts

University of Palermo

from January to May. At Piana degli Albanesi, near Palermo, Sicilians don colorful costumes for the celebration of the Epiphany according to the Greek tradition every January. Late in May and early in June the Mediterranean Fair is held in Palermo; in July the traditional feast of Saint Rosalia, "Il Festino," is celebrated; October–November is the concert season at the Massimo Theater. Hospitality is traditional with Sicilians and university students are well versed in the art of making foreign students feel at home. Trips to points of interest are planned by and for students and the Sicilians know how to take good advantage of sight-seeing hours.

UNIVERSITY OF PARMA

Parma has been a mecca for Italian music students and it is famous not only as the home of Verdi and Arturo Toscanini, but also for its Conservatory and for its Royal Theater, or *Teatro Regio,* the opera house where opera performances are given in December and January. Besides the Cathedral, the Baptistery, and the National Museum of Antiquities, the Palatine Library is important for its fine exhibitions of manuscripts, incunabula, and nearly a half million volumes. Various churches and monuments also rank as tourist attractions. The University of Parma was founded in 1025 as a school of liberal arts; it can trace its origin back to the eighth century, however, when schools of medicine and of law were established in Parma.

SIZE ... Student enrollment about 8,000 with about 60 foreign students.

CALENDAR ... The academic year is from the beginning of November to the end of October; classes begin in November and end in May and examinations follow. There are no terms or semesters.

COURSES OF STUDY ... The University has a Faculty of Law; Faculty of Economics and Commerce; Faculty of Medicine and Surgery; Faculty of Mathematics, Physics and Natural Sciences, with a preliminary course in Engineering, and, courses in Biology, Geology, Chemistry, Physics, Mathematical Sciences, Mathematics and Physics, Natural Sciences; Faculty of Pharmacy; Faculty of Veterinary Medicine; and a Special School of Musical Palaeography. There are also postgraduate and specialization schools and courses.

TUITION ... Registration fees are about $8, enrollment fees about $30 and examination fees about $12. There are additional charges for some courses.

ADMISSION REQUIREMENTS ... See the Admission Requirements section in the opening summary on Italy.

LANGUAGE OF INSTRUCTION ... Italian.

ACCOMMODATIONS ... Although it is difficult for foreign students to obtain lodgings at the student hostel, the restaurant of the *Casa e Mensa dello Studente* (Student's Hostel and Canteen) is open to all students and serves meals for about 50 cents each. Many students eat their meals at the *Mensa* and take a room with an Italian family; the cost of a room alone may be $30 to $40 per month. Other students live in boardinghouses or in small hotels. A single room in a hotel may cost about $1.20 to $2.10 per day, a double room about $2 to about $3.70 per day; full board from $3 to $5.30 per day. Meals are available in some

University of Parma

restaurants for about $1. The local tourist office will assist students to find accommodations.

AVERAGE COSTS ... Fees about $100 per academic year. Room and board about $75 and up per month.

STUDENT LIFE ... Near Parma in the smaller town of Busseto are many spots made famous by Verdi, and music lovers will find a visit to them rewarding. The galleries, monuments, museums, and libraries of Parma also beckon; many of them are free to students who present their University card. But the less exacting haunts of students also offer relaxation, and Italian students will hospitably introduce newcomers to the *caffè* routine. There are tennis courts, and swimming pools for the athletics-minded.

UNIVERSITY OF PAVIA

One of the most interesting sections of Pavia lies around the University. Near its main building are the Collegio Ghislieri and the Collegio Borromeo, an imposing sixteenth-century building with frescoes on the ceilings. The Ghislieri, which was built in 1569, houses an important collection of art works. Several churches in the city are of artistic and architectural interest. About five miles from the city of Pavia is the Certosa, a famous Carthusian Monastery which today houses masterpieces of painting and sculpture and is itself a fine example of architecture. The University of Pavia was famous during the Middle Ages for its school of law; it ranked with the Universities of Bologna, Oxford, and Paris. The University of Pavia dates back to May 825; it became a university in April 1361.

SIZE ... About 5,500 students attend the University; this number includes about 170 students from foreign countries.

CALENDAR ... The academic year runs from the beginning of November to the end of October; classes begin in November, end in May and examinations follow. There are no terms or semesters.

COURSES OF STUDY ... The University of Pavia has a Faculty of Law, Faculty of Political Science, Faculty of Letters and Philosophy, Faculty of Medicine and Surgery, Faculty of Mathematics, Physics and Natural Sciences, Engineering and a Faculty of Pharmacy. There are also postgraduate and specialization schools and courses.

TUITION ... Registration fees are about $8, enrollment fees about $30 and examination fees about $12. Some additional charges may be made.

ADMISSION REQUIREMENTS ... See the Admission Requirements section in the opening summary on Italy.

LANGUAGE OF INSTRUCTION ... Italian.

ACCOMMODATIONS ... Several residence halls are maintained by the University of Pavia; three of them are for men and admission is by competition among honor students; those who live there follow special courses in addition to their regular courses at the University. These halls, Collegio Ghislieri, Collegio Borromeo, and Collegio Universitario Cairoli, are mainly for Italian students, but foreigners who are working for a degree from the University of Pavia may be eligible to compete for admission. Some students live in boardinghouses, take a room with a family, or stay in small hotels. Average cost per day for a single room in a hotel is about $1.20 to $1.90, for a double room about $2.20 to $3 per day, full board $3.20 to $4.50 per day. Other types of accommodations are available at varying prices; the tourist organization will assist students to find suitable rooms.

University of Pavia

AVERAGE COSTS ... Fees about $100 per academic year. Room and board about $70 and up per month.

STUDENT LIFE ... Long a center of culture and learning, the city of Pavia has given its people a traditional respect for students. Foreign students will feel themselves at home on a bicycle ride through the countryside, on walks in the city's parks, or in museums and on visits to monuments. A dozen spectator sports can be watched in Pavia or in nearby cities of Lombardy. Students organize their own excursions and welcome foreign students on these occasions.

ITALIAN UNIVERSITY FOR FOREIGNERS, PERUGIA*

Italy's only province not bordering on the sea is Umbria, a region of scenic valleys, historic Lake Trasimene where Hannibal fought the Romans, and countless mountains made more picturesque by the towns that were built on these hillsides in order to defend themselves in ancient times. Perugia, Umbria's capital, is but a few hours from Rome to the south, Florence to the north. Its most famous monuments are the Etruscan Arch or Gate, with Roman and Renaissance superstructure, and the Etruscan walls, the only remnants of Perugia's great importance under the Etruscans. That Perugia has always fostered the arts is evidenced by its several universities, art and music academies, museums, and musical and theater festivals. The National Gallery of Umbria, Pre-Historic, Etruscan, Roman, and Medieval museums have important collections. The University of Perugia was founded in 1200.

The Italian University for Foreigners was established in October 1925. It grew out of the Summer Courses in Advanced Cultural Studies started in 1921. Its home is the beautiful Palazzo Gallenga, built in 1758.

SIZE ... About 200 students; all are foreign students and generally there are representatives from every continent.

CALENDAR ... The academic year has three terms: from the beginning of April to the end of June; the first of July to the last of September; and the beginning of October to late December. Students may enter at the beginning of any session and enroll for one, two or three courses. Summer session is from July through September.

Advanced courses are given in the History of the Italian Language, Italian Pronunciation, Syntax, History of Italian Literature, the *Divine Comedy,* the History of Italian Philosophy, Italian History, Italian Geography, History of Italian Art, and History of Italian Music. Courses on Italy in the Fifteenth Century cover Literature, with lectures on Latin and Vernacular Poetry, Prose, Religious Prose, Epic Poems, Theater, Classical World, the Greeks and their Language, Family Life, and Entertainment and Dances; Political and Economic History, with lectures on Political Ideas, Ideas on Economics, and Political History; the History of the Church, with lectures on the Papacy; Philosophy, with lectures on Humanism; Humanism and Christianity, and Platonism; Educational and Scientific Thought with lectures on Education Ideas and Medicine; History of Art with lectures on Florentine Painting, Painting outside Florence, Architecture, and Sculpture; History with lectures on Secular Polyphony; and Sport with lectures on Knights and Tournaments. Courses in Contemporary Italy cover Contemporary Italian Prose Writers, Italian Poets of Today, Economic Development of Southern Italy, Italian Theater, Agricultural Changes in Southern Italy, and Contemporary Italian Cinema. Courses in Etruscology and Italic Antiquities cover Etruscology in the Last Forty Years, Etruscan History and Antiquities, Epigraphy and Language of the Etruscans, Etruscan Art, Italic Antiquities and Languages, and Etruscan-Italic Topography. Etruscology courses are offered in the summer only. The Center of Pedagogic Studies offers courses covering the general topic of the primary school as a school for self-expression with lectures on the Importance of Games in the Child's Self-Expression, The Idea of Creation and Self-Expression in John Dewey, Manual Work in the Primary School, Physical Education, Native Language and Self-Expression, the Teaching of Art, Teaching of Music, Self-Expression and Religious Development, and others.

* Not to be mistaken for The State University of Perugia.

Italian University for Foreigners

SUMMER COURSES ... Summer courses are given in Italian language and culture.

TUITION ... Registration fees are $10 a month; examination fees are $2.40 to $3.20; diploma fees range from $2.40 to $4.80.

ADMISSION REQUIREMENTS ... A secondary school certificate (high school diploma) is required for students who wish to take the advanced course examinations; no documents are required for other foreign students.

See also the Admission Requirements section in the opening summary on Italy.

LANGUAGE OF INSTRUCTION ... Italian is the language for all lectures and practical courses.

ACCOMMODATIONS ... Many students live with Italian families and take their meals at small restaurants or the student canteen; others live in boardinghouses. With a private family full board and a room may cost from about $2.50 to $4 a day. A room alone in a private home may cost from about $20 to about $30 per month. Boardinghouses may cost from about $2.50 to about $4 a day for room and full board. Full board and a room in a hotel range from about $4.50 to about $6.75 daily. A room and full board in a convent cost about $65 per month. Students who live in the convents must observe hours and generally be indoors by 9 p.m. The Secretary of the University will give students addresses of families, hotels, and pensions, upon request, after the student arrives in Perugia. The Tourist Office will also assist students to find accommodations.

AVERAGE COST ... Fees about $11 per month. Room and board about $70 and up per month.

STUDENT LIFE ... "Meeting downstairs at the coffee bar after class" is an old tradition at the Palazzo Gallenga, and though the bar changed its shape about five years ago from an intimate room with plush brocade walls to a spacious lounge (ping pong tables, jukebox), the elbow room has not muted the spirited conversations that go on, on and on. Properly called the Students' Club, it is a meeting place for students and professors from all corners of the earth—100 nations have been represented at the school in its 35 years. Dances, concerts, movies, discussions and debates take place there. Holidays celebrated by various nationalities are observed, and sometimes for these occasions students turn up in colorful costumes from their home countries. Americans, for instance, celebrate July 4th. Professors of the University receive students at certain times during the week, and any problems or questions may be discussed. There are regular student excursions to galleries, monuments, historic and artistic cities of the province of Umbria. Tennis courts, gymnasiums, swimming pools, and theaters are available for students. In the fall an international festival of religious music is held in Perugia. During the winter there is skiing on slopes only 35 miles away.

UNIVERSITY OF PISA

Besides the celebrated Leaning Tower identified throughout the world with the city, Pisa claims its share of palaces, old monuments, churches, and museums. The Arno River flows through the city and provides reason for several artistic bridges. Because of special adaptations of the Romanesque tradition of architecture, many buildings of the city are considered to be "Pisan style," a mode that spread to other provinces of Italy and Sardinia. Pisa's most famous son is perhaps Galileo Galilei, the astronomer. The University of Pisa was founded in 1343, although a document dated 1194 refers to law students in the city. The University has had among its students and teachers some of Italy's most famous poets and scholars.

SIZE ... About 6,500 students, including 80 foreign students.

CALENDAR ... The academic year runs from the beginning of November to the first of October; the year is not divided into terms or semesters, but a summer session for foreign students is held during July and August at Viareggio.

COURSES OF STUDY ... The University of Pisa has Faculties of Law, Economics and Commerce, Letters and Philosophy, Medicine and Surgery, Mathematics, Physics and Natural Sciences, Pharmacy, Engineering, Agriculture, and Veterinary Medicine, and also certain postgraduate and specialization courses and schools.

SUMMER COURSES ... Italian language and culture courses for foreign students are offered by the University of Pisa at Viareggio during July and August. Elementary, intermediate and advanced language classes are offered as well as courses in Italian literature, history of the language, comparative literature, history of art, history of music, Etruscology, history of philosophy, history of politics, and geography.

TUITION ... Fees for registration are about $8, for enrollment about $30 and for examinations about $12. Reduced fees are sometimes earned by students with very high marks.

For summer courses, fee for enrollment in a course is $16.60. Room and board are available in hotels for about $62 monthly.

ADMISSION REQUIREMENTS ... No academic qualification is needed for admission to the summer courses.

See also the Admission Requirements section in the opening summary on Italy.

LANGUAGE OF INSTRUCTION ... Italian.

ACCOMMODATIONS ... Many Italian students take a room with a private family but eat their meals at the student canteen: meals may cost from 50 cents to 60 cents each. Prices at *pensioni* (boardinghouses) range from about $3 to $5 per day for full board; about $1 to $2 for a single room; or $2 to $3 for a double room per day. Certain religious institutions also offer accommodations with prices varying from $1.30 to $1.60 per day for full board. The tourist office will assist students to find suitable accommodations.

AVERAGE COSTS ... Fees about $100 per academic year. Room and board about $75 per month.

STUDENT LIFE ... Not far from Pisa is a large motor-scooter manufacturing center; owning a scooter is the ambition of many an Italian student. Once he owns one, he will gladly introduce his fellow foreign student to the world of motor-scooter riding. Visiting students will find their Italian counterparts also willing to conduct them on walking tours of the city's famous section of monuments, or to pilot them through the celebrations at any of the summer festivals in Pisa. There are concerts and drama offerings the year round. Swimming, boating, fishing, tennis, skating, riding, and netball are popular with Pisa students.

UNIVERSITY OF ROME

The University of Rome was founded as Studium Urbis by Pope Boniface VIII in April 1303; however, it was combined with the Schola Palatina founded by Pope Onorio III in 1200. Studium Urbia was set up for impoverished and poor students from foreign countries, or from other parts of Italy, who came to Rome to study. For many years the University was located in the center of the city, called *Sapienza,* a word meaning "wisdom" in Italian. Undergraduates at the University are sometimes called *Sapientino.* In recent years the University has moved to Città Universitaria, University City, which is being developed near the Campo Verano section of Rome. Its buildings and equipment are all modern.

SIZE ... About 46,000 students attend the University of Rome, including 850 foreign students.

CALENDAR ... The academic year runs from the beginning of November to the end of October; classes are held from November to June. Examination periods are the summer and fall. The Società Dante Alighieri has a summer session in June and July.

COURSES OF STUDY ... The University of Rome has the following faculties: Faculty of Law, Faculty of Political Science, Faculty of Statistical, Demographic, and Actuarial Sciences, Faculty of Economics and Commerce, Faculty of Letters and Philosophy, Faculty of Education, Faculty of Medicine and Surgery, Faculty of Mathematics, Physics, and Natural Sciences, Faculty of Pharmacy, Faculty of Architecture, Faculty of Engineering and a School of Aeronautical Engineering, and postgraduate schools and specialization schools and courses.

SUMMER COURSES ... The Società Dante Alighieri of Rome sponsors courses in the Italian language and culture especially for foreigners during June and July. The courses are offered in Rome, and sessions last one month. Besides language, history of art and Italian literature courses are offered. The Società also offers courses in the Italian language from October to May, each course being of two months' duration. All the courses are given in Rome.

TUITION ... Registration fees are approximately $8, enrollment fees about $30, and examination fees about $12. Some faculties make additional charges.

For the summer courses registration fees are about $1.70, examination fees about $1.70, language courses about $14 and literature courses about $8.50.

ADMISSION REQUIREMENTS ... See the Admission Requirements section in the opening summary on Italy.

LANGUAGE OF INSTRUCTION ... Italian.

ACCOMMODATIONS ... Italian students live with families, in boardinghouses, small hotels, or in the student hostel. In summer one can obtain a room at the student hostel, the *Casa dello Studente,* and meals can be taken there also. The cost is about 50 cents per meal. Average boardinghouse prices are about $1.70 to $2.50 per day for a single room, about $2.50 to $4 per day for a double room, and about $4.50 to $6 per day for full board. At boardinghouses maintained by religious groups the cost

University of Pisa

University of Rome

is about $2.50 to $3.25 per day for full board. Most of these houses require students to keep hours. Students can stay at the Casa Internationali dello Studente, Viale Ministerio degli Affari Esteri 6; and at the Residenza Universitaria Internazionale, Via dello Sierra Nevada 10; average cost about $3.50 a day. A room with an Italian family may cost about $30 and up per month. The tourist office and some student groups will help students to find accommodations.

AVERAGE COSTS ... Fees about $100 per academic year. Room and board about $150 and up per month.

STUDENT LIFE ... The University student office has helpful information designed to help students make the best use of their time in seeing Rome. There is every kind of cultural, athletic, or social activity that a student could ask for. The University card will give students free admission to many of the museums and monuments about the city. The environs of Rome can be reached by bicycle or by energetic walkers.

UNIVERSITY OF SASSARI

Sassari, with a population of 76,000 inhabitants, is the second largest town on the island of Sardinia. The city is quite modern in aspect, although the Cathedral was built in the eighteenth century and has a baroque façade. The National Museum has a collection of archaeological works as well as paintings of note. The University occupies a historic palace which dates from 1562; other buildings, especially those of the Faculty of Medicine and Surgery, are modern and date from the 1930s. The University was founded in 1565 by the Jesuit fathers: it became a university in 1617 by a charter from Philip III.

SIZE ... About 2,000 students, including 10 foreign students.

CALENDAR ... The academic year runs from the beginning of November to the end of October; classes begin in November, end in May. There are no semesters or terms.

COURSES OF STUDY ... The University has the following faculties: Faculty of Law, Faculty of Medicine and Surgery, Faculty of Pharmacy, Faculty of Veterinary Medicine, Faculty of Agriculture, and Faculty of Mathematics, Physics, and Natural Sciences.

TUITION ... Registration fees are about $8, enrollment fees about $30 and examination fees about $12. In addition there may be charges for special courses.

ADMISSION REQUIREMENTS ... See the Admission Requirements section in the opening summary on Italy.

LANGUAGE OF INSTRUCTION ... Italian.

ACCOMMODATIONS ... Room and board are available at students' hostels and canteens, boardinghouses, dormitories maintained by religious institutions, with Italian families and in hotels. The costs vary considerably according to the accommodations, but in hotels the average daily cost for a single room is about $1 to $1.50, for a double room about $2 to $3. Some restaurants serve meals for about $1. The tourist office keeps lists of accommodations suitable for students.

AVERAGE COSTS ... Fees about $100 per academic year. Room and board about $75 and up per month.

STUDENT LIFE ... The island of Sardinia offers students places to hike, cycle, and swim. There are also excursions to the mainland, arranged by students. The University has a small and friendly student body, and foreign students will have an opportunity to see Sardinian life at close range.

UNIVERSITY OF SIENA

Siena, in the historic region of Tuscany, is a city on three hills; its thirteen towers and the special adaptation of Gothic architecture in its buildings make it singular among Italian towns for its look of the Middle Ages. Art galleries, palaces, churches of interest abound. Of special appeal is the *Palio delle Contrade,* a horse race which is preceded by a parade with marchers in fifteenth-century costume. The event takes place on July 2 and again on August 16 in the Piazza del Compo, the center of the city, as it has for several centuries. Siena is not far from Florence, to the north, and the famous Chianti wine-producing area is nearby. The University of Siena was founded in 1241.

University of Siena

SIZE ... There are more than 1,400 students.

CALENDAR ... The academic year runs from the beginning of November to the end of October; classes are held from November to June. A summer session for foreign students is held from July to September.

COURSES OF STUDY ... The University of Siena has Faculties of Law, Medicine and Surgery, Pharmacy and Economics, and certain postgraduate and specialization schools and courses.

SUMMER COURSES ... Each summer the School of Italian Language and Culture for Foreigners of the University of Siena offers graded language courses for elementary, intermediate and advanced students; Italian culture courses cover literature, social and political history, and history of art; a conversation course gives students an opportunity to discuss art, literature or current affairs with a teacher who speaks English, French or German as well as Italian, in which the course is conducted; courses on Italian civilization cover history of Italian painting, Dante, and figurative arts in Siena.

TUITION ... Registration fees are about $8, enrollment fees about $30, examination fees about $12.

At the School of Italian Language and Culture for Foreigners the enrollment fee for the entire course is $16, examination fee is $3.20, and diploma fee $1.60.

ADMISSION REQUIREMENTS ... A secondary school certificate (high school diploma) is acceptable for courses of the School of Italian Language and Culture for Foreigners of the University. For admission as an auditor (special student) or as a regular student at the University see the Admission Requirements section in the opening summary on Italy.

LANGUAGE OF INSTRUCTION ... Italian. Some of the instructors at the School of Italian Language and Culture for Foreigners speak English, but classes are conducted in Italian.

ACCOMMODATIONS ... Deserving and needy students from every country of the world are given an opportunity to live at the students' hostel in Siena. Residents are selected from those who apply at the beginning of the academic year. Rates are very low. The student canteen, *Mensa Universitaria,* is also open to all students, and meals can be purchased for around 50 cents. Many students live with families or in boardinghouses. A double room may cost from $2 to $3.50 per day, a single room from about $1 to $2 per day; full board costs from about $2.30 to $6 per day. The tourist office keeps a list of boardinghouses and private homes with accommodations for students and assists students to get settled in the new university surroundings.

AVERAGE COSTS ... Fees about $100 per academic year. Room and board about $80 and up per month.

STUDENT LIFE ... During the summer students are among the liveliest spectators at the historic pageant, *Palio delle Contrade,* a parade and horse-racing show. Throughout the year students arrange their own tours to historic and artistic centers in Siena and nearby. The Centro Turistico della Città di Siena provides information for students, journalists and visitors interested in the city's art and history. Students are issued a card entitling them to free admission to all museums, galleries and libraries of the city, and to concerts of the Chigiana Academy. The student habit of *caffè* drinking is contagious, pleasant, and a long-established part of student life in Siena.

UNIVERSITY OF TRIESTE

Trieste is the most important international port on the Adriatic Sea, and its maritime industries are the principal resource of the economic life of the city. Attractions which should be visited are the city's monuments, theaters, museums, art galleries, gardens, the characteristic environs, the promenades along the sea and the harbor, as well as the Canal area.

Sports spectacles and games take place during the entire year. The international championship games and contests commence in Trieste during the early days of the summer season. In the winter there is a period devoted to poetry, prose and symphonic concerts. During the summer there are various art exhibitions open to the public in the Castello di S. Giusto and in the park of the Castello di Miramare.

The University of Trieste was founded in 1877 as a private institution of learning. At that time it was a secondary school for skilled trades and commerce; in 1924, the Italian government elevated the school to the status of a university. Additional courses were added from time to time during the period from 1938 to 1960.

SIZE ... About 3,500 students, of whom about 60 are foreigners.

CALENDAR ... The academic year runs from the first of November to the end of October. The lectures and courses start in November and end in May. The examinations take place in June and October.

COURSES OF STUDY ... The curriculum of the University of Trieste comprises Jurisprudence, Economics, Commerce, Belles Lettres, Philosophy, Education, Mathematics, Physical and Natural Science, Pharmacy, Engineering. In addition, the School of Jurisprudence includes courses of advanced studies and specialization in labor and social security laws; the School of Economics and Commerce includes the Institute of Modern Languages for conference translators and interpreters. There are also special scientific and seminary courses.

TUITION ... The fee for matriculation is about $8, for registration around $30 and the fee for examinations is about $12. In addition, the students pay fees for use of the library and the laboratory, the amount varying according to the course of graduate studies (studies leading to a degree) for which they are enrolled.

ADMISSION REQUIREMENTS ... See the Admission Requirements section in the opening summary on Italy.

LANGUAGE OF INSTRUCTION ... Italian.

ACCOMMODATIONS ... A dormitory for students with 92 single rooms, service, study and recreation halls has recently been completed.

Most of the foreign students prefer to live with an Italian family or in pensions, in lodgings managed by religious groups, or in small hotels. In the hotels the average cost runs from about $1.20 to $2 daily for a single room, and from $2.50 to $4 daily for a double room. A room rented from an Italian family will probably cost about $30 monthly.

The Ente Provinciale Turismo (Provincial Tourist Association) offers assistance to the students in finding suitable and reasonable lodgings. All students enrolled with the University have access to free medical assistance.

AVERAGE COSTS ... Fees about $70 per academic year; meals and lodgings around $75 per month additional.

STUDENT ACTIVITIES ... In addition to the cultural activities mentioned above, Trieste offers in the field of sports a hippodrome (stadium), football field, facilities for tennis, basketball, Rugby, baseball, rollerskating, golf, fields and gymnasium for light and heavy gymnastics, clubs for nautical sports, canoes, sail and motor boating, indoor swimming pool, facilities for horseback riding. Transportation facilities—surface, railroad, maritime and airline transportation connect the city with all the national and international centers. There are numerous places of amusement, recreation and entertainment.

The Students' Organization has its own sports, moving-picture, musical and theatrical clubs, which engage in constant activities. These clubs and associations collaborate with the foreign students, offering them information and assistance in getting acquainted with the city and the neighboring regions. This organization meets periodically with international and European groups. The American students are welcome at all times.

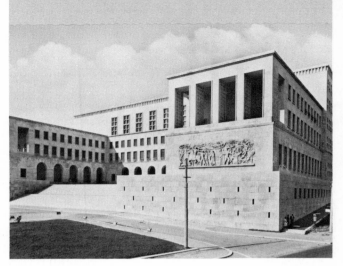

University of Trieste

UNIVERSITY OF TURIN

The Italian Alps form a background for Turin, one of the gateway cities of Italy. Located in the historic region of Piedmont, Turin is noted for its artistic, historic, and scientific collections, and for its natural scenic setting on the Po River. Its industries range from the production of automobiles to vermouth; its salons have taken an important place in the world of international fashion. Among the outstanding museums in the city are the Museum of Antiquity, Egyptian Museum, Sabauda Gallery, Royal Palace, Royal Armory, Gallery of Modern Art, Museum of Art and Furnishings, and the Civic Museum of Ancient Art. The University of Turin is situated on the Via Po, an impressive wide avenue which runs to the river a few blocks from the University. Founded in 1404 by Benedetto XIII, the University of Turin was long a center of movements and ideas espousing the unification of Italy.

SIZE ... About 8,000, including 80 foreign students.

CALENDAR ... The academic year runs from the beginning of November to the end of October; classes end in May and examinations follow.

COURSES OF STUDY ... The University of Turin has the following faculties: Faculty of Law, Faculty of Economics and Commerce, Faculty of Letters and Philosophy, Faculty of Education, Faculty of Medicine, Faculty of Mathematics, Physics, and Natural Sciences, including a preliminary course in Engineering, Faculty of Pharmacy, Faculty of Agriculture, Faculty of Veterinary Medicine, and postgraduate and specialization schools and courses.

TUITION ... Registration fees are about $8, enrollment fees about $30 and examination fees about $12.

ADMISSION REQUIREMENTS ... See the Admission Requirements section in the opening summary on Italy.

LANGUAGE OF INSTRUCTION ... Italian.

ACCOMMODATIONS ... Many Italian students live with families, in boardinghouses, small hotels, or in the student hostel. The *Collegio e Mensa Universitaria*, student hostel and canteen, serves meals to all students at a cost of about 50 cents each. Rooms at the hostel are inexpensive, but hard to come by because there are not enough to go around among the Italian students. Average boardinghouse prices are about $1.30 to $2.50 per day for a single room, $2.50 to $4 per day for double room, and about $3 to $6 per day for full board. Some religious organizations maintain student houses; prices are approximately $3 per day for room and board. A full meal at some restaurants costs about $1. The tourist office keeps lists of accommodations suitable for students and will help foreign students to find a place to live.

AVERAGE COSTS ... Fees about $100 per academic year. Room and board about $90 per month and up.

STUDENT LIFE ... The calendar of outdoor activities changes with the seasons in Turin; the variety ranges from mountain climbing, hiking, camping, cycling, and swimming to skiing and sledding. Songs and dances of the region can be heard and seen at festivals during the year; another spectator activity is watching games of "elastic ball" played on outdoor courts. In

Free University of Urbino

University of Turin

Turin there is such a court on the Via Napione; this game originated in Piedmont, though its popularity has spread to other areas. There are student-organized tours to various spots near Turin as well as to other cities in Italy.

FREE (PRIVATE) UNIVERSITY OF URBINO

Urbino is the home town of Raphael, and today the house where the painter was born is a tourist attraction. The National Gallery of the Marches, a ducal palace, houses many of Raphael's paintings as well as other masterpieces. There are excellent examples of fifteenth-century architecture about the town, a quiet, peaceful one spread over two small hills. At an early date the book-production trade flourished in Urbino and today the city is the seat of the Institute for Book Decoration and Illustration, the only such organization in Italy. Students are welcome to visit it. The Free University of Urbino was founded in 1506 and is one of the oldest universities in Italy.

SIZE ... About 5,000 students, including 50 students from foreign countries.

CALENDAR ... Classes are held from the beginning of November to the end of June; the academic year continues to October 31. A summer course for foreigners is held during August.

COURSES OF STUDY ... The Free University of Urbino has a Faculty of Law, Faculty of Economics and Commerce, Faculty of Letters and Philosophy, Faculty of Education, Faculty of Pharmacy.

SUMMER COURSES ... A summer course for foreigners offers elementary and advanced courses in the Italian language and culture.

TUITION ... Registration fees are about $8, enrollment fees about $30, examination fees about $12. In addition there may be other fees for certain courses of study. Students who achieve exceptionally high marks may have their fees reduced somewhat.

For the summer course for foreigners, the fee for the entire course is $16.

ADMISSION REQUIREMENTS ... No academic qualifications are needed for admission to the summer course. For admission as a regular or special student see the Admission Requirements section in the opening summary on Italy.

LANGUAGE OF INSTRUCTION ... Italian.

ACCOMMODATIONS ... The student hostel and canteen at the University is open the year round; it offers single rooms for about 50 cents per day, meals at 40 cents each, full board for about $1.50 per day. There are not enough rooms to house all the students, however, and many Italian students as well as foreign students live with families or in boardinghouses. Some students prefer a room in a small hotel. Hotel prices vary according to room size and hotel classification. A double room may cost from $1 to $2 per day, a single from $1.50 to $2 per day. Full board at a hotel ranges from $1.75 to $5 per day. The tourist office will assist students to find lodgings.

For the summer course for foreigners accommodations in a boardinghouse, room and three meals a day, are available for $2 to $3 per day.

AVERAGE COSTS ... Fees about $100 per academic year. Room and board about $75 and up per month.

STUDENT LIFE ... Students will find that their student cards admit them without charge to many of the museums of the town of Urbino; an Italian student will be willing to serve as guide to the city's treasures. Tennis, volleyball, basketball, and badminton are sports liked by the students; bicycling is another that is popular. Hiking and walking should not be overlooked, for there are many scenic as well as historic spots to see.

JAPAN

Japan, isolated from the outside world until a century ago, is today within the mainstream of international, economic, political and cultural movements. As one of the representative nations of Asia, it is a mecca for both tourists and students from throughout the world.

In growing numbers, American students, both undergraduate and graduate, are studying in this country, which is known for its advanced educational institutions. They are learning on the spot the language, the life, the culture of one of the world's oldest nations.

Traditional Japanese hospitality is extended to all foreign students, who are considered "guests" in the true sense of the word.

In this world of rapid communication, the many friendships developed in Japan by these students continue even after departure. It is through these channels that the hope for world peace grows.

Masahide Kanayama
Consul General

JAPANESE UNIVERSITY SYSTEM ... Most Japanese universities are now of the "comprehensive" or multiple-faculty type, although some single-faculty institutions still exist. In addition some 2- and 3-year junior colleges have recently been established. Three categories of university exist in Japan. The *national,* or governmental, universities are supported by the central government. In 1949 the several hundred national institutions of higher education, including the former imperial universities and many professional schools, were merged into 70 national universities, with at least one located in each of the 46 prefecture or state units. Admission to all of the governmental universities is by competitive examination. The *public,* or prefectural and municipal, universities are supported by these local bodies. The *private* universities, several of which were founded through foreign missionary efforts, are maintained by private support and fee structure. All three categories are under the jurisdiction of the National Ministry of Education, although the Ministry's control over individual institutions is less than it was in prewar years.

Like the American liberal arts college, and unlike the European university, Japanese universities now devote a certain amount of time to "general education" courses, although to a lesser extent than in the United States. A credit system like that used in the United States is now in operation, but university teaching in Japan is still based largely on the lecture. Graduate schools of the American type have been established at some of the large universities. The new system of education is not yet firmly established in Japan, since the process of reorganization and reorientation is a long and difficult one. Many critics feel that this system is not the answer and that changes must be made in the interests of the needs and potential of the country.

UNIVERSITIES OF JAPAN ... Under the new system there are 72 national universities, 34 public universities and 183 private universities. In addition, there are 337 junior colleges. In Japan many private institutions were founded by religious sects or by missionary groups; institutions are non-sectarian as well as sectarian. A number of the schools founded by Christian missionaries offer some courses with instruction in the English language.

ADMISSION REQUIREMENTS ... For admission to universities, Americans must have had 2 years of college, take a scholastic attainment test, physical examination and show their previous scholastic records. All examinations are given in the Japanese language, and in some cases proficiency tests will be given non-Japanese students to determine their ability to read, write and speak the Japanese language. A number of private institutions do not require students to pass examinations given in the Japanese language if they plan to study at the university for only one year. Some of these schools offer certain courses in the English language.

REGULATIONS ... American students must have an American passport and a Japanese student visa to enter Japan. Application for the visa must be made at the nearest Japanese Consulate in the United States. It is wise to apply for the visa well in advance of the anticipated departure date because processing of documents takes at least two months. Certain documents must be presented to receive a student visa; detailed information on procedure for obtaining a student visa is available from Japanese consular offices in various cities of the United States. Students should inform themselves of the currency and other regulations for entering Japan.

TUITION ... Tuition fees vary at government, public and private institutions, but all national universities have the same charges for tuition, matriculation and application fees. Written applications for entrance to a national institution must be accompanied by $2.78 (1,000 yen); when a student is admitted he must pay an additional $2.78 as a matriculation fee; tuition for the undergraduate course for the academic year is $33.34. Generally, an American student's tuition and other costs outside living expenses would not exceed $150 per academic year.

LIVING COSTS ... Not all universities have dormitories, and those which do have insufficient rooms to house all students. Some universities do have a cafeteria or a dining room where meals are available at moderate prices. If students want to eat Western style food, they must allow a larger part of their budget for food than if they choose to eat Japanese style meals. Many students live in rooming houses or with private families. In Tokyo the International Students' Institute operates an International Students' House (much like those found at Columbia University or the University of California) which has single rooms for foreign students; meals are served at the House. Room and board cost approximately $200 per month. It is very difficult for foreign students to find work in Japan. Most universities do have a student bureau or committee which maintains a bulletin board for notices of part-time jobs available to students. American students may find their best bet for earning extra money is English language tutoring.

COMMON COURTESIES AND LOCAL CUSTOMS ... In spite of much Westernization in Tokyo, it is still the custom there, and elsewhere in Japan, to remove one's shoes when entering a Japanese-style hotel, and, of course, a private home or temple. If one attends a true Japanese tea ceremony, silence is the best policy unless one's host engages in conversation. Japanese persons will bow graciously during introductions. As in many countries outside the United States, name cards are common and may be presented to newly met persons. Automobile traffic keeps to the left in Japan. The Japanese never use soap in the bathtub. The custom is to lather themselves thoroughly, then rinse themselves, after which they enter the tub or big open bath, and soak themselves in the hot water.

FOR FURTHER INFORMATION ... Write directly to the Director of Admissions of the university of your choice.

For travel particulars and documentation, write to Educational Department, NHE, Pan American Airways, Pan Am Building, New York, N. Y. 10017.

HOW TO GET THERE ... By Pan American Jet Clipper to Tokyo from United States West Coast via "Great Circle" route, 13 hours; via Honolulu, about 14½ hours (elapsed time); 3¾ hours from Hong Kong. Tokyo is on Pan American's Round-the-World Route. By ship, the journey from the United States West Coast takes about 12 to 14 days.

DOSHISHA UNIVERSITY, KYOTO

SIZE . . About 15,000 students in the University, including foreign students. Doshisha Women's College, which has been set up separately by the same founder as that of Doshisha University, has an enrollment of 1,300 students.

CALENDAR ... The academic year begins in April and ends the following March.

COURSES OF STUDY ... The University has faculties as follows: Faculty of Theology, Faculty of Letters, Faculty of Law, Faulty of Economics, Faculty of Commerce, and Faculty of Technology; there is also an Institute for the Study of Humanities and Social Sciences. The Women's College has a Department of English Literature, a Department of Music, and a Department of Home Economics. There are several secondary and primary schools attached to the Doshisha.

TUITION ... Average tuition fees are about $350 per academic year.

ADMISSION REQUIREMENTS ... Foreign students must present a transcript of their previous scholastic record with a letter of recommendation from their former school head. Students must pass an entrance examination, which may be taken in English, French or German, as well as in Japanese. See also the Admission Requirements section in the opening summary on Japan.

LANGUAGE OF INSTRUCTION ... Japanese. Some courses in literature, sociology, pedagogy, and religious education are taught in other languages.

ACCOMMODATIONS ... There is not enough dormitory space provided by the University to house all students. Foreign students usually take a room in a boardinghouse, or sometimes live with a Japanese family. Expenses are a bit less in Kyoto than in Tokyo. Students will find a committee of the University ready to assist them in finding accommodations.

AVERAGE COSTS ... Fees about $350 per academic year. Room and board about $800 per academic year.

STUDENT LIFE ... Kyoto is an "art city" and students will find a wealth of cultural activities available to them. The Doshisha campus is covered with trees and green lawns and there are many spots for meditation and paths for strolling. Recreation halls provide space for athletic activities; there are various religious centers for students of different beliefs. The University has a crew, baseball team, judo group, football team, and fencing and lawn tennis groups.

KYOTO UNIVERSITY

Kyoto has been called the "classic" city of Japan. Former capital of the country, it is rich in historical relics. It is an art center, the center of culture in western Japan, a city of festivals. Kyoto has more than two hundred Shinto shrines, fifteen hundred Buddhist temples, and museums, parks and palaces. Less than an hour from Kyoto is Nara, considered the cradle of Japanese art, craft and literature, and a city with luxurious palaces, temples and mansions open to the public. From industrious Kyoto craftsmen come magnificent silk fabrics, embroidery work, porcelain and lacquer, all for sale in the network of bazaars and shops. Kyoto is also the educational center of western Japan, and the University, founded in 1897, is the second oldest national university in the country. The campus stretches over a wide area with trees, lawns and gardens.

SIZE ... About 9,000 students, including about 100 from foreign countries.

CALENDAR ... First of April to the end of March. The year is divided into two semesters of April–October and October–March. Summer vacation is from mid-July to mid-September; winter vacation is from late December to early January; spring vacation is the first week of April. There are also holidays on national festival days.

COURSES OF STUDY ... The University has a School of Liberal Arts and Sciences. There is a Medical School, a Postgraduate School, various institutes, observatories, laboratories, and a botanical garden. The College of Liberal Arts and Sciences embraces the Faculty of Letters, with Departments of Philosophy, History, Literature and the Museum of the Faculty of Letters; Faculty of Education; Faculty of Law; Faculty of Economics; Faculty of Science with Departments of Mathematics, Physics, Astronomy, Geophysics, Chemistry, Zoology, Botany, Geology and Mineralogy and various laboratories; Faculty of Engineering offering Civil, Mechanical, Electrical, Aeronautical, Nuclear and Sanitary Engineering, Precision Engineering, Mathematical Engineering, Mining, Metallurgy, Industrial Chemistry, Fuel Chemistry, Textile Chemistry, Chemical Engineering, Synthetic Chemistry, Architecture and Electronics; Faculty of Agriculture with Departments of Forestry, Agriculture, Chemistry, Agricultural Biology, Agricultural Engineering, Agricultural Economics, Fisheries and the Kyoto Farmstead; the Faculty of Medicine with School of Nursing, Leprosy Research Laboratory, and University Hospital; and the Faculty of Pharmacy.

TUITION ... Written application to the University must be accompanied by $2.78 as examination fee; a matriculation fee of $2.78 must be paid at the time of admittance; tuition for the undergraduate course is $33.34 for the academic year; tuition for the postgraduate course is $36.11 for the academic year. Some scholarships and fellowships are available for foreign students.

ADMISSION REQUIREMENTS ... Approval of the faculty to which the student wishes admission must be obtained. Some students may be admitted as irregular students; foreign students who wish to become irregular students must apply through the embassy or legation of their own government in Japan; this organization then submits the application to the Ministry of Education of Japan for consideration by the University. See also the Admission Requirements section in the opening summary on Japan.

LANGUAGE OF INSTRUCTION ... Japanese. The University catalogue is available in an English edition.

ACCOMMODATIONS ... The University maintains two men's dormitories; each has a dining room but rooms are few and needy students are given first choice. Many students live in private homes or in a Japanese rooming house. The Student Bureau of the University keeps a list and assists students to find accommodations.

AVERAGE COSTS ... Fees about $35 per academic year. Room and board about $100 per month.

STUDENT LIFE ... Cultural activities are offered at every turn for students in Kyoto. Students themselves have clubs to pursue their interests in such subjects as literature, history, philosophy, religion, journalism, aesthetics, agriculture, engineering, economics, science, drama, music and movies. There are discussion groups to consider problems of military affairs and the hydrogen bomb. There is always a Japanese student who will help initiate Westerners into the mysteries of the tea ceremony, arts, calligraphy or flower arrangement. A University center offers a dining room, small store, barber shop, student assembly hall and lounges, very much like Western colleges. There are gardens and walks about the campus designed for the Eastern practice of meditation; these are popular with students.

TOKYO

Japan's capital city, with a population of about 10,000,000, is the industrial center of the country. Although the city is highly modernized, there is still an old-world charm in its blend of East and West. Kimono-clad women can be seen occasionally mingled with the more predominant Western-dressed women. Major tourist attractions are still those characteristic of traditional Japan: the Imperial Palace, with outer gardens open to the public; the Outer Garden of the Meiji Shrine, the Diet Building, teahouses, the museums and the cherry blossom festival. Students will find the Kanda Bookstore Street of special interest and often inhabited by their Japanese counterparts; the street has become the Latin Quarter of Tokyo. The best way to prepare for a Kabuki performance or a noh drama is to have a Japanese student explain it ahead of time. Introductory discussions of these fine arts are offered at the various universities of the city. Newest of the city's several colleges and universities is the International Christian University founded in 1953; its first students were graduated in March 1957. The I.C.U. is located in Mitaka, a western suburb of Tokyo about 17 miles from the city center, on a 317-acre campus. The University of Tokyo was established in 1877 on the site of a large estate; it has a sprawling campus with lawns, trees, ponds and gardens and the Akamon, a national treasure, built in 1828 as one of its gates. It is commonly called "The Red Gate" and is a tile-roofed wooden structure with a porter's lodge on either side. The Tokyo University of Foreign Studies grew out of the Tokyo Academy of Foreign Languages in 1897; the Special Course of one-year study which was established within the University in November 1954 has been reorganized since April of 1960 into the Intermediate College for foreign students, the course of which covers three years. St. Paul's University was founded as St. Paul's School in 1874 by American missionaries in Japan.

INTERNATIONAL CHRISTIAN UNIVERSITY, TOKYO

SIZE ... Enrollment in the University is about 1,150 students; 150 students are from countries outside Japan.

CALENDAR ... The winter term is from December through March with two weeks' vacation at Christmas time, and the spring term is April through June. Although the academic year begins in April, it is possible for foreign students to enter the University in the autumn term.

COURSES OF STUDY ... The University consists of undergraduate courses in Humanities, Natural Sciences, Social Sciences and a Graduate School of Education, an Institute of Rural Welfare Research and an Institute of Nutritional Research.

TUITION ... In general, fees average about $364. This includes a fee of about $11.11 to accompany the application for admission to the University and an admission fee of $83.35, which is paid only once.

ADMISSION REQUIREMENTS ... Students are admitted as regular students, one-year regular students, transfer regular students, or special students. All except special students, those who are not enrolled for credit, must meet the two years of college requirement. Regular students enroll for the 4-year course leading to a Bachelor's degree; one-year regular students include Junior-Year-Abroad students; they must be students working for a degree from a college or university abroad who wish to study for one year at the University and who plan to return to their own college or university; transfer regular students are those who have completed a year or more of study outside Japan as regular college or university students and who wish to matriculate for a degree from the University. Certain fees must be paid by each student with his application and at registration time.

See also the Admission Requirements section in the opening summary on Japan.

LANGUAGE OF INSTRUCTION ... Japanese and English. Students who plan only one year at the University are not required to master Japanese; 4-year students must speak, read and write the Japanese language. Facilities for meeting these requirements are provided at I.C.U. The University catalogue is available in an English edition.

ACCOMMODATIONS ... Two dormitories for men and three dormitories for women are maintained by the University for undergraduate students. There is also a dormitory for graduate students which has both single rooms and a few apartments. Dormitories have hot water, central heating, a Japanese bath and laundry facilities. An initial dormitory admission fee of $5.56 must be paid to secure a room; this fee is paid only once. The University has a dining hall. Dormitory space cannot accommodate all students of the University, and foreign students and Japanese students alike sometimes take a small house, an apart-

International Christian University

ment or a room with a Japanese family, or live in a rooming house.

AVERAGE COSTS ... Tuition fees, health examination, registration and books about $270 per academic year. Room and board about $200 to $250 per month.

STUDENT LIFE ... It is the aim of the University to have 25 per cent of its student body from countries outside Japan; at present about 10 per cent of the students are non-Japanese, a figure large enough to give an international character to the clubs and activities of the University. Students arrange excursions to parts of Japan they have not seen; mountain-climbing can also be arranged and a mountain-climbing club has been formed. There are also automobile, basketball, broadcasting, camera, chamber music, drama, English-speaking, fine arts, glee, music appreciation, and tennis clubs. Of special note are the Flower Arrangement Club, Tea Ceremony Club and the International Cultural Exchange Club. Tennis courts, soccer grounds, a picnic ground and a basketball court are found on the campus. Debates, sports events, work camps, seminars, conferences and recreation programs are part of the International Christian University (I.C.U.) college life.

NOTE ... For further information write to the Japan International Christian University Foundation, Room 1220, 475 Riverside Drive, New York, N. Y. 10027.

KEIO UNIVERSITY, TOKYO

Keio University traces its beginning to 1858, when the University's founder, Yukichi Fukuzawa, opened classes in his own home. It is therefore the oldest educational institution in Japan. Keio University has its main campus in Tokyo, with the Engineering Faculty in a Tokyo suburb and the General Education courses buildings on the Hiyoshi campus in Yokohama.

SIZE ... About 22,690 students enrolled in the University. This number includes foreign students and those on all campuses of the University.

CALENDAR ... Early April to late March. Entrance examinations are given on February 28 and entrance exercises take place on April 11. Summer vacation extends from early July to mid-September; winter vacation from late December to early January.

COURSES OF STUDY ... The University offers courses in the six faculties of which it is composed: Faculty of Literature, Faculty of Economics, Faculty of Law, Faculty of Business and Commerce, Faculty of Medicine, and Faculty of Engineering. The Faculty of Literature offers courses in Library Science through a Library School attached to it, and courses in History including Japanese, European, and Oriental; Literature including Japanese, English, German, Chinese, and French; and Philosophy including Psychology, Sociology, Ethics, Pedagogy, and Aesthetics and History of the Fine Arts. The Faculty of Engineering is divided into the five departments of Mechanical Engineering, Electrical Engineering, Applied Chemistry, Instrumentation and Measurement Engineering, and Administration Engineering. The University has an Institute of Journalism, Institute of Linguistics including a School of Foreign Languages, Institute of Management and Labor Studies, and various other research institutes and laboratories.

TUITION ... In general, fees range from about $344 to $1,344 depending on the faculty a student enters. The admission fee (paid only once) for the Faculty of Medicine is about $278; for all other faculties the admission fee is about $167.

Keio University

ADMISSION REQUIREMENTS ... The number of admissions to each faculty of the University is specifically limited; for instance, the Medical Faculty takes only 80 students each year, the Literature Faculty takes exactly 500 students. Competitive entrance examinations are given each year in February, in Japanese, and foreign students must compete in these examinations with no special consideration given them. Foreign students are accepted on the same basis as Japanese students. See also the Admission Requirements section in the opening summary on Japan.

LANGUAGE OF INSTRUCTION ... Japanese.

ACCOMMODATIONS ... A few dormitory facilities are maintained by the University, but it is usual for foreign students to find their own accommodations. The Office of the Dean of Students will give students information on available living quarters suitable for students. Foreign students can live at the International Student House in Tokyo and have three meals a day, Japanese style. There are also many rooming houses; or a student may take a room and eat his meals with a Japanese family for about the same price. A student association will help foreign students to find lodgings, if necessary.

AVERAGE COSTS ... Tuition fees, outside Medicine, about $344 to $1,344 per year. See Tuition section above. Room and board about $200 to $250 per month.

STUDENT LIFE ... Facilities are provided on the Mita campus for volleyball, boxing, wrestling, football, Japanese wrestling, and swimming. The University also has access to ski areas and facilities for tennis, sailing, skating, hiking, rowing, track, horseback riding, ping pong, soccer, and rugby. The student Autonomous Organization maintains a Co-operative Society which operates stores to sell textbooks, magazines, to lend books; it maintains a tea room and dining rooms, repair shops for shoes, watches, and fountain pens, and a barber shop, laundry and tailor shop. An Institute of International Relations is run by students; there are various student academic and research societies, cultural societies, an athletic association and the Keio Student Association. The *Mita Shinbun* is a student newspaper as is *Mita Campus*, a monthly paper published in English.

ST. PAUL'S UNIVERSITY, TOKYO

SIZE ... Enrollment includes 10,000 students with about 40 foreign students.

CALENDAR ... The regular session begins in April and ends the following March. Generally students must register at the beginning of the academic year. Sometimes, however, students will be accepted at other times.

COURSES OF STUDY ... The University has a College of Arts, College of Economics, College of Sociology, College of Science, College of Law, and the Institute for American Studies. English and American literature, history, economics, and religion courses are among those offered.

TUITION ... In general, fees range from about $341 to $425, depending on the college entered, and include an admission fee, paid only once, of about $139.

ADMISSION REQUIREMENTS ... There is a written examination testing the student's general knowledge, intelligence and ability in the English language. The examination is given in English. See also the Admission Requirements section in the opening summary on Japan.

LANGUAGES OF INSTRUCTION ... Japanese and English. Courses in English literature, American literature, history, economics, and religion are given in English.

ACCOMMODATIONS ... St. Paul's University does not operate a dormitory for its students. Most of the men live in private homes or in boardinghouses. The Japanese Student Association with offices in Tokyo will assist students in finding lodgings.

AVERAGE COSTS ... Fees are from around $200 to $290 per academic year. Room and board about $100 to $200 per month.

STUDENT LIFE ... No student will find time on his hands in Tokyo. The International Student Institute and the Japanese Student Association provide a long list of activities for students from all the universities and colleges of the city. Some English-speaking students find it rewarding to teach English to Japanese students in return for lessons in the Japanese language. There are also special hobbies such as archery and Japanese-style boxing which Westerners may find interesting to learn.

SOPHIA UNIVERSITY, INTERNATIONAL DIVISION, TOKYO

Sophia University, founded by Jesuits in 1906, includes an International Division to provide university courses conducted in English for those wishing to work toward a Bachelor's degree, or study without working for a degree. The academic year runs from September to June, and a summer course conducted in English has recently been established.

SIZE ... About 350 students representing 25 foreign countries, mostly residents in and around the Tokyo area.

CALENDAR ... The academic year—two semesters—begins the second week in September and ends the second week in June. Classes are held on Monday, Tuesday, Thursday and Friday evenings and on Wednesday and Saturday afternoons. There is a summer session July to August.

SUMMER COURSES ... Japanese Language, Literature in Translation, History, Art, Politics, Economics, Sociology, Education, Comparative Religion, Comparative Government, etc.

SOPHIA UNIVERSITY, DAY DIVISION, TOKYO

SIZE ... About 5,000 students are enrolled at the University.

COURSES OF STUDY ... The University has Faculties of Theology, Literature, Law, Economics, Foreign Languages and a Graduate School. The undergraduate faculties are comprised of the Departments of Theology, Philosophy, Education, History, Japanese Literature, English Literature, German Literature, Journalism, Economics, Commerce, Law, English Language, French Language, German Language, Russian Language and Spanish Language.

TUITION ... In general, fees range from about $370 to $508 and include an admission fee, paid only once, of about $83.35.

ADMISSION REQUIREMENTS ... Foreign students who wish to receive academic credits toward a degree for their work at Sophia University must submit certified copies of their previous academic records. See also the Admission Requirements section in the opening summary on Japan.

ADVANCED STANDING ... A candidate for admission to advanced standing from another institution of collegiate rank must present an official transcript showing his entrance qualifications for that institution and his college record in each subject taken while in that institution.

LANGUAGES OF INSTRUCTION ... Japanese, English, French, German, Latin, Russian and Spanish.

ACCOMMODATIONS ... Foreign students attending the University do not live in the dormitories operated by the University. Accommodations can be obtained in private homes, in rooming houses or in apartments.

AVERAGE COSTS (Foreign Students) ... Tuition and fees are from about $285 to $425 per academic year. Room and board, about $200–$250 per month.

STUDENT LIFE ... Many recreational activities are popular with the students: tennis, swimming, volleyball, baseball, boxing, wrestling, table tennis, badminton, mountain climbing, fishing, skiing, rowing. The more sedentary forms of relaxation—debates, discussions, club meetings—are also popular, and students form groups to follow their hobbies from literature, language, music, drama to archery. Foreign students are welcome to join any of these groups.

TOKYO UNIVERSITY OF FOREIGN STUDIES— INTERMEDIATE COLLEGE FOR FOREIGN STUDENTS

SIZE ... Thirty students are admitted each year to the 3-year course of the Intermediate College for Foreign Students. The University has a total of 1,750 students.

CALENDAR. ... First of April to the end of March. The year is divided into two semesters of April–October and October–March. Summer vacation is from mid-July to mid-September; winter vacation is from late December to mid-January and spring vacation lasts the month of March.

COURSES OF STUDY ... The Intermediate College for Foreign Students of Tokyo University aims at providing foreign students with instruction in Japanese language, general subjects and some professional studies.

The course covers three years. In the first year, the course provides training of fundamental scholastic ability, putting stress on teaching Japanese language in addition to basic subjects of senior high school level. In the second year, general education is given and in the third year, basic subjects for professional studies. The second and third years of this course correspond to the first and second years of study at a university with a 4-year course.

TUITION ... An entrance examination fee of approximately $2.78 is charged along with a registration fee of $2.78. Tuition is $60. Fees are waived for certain scholarship students.

ADMISSION REQUIREMENTS ... Foreign students who have completed 12 years of school education may apply for admission. Enrollment must be at the beginning of the academic year and applications for enrollment must be accompanied by certain documents including a curriculum vitae, transcript of previous academic records, physical examination certificate, and recent photographs. See also the Admission Requirements section in the opening summary on Japan.

LANGUAGE OF INSTRUCTION ... Japanese.

ACCOMMODATIONS ... The University has available a limited amount of dormitory space. Most students, however, find it necessary to live off campus in boardinghouses or with families. The Welfare and Guidance Section of the University keeps a list of boardinghouses and homes which accept student boarders.

Tokyo University of Foreign Studies

AVERAGE COSTS ... Fees about $60 per academic year. Room and board about $200 to $250 per month.

STUDENT LIFE ... Among the clubs on campus are the Society for Chinese Study, the Society for German Study, the Society for Latin-American Study, Dramatic Club, English-Speaking Society, "Clover" Chorus Group, Music Club, Photography Club, and the Mountaineering and Bowmen's Clubs. Students put out their own newspaper and have a student government that offers a number of student activities. There is a wide range of athletics and sports, popular at the University.

UNIVERSITY OF TOKYO

SIZE ... About 12,350 students, including about 25 foreign students and nearly 2,000 graduate students.

CALENDAR ... First of April to the end of March. Students are admitted only in April at the opening of the academic year. There are winter, spring and summer vacations. Japanese national holidays are also observed.

COURSES OF STUDY ... The University has a College of General Education with faculties and departments as follows: Faculty of Law; Faculty of Economics; Faculty of Letters with Departments of Japanese Literature, Japanese History, Chinese Philosophy, Chinese Literature, Oriental History, Occidental History, Philosophy, Indian Philosophy and Sanskrit Literature, Psychology, Ethics, Science and History of Religion, English Literature, French Literature, German Literature, Linguistics, Archaeology, Sociology, Aesthetics and History of Fine Arts; Faculty of Science with Divisions of Mathematics, Physical Science, Chemistry, Biophysics and Biochemistry, Biological Science and Geological Science; Faculty of Medicine with a School of Medicine and a School of Health Care and Nursing; Faculty of Pharmaceutical Sciences; Faculty of Education; Faculty of Engineering; and Faculty of Agriculture with nine departments—Agriculture, Agricultural Chemistry, Forestry, Fisheries, Agricultural Economics, Agricultural Engineering, Zootechnical Science, Veterinary Science and Forest Products. There are also a Graduate School and various institutes.

TUITION ... A student must pay an examination fee of about $2.78 with his application to the University; upon admittance he pays approximately $2.78 more as the matriculation fee; tuition fee for the undergraduate course is about $33.34 per academic year; $36.11 per year for a postgraduate course.

ADMISSION REQUIREMENTS ... Students who have completed 12 years of education in a country outside Japan are eligible to take the entrance examination, which is given in Japanese. See also the Admission Requirements section in the opening summary on Japan.

University of Tokyo

Waseda University

LANGUAGE OF INSTRUCTION ... Japanese. The University catalogue is available in an English edition.

ACCOMMODATIONS ... The University of Tokyo provides no living accommodations for students. There are several English-language newspapers in Tokyo which advertise rooms with families, apartments, small houses, rooming houses. The International Student Institute maintains a dormitory, International Student House, where foreign students can have a single room and three meals a day. The Japanese Student Association will assist students in finding a room with a family or in a rooming house.

AVERAGE COSTS ... Fees about $30 to $35 per academic year. Room and board about $200 to $250 per month.

STUDENT LIFE ... There is some kind of festival every month in the year in Japan, and students are willing to explain to newcomers the traditions behind these events. They will also help foreign students plan visits to villages outside Tokyo, introduce them to the best beaches, mountain climbs or skiing resorts. Japanese students have many clubs which cover a range of activities from archery to zoology; they may also share with Westerners their enjoyment of quieter activities such as painting, reading, fishing, or the wonders of the botanical garden on the campus, or swimming, concerts, movies and the opera. Popular sports are tennis, volleyball, baseball, basketball, table tennis, boxing and wrestling and rowing. A quiet corner of the campus is the "Garden for the Cultivation of Virtue"—pleasantly landscaped with trees and ponds.

WASEDA UNIVERSITY, TOKYO

SIZE ... About 35,000 undergraduate students, of whom about 200 are foreign students.

CALENDAR ... First of April to the end of March. The winter term opens in October and ends in February; the spring term opens in April and ends in October. An examination period is held at the end of each term. Winter vacation begins about December 20 and ends about January 10; summer vacation begins about July 1 and ends about September 5. A summer session is held during July.

COURSES OF STUDY ... The University is composed of the School of Political Science and Economics, the School of Law, the School of Literature, the School of Education, the School of Commerce, and the School of Science and Engineering. In addition, several research institutes are attached to the University including the Casting Research Laboratory, the Science and Engineering Research Institute, the Ohkuma Institute of Social Sciences, and the Institute for Research in Productivity. The School of Political Science and Economics offers courses in Political Science, Economics, Journalism, and Local Government; the School of Literature offers courses in Oriental Philos-

ophy, Western Philosophy, Psychology, Sociology, Pedagogy, Japanese Literature, English Literature, French Literature, German Literature, Russian Literature, Dramatic Art, Fine Arts, Japanese History, Oriental History, and Western History; the School of Education offers courses in Pedagogy, Japanese Language and Literature, English Language and Literature, and Social Studies; the School of Science and Engineering offers courses in Mechanical, Electrical, Mining, Metallurgical, and Civil Engineering, Architecture, Applied Chemistry, Electrical Communications, Industrial Management, Applied Physics, and Mathematics.

SUMMER SESSION ... The summer session lasts for five weeks, opening the beginning of July each summer. There are both daytime and evening sessions. Courses are offered in the Humanities including Philosophy, Logic, Psychology, Introduction to Literature, History, English and American Literature; in Social Science including Law, Economics, Sociology, and Political Science; in Natural Science including Biology, Anthropology, Mathematics, and Theory of Natural Science; Foreign Languages; various specialized courses, teacher-training courses.

TUITION ... In general, fees range between $361 and $553 depending on the school in which the student is enrolled, and include an admission fee, paid only once, of about $83.35.

ADMISSION REQUIREMENTS ... Foreign students are screened on the basis of a transcript and other documents sent to Waseda University. If a student is accepted he is mailed a certificate of admission; when he arrives at the University he must go through a second screening which determines the training necessary. Students must register with the proper authorities upon their arrival in Japan and then must present to the University a certificate of alien registration. Applicants are interviewed personally. See also the Admission Requirements section in the opening summary on Japan.

LANGUAGE OF INSTRUCTION ... Japanese.

ACCOMMODATIONS ... Although there are several dormitories near the University athletic field, they cannot accommodate all students of the University. Many Japanese students live with families, in rooming houses, or the International Student House. The University does operate a student cafeteria in the Student Center; meals are available at low cost.

AVERAGE COSTS ... Fees average from about $280 to $470 per academic year. Room and board about $200 to $250 per month.

STUDENT LIFE ... Each school of the University has its own student government organization which organizes various student activities. There are scientific societies, art and social clubs, religious organizations, and groups devoted to cultural activities. The campus has a Student Center opened in 1954 which provides meeting rooms, lounges, a cafeteria, a small store, and reading rooms. An athletic hall, gymnasium, athletic fields, and baseball grounds are available for students. Tennis, swimming, and hiking are popular sports. Students interested in journalism may find a niche working on one of the many journals published by students. One publication, the *Waseda Guardian,* is in English.

LEBANON

LEBANON

★ BEIRUT

The strategic location of the American University in Beirut, the meeting place of Western and Near Eastern civilizations, creates an opportunity and a responsibility for integrating the positive values of both civilizations. The University aims to produce in each student the perception and the objectivity which will enable him to create a worthy personal synthesis for today and the future.

The American University of Beirut is American both in its democratic spirit and in its educational philosophy. However, it builds on the foundation laid by the educational systems of the national governments of the Near East. It makes every effort to harmonize the values of these governmental systems with the values which have been derived from American experience, avoiding both absorption in any one national educational system and an attitude of indifference toward them.

In many regards, both in its educational philosophy and in its student body, the American University is as comprehensive as any university in the world. As such it has an opportunity to serve young people from a tremendous population scattered over a wide area. In this service the University hopes to measure up to its motto: "That they may have life and have it more abundantly."

The University offers opportunities for a limited number of American students, particularly in the Faculty of Arts and Sciences. Facilities are usually not available in Engineering and Medicine. Recent limitations in enrollments have made it impossible for the University to accept students from outside the area into the freshman and sophomore classes. Admission to the other classes is open to students with an exceptionally good academic record.

Norman Burns
President

AMERICAN UNIVERSITY OF BEIRUT

Beirut is the capital of Lebanon; the city and the country are filled with contrasts, the East and the West mixing and mingling the old and the new, the truly ancient and the truly modern: magnificent ruins and ultra-modern hotels; swimming in the blue Mediterranean Sea, skiing in the nearby snow-capped mountains. Olive and orange groves rival the beautiful stands of wild flowers for scenic grandeur. The bazaars and markets and mosques are Eastern, the automobiles, influx of "modern" dress, the coming of refrigerators and air conditioners are Western. Beirut stands in the center of Lebanon's coast; it has been an important trading center for centuries, because of Lebanon's position in the center of the Near East. One can hear English and French, as well as Arabic, spoken in the city. Lebanon has the highest rate of literacy in the Arab world. The American University of Beirut was chartered in 1863 and opened in 1866 with 16 students. It was then called the Syrian Protestant College; the name was changed in 1920.

SIZE . . . About 2,500 students representing 52 nationalities and 24 religious sects. A high percentage of the student body comes from outside Lebanon. The University is co-educational. However, only men students are admitted to the School of Engineering.

CALENDAR . . . October–June. Registration may begin at the end of September; classes begin in October. The year is divided into semesters: October–February, February–June. Entrance and make-up examinations are given in September. Summer session of 9 weeks begins in July.

COURSES OF STUDY . . . The University is made up of the following schools: School of Arts and Sciences, School of Medicine, School of Pharmacy, School of Nursing, School of Public Health, School of Engineering, and School of Agriculture. Students in the School of Arts and Sciences may major in any of the following programs: Arts, Science, including Biology, Chemistry, Physics, Mathematics, and Statistics; Business Administration; Theology; Social Sciences; pre-Medicine, pre-Pharmacy, pre-Engineering, pre-Agriculture.

SUMMER COURSES . . . The School of Arts and Sciences holds a summer session of 9 weeks in addition to special institutes beginning about July 1. The summer school repeats some courses offered during the regular academic year and gives students an opportunity to make up deficiencies or prepare for examinations. Students may not take more than nine credit hours of work during the summer.

TUITION . . . Tuition charges vary according to the school. The School of Arts and Sciences charges $365 for tuition per academic year for undergraduate students taking twelve or more credits per semester, and $14.30 per credit hour for graduate courses; auditors pay $9.60 per hour. Tuition per academic year for a full-time student (fifteen hours or more) of the School of Engineering is $550. Tuition for full-time students (ten or more credits per semester) of the School of Agricultural Sciences is $659 per academic year. Tuition per academic year is as follows for the medical faculties: School of Medicine, $565; School of Pharmacy, $432; School of Public Health, $548; School of Nursing, $96 first year, $32 second and third years. These fees also cover hospitalization, insurance and service and graduation fees. They do not cover fees for special services, books, supplies, athletic equipment, bedding, board and room. A general deposit of $32 is required of all students who enter the University for the first time; this sum, less any indebtedness to the University, is returned to the student when he graduates or discontinues his studies at the University.

For summer courses, fee per summer term for six or more credit hours is $128; for five or fewer credits, $80 in the Faculty of Arts and Sciences.

ADMISSION REQUIREMENTS . . . Each school has its own admission requirements. In general, however, to enter as a freshman a student must have an approved secondary school certificate with quality grades and must successfully pass the entrance examinations, if required by the faculty. Non-Arabic-speaking students who are English-speaking must have completed two units in a foreign language, that is, at least 240 hours of classroom instruction (a unit being equal to 120 hours of instruction); and must meet certain requirements in mathematics, English, social sciences, and sciences. Promotion from the freshman class to sophomore standing in an American university will generally admit a student to the sophomore year at the American University of Beirut in the School of Arts and Sciences. Students who have successfully completed two years of college in the United States may be given advanced standing (junior or senior year standing) at the American University provided all requirements of the Beirut University have been satisfied. Some departments may require students to pass departmental examinations. For admission to the School of Medicine and the School of Pharmacy, students must have completed the pre-medicine or the pre-pharmacy courses and meet other departmental requirements.

LANGUAGE OF INSTRUCTION ... English.

ACCOMMODATIONS ... The University maintains dormitories for both men and women students and also operates a self-service cafeteria and restaurant for students. All women students whose homes are not in Beirut are required to live in the University residence halls. Two new halls, housing 170 women students, have just been completed and have central heating, constant hot water, and complete furnishings. Most rooms are for two students and the cost per person per semester is about $100; students can either provide their own bed linens or rent them. A few suites of two rooms and a bath, for four students, are available. Some students live off campus and the University Housing Office keeps a list of available rooms. These students may eat at the University cafeteria, however, and can pay by the semester or by the meal, about $150 per semester; meals are not served during vacation period. There are several milk bars where sandwiches, ice cream, coffee and tea are available at moderate cost.

AVERAGE COSTS ... Tuition fees about $400 for the School of Arts and Sciences for the first year. Incidental expenses for books, stationery, supplies, and laundry range from about $100 to $200 per academic year.

American University of Beirut

STUDENT LIFE ... A Student Life Committee has charge of student activities; there are some twenty student societies, twelve student clubs, and other organizations. The student newspaper, *Outlook,* is managed and run by students. Football, basketball, volleyball, track, tennis, archery, swimming, skiing, and table tennis are some of the sports popular with the students.

FOR FURTHER INFORMATION ... For complete information about the University and how to enroll, write to the Consulate General of Lebanon, 9 East 76th Street, New York, N. Y. 10021.

For travel particulars and documentation, write to Educational Department, NHE, Pan American Airways, Pan Am Building, New York, N. Y. 10017.

HOW TO GET THERE ... By Pan American Jet Clipper service from New York to Beirut, only 13¾ hours. By ship, about 14 to 21 days depending on the steamship line.

MEXICO

UNIVERSITIES OF MEXICO ... Mexico has numerous institutions of higher learning. There is The National Autonomous University of Mexico, founded in 1551, which includes 17 teaching faculties and schools and 15 research institutes, a Graduate School and a School for Foreign Students. In addition there are the Women's University of Mexico, University of the Americas, Ibero-American University. Most of the states support a university and Jalisco maintains two. Although state institutions are more limited in comparison with the National University, their programs of study and their degrees correspond closely to those of the National Autonomous University. The National Polytechnic Institute, one of the major divisions of the Department of Public Education, is made up of eight professional schools and is located in Mexico City. Other federal institutions are the National School of Anthropology and History, the Institute of Health and Tropical Diseases, the National Institute of Scientific Research. The federal government has complete control, administrative and technical, over education in the Federal District and in the schools which it establishes and maintains in the states.

ADMISSION REQUIREMENTS ... There are several steps to follow when applying to a university in Mexico. A student must first submit the following documents for approval by the evaluation committee of the university: letter of application specifying the school in which the applicant wishes to enroll; completed medical form; two letters of recommendation from persons qualified to judge the applicant's character and intellectual capacity; letter of good financial standing stating that the applicant will pay accordingly for his fees at the university; a transcript indicating graduation from high school with satisfactory grades—or an official record stating that the high school G.E.D. tests have been passed with an average score of 45. Students from countries other than the U.S. must have their preparatory studies evaluated by examination.

All documents in a language other than Spanish, English or French must be accompanied by official Spanish translations. In addition, an ample knowledge of Spanish is necessary for any activity in a university, as all instruction is given in Spanish. Entering students whose native language is other than Spanish will be required to take and pass an examination in Spanish before being admitted to the regular session of a university.

An applicant who comes from an approved college or university must submit an official transcript describing his entrance credits, courses of study and his scholastic record, as well as a letter of recommendation from the school. Transfer credits will be given on the basis of this transcript, full credit being given for all work satisfactorily completed.

CREDIT TOWARD AN AMERICAN DEGREE ... Undergraduate as well as graduate foreign students may transfer credits obtained at most universities in Mexico as long as their respective colleges or universities approve them previously. The courses offered by the School of University Courses for Foreign Students at the National University of Mexico are definitely recognized by U.S. colleges and universities.

REGULATIONS ... Upon arrival in Mexico the student must bring the originals of his transcripts, diploma and birth certificate, duly legalized by the Mexican Consul, and report to the Departamento de Coordinación de Estudios at the university.

TUITION ... Tuition varies with each university. The National University, for example, costs $160 per year, whereas a student attending Mexico City College must pay a quarterly tuition of $185. The Women's University of Mexico charges $243 per year for enrollment. These fees generally include registration.

LIVING COSTS ... Room and board in Mexico City average $60-$80 per month. It is estimated that a student can plan to live on $120–$170 per month. Living costs in Mexico City are somewhat lower than in the average U.S. city.

COMMON COURTESIES AND LOCAL CUSTOMS ... Luncheon, served from 1-3, is the big meal of the day. Women in slacks and shorts are not permitted on the streets of Mexico City. Women, unless they are in the heart of the city, should not be unescorted.

FOR FURTHER INFORMATION ... For complete information about a university and how to enroll, see the How to Enroll heading at the end of each university.

For travel particulars and documentation, write to Educational Department, NHE, Pan American Airways, Pan Am Building, New York, N. Y. 10017.

HOW TO GET THERE ... By Pan American or connecting airlines, Mexico City is 1¾ hours from Houston, 3¼ hours from Los Angeles; by connecting airlines through Houston, elapsed time to Mexico City is 7¼ hours from St. Louis; 10¼ hours from Washington, D. C. Nonstop service from New York and Chicago, 4¼ hours and 3½ hours, respectively. Mérida is 1½ hours from New Orleans and 1¾ hours from Miami. By train, Mexico City is 3 days and 3 nights from New York.

NATIONAL AUTONOMOUS UNIVERSITY OF MEXICO, MEXICO CITY

The National Autonomous University of Mexico was founded in 1551 as the Royal and Pontifical University of Mexico. In 1910 it became the National University of Mexico and in 1929 it was granted autonomy. In 1946 the Mexican Government awarded the University more than 1,500 acres of land located south of Mexico City on the Cuernavaca Highway. Construction of the new campus, or University City as it is called, began in 1949 under the supervision of the professors and students of the National School of Architecture.

SIZE ... The student body totals 74,000 with 6,270 professors and 5,757 employees. There are 17 faculties and schools, 15 research institutes, a Graduate School and a School for Foreign Students.

CALENDAR ... The school year at the University begins in March and ends in October. Examinations are given during the months of November and December. The vacation period is scheduled from the middle of December to the beginning of March. Summer sessions are held in July and August.

The climate in Mexico is springlike. There are no sharply defined seasons, but there are light afternoon rains from June to October. Mornings are invariably sunny.

COURSES OF STUDY ... The University is composed of the Schools and Faculties of Law, Philosophy and Letters, Science, Architecture, Engineering, Economics, Dentistry, Chemical Science, Commerce and Business Administration, Medicine, Music, Nursing and Midwifery, Plastic Arts, Political and Social

National Autonomous University of Mexico

Science, Odontology, Veterinary Science and Zootechnics. There are also numerous institutes for specialized study, a summer school, and special courses for foreign students.

SUMMER COURSES ... The summer session at the University is generally held during the months of July and August. Classes are conducted only in the mornings. The courses, which are mostly given in Spanish, include: Spanish (Beginning, Intermediate, and Advanced), and Spanish and Mexican Culture. The registration and tuition fee is approximately $110 for the entire session. There are no special requirements for admission if the student is not working toward his M.A. Students working for credit must bring with them transcripts of their previous studies.

As for housing facilities, the University maintains a list of approved private homes. Apartments in Mexico City are available from $60 a month.

For additional information on the Summer School, write to the Registrar, Summer School, Philosophy and Letters Building, University City, Mexico 20, Mexico, D. F.

TUITION ... Tuition and registration fee for the entire year is $160. This is to be paid by the student upon arrival at the University.

ADMISSION REQUIREMENTS ... In addition to the documents listed under the Admission Requirements section in the opening summary on Mexico, an applicant must also submit six 1½" x 2" photographs as well as a photostatic copy of high school and college transcripts leading to a B.A. or B.S. degree (a minimum of 60 semester college credits required), a photostatic copy of the original diploma, all duly legalized by the corresponding Mexican Consul, *unless sent directly by the issuing institutions.* Some colleges require only photostatic copies of high school transcripts and of the original diploma. (Check with the University.) A general catalogue or official programs of the institution(s) where the credits were obtained must also be enclosed.

When the applicant is formally approved by the Evaluation Committee, he will receive an official letter of acceptance signed by the corresponding authorities. With this letter the applicant may obtain the proper student's visa from the Mexican Consul.

A student who wishes to enroll for certain courses without matriculating should present his request in writing to Dirección General de Servicios Escolares, Torre de la Rectoría, Ciudad Universitaria, México 20, D. F.

LANGUAGE OF INSTRUCTION ... Most courses are conducted in Spanish. During the summer session, however, there are several subjects taught in English.

ACCOMMODATIONS ... The campus has no dormitory facilities. However, the University maintains a list of desirable private homes and boardinghouses for foreign students.

AVERAGE COSTS ... A student can live comfortably on $120 to $170 per month. This, of course, does not include his tuition at the University.

STUDENT LIFE ... The students at the National University participate in numerous campus activities. They have an olympic stadium which holds 90,000 and a beautiful swimming pool. Social and cultural activities are planned by the students.

HOW TO ENROLL ... For complete information on the National Autonomous University of Mexico, write to the UNIVERSIDAD NACIONAL AUTÓNOMA DE MÉXICO, Departamento de Información al Extranjero, Torre de la Rectoría, Ciudad Universitaria, México 20, D.F.

UNIVERSITY OF THE AMERICAS, MEXICO CITY

The University of the Americas, formerly Mexico City College, founded in 1940, is situated on a lovely hilltop campus on the edge of Mexico City. The only school of its kind in Latin America, it is private, non-profit, non-sectarian and essentially an American-type liberal arts institution. Its chief emphasis has been on Latin American studies and it offers the Master's degree in eight distinct areas of specialization. In 1959 the University was made a full member of the Southern Association of Colleges and Schools.

SIZE ... The average enrollment is 1,000 students, 75 per cent of whom are from the United States.

CALENDAR ... The University is operated on the U.S. quarter system. The sessions run approximately as follows: fall—late September to mid-December; winter—early January to mid-March; spring—late March to early June; summer—mid-June to late August. Final exams are given at the end of each quarter.

ADMISSION REQUIREMENTS ... The University requires that an application fee of $15 accompany the documents listed under the Admission Requirements section in the opening summary on Mexico.

COURSES OF STUDY ... The University offers undergraduate studies with majors in Spanish Language and Literature, Anthropology, Business Administration, Economics, Education, English, Creative Writing, Fine Arts, History, International Relations, Philosophy, and Psychology. Basic courses in pre-Engineering and pre-Medicine are also offered.

The graduate program includes majors in Spanish and Spanish American Language and Literature, Creative Writing, Business Administration, Economics, Fine Arts, History, and International Relations.

The College also offers a Junior Year Program in Mexico for students who wish to concentrate on Spanish or other Latin American studies.

A student may earn a degree of Bachelor of Arts, Bachelor of Fine Arts, Master of Arts, Master of Fine Arts or Master of Business Administration.

SUMMER COURSES ... The University of the Americas offers two summer sessions: one 11-week summer quarter, mid-June to late August, and one 6-week intensive special summer session for those unable to attend the full quarter, early July to mid-August. The only requirement for admission is that the student be a high school graduate with a C average. Tuition is $200 for the summer quarter, or $115 for the intensive summer session. The application fee is $15. Students should budget $5.60 per month for daily bus service between the University and downtown Mexico City. The University will arrange housing for the student. The special 6-week session offers intensive courses primarily concerned with Mexico and Latin America. The University also operates summer workshops especially designed for teachers, sociologists, government and social workers. The workshops deal with the study of the Latin American culture. There are also courses in liberal arts and the Spanish language.

TUITION ... Quarterly tuition at the University of the Americas is $200. This fee also includes medical, library, athletic, and recreational services, college publications, theater productions and other college activities. In addition, there is a graduating fee of $25. Students should plan to allot approximately $25 for textbooks during their first quarter at the University.

LANGUAGE OF INSTRUCTION ... Most classes at the University of the Americas, except those in the Spanish Department, are given in English.

ACCOMMODATIONS AND AVERAGE COSTS ... Since the college does not have dormitory facilities, students are referred to approved private homes or boardinghouses. The cost of room and board will range from approximatey $60 to $80 per month. This generally includes only two meals a day (breakfast and supper). Married students will find a wide selection of furnished and unfurnished apartments available at prices ranging from $120 to $170 per month. Living costs in general are somewhat lower than in the average U.S. city.

STUDENT LIFE ... The Student Council and the Administration work together in planning lectures, parties, dances and plays. Recreational facilities are available on the campus for basketball, volleyball, badminton, fencing, etc. The University also offers numerous clubs for students to join, such as the International Relations Club, Chess Club, Newman Club, Fireside Club, Drama Workshop, etc. An informal theater group has been active at the University for several years. The students publish a biweekly newspaper called the *University of the Americas Collegian.*

HOW TO ENROLL ... For complete information on the University of the Americas, write to the UNIVERSITY OF THE AMERICAS, Apartado Postal 968, México 1, D. F.

WOMEN'S UNIVERSITY OF MEXICO (UNIVERSIDAD FEMENINA DE MEXICO), MEXICO CITY

The Women's University of Mexico, founded in 1943 by Mrs. Adela Formoso de Obregon Santacilia, is located within the Federal District in front of Chapultepec Park. This institution, the only one of its kind in Mexico, was founded exclusively for women, to give them an opportunity to acquire a good education as well as learn a particular trade.

SIZE ... The University has a total enrollment of 1,000 students in its eight Schools.

CALENDAR ... Students begin registering on November 1. Classes start the first week of February. Vacations are scheduled for December and January.

COURSES OF STUDY ... The University offers courses in Liberal Arts, Law, Social Science, Languages, Literature, Physical Science, Administrative Science, Education, Decoration, Publicity, and Social Work. The University also conducts a summer school during the months of July and August. At this time a group of students from Oklahoma College for Women generally attends the session. Courses in Spanish, Mexican Literature and the Art of Mexico are conducted.

TUITION ... Tuition is approximately $250 per year.

ADMISSION REQUIREMENTS ... See the Admission Requirements section in the opening summary on Mexico.

Women's University of Mexico

LANGUAGE OF INSTRUCTION ... All classes at the University are conducted in Spanish.

ACCOMMODATIONS ... The University has enough dormitory facilities to house 50 students. The remaining students have to find rooms in the city or live with families.

AVERAGE COSTS ... One can live in a boardinghouse in Mexico City for approximately $80 per month. It is estimated that a student's average expenses, not including tuition, would range from $120 to $170 per month.

STUDENT LIFE ... The University offers to its students various intramural sports, in addition to cultural and social activities. It arranges conferences, concerts and social gatherings.

HOW TO ENROLL ... For complete information on the Women's University of Mexico, write to the UNIVERSIDAD FEMENINA DE MÉXICO, Avenida de los Constituyentes Num. 151, Tacubaya, México, D. F.

THE NETHERLANDS

For many centuries the standard and quality of higher education in Holland have been internationally known; and this is owing both to its level of scholarly achievement and to the age-old tradition of academic freedom.

A university in Holland always has a dual task: it must enable a student to develop his personality as well as his mental aptitudes. For this purpose, academic freedom in the widest sense is indispensable. Our country opens her doors to the student from America, offering him the finest traditions of her finest institutions—and her warm friendship.

J. van den Bogaert
Director
The Netherlands Information Service

One consequence of that major period in Dutch history, the 80-year war against Spanish rulers, was the fact that at its conclusion in 1648 Holland had not only acquired independence but had even attained a leading position in the cultural, political and economic life of Europe. The inspiring leader of the revolt against Spanish rule was Prince William of Orange (William the Silent), himself a great champion of the principles of tolerance and freedom. In 1568 he had taken the field against the Spaniards and it was his leadership which inspired the seven northern provinces to unite and continue the struggle as the Republic of the United Netherlands. In this atmosphere of suppression and revolt the need arose for an institute of higher learning that would cherish the national principles of freedom and tolerance. In 1575, Prince William of Orange founded the University of Leyden as a tribute to the citizens of that city for their splendid resistance to the Spaniards during the siege of Leyden in 1572.

Soon the other provinces followed suit: schools were established in several places, but Leyden University remained the most important one. Latin being the language of instruction, there was no linguistic bar to the admission of foreigners. Names such as René Descartes, Scaliger and Junius may suffice as illustrious examples.

As the universities of other countries grew, Holland lost her leading position in higher education, and it was not until the nineteenth century that the Dutch system of higher education was reorganized and won international acclaim once more.

In 1876 the Education Act established the State Universities of Leyden, Groningen and Utrecht, and the Municipal University of Amsterdam. In 1880 the Free University at Amsterdam was established by the Reformed Church, and in 1923 the Roman Catholic Church founded its University at Nijmegen. Specialized education demanded the establishment of technical institutes, and the Technological University at Delft, the Agricultural University at Wageningen, Schools of Economics at Rotterdam and Tilburg, and a second Technological University at Eindhoven are the result.

DUTCH UNIVERSITY SYSTEM ... The academic standard and the degrees to be acquired are the same at all the universities. They are governed by a Board of Curators, or Directors. The internal affairs are directed by the Academic Senate, which is presided over by the Rector Magnificus.

There are usually seven departments or faculties at Dutch universities: Theology, Law, Medicine, Science, Arts, Economics, and Political and Social Sciences.

The university student in Holland is almost completely free to arrange his course of study and to decide in what order to take his preliminary examinations. Attendance in class is voluntary and in general a student's success depends on his own initiative and perseverance.

Teaching consists of lectures, seminars, and laboratory work. In all faculties the student must take the *candidaatsexamen* after two or three years of study before being admitted to the final degree examination (the *doctoraal examen*). The subject matter a student must master for these examinations is divided into sections. Proficiency in each section has to be shown by a preliminary examination called *tentamen*.

ADMISSION REQUIREMENTS ... Foreign students must have the equivalent of the secondary school education required for Dutch students in order to be admitted into a university. In the case of United States students, this means that the minimum academic requirement is a high school diploma, plus two years at an accredited college. Generally speaking, however, a Bachelor's degree is required for admission to a Dutch university. (For medical students: B.Sc. with A or B average.)

Application for admission to a medical school should be sent to the Ministry of Education together with transcripts and a recommendation by two authorized persons.

REGULATIONS ... For student visa and entrance procedure, see the For Further Information heading at the end of this section.

CREDIT TOWARD AN AMERICAN DEGREE ... Students who are candidates for a degree in an American university must make arrangements with their dean regarding transfer of credits before applying for admission to a Dutch university.

SUMMER SESSION ... The annual summer session of the Netherlands Universities (NUFFIC) consists of a 3-week course at one of the universities on a subject of international importance. Lectures are given in English. Excursions are organized to places of interest in several parts of the Netherlands.

TUITION ... A registration fee of $2.60 and a tuition fee of $30 are charged before enrollment. In some faculties, laboratory fees are charged. Fees for the various examinations are about $15.50 each.

LIVING COSTS ... Most students find rooms in private homes or boardinghouses. Breakfast and lunch are supplied at some boardinghouses, but dinner must be eaten out. Nearly all universities have a special student restaurant (*Mensa Academica*).

About $110 per month should cover living expenses. Tuition and fees will amount to about $80, and some faculties charge fees for laboratory and supplies, which may be quite high.

COMMON COURTESIES AND LOCAL CUSTOMS ... The student clubs and associations are very active in the Netherlands. The freshman student will have to prove himself, and an initiation period is accompanied by some mild hazing in some groups. Students from the United States, if they want to take full advantage of their student days in Holland, are advised to join one or more of the many student societies.

The student cabarets, or shows, have become popular in recent years, and festivals of all kinds are frequent through the academic year.

When Dutch people are introduced to each other, they

always shake hands and mention their own names—they never use "How do you do" or some such phrase.

If a student wishes to see a professor he is advised to make an appointment by mail or call at the regular visiting hours arranged for the purpose.

FOR FURTHER INFORMATION ... For complete information about a university and how to enroll, write to the Netherlands Information Service, 711 Third Avenue, New York, N. Y. 10017.

For travel particulars and documentation, write to Educational Department, NHE, Pan American Airways, Pan Am Building, New York, N. Y. 10017.

HOW TO GET THERE ... By Pan American Jet Clipper, nonstop flights to Amsterdam from New York, 8 hours; 1 hour from London. By boat from New York, 7 to 11 days.

AMSTERDAM

Amsterdam is the capital and largest city of the Netherlands. Rulers of the Netherlands are enthroned in Amsterdam but the official residence and the seat of the government are at The Hague. Most of the city rests on piles like Venice. The canals, crossed by over three hundred bridges, divide the city into about ninety islands. The city is great because of its commerce. It was founded in 1275 and has long been one of the foremost ports of the world; it is famous for its diamond-cutting industry. Amsterdam was the home of Rembrandt, and many of his works, including the famous "Night Watch," are in the Rijks Museum; it was the birthplace of the great philosopher Spinoza.

FREE UNIVERSITY OF AMSTERDAM

When the Education Act of 1876 converted the old academies and universities into the state universities, it also made provision for the founding of universities by private corporations. In 1880 the Free (Calvinistic) University at Amsterdam was established by a group of members of the Reformed Church.

SIZE ... There are about 3,500 students, including 120 foreign students.

CALENDAR ... There is no division of the academic year into semesters in the Netherlands. The university session begins in the last week of September and ends at the beginning of July, with vacations of about four weeks at Christmas and three weeks at Easter.

COURSES OF STUDY ... The Free University of Amsterdam has the usual seven faculties: Theology, Law, Medicine, Science (Natural Sciences, Mathematics), Arts (Humanities), Economics, Political and Social Sciences. However, the Free University does not have as great a variety of subjects as the Municipal University.

ADMISSION REQUIREMENTS ... See the Admission Requirements section in the opening summary on the Netherlands.

LANGUAGE OF INSTRUCTION ... Dutch. Some of the summer courses are conducted in English, French, or German.

ACCOMMODATIONS ... All students must find their own rooms in private homes or boardinghouses. The Student Information Office has a special lodgings department to assist the students in finding suitable accommodations. Most students have breakfast and lunch at their lodgings but get dinner out. About $110 a month should be allowed for living expenses. Another $80 a year will be necessary for tuition fees, etc.

STUDENT LIFE ... There are a large number of student organizations at Dutch universities; the *Corpora,* the oldest of these, still adhere to the old customs. There is an initiation period during which the freshman is indoctrinated.

The general student association which has been instituted at all universities will, it is hoped, provide a vital force for the enormously increased student population. It has the function too of looking after the general social and cultural well-being of the student community.

Municipal University, Main Building

MUNICIPAL UNIVERSITY OF AMSTERDAM

The Municipal University of Amsterdam was established in 1632 originally as the Athenaeum Illustre. It enjoyed a considerable period of renown after its founding but declined' in importance along with other Dutch universities during the period of intellectual growth in other European countries, culminating during the Napoleonic Wars, when Holland was annexed by France. The social revolutions of the nineteenth century hardly affected the Netherlands. However, during the course of a few decades the form of government changed from an absolute monarchy to a liberal democracy.

In 1848 the principle of complete freedom of education was incorporated in the constitution. The Education Act of 1876 converted the old academies and universities into the State Universities of Leyden, Groningen, Utrecht, and the Municipal University of Amsterdam. The University is governed by a Board of Curators, or Directors, who form a mediating body between the government and the State University. The internal affairs are directed by the Academical Senate, consisting of the entire body of professors and presided over by one of these called Rector Magnificus.

SIZE ... There are about 6,500 students, including 400 foreign students.

CALENDAR ... There is no division of the academic year into semesters in the Netherlands. The university session begins in the last week of September and ends at the beginning of July, with vacations of about four weeks at Christmas and three weeks at Easter.

COURSES OF STUDY ... The Municipal University of Amsterdam has seven departments or faculties: Theology, Law, Medicine, Science, the Arts, Economics, and Political and Social Sciences.

At Amsterdam students may also find the State Academies of Fine Arts and of Dramatic Arts, the Conservatory of Music, and the Physical Culture Academy.

TUITION ... See the tuition section in the opening summary on the Netherlands.

ADMISSION REQUIREMENTS ... See the Admission Requirements section in the opening summary on the Netherlands.

LANGUAGE OF INSTRUCTION ... Dutch. Some of the summer courses are conducted in English, French, or German.

ACCOMMODATIONS ... All students must find their own rooms in private homes or boardinghouses. The Student Information Office has a special lodgings department to assist the students in finding suitable accommodations. Most students have breakfast and lunch at their lodgings but get dinner out. About $110 a month should be allowed for living expenses. Another $80 a year will be necessary for tuition fees, etc.

STUDENT LIFE ... There are a large number of student organizations at Dutch universities; the *Copora,* the oldest of these, still adhere to the old customs. There is an initiation period during which the freshman is indoctrinated.

The general student association which has been instituted at all universities will, it is hoped, provide a real binding force for the enormously increased student population. It has the function too of looking after the general social and cultural well-being of the student community.

University of Groningen, Main Building

UNIVERSITY OF GRONINGEN

Groningen is one of the most important trading cities of the Netherlands. It lies about 22 miles inland from the northern coast. Canals connect Groningen with the sea, and the city has many docks. It has a 2,000-year history starting with a Roman camp in A.D. 48, through its important shipbuilding days in the twelfth century, providing ships for the Crusades, to the period when it joined the Hanseatic League in 1284. In 1579 it joined the Union of Utrecht and was captured and recaptured in the battles with the Spaniards.

The University of Groningen was founded in 1614 and enjoyed European prestige for many years. The social revolutions of the nineteenth century hardly affected the Netherlands. However, during the course of a few decades the form of government changed from an absolute monarchy to a liberal democracy. In 1848 the principle of complete freedom of education was incorporated in the constitution. The Education Act of 1876 converted the old academies and universities into the State Universities of Groningen, Leyden, Utrecht, and the Municipal University of Amsterdam. The University is governed by a Board of Curators, or Directors, who form a mediating body between the government and the State University. The internal affairs are directed by the Academical Senate, consisting of the entire body of professors and presided over by one of these called Rector Magnificus.

SIZE ... There are about 4,500 students, including 100 foreign students.

CALENDAR ... There is no division of the academic year into semesters in the Netherlands. The university session begins in the last week of September and ends at the beginning of July, with vacations of about four weeks at Christmas and three weeks at Easter.

COURSES OF STUDY ... The University of Groningen has seven departments or faculties: Theology, Law, Medicine, Science, the Arts, Economics, and Political and Social Sciences. The annual summer session of the Netherlands universities consists of a 3-week course at one of the universities on some subject of international importance. Lectures are given in English. Excursions are organized to places of interest in several parts of the Netherlands. At the University of Groningen there is a biannual postgraduate course in Thoracic Clinical Science and Surgery. The course is given in English and lasts three weeks.

TUITION ... See the section on Tuition in the opening summary on the Netherlands.

ADMISSION REQUIREMENTS ... See the Admission Requirements section in the opening summary on the Netherlands.

LANGUAGE OF INSTRUCTION ... Dutch. Some of the summer courses are conducted in English, French or German.

ACCOMMODATIONS ... All students must find their own rooms in private homes or boardinghouses. The Student Information Office has a special lodgings department to assist the students in finding suitable accommodations. Most students have breakfast and lunch at their lodgings, but get dinner out. About $110 a month should be allowed for living expenses. Another $80 a year will be necessary for tuition fees, etc.

STUDENT LIFE ... There are a large number of student organizations at Dutch universities; the *Corpora,* the oldest of these, still adhere to the old customs. There is an initiation period during which the freshman is indoctrinated.

The general student association which has been instituted at all universities will, it is hoped, provide a real binding force for the enormously increased student population. It has the function too of looking after the general social and cultural well-being of the student community.

UNIVERSITY OF LEYDEN

The city of Leyden lies 22 miles southwest of Amsterdam on the Rhine River. It is the birthplace of the great painters Rembrandt van Rijn, Jan Steen and Gerard Dou. Prince William of Orange founded a university here in 1575 to reward the citizens for their heroic defense against a siege by the Spaniards in 1572. The Pilgrims lived in Leyden for eleven years before sailing for America. Avenues of trees border Leyden's canals, which serve as commercial routes in summer and as skating rinks in winter.

The University at Leyden was founded in 1575 by Prince William of Orange. Great festivities attended the opening. A pageant was held in which symbolical figures represented the four faculties of Divinity, Law, Medicine and Philosophy.

The social revolutions of the nineteenth century hardly affected the Netherlands. However, during the course of a few decades, the form of government changed from an absolute monarchy to a liberal democracy. In 1848 the principle of complete freedom of education was incorporated in the constitution. The Education Act of 1876 converted the old academies and universities into the State Universities of Leyden, Groningen, Utrecht, and the Municipal University of Amsterdam. The University is governed by a Board of Curators, or Directors, who form a mediating body between the government and the State University. The internal affairs are directed by the Academical Senate, consisting of the entire body of professors and presided over by one of them called Rector Magnificus.

SIZE ... There are about 6,300 students, including 200 foreign students.

CALENDAR ... There is no division of the academic year into semesters in the Netherlands. The University session begins in the last week of September and ends at the beginning of July, with vacations of about four weeks at Christmas and three weeks at Easter.

COURSES OF STUDY ... The University of Leyden has seven departments or faculties: Theology, Law, Medicine, Science, the Arts, Economics, and Political and Social Sciences.

TUITION ... See the section on Tuition in the opening summary on the Netherlands.

ADMISSION REQUIREMENTS ... See the Admission Requirements section in the opening summary on the Netherlands.

LANGUAGE OF INSTRUCTION ... Dutch. Some of the summer courses are conducted in English, French and German.

University of Leiden, Main Building

ACCOMMODATIONS ... All students must find their own rooms in private homes or boardinghouses. The Student Information Office has a special lodgings department to assist the students in finding suitable accommodations. Most students have breakfast and lunch at their lodgings, but have dinner out. About $110 a month should be allowed for living expenses. Another $80 a year will be necessary for tuition fees, etc.

STUDENT LIFE ... There are a large number of student organizations at Dutch universities; the *Corpora,* the oldest of these, still adhere to the old customs. The general student association which has been instituted at all universities will, it is hoped, provide a real binding force for the enormously increased student population. It has the function too of looking after the general social and cultural well-being of the student community.

UNIVERSITY OF NIJMEGEN

Nijmegen is near the German border. It is an inland shipping center ten miles from Arnhem on the Waal River. Among the interesting sights of the city are a sixteenth-century Latin school, and the remains of Palace Valkhof built by Charlemagne in 777. In the Second World War, in 1944, Nijmegen was the scene of a United States airborne landing.

SIZE ... There are about 3,500 students, including 70 foreign students.

CALENDAR ... There is no division of the academic year into semesters in the Netherlands. The university session begins in the last week of September and ends at the beginning of July, with vacations of about four weeks at Christmas and three weeks at Easter.

COURSES OF STUDY ... The University of Nijmegen has six faculties: Theology (only graduates of a Roman Catholic seminary are admitted to the 3-year course in Theology at Nijmegen University), Law, Medicine, Science (Natural Sciences), Arts (Humanities), and Social Sciences. The University at Nijmegen does not have as great a variety of subjects as do the state universities.

TUITION ... See the section on Tuition in the opening summary on the Netherlands.

ADMISSION REQUIREMENTS ... See the Admission Requirements section in the opening summary on the Netherlands.

LANGUAGE OF INSTRUCTION ... Dutch. Some of the summer courses are conducted in English, French, or German.

ACCOMMODATIONS ... All students must find their own rooms in private homes or boardinghouses. The Student Information Office has a special lodgings department to assist the students in finding suitable accommodations. Most students have breakfast and lunch at their lodgings but get dinner out. About $110 a month should be allowed for living expenses. Another $80 a year will be necessary for tuition fees, etc.

STUDENT LIFE ... There are a large number of student organizations at Dutch universities; the *Corpora,* the oldest of these, still adhere to the old customs. There is an initiation period during which the freshman is indoctrinated.

The general student association which has been instituted at all universities will, it is hoped, provide a real binding force for the enormously increased student population. It has the function too of looking after the general social and cultural well-being of the student community.

UNIVERSITY OF UTRECHT

The City of Utrecht, in the very center of the Netherlands, is located on the Rhine River about 22 miles southeast of Amsterdam. Utrecht is called the city of spires and bridges because of its many churches and the bridges over its two canals. Utrecht has seen long centuries of history. It was a Rhine River crossing in Roman times, became a bishopric in 696 and received a town charter in 1122. Utrecht revolted against Spain in 1577; it became the headquarters of the anti-Spanish Union of Utrecht in 1579, resulting in the formation of the United Provinces. The Treaty of Utrecht in 1713 ended the War of Spanish Succession.

The University of Utrecht was founded in 1636, although as early as 1470 the Town Council had been considering the foundation of a university. This university enjoyed European prestige for many years. The social revolutions of the nineteenth century hardly affected the Netherlands. However, during the course of a few decades the form of government changed from an absolute monarchy to a liberal democracy. In 1848 the principle of complete freedom of education was incorporated in the constitution. The Education Act of 1876 converted the old academies and universities into the State Universities of Utrecht, Leyden, Groningen, and the Municipal University of Amsterdam.

The University is governed by a Board of Curators, or Directors, who form a mediating body between the government and the State University. The internal affairs are directed by the Academical Senate, consisting of the entire body of professors and presided over by one of these called Rector Magnificus.

SIZE ... There are about 6,000 students, including 200 foreign students.

CALENDAR ... There is no division of the academic year into semesters in the Netherlands. The university session begins in the last week of September and ends at the beginning of July, with vacations of about four weeks at Christmas and three weeks at Easter.

COURSES OF STUDY ... The University of Utrecht has seven departments or faculties: Theology, Law, Medicine, Science, Arts, Economics, and Political and Social Sciences.

TUITION ... See the section on Tuition in the opening summary on the Netherlands.

ADMISSION REQUIREMENTS ... See the Admission Requirements section in the opening summary on the Netherlands.

LANGUAGE OF INSTRUCTION ... Dutch. Some of the summer courses are conducted in English, French, or German.

ACCOMMODATIONS ... All students must find their own rooms in private homes or boardinghouses. The Student Information Office has a special lodgings department to assist the students in finding suitable accommodations. Most students have breakfast and lunch at their lodgings but get dinner out. About $110 a month should be allowed for living expenses. Another $80 a year will be necessary for tuition fees, etc.

STUDENT LIFE ... There are a large number of student organizations at Dutch universities; the *Corpora,* the oldest of these, still adhere to the old customs. There is an initiation period during which the freshman is indoctrinated.

The general student association which has been instituted at all universities will, it is hoped, provide a real binding force for the enormously increased student population. It has the function too of looking after the general social and cultural well-being of the student community.

University of Utrecht, Main Building

NEW ZEALAND

In New Zealand there are institutions of higher learning in various parts of the country, each of them preparing and examining students and awarding degrees. These include the University of Otago at Dunedin; the University of Canterbury at Christchurch; the University of Auckland at Auckland; the Victoria University of Wellington at Wellington; Massey University of Manawatu at Palmerston North and the University of Waikato at Hamilton (which began enrolling students in 1965). There is also Lincoln College, a constituent of the University of Canterbury, specializing in agriculture. The government has recently decided that a School of Veterinary Science should be opened at Massey University. Previously, New Zealand veterinarians were trained in Australia.

Each of the six universities conducts the usual courses in the Liberal Arts, Law, Science, Commerce and Music, in addition to first-year courses for certain professional degrees. Each, in addition, specializes in certain fields. The University of Otago: medicine, dentistry, home science, theology, physical education, mining and metallurgical engineering. The University of Canterbury: fine arts, engineering (mechanical, civil, electrical and chemical). The University of Auckland: architecture (including town planning), engineering (electrical, mechanical and civil) and fine arts. It also has a postgraduate Department of Obstetrics and Gynecology. Victoria University of Wellington: public administration, social science (social work) and nuclear science. There is also a Department of Asian Studies. Massey University of Manawatu: various branches of agriculture, food science and biotechnology. Special facilities are provided for extramural studies and Colombo Plan students. The English Language Institute offers a diploma course in the techniques of teaching English for selected teachers from Southeast Asia, and a course in English for Colombo Plan students. The first year in most professional courses may be taken at any of these six universities. Lincoln College prepares students for degrees in Horticulture, Agriculture and Agricultural Science and for diplomas in a variety of branches of agriculture and horticulture.

NEW ZEALAND UNIVERSITY SYSTEM ... The New Zealand University System differs considerably from that of the United States. Courses for the First degrees of B.A., B.Sc. and B. Com. require a minimum of three years' study and are made up of units. Each unit represents one year's work in a subject, e.g., eight units are required for B.Sc. degree and nine units for B.A. degree. Examinations for Bachelor's and Master's degrees are taken annually in October/November. The minimum number of years of study for other First degrees is as follows: B.Agr., 3 years; B.H.Sc., B.Agr.Sc., B.E. (civil, electrical mechanical, metallurgical or mining), Mus.B., 4 years; LL.B., B.E. (Chem.), B.D.S., B.Med.Sc., 5 years; M.B., Ch.B., 6 years.

ADMISSION REQUIREMENTS ... Normally, to gain entrance as an undergraduate to any of the teaching institutions, an applicant must have passed the New Zealand Universities' Entrance Examination, but any person who has taken a similar course and who has attained a standard substantially equivalent to that required for the entrance examination may be admitted.

To gain entrance to graduate courses, the courses taken and the standards attained by students at universities in other countries must be substantially equivalent to the courses and standards required of graduates of New Zealand universities.

An applicant who has not passed the entrance examination but who meets the requirements as above, or who is not a graduate of one of the universities of New Zealand but is equivalent thereto, is entitled to be admitted *ad eudem gradum*. An applicant for admission *ad eundem gradum* must make written application to the Registrar of the university concerned, enclosing:

a) evidence of his academic standing and of any degree obtained at his former university

b) a statutory declaration of identity

c) a prescribed fee (approximately $7 entrance status; $14 graduate status or with credits toward a degree).

CALENDAR ... In most degree courses the university year commences in March and is divided into three terms, usually March–May, June–August, and September–November. The long vacation is from November to March and there is a 3-week vacation between terms. Graduation exercises take place at the end of the first term, usually the first week in May.

Each course for a Bachelor's degree consists of a certain number of units and at least a minimum number of subjects, a unit being defined as one year's work in one of the subjects prescribed for the degree. A first-year course (Stage I) must be passed before a second-year course (Stage II) can be taken. A candidate for a Master's degree studies one, or at most two, subjects at an advanced level.

SUMMER COURSES ... Although no official summer courses are offered by the universities, special agriculture courses, as well as refresher courses in methods for teachers, are given at Massey and Lincoln Universities.

TUITION AND OTHER COSTS ... Most fees range from $44 to $88 per subject per year. Student Association fees are approximately $14 per annum. The approximate cost of study and residence for a full-time student from overseas is as follows: tuition, examination and miscellaneous fees, $84 to $154; board (either private or hostel during term and private during vacation), $700; clothes, books, travel, etc., $420 to $560.

Annual tuition fees for lectures and laboratories in each subject for various degree courses are approximately as follows: Liberal Arts, $44; Science, $31; Law, $33; Commerce, $44; Engineering, $192. Medicine: first year, approximately $270 tuition, $6 exam; second to fifth years inclusive, approximately $756 tuition, $364 exam; sixth year, approximately $33 tuition.

CREDIT TOWARD AN AMERICAN DEGREE ... A student must make arrangements for receiving credit toward an American degree from his own university before he leaves home. A student may get "Terms" from the professor or lecturer in a course if he has attended over 70 per cent of the lectures, and has completed all laboratory work and assignments satisfactorily. This is not an official recognition by the University but is only the student's permit to sit the exam at the end of the school year. A student may earn a C.O.P. (certificate of proficiency) if he passes the course examination but is not taking the course toward a degree. The C.O.P. is an official statement by the University.

REGULATIONS ... A visa is necessary for a student who will spend more than three months in New Zealand. Students should check on this and on customs regulations at the nearest

New Zealand Consulate. The New Zealand Government does not offer assistance to any foreign students apart from those who are nominated by recipient governments under the Colombo Plan, which is confined solely to Southeast Asia.

ACCOMMODATIONS . . . There are accommodations in the University Hostel (dormitory); private home accommodations can also be found and students can share a flat and do some of their own cooking to cut expenses. All students may eat their noon and evening meals at the University dining halls, whether or not they live in the hostels.

COMMON COURTESIES AND LOCAL CUSTOMS . . . Virtually all stores are closed on Saturdays and Sundays. People retire early at night, and it is safe to say you will find very little night life. Traffic drives on the left. There are many cars and a fair number of bicycles. Morning and afternoon tea are served.

FOR FURTHER INFORMATION . . . For complete information about a university and how to enroll, write to the Registrar of the university concerned.

For travel particulars and documentation, write to Educational Department, NHE, Pan American Airways, Pan Am Building, New York, N. Y. 10017.

HOW TO GET THERE . . . By Pan American Jet Clipper from San Francisco, Los Angeles, Seattle or Portland, to Auckland via Honolulu. The elapsed time is about 14¾ hours from the Pacific Coast, 12 hours from Honolulu, or 5 hours from Fiji. By ship, about 17 days from San Francisco.

NORWAY

NORWAY

BERGEN
★
OSLO

I take this opportunity to welcome American students to Norway to pursue their academic studies in my country.

As in most other countries, education in Norway is on the move. More children need more classrooms, adequately equipped, for primary education; more youngsters than ever before go on to secondary schools, and an increasing number of students receive academic training in our universities or other institutions of higher learning.

The large number of Norwegian applicants, unfortunately, restricts the admission of foreigners in certain fields of study—especially engineering, medicine and dentistry. In other fields, however, well qualified students from abroad will find ample opportunities. They may rest assured that their stay in Norway will be worth their while, and that they will be made to feel at home by Norwegian hospitality.

Arvid Sveum
Director-General
Office of Cultural Relations
Oslo, Norway

HIGHER EDUCATION IN NORWAY ... Education on a university level in Norway dates back to the beginning of the last century, when Norway's first university was founded in Oslo by Royal Order in 1811. It was opened in 1813, one year before the union between Denmark and Norway was dissolved. This was the only university until 1946, when Norway's second university was established in Bergen. Both universities are state institutions.

Special institutions of university rank have been established to offer instruction in the fields of agriculture, engineering, business administration, economics, etc. These include: the Technical University of Norway, which has Departments of Architecture, Geology, Civil, Electrical and Mechanical Engineering, Chemistry, Naval Architecture and Aeronautics; the State College for Physical Education; the State College for Teachers; the State College of Business Administration and Economics; the State College of Agriculture; the State Veterinary College; and the Independent Theological College. The technical schools are very crowded and could probably not take foreign students. The Scandinavian Seminar offers a 9-month study program in Norway based on the Folk High Schools. It extends from early August until May. (For a more detailed description, see under Denmark.)

NORWEGIAN UNIVERSITY SYSTEM ... The Norwegian university system is similar to that of other European universities in that it aims at giving students instruction in academic subjects and introducing them to methodical scientific research. In general, students are not required to attend lectures or classes, and it is up to them whether they acquire their knowledge from the courses or on their own, since they are generally permitted to present themselves for examination when they feel prepared. After enrollment there is a fundamental course in philosophy which is required of all students. There are also prerequisite courses in some faculties; in Liberal Arts, for instance, students must qualify in phonetics and linguistics, and also in Latin, if they have not matriculated "on the Latin side" (as a major course of secondary school study),

ADMISSION REQUIREMENTS ... The matriculation examination, or "school leaving examination," forms the basis for entrance to specialized studies at universities and institutes of higher learning. Students from the United States must have a high school diploma and two years at an accredited college in order to matriculate at a Norwegian university. Scandinavian Seminar is open to qualified college undergraduates (except

freshmen), graduates and other adults. There are no specific education prerequisites. Each applicant is considered on his merits. No knowledge of the Scandinavian language is required prior to acceptance; however, the student generally attains fluent knowledge of Norwegian before the end of the Seminar year.

CREDIT TOWARD AN AMERICAN DEGREE ... Students who are candidates for a degree in an American university must make arrangements with their dean regarding transfer of credits before applying for admission to a university in Norway.

A certificate of attendance and grades may be transferred provided the student is a regular student at the university for at least one semester. A certificate is awarded for attendance at a summer school course.

The Scandinavian Seminar program issues a certificate of completion, and an evaluation of the student's performance may be sent to his college upon request as a basis for granting credit.

REGULATIONS ... For student visa and entrance procedure, see the For Further Information heading at the end of this section.

TUITION ... None, except in summer school and Scandinavian Seminar. There is a small charge for the use of laboratories and for examinations.

All students are required to become members of the Student Union. Each student pays a matriculation fee of about $14 and a semester fee of about $3.

The 6-week summer school course at the University of Oslo charges a total basic fee of $357.

The Scandinavian Seminar fee for board, room, tuition and travel in Norway amounts to about $1,800.

LIVING COSTS ... The cost of living in Norway is considerably lower than in the United States, especially for food and rent. Student Town in Oslo, run by the Student Union, will house about 1,200 students at very reasonable rates. Groups of five students share a kitchen and bathroom.

The Student Union also runs student restaurants and cafeterias, and its policy is to produce one decent hot meal a day "at such a price that the students simply cannot afford to miss it."

The exchange rate is 7.15 kroner to the dollar.

LOCAL CUSTOMS ... The Norwegians are an active, outdoor people. Dress is informal and sweaters and some warm clothing are desirable even in summer. In winter, warm, heavy clothing is essential, because of Norwegian ideas of heating.

Eiderdowns take the place of top sheets even in the hotels.

FOR FURTHER INFORMATION ... For complete information about a university and how to enroll, write to the Norwegian Information Service, 290 Madison Avenue, New York, N. Y. 10016. Those interested in the Scandinavian Seminar program should contact Scandinavian Seminar for Cultural Study, 62 West 58th Street, New York, N.Y. 10019.

For travel particulars and documentation, write to Educational Department, NHE, Pan American Airways, Pan Am Building, New York, N. Y. 10017.

HOW TO GET THERE ... Through-plane service by Pan American Jet Clipper to Oslo, 7 hours from New York (or connect from Jet Clippers to Copenhagen). By ship, 7 days to Bergen, 8 days to Oslo.

UNIVERSITY OF BERGEN

Bergen is Norway's second largest city. It is a happy blend of medieval, Renaissance and modern architecture.

Edvard Grieg, the great Norwegian composer, made his

University of Bergen, Geophysical Institute

University of Oslo

home here. Bergen is the starting point for the famous coastal express steamers to the Land of the Midnight Sun. The fjord country in western Norway which these steamers visit is unforgettably beautiful.

The University of Bergen was developed from the Bergen Museum, which was established in 1825. The Museum was originally primarily a scientific institution. It was recognized as a university by the National Assembly in 1946 but, without examination rights, had served as a research and teaching institution of university rank for many years prior to this date.

The govering body of the University of Bergen is the University Senate, which administers the University as a whole. At present the University of Bergen has three faculties: Liberal Arts, Natural Science (Mathematics and Science) and Medicine. There is keen competition among Norwegian students for admission to the so-called closed studies (medicine, dentistry), and for this reason, foreign students are not eligible.

A number of institutes for research work and teaching have been established within each faculty at this university as at Oslo.

At the University of Bergen, the Faculty of Medicine operates in conjunction with Haukeland Hospital, which serves as a university clinic.

SIZE ... There are 2,000 students, including 100 foreign students.

CALENDAR ... The academic year is divided into two terms: first week of September to mid-December, and mid-January to mid-June.

In the spring term, classes are interrupted for about 12 days at Easter.

There is a summer session from mid-July to mid-August.

SUMMER COURSES ... A course in Norweigian language and culture is offered in July and August.

ADMISSION REQUIREMENTS ... It is recommended that foreign students begin their studies at the University of Bergen by attendance at the earlier mentioned special 6-week summer session. See also the Admission Requirements section in the opening summary on Norway.

LANGUAGE OF INSTRUCTION ... Norwegian.

ACCOMMODATIONS ... The Student Union provides accommodations at low rates and also operates a billeting office where students may sign up for rooms with private families.

The Student Union also operates a restaurant and cafeteria to provide good meals at reasonable prices.

AVERAGE COSTS ... Board and room will be about $23 per week; matriculation fee, $14, and a semester fee of about $3; books and supplies, about $15 per term; incidentals, about $30 per month.

STUDENT LIFE ... A great number of student associations, societies, and clubs have been organized at the universities. Membership is voluntary, but most students join one or more during their period of study.

Exploring the city will be a rewarding experience. This was a Hanseatic town, and the museum gives an excellent idea of the culture of old Norway.

The art gallery and the ethnological collection at Bergen University are outstanding.

UNIVERSITY OF OSLO

The 900-year-old city of Oslo is surrounded by wooded hills. The oldest part of the city still standing is a survival of 300 years ago. The Castle Akershus, partly built by Haakon the Fifth

(1299–1319), is its high point. The rest of the city is beautifully laid out on the harbor with the Oslo Fjord beyond and parks all around.

The University of Oslo was opened in 1813. Its beautiful buildings are near the Royal Palace in downtown Oslo. New science buildings have been added to the University at Blindern just outside the city. The governing body of the University is the Senate (Collegium Academicum), which administers the University as a whole.

The University of Oslo is organized in seven faculties: Theology, Law, Medicine, Liberal Arts (History and Philosophy), Natural Science (Mathematics and Science), Odontology, Social Sciences.

In 1947 the University of Oslo organized its first Summer School of Norwegian Civilization for English-speaking foreign students. In 1958, the name was changed to the International Summer School. The core of the curriculum is a general survey course of Norwegian civilization. The essential purpose of the Oslo School is academic. Instruction is in English. During the regular sessions of the University, Norweigian language courses are arranged for foreigners.

SIZE ... About 6,300, including 250 foreign students.

CALENDAR ... The academic year is divided into two terms: first week of September to mid-December, and mid-January to mid-June. In the spring term, classes are interrupted for about twelve days at Easter.

The summer session is held each year from the end of June to the first week in August.

SUMMER COURSES ... Courses in Norwegian language, Norwegian literature, history, art, music, social problems, international relations and geography. International Teachers' Institute: educational system of Norway and physical education in Scandinavia. Special course on medical care and public health services in Norway.

ADMISSION REQUIREMENTS ... It is recommended that foreign students begin their studies at the University of Oslo by attendance at the special 6-week summer session. See also the Admission Requirements section in the opening summary on Norway.

LANGUAGE OF INSTRUCTION ... Norwegian. (Instruction at the summer school is in English.)

ACCOMMODATIONS ... Student Town in Oslo, run by the Student Union, will house about 1,200 students at very reasonable rates. Groups of five students share a kitchen and bathroom.

The Student Union also runs student restaurants and cafeterias, and its policy is to produce one decent hot meal a day "at such a price that the students simply cannot afford to miss it." During the summer session single students will be housed at the Blindern Students' Hall, and accommodations for married couples will be found in the central dormitory building or in rooms with private families.

Meals during the summer session are served in the cafeteria.

AVERAGE COSTS ... Board and room will be about $23 per week. Matriculation fee, $14, and a semester fee of about $3. Books and supplies, about $15 per term; incidentals, about $30 per month. The summer course charges a total basic fee of $357. Single students should allow about $110 per month for room, board and incidentals.

STUDENT LIFE ... Norwegians are an active, outdoor people, and the student from the United States will find hiking and skiing everywhere in Norway. Ski touring is very popular and huts and lodges dot the routes of cross-country runs. Students will enjoy seeing the Viking Ship Museum, the Kon-Tiki raft and many other sights in Oslo. (There are regular sightseeing tours by boat down the Oslo Fjord.)

The Student Union runs a bookshop, a housing office, a travel bureau, a publishing house, and a kindergarten for students' children.

PERU

PERU

★ LIMA

UNIVERSITIES OF PERU ... The three main universities in Peru are the University of San Marcos, which is the oldest university in the Western Hemisphere, Catholic University and the University of Trujillo. All three universities offer a wide range of educational opportunities. Peru has a long tradition of private, Catholic education on a high academic level. The Catholic University of Peru, founded in 1917, is the focus of Catholic thought today. This university with its 3,000 students is located in the heart of Lima.

PERUVIAN UNIVERSITY SYSTEM ... Due to the rapidly increasing population, a new Peruvian Education Plan was adopted in 1956. This nationwide plan of educational expansion called for the reorganization of technical education for young men and women, including agricultural, industrial, and commercial courses, home economics, engineering and related studies. It also began teacher-training programs to raise the standards of the teaching profession. Education in Peru is largely controlled by the Ministry of Education and is to a great extent financed and subsidized by the Ministry.

ADMISSION REQUIREMENTS ... All foreign students applying for admission as regular students must have completed high school and must be acquainted with the Peruvian culture as well as the language and are compelled to pass the entrance examinations at San Marcos. Requests for admission must be presented during the months of November and December and records must be duly legalized by the Peruvian Consulate. If students have spent a year in a foreign university they are exempt from the entrance examination requirements. Documents certifying this fact must be validated by the Ministry of Education in Peru.

CREDIT TOWARD AN AMERICAN DEGREE ... In order for a U.S. student to receive credit for work done at a Peruvian university, he must have his courses evaluated by the American university in which he is enrolled.

REGULATIONS ... For student visa and entrance procedure, see the For Further Information heading at the end of this section.

TUITION ... Tuition fees at Peruvian universities are generally very low as the Peruvian government wants to make college training available to a greater number of students.

LIVING COSTS ... Board and lodging in Lima may be had from about $90 per month. The total cost for tuition and other fees involved in studying at a Peruvian university for the year is about $20.

COMMON COURTESIES AND LOCAL CUSTOMS ... Lima is proud of its traditions and preserves many old customs. Life goes on at a comparatively leisurely pace and social activities are inclined to be formal. Tea, from 5:30 to 7:00 p.m., is an important daily event. The dinner hour is from 9:00 p.m. on. As in most Latin American countries, both men and women shake hands on meeting and saying good-bye.

FOR FURTHER INFORMATION ... For complete information about a university and how to enroll, write to the individual university. For information on the University of San Marcos, write to: UNIVERSIDAD NACIONAL MAYOR DE SAN MARCOS, Avenida Nicolas de Pierola 1222 (Parque Universitario), Lima, Peru.

For travel particulars and documentation, write to Educa-

tional Department, NHE, Pan American Airways, Pan Am Building, New York, N. Y. 10017.

HOW TO GET THERE ... By National, Pan American and Panagra interchange, direct Jet service, about 6½ hours from Miami; 10 hours from New York. Lima is a popular stop on Round-South-America itineraries.

UNIVERSITY OF SAN MARCOS, LIMA

San Marcos, the oldest university on the South American continent, had its beginnings in the Dominican monastery in Lima. The University was founded on May 12, 1551, by Royal Decree of his Spanish Majesty Charles V and organized on the basis of the University of Salamanca, which had existed in Spain since 1181.

Although the University is situated in the heart of Lima, faculties and institutions are functioning not only within the city, but on the outskirts and in the suburbs as well.

San Marcos, from its beginning to the present day, has been considered the most advanced university in Latin America.

SIZE ... There are approximately 13,500 students (co-educational) enrolled in the University's ten faculties.

CALENDAR ... The academic year begins in May and the final exams take place in December. January, February, and March are vacation months. Toward the end of March, however, examinations are held for those students who were unable to take their examinations in December. The summer school for foreign students is conducted during the months of July and August. The seasons, as in other Latin American countries, are reversed in Peru. Spring begins in September. Summer starts in December. January through April is the ideal season in Lima.

COURSES OF STUDY ... The University of San Marcos is composed of the following ten faculties: Law, Medicine, Letters, Science, Economic Science, Pharmacy and Biochemistry, Odontology, Education, Chemistry, and Veterinary Medicine.

SUMMER COURSES ... The summer school at the University of San Marcos offers a 7-week course for foreign students beginning in July and terminating in August. Classes are conducted in both Spanish and English. For those classes taught in Spanish, the students will be provided with outlines in English. The summer course offers the following nine subjects, three of which are compulsory: The compulsory subjects: 1) Spanish (beginning, intermediate, and advanced); 2) Peruvian Art and Folklore; 3) History of Peruvian Culture. The optional subjects: 4) Latin American Literature; 5) American Archaeology; 6) General American Culture and Economic Problems; 7) Latin American Geo-Sociology; 8) Education in Peru; 9) History of Latin American Art.

In all the courses the emphasis is on the Peruvian aspect. In addition to the classes mentioned above, there are excursions to points of interest in and near Lima, and also lectures and social activities sponsored by the University of San Marcos.

If the students so wish, they may attend summer school courses in the city of Cuzco. The subjects offered in Cuzco are 1) Archaeology, 2) Ethnology, 3) Art and Folklore. Five credits are granted for each subject. The prices of the summer school courses, which are subject to change, are as follows: in Lima—$100; in Cuzco—$150.

Transportation to and from Cuzco and accommodations, if included in students' plans, will cost approximately $80.

TUITION ... The total cost for tuition and other fees for a year is approximately $20, depending on the faculty. (Medicine, for example, is much more.)

ADMISSION REQUIREMENTS ... A foreign student must sit for an entrance examination according to a questionnaire published each year in advance. If the pupil has already been registered in a foreign university, his matriculation in the University of San Marcos would not be subject to the entrance exam. Registration can be for all courses or only some, according to the student's wishes. See also the Admission Requirements section in the opening summary on Peru.

LANGUAGE OF INSTRUCTION ... All classes at the University of San Marcos are in Spanish. During the months of July and August, however, a special summer school course is given in English and Spanish for the benefit of foreign students.

ACCOMMODATIONS ... The University of San Marcos provides a list of approved accommodations in hotels, boarding-houses and private homes and will make reservations for lodging upon the request of a student, since the University has no dormitory facilities.

AVERAGE COSTS ... Pensions cost from $4.40 to $6 a day. A de luxe hotel runs about $12 to $14 per day with meals. The University can assist in locating board and lodging in Lima for approximately $90 per month.

STUDENT LIFE ... Generally speaking social life for the student at the University of San Marcos is not very active. The premises are designed in true colonial fashion for purely academic pursuits. There is a gymnasium attached to the University which is used for sporting events, etc. Dances and social gatherings are not very common. There are, however, a spring festival and a Christmas party arranged by the Students' Union.

THE PHILIPPINES

QUEZON CITY
MANILA

THE PHILIPPINES

The avidity of the Filipino people for education is unsurpassed. It is the paramount ambition of every Filipino parent to send his or her children to school and, if possible, to college. This accounts for the fact that about 5 million young people are enrolled in the public and private schools and institutions of higher learning and about one-third of the annual budget is allocated to education.

The history of higher education in the Philippines dates back to 1611, when the Pontifical University of Santo Tomás was established.

The universities in the Philippines are for the most part patterned after the universities in the United States. They offer courses in practically all professions. Their curricula and methods of instruction are very similar to those in American universities. The medium of instruction is English. Most of the colleges and universities are co-educational.

Etta C. Enriquez
Cultural Attaché
Philippine Mission to the United Nations

UNIVERSITIES OF THE PHILIPPINES ... Over 100 college-level institutions in the Philippines; these include the one state university—the University of the Philippines in Manila and its branch, Iloilo College at Iloilo City—and the private universities and colleges. Public and private education are controlled by separate bureaus of the Philippine Department of Public Instruction. The Bureau of Public Schools of the Department administers public education; this system usually consists of a 4-year primary school, a 3-year intermediate school, and a 4-year secondary school. The Bureau of Private Schools of the Department administers private educational institutions; the usual pattern for this system is a one-year kindergarten, 4-year primary school, 3-year intermediate school, and 4-year secondary school. Many of the private institutions include elementary and secondary schools as well as universities. The University of the Philippines is co-educational, as are many of the private institutions. Religious groups, including some missionary groups from the United States, founded or maintain a number of the college-level institutions in the Philippines, including De La Salle, Ateneo de Manila, and San Juan de Letran Colleges.

PHILIPPINE UNIVERSITY SYSTEM ... The state university in Manila, the University of the Philippines, is organized much like a state institution in the United States; its teaching methods and procedures are similar. In general a Bachelor's degree requires four years' study. Certain courses leading to advanced or special degrees require a longer period of study. English is the language of instruction for all universities in the Philippine Islands. Most of the private institutions are 4-year colleges which grant a Bachelor's degree upon completion of the course, but again, certain courses require longer study and lead to advanced degrees.

ADMISSION REQUIREMENTS ... These vary from university to university. Generally, foreign students must have graduated from an accredited secondary school and have two years of college to be eligible for admission. For some private institutions, application must be made to the Bureau of Private Schools, Department of Public Instruction. Certain private universities require foreign students to submit their entire previous academic record to the Bureau of Private Schools for evaluation and classification; some institutions have special entrance examinations for foreign students; others except American students

from some of these formalities. Entrance examinations are conducted in the English language.

CREDIT TOWARD AN AMERICAN DEGREE ... A student must make arrangements for receiving credit toward an American degree from his own university before he leaves the United States. Because of the variations in credit systems within American universities, it is impossible to generalize about the number of credit hours a student may receive. Each student should discuss with his own dean or guidance counselor the requirements for receiving credit and the number of credit hours toward his American degree that may be awarded for the study abroad. Sometimes full credit may be given for the period of study in the Philippines if the student passes the Philippine examinations. It is well for students to remember that some Philippine universities do not give credit for the work done unless the examinations are taken—and that examinations cannot be taken unless a full academic load is carried. Other Philippine universities are very strict about admitting students of other universites and require a letter of permission from the dean or director of the student's original college or university. On the other hand, some Philippine universities are set up according to a pattern much like American universities and the transfer of credit will not be difficult. Each American university will make its own evaluation of the study at each Philippine university. Certain diplomas or certificates can be earned from some Philippine universities.

REGULATIONS ... Besides a valid American passport, the American student must have a visa for entry into the Philippines. He must have also a smallpox vaccination certificate (considered valid in the Philippines up to three years from date of issue). The nearest Philippine Consulate can give full details of documents required for obtaining the student visa, which costs $15 and is valid for one year. An unlimited amount of foreign currency may be taken into the Philippines but it must be declared at the time of entry into the country. Students should inform themselves of the currency and other regulations regarding entry into the Philippine Islands.

TUITION AND OTHER COSTS ... Cost of tuition and other expenses of matriculation, registration, student health, activities, and special courses vary greatly from one university to another and from one faculty or college to another within the university. Tuition is charged each semester and varies from about $55 to about $250, depending upon the faculty concerned. Students should expect to pay in addition to the tuition a minimum of $10 per semester for medical, laboratory, matriculation, new student, and activities fees. As in American universities, there are fees for late registration, above the regular charge. A minimum tuition of about $150 should be allotted for one academic year.

LIVING COSTS ... There is not enough space in dormitories to accommodate all students, and many must live off the campus—in private homes, in boardinghouses, sometimes in apartments, and sometimes in privately operated dormitories. Room and board with a family or in a private dormitory cost from about $40 to about $80 per month. Food will be typical of the country, however, and students who want Western-style food must expect to pay a little more for it.

COMMON COURTESIES AND LOCAL CUSTOMS ... Philippine students carry on the tradition of extending lavish hospitality to visitors; American students will feel very much at home. But the scenery and the people and many of the customs will be unfamiliar. University students follow the local mode of dress and men will be seen in long or short-sleeved shirts of cotton, silk, or rayon with plain or Hawaiian prints, with shirt tails designed to be worn outside the trousers. The *barong Tagalong,* made of Philippine piña cloth, ramie cloth and sometimes of very fine synthetic textiles as nylon and dacron, will also be seen, mostly in the evenings. Coats and ties are generally worn in offices.

FOR FURTHER INFORMATION ... For complete information about a university and how to enroll, write directly to the university.

For travel particulars and documentation, write to Educational Department, NHE, Pan American Airways, Pan Am Building, New York, N. Y. 10017.

HOW TO GET THERE ... By Pan American Jet Clipper from Los Angeles via Honolulu, about 18½ hours (elapsed time) to Manila. Saigon is 2½ hours and Singapore is another 1¾ hours. By ship from San Francisco, 17 to 21 days.

MANILA

Manila is on Luzon, the largest of the 7,109 islands in the Philippine group. A warm-weather country, the average temperature remains in the seventies and eighties. There are flowers blooming the year round and many holidays and gay and colorful fiestas make the city a pleasant one. The National Museum and the Art Gallery of the University of the Philippines have good collections of costumes and art, literature, and weapons; the Manila Symphony Orchestra offers concerts; there are frequently ballet or other dance performances. Intramuros, the Spanish walled city, now in ruins, and the Malacañang Palace, official residence of the Philippine President, are spots to see. Beach resorts are less than an hour from Manila. The University of Santo Tomás, founded in 1611, is the oldest university in the Philippine Islands and is itself a tourist attraction. The University of Manila, a private institution, was founded in October 1913. It is a member of the International Association of Universities and has a campus in the Sampaloc district of Manila, another campus in the Tondo district.

UNIVERSITY OF THE EAST, MANILA

The University of the East had its beginnings in the Philippine College of Commerce and Business Administration which was set up in April 1947 as an outgrowth of an educational corporation. The University of the East reached university rank on July 3, 1950.

SIZE ... Nearly 37,000 students, including foreign students, attend the University.

CALENDAR ... The academic year opens about the middle of June and closes about the middle of March; there are two semesters, from June to September and from October to March.

COURSES OF STUDY ... The University offers courses in its constituent colleges: College of Liberal Arts, College of Commerce, College of Education, College of Engineering, College of Dentistry, College of Law, and in the Graduate School. Liberal Arts majors offered include English, Filipino, Mathematics, Economics, History, Nursing, Science, and Political Science. The College of Commerce embraces courses in Accounting, Economics, Banking and Finance, Business Management, Taxation and Tariff, Business Administration. Electrical, Mechanical, and other Engineering courses are offered in the College of Engineering.

TUITION ... This varies according to the college entered. Tuition fees start from about $55, depending on the course chosen, per semester plus various additional fees. Medical College students pay $125 tuition and $125 laboratory fees each semester. In addition, a total of about $75 each semester is charged for library, entrance, registration, and other fees. A refundable deposit of $25 must also be made for laboratory

equipment. Students in all other colleges pay miscellaneous fees totaling about $9 per semester.

ADMISSION REQUIREMENTS ... A foreign student from a university abroad which has already been accepted for the "accredited list" of foreign universities established by the University of the East need only present his authenticated credentials to the Registrar of the University of the East. A foreign student from a university abroad not yet appearing on the University of the East accredited list must present his credits for evaluation by the Philippine Bureau of Private Schools; this bureau must certify the student's eligibility to be admitted to the University of the East. See also the Admission Requirements section in the opening summary on the Philippines.

LANGUAGE OF INSTRUCTION ... English.

ACCOMMODATIONS ... Residence halls are not maintained by the University; there are, however, a number of snack bars, canteens, and soda fountains on the campus which serve complete meals at low prices. Many students live with families, in independently operated student houses, or in boardinghouses. The cost of room and board per month ranges from about $40 to about $80.

AVERAGE COSTS ... Tuition fees and other fees about $65 per semester. Room and board about $75 per month.

STUDENT LIFE ... An active Student Government offers a program of activities giving students of widely divergent interests opportunities to participate in extracurricular events. Various professional and social societies, the Women's Club, Historians' Club, Young Educators' Club, recreational groups, and cultural organizations welcome foreign students.

FAR EASTERN UNIVERSITY, MANILA

Far Eastern University was founded in 1934 when the Far Eastern College and the Institute of Accounts, Business and Finance, which was set up in 1928, were merged. The University has a large campus in the heart of the city of Manila.

SIZE ... Nearly 43,000 students attend the University; this includes foreign students and those of all the schools and institutes.

CALENDAR ... The academic year is divided into two semesters, the first from early June to the first half of October, the second from the end of October to about the middle of March. A summer term is also held from about the first of April to mid-May.

COURSES OF STUDY ... Far Eastern University is made up of the Institute of Accounts, Business and Finance, Institute of Arts and Sciences, Institute of Education, Institute of Law, Institute of Medicine, Institute of Technology, School of Nursing, and the Department of Military Science and Tactics. The Institute of Arts and Sciences offers such courses as Economics, English, History, Mathematics, Philosophy, Political Science, Psychology, Sociology, Spanish, Speech, Arts and Speech, and Drama, Botany, Chemistry, Physics and Zoology and many others. The Institute of Technology includes courses for majors in Architecture, Civil, Electrical, Mechanical, and Chemical Engineering, and Surveying. There is also a Graduate Institute.

TUITION ... Tuition varies from institute to institute. For the Arts and Sciences Institute the tuition fee per semester is about $65 for undergraduates carrying the usual load of 18 units. Various charges are made for laboratory classes.

ADMISSION REQUIREMENTS ... Foreign students wishing to enter the University from other colleges or universities must present a transcript of their academic records to the dean or director of the institute or school they wish to enter; a certificate of honorable dismissal from the school previously attended should also be obtained for presentation to the dean or director. Foreign students must file with the Registrar of the University a certified copy of their scholastic records as evaluated by the Bureau of Private Schools of the Philippines. The Bureau will supply students with a Certificate of Eligibility if they meet the standards set up by that Bureau. See also the Admission Requirements section in the opening summary on the Philippines.

LANGUAGE OF INSTRUCTION . . . English.

ACCOMMODATIONS . . . There are a number of canteens or snack bars on the campus where students can take their meals at low cost. The University does not, however, maintain dormitories, and students must look after their own living quarters. Many students live with families, in boardinghouses, or in other student houses. The cost of room and board per month ranges from $20 to $60.

AVERAGE COSTS . . . Tuition and other fees about $65 per semester. Room and board about $75 per month.

STUDENT LIFE . . . Recreational, social, cultural, and intellectual socities and groups exist on the F.E.U. campus; there is an active student government organization, Central Student Organization (FEUCSO). Among the publications are a student newspaper, *Advocate,* a literary journal, *Transition,* the college yearbook, and various technical journals. The University auditorium is used for performances of many internationally famous performers in the arts. There is a club for almost every student interest.

UNIVERSITY OF MANILA

SIZE . . . There are about 5,000 students enrolled in the University, including a few foreign students.

CALENDAR . . . The academic year runs from June to March; there are two semesters: June to October and November to March. A summer session is held during April and May.

COURSES OF STUDY . . . The University of Manila is made up of the College of Liberal Arts, College of Law, College of Education, College of Business Administration, Normal College, School of Foreign Service, and the Graduate School of Law, Graduate School of Education, and the Graduate School of Arts. Among the courses offered are the following: Accounting, Advertising, Anthropology, Banking, Botany, Chemistry, Economics, Education, English Literature, Finance, Foreign Trade, French, Geography, German, Health Education, History, Home Economics, Journalism, Law, Library Science, Management, Marketing, Mathematics, National Language, Philosophy, Physics, Political Science, Sociology, Science, Retailing, Spanish, Statistics, Transportation, and Zoology. Courses designed for pre-law, pre-medicine, pre-nursing and pre-dentistry students are also offered.

TUITION . . . Fees are payable each semester. Tuition varies depending on course chosen, starting at about $55.

ADMISSION REQUIREMENTS . . . A secondary school certificate (high school diploma) from an accredited school is necessary for admission as a freshman student. Students with college or university credits are accepted as transfer students, subject to the authentication of their records by the Bureau of Private Schools of the Philippine Department of Education. Transfer students must present a transcript of their college records for admission to the Department of Education. Any student "on leave" from another university from which he hopes to obtain a degree must have a letter of permission for the absence from his college dean or director in order to attend the University of Manila. In all cases, the student's transcript of records shall be evaluated by the Philippine Department of Education. See also the Admission Requirements section in the opening summary on the Philippines.

LANGUAGE OF INSTRUCTION . . . English.

ACCOMMODATIONS . . . The University does not operate residence halls. A privately maintained dormitory for women is located on the campus, however, and room and board cost about $25 monthly in these accommodations. Board and room in boardinghouses near the campus range from $40 to $80 per month. Laundry fees are from $5 to $7 per month. It is possible for students to take a room in a lodging house for about $5 a month; some houses have cooking facilities and students can prepare their own meals at a cost of about $20 per month.

AVERAGE COSTS . . . Fees about $60 per semester. Room and board about $75 monthly.

STUDENT LIFE . . . The Central Student Council of the University is the main student organization and it arranges athletic events and other recreational, cultural, and social activities for students. There are a number of student publications to which students may contribute; there are class picnics and other social events; there are libraries for study and relaxing reading.

UNIVERSITY OF SANTO TOMÁS (THE CATHOLIC UNIVERSITY OF THE PHILIPPINES), MANILA

SIZE . . . The University has an enrollment of about 27,000 students; this includes about 100 foreign students.

CALENDAR . . . The academic year is divided into semesters: the first semester from June to October; the second semester from the end of October to the end of March. Christmas vacation begins December 22 and ends January 6. A summer session is held during April and May.

COURSES OF STUDY . . . The University has three ecclesiastical faculties including the Faculty of Sacred Theology, the Faculty of Canon Law, and the Faculty of Philosophy. It also has the following civil faculties and colleges: Faculty of Civil Law, Faculty of Medicine and Surgery, Faculty of Pharmacy, Faculty of Philosophy and Letters, Institute of Spanish, Faculty of Engineering, College of Education, including a Department of Home Economics and the Junior Normal School, College of Liberal Arts, College of Commerce and Business Administration, College of Architecture and Fine Arts, including a Department of Painting and Sculpture, Conservatory of Music, College of Nursing, and the Graduate School. Full courses of instruction are offered in each of these faculties, colleges and departments.

TUITION . . . Tuition and common miscellaneous fees vary according to course chosen, starting at about $65.

ADMISSION REQUIREMENTS . . . A secondary school certificate (high school diploma) is required for admission. See also the Admission Requirements section in the opening summary on the Philippines.

LANGUAGE OF INSTRUCTION . . . English.

ACCOMMODATIONS . . . Residence halls are not maintained by the University. Room and board are available in private homes at a cost of about $50 to $75 per month.

STUDENT LIFE . . . The University operates a student restaurant—a popular gathering place for upperclassmen as well as freshmen. There are also a swimming pool, a gymnasium, and a co-operative store for students. The University maintains a museum, a library, and a chapel. Students have fraternities, clubs and organizations of an extracurricular character.

University of Santo Tomás

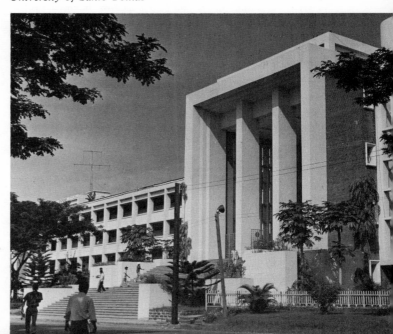

Santo Tomás

QUEZON CITY

The official capital of the Philippines is Quezon City, a suburb of Manila that since December 1948 has been the home of the Philippines' only state university, the University of the Philippines. The city is named after Manuel Quezon, who was President of the Philippine Commonwealth from 1935 until his death in 1944. Señor Quezon was instrumental in planning the move of the University from its former home, Manila, to a site of about 500 hectares at Diliman, a section of Quezon City. The University was founded in 1908. All its buildings and the library were burned during the Second World War. The present modern campus covers gently rolling grounds and is an attraction for tourists. The Carillon Tower houses 45 bells which ring forth periodically during the day. The Tower was built through financial gifts from the University's alumni. The University Medical School remains in Manila.

UNIVERSITY OF THE PHILIPPINES

SIZE ... From 15,000 to 16,000 students attend the regular session of the University; nearly 5,000 the summer institute. Foreign students for both sessions number together 639. Faculty strength more than 1,200. The strong incumbent president, Dr. Vicente G. Sinco, has effected bold and basic reforms in university education. Stiff scholarship standards. Intensive instruction and research.

CALENDAR ... There are six terms of 6 weeks each during the school year (three terms a semester).

COURSES OF STUDY ... The University of the Philippines offers courses in the following colleges and schools: Colleges of Agriculture, of Business Administration, of Education, of Engineering and of Law (Quezon City Unit and Manila Unit); Colleges of Liberal Arts, of Medicine, of Pharmacy and of Veterinary Science; the Conservatory of Music; the Extension Division with centers at Iloilo (Upper Division), at Manila, at Clark Air Base, at Baguio City, Davao City, Hundred Islands (LA), San Pablo City, Subic Bay, Zamboanga City; a Graduate Department; the Institute of Public Administration; the Postgraduate School of Medicine; Schools of Dentistry, of Fine Arts, of Fisheries, of Forestry, of Hygiene, of Nursing and of Public Health Nursing.

TUITION ... Foreign students: about $30 non-resident's fee per semester, unless countries of origin exempt Filipino students studying in those countries from such alien fees.

ADMISSION REQUIREMENTS ... A transcript of record, honorable dismissal and eligibility to transfer are required for admission.

Validation of credits of transfer students from other colleges is required. All freshmen submit to entrance examination. All foreign students are considered for admission on the same basis as Filipino students. Language of instruction is English. See also the Admission Requirements section in the opening summary on the Philippines.

ACCOMMODATIONS ... There are two men's dormitories and three women's dormitories consisting of several buildings on the Diliman campus but only space for a little over 2,000 students is provided and it is difficult for foreign students to secure rooms. Many Philippine students live with private families near the campus, in the suburbs, or in Manila. There are also a few privately operated dormitories for students. Costs for room and board range from about $50 to $75 per month.

STUDENT LIFE ... American students will find themselves made to feel at home by their Filipino counterparts. Among numerous holidays—which provide school vacation days —there are Thanksgiving, National Heroes Day, Good Friday, Maundy Thursday, Labor Day, Philippine Independence Day, and Christmas. All provide students an opportunity to see Philippine-style celebrations, and a Filipino student will be happy to show newcomers the gaiety or the solemnity of the day. The University of the Philippines Symphony Orchestra has established itself in Manila and plays a concert season open to the public. Orchestra members are students at the University's Conservatory of Music. Students will find the new campus at Quezon City a quiet and pleasant place for study and recreation.

POLAND

WARSAW ★
POLAND

●KRAKÓW

Poland's history has been a long succession of violent changes during which the country has grown or shrunk in size and at times disappeared altogether from the map. The Polish people have nevertheless retained a strong national loyalty and patriotism.

Education in Poland has had a long struggle against great odds. During the nineteenth century, after the partition of Poland, teaching in the German section was entirely in German; in the Russian sector, teaching was in Russian only. In Austria alone were Poles allowed to have schools of their own.

When Poland was reborn after World War I, a good educational system was one of the primary objectives of the state. Great strides were made, only to be undone again during World War II.

INSTITUTIONS OF HIGHER LEARNING IN POLAND ... From 1960 to 1966, Poland will be celebrating a thousand years of history as a nation, and for that reason, many special events will take place. The sense of history will be particularly felt in Polish higher institutions of learning, one of which was established in 1364. Jagiellonian University in Krakow has had many noted teachers and students, among them the greatest of Polish scientists, Nicholas Copernicus, who studied in that school during the last decade of the fifteenth century.

There are 76 institutions of higher learning in Poland, with a total student enrollment of about 157,000. Among such schools are eight universities, ten polytechnic institutes, seven schools of agriculture, eight schools of economics, ten medical schools, four teachers colleges, four physical training institutes, two theological academies, five evening engineering schools, seventeen art academies including seven music schools, six schools of the fine arts, three drama colleges and one film college.

Universities where foreign students may enroll are Warsaw University; Jagiellonian University, Krakow; Adam Mickiewicz University, Poznan; and Boleslaw Bierut University, Wroclaw (Breslau). Other higher schools which accept foreign students include the following: Warsaw Polytechnic Institute; Gdansk Polytechnic Institute; the Academy of Mining and Metallurgy in Krakow; the Central School of Agricultural Economy, Warsaw; the Central School of Planning and Statistics, Warsaw; The Academy of Fine Arts, Warsaw; the State Higher Schools of Plastic Arts in Lodz, Wroclaw and Sopot; and the State Higher Schools of Music in Krakow and Warsaw.

POLISH UNIVERSITY SYSTEM ... The universities of Poland and most other institutions of higher education come under the authority of the Ministry of Higher Education. All are state institutions, with the exception of the Catholic University in Lublin, which is under private control.

The first degree conferred by the Polish universities is the Master's degree, and in every field except that of medicine it is achieved after the completion of a 4-year course, a thesis in the subject of specialization, and a final examination. In the field of medicine, studies last for six years and are divided into a 2-year theoretical course and a 4-year practical course.

The University student in Poland is relatively free to arrange his course of study. Attendance in class is voluntary, and in general, a student's success depends on his own initiative and perseverance.

ADMISSION REQUIREMENTS ... A minimum of two years of college (a college degree is preferred) and a recent health certificate are required for all who plan to begin their university studies in Poland. Foreign students are not required to take entrance examinations. However, those without an adequate knowledge of the Polish language must take a one-year course in Polish given by the Ministry of Higher Education prior to admission as first year university students.

CREDIT TOWARD AN AMERICAN DEGREE ... Students who are candidates for a degree in an American university must make arrangements with their dean regarding transfer of credits before applying for admission to a Polish university.

REGULATIONS ... In addition to a valid passport and smallpox certificate, a student requires a visa. He should apply to the Polish Embassy in Washington.

TUITION ... Foreign students pay $50 monthly. This covers the cost of their tuition and their maintenance. It is suggested that an additional $20 per month should cover such extra costs as laundry, excursions, entertainments, etc.

LIVING COSTS ... The student will receive without additional fee a place in a student dormitory, medical care and a stipend of 880 zlotys (about $37) per month. From the latter he will pay approximately 210 zlotys (about $9) per month for meals at a student boardinghouse if he chooses to eat at such an institution.

It is estimated that about $100 per month will cover all costs while in Poland. This, however, does not cover cost of travel to and from Poland, which is the responsibility of the student. The zloty is the unit of currency in Poland. The tourist rate of exchange is 24 to the U.S. dollar.

COMMON COURTESIES AND LOCAL CUSTOMS ... Polish social customs are quite informal. Poles are hospitable and frank. People gather in coffeehouses to exchange views. University students have their own clubs, and some groups have their own cabarets. The chief source of social activities is the Polish Students' Association (Zrzeszenie Studentow Polskich—ZSP).

FOR FURTHER INFORMATION ... For complete information about a university and how to enroll, write to the Cultural Affairs Officer, Embassy of the Polish People's Republic, 2640 16th Street, N.W., Washington, D. C. 20009. Applications for admission should be made prior to May 1 of the academic year in which the student plans to begin his studies.

For travel particulars and documentation, write to Educational Department, NHE, Pan American Airways, Pan Am Building, New York, N. Y. 10017.

HOW TO GET THERE ... By Pan American Clipper to London (6½ hours), Paris, Berlin, Copenhagen or Vienna, then by Polish airlines LOT to Warsaw and all tourist centers.

UNIVERSITY OF WARSAW

The University of Warsaw was founded in 1816 as the Royal University. It was closed by the Russians in 1831 and reopened as the General School in 1862. Seven years later it was closed again, this time until 1915 when it was renamed the University of Warsaw. In 1935 it became Joseph Pilsudski University. In 1939 it was closed by the Germans but opened again in 1945 as the University of Warsaw as before. University buildings are located in various sections of the city. The oldest part of the University and the John Casimir Palace (named for King John Casimir), erected in the seventeenth century, are located on the main campus; also, parts of the former Royal University, founded in the early part of the nineteenth century and extensively damaged during the war, are being repaired so that they will soon be entirely restored.

The governing body is composed of the Rector and the members of the University Senate. Representative professors from the university staff are either appointed or elected to serve on the Senate.

SIZE ... There are approximately 7,000 students in day classes at the University of Warsaw, and more than 2,000 evening students.

CALENDAR ... The regular university session runs from the first week in September to the end of June. The autumn session is from the first of September to the middle of December; the winter session from the first week in January to the middle of March; and the spring session from mid-April to the end of June.

COURSES OF STUDY ... In recent years, the University of Warsaw has become a research center in atomic physics, and it is also world-famous for its Department of Mathematics. It is an outstanding institution in connection with developments in Marxist philosophy and socialist economics. Current departments are Biology, Geophysics, Geology, Chemistry, Journalism, Philology, Political Economics, Philosophy, History, Law, Mathematics and Physics, and Education.

ADMISSION REQUIREMENTS ... See the Admission Requirements section in the opening summary on Poland.

LANGUAGE OF INSTRUCTION ... Polish. Foreign students must have an adequate knowledge of Polish to understand the lectures. Required theses and dissertations may be written in a foreign language.

ACCOMMODATIONS ... The student will receive without additional fee a place in a student dormitory, medical care and a stipend of 880 zlotys (about $37) per month. From the latter he will pay approximately 210 zlotys (about $9) per month for meals at a student boardinghouse if he chooses to eat at such an institution.

AVERAGE COSTS ... It is estimated that about $100 per month will cover all costs while in Poland. This, however, does not cover costs of travel to and from Poland, which are the responsibility of the student. The zloty is the unit of currency in Poland. The tourist rate of exchange is 24 to the dollar.

STUDENT LIFE ... University students have their own clubs and some groups have their own cabarets. The chief source of social activities is the Polish Students' Association (Zrzeszenie Studentow Polskich—ZSP).

University of Warsaw

Jagiellonian University

JAGIELLONIAN UNIVERSITY OF KRAKOW

Krakow was the capital of the kingdom of Poland from 1320 to 1609. It is a city of many churches and towers. Situated on the Vistula, it is known for its trade in lumber, grain, cattle and salt. Some of the world's largest salt mines are only eight miles away. Krakow's famous buildings include the castle of Wavel and the Gothic Cathedral of Stanislaus of Krakow, where Polish kings were crowned and buried. The Polish heroes Thaddeus Kosciusko and Adam Mickiewicz are also buried here.

Poland's most ancient university and second oldest in Central Europe, this institution was established in 1364 by King Casimir the Great and has been a center of Polish scholarship for six centuries. Nicholas Copernicus, the father of modern astronomy, was a student here from 1491 to 1496, and the University library contains the first edition of his book. One of its original structures, Collegium Maius, now reconstructed, is still in use.

SIZE ... There are about 3,200 day students enrolled at the Jagiellonian University.

CALENDAR ... The regular university session runs from the first week in September to late June. The autumn session is from the first of September to the middle of December; the winter session from the first week in January to the middle of March; and the spring session from mid-April to the end of June.

COURSES OF STUDY ... The departments of the University are Law, Mathematics, Physics and Chemistry, Philology, Philosophy and History, Biology, and Geophysics. The University is particularly known for its research activities in the fields of linguistics, history of material culture, geology and chemistry, among others.

ADMISSION REQUIREMENTS ... See the Admission Requirements section in the opening summary on Poland.

LANGUAGE OF INSTRUCTION ... Polish. Foreign students must have an adequate knowledge of Polish to understand the lectures. Required theses and dissertations may be written in a foreign language.

ACCOMMODATIONS ... The student will receive without additional fee a place in a student dormitory, medical care and a stipend of 880 zlotys (about $37) per month. From the latter he will pay approximately 210 zlotys (about $9) per month for meals at a student boardinghouse if he chooses to eat at such an institution.

AVERAGE COSTS ... It is estimated that $100 per month will cover all costs while in Poland. This, however, does not cover cost of travel to and from Poland, which is the responsibility of the student. The zloty is the unit of currency in Poland. The tourist rate of exchange is 24 to the dollar.

STUDENT LIFE ... University students have their own clubs and some groups have their own cabarets. The chief source of social activities is the Polish Students' Association (Zrzeszenie Studentow Polskich—ZSP).

PORTUGAL

Portugal, one of the friendliest countries in Europe, has three first-rate universities which are looking forward to having their classes enriched with American students.

The Portuguese students, broad-minded about foreigners, are anxious to meet the young intellectuals of a country they admire so much.

Well known as a country of sunshine and easygoing people, Portugal has a way of winning all newcomers into its fold. The eventual parting time for the students to return to their homeland will be very sad for them and their newly made friends.

José Cabral
Director
Casa de Portugal
New York, N. Y.

UNIVERSITIES OF PORTUGAL ... Portugal has four universities and a number of special schools of music and art, medical research institutes, and technical schools. The country's oldest institution is the University of Coimbra, which was founded in 1290. The University of Lisbon and the University of Oporto were both founded in 1911. The fourth university of Portugal is the Technical University of Lisbon, which was founded in 1930 under its present title; it brought together the Army School, which was founded in 1837, the School of Veterinary Medicine, which dates back to 1830, the Higher Agricultural Institute, which was set up in 1852, the Higher Institute of Economics and Finance, which was established in 1913, and the Naval School, founded in 1845. Foreign students are accepted by Portuguese universities during the regular academic year but students must compete on the same basis as Portuguese students in the entrance examinations and they must, of course, be completely fluent in the Portuguese language. The University of Coimbra and the University of Lisbon offer summer courses in the Portuguese language and culture; these courses are designed for foreign students.

PORTUGUESE UNIVERSITY SYSTEM ... Portugal has a Ministry of Education which concerns itself with the educational system throughout the country. The universities are generally autonomous institutions although the Ministry of Education may have a representative on the administrative body of the university. A number of faculties make up each of the universities of Portugal. A student enters a faculty when he enters the university and he may study four, five, or six years for his *licenciado* degree. A Doctoral degree requires longer study and a written thesis. The universities of Portugal are open to all students who have completed a prescribed course in a secondary school. The classical universities—at Lisbon, Coimbra, and Oporto—require students to be prepared in the humanities and classics, whereas the Technical University of Lisbon requires students to have a scientific background. Students may enter the technical or the classical specialization in secondary school to prepare for their university work.

ADMISSION REQUIREMENTS ... Students must have completed the secondary school course prescribed for entrance to the field they wish to enter. For American students, a minimum of two years of college is required; generally speaking it is recommended that Americans have a Bachelor's degree before applying for admission to a Portuguese university. A science background is required for entry to the Technical University of Lisbon; a classical background is required for entry to the Uni-

versity of Coimbra, the University of Lisbon, or the University of Oporto. Entrance examinations must be completed satisfactorily for admission to a university. Foreign students are accepted on the same basis as Portuguese students but must have their academic records evaluated by Portuguese authorities and must sit for the examinations which are given in the Portuguese language. The ability to read, write, speak and understand the language is essential. The summer courses for foreigners given at the University of Coimbra and the University of Lisbon are open to all foreign students without formal presentation of academic credentials.

CREDIT TOWARD AN AMERICAN DEGREE ... A student must make arrangements for receiving credit toward an American degree from his own university before he leaves the United States. Because of the variations in credit systems within American universities, it is impossible to generalize about the number of credit hours a student may receive. Each student should discuss with his own dean or guidance counselor the requirements for receiving credit and the number of credit hours toward his American degree that may be awarded for study abroad. Sometimes full credit may be given for the period of study in Portugal if the student passes the Portuguese examinations. But each American university will make its own evaluation of the study at each foreign university. In some faculties certificates may be earned for the period of study in Portugal.

REGULATIONS ... American students must have an American passport and a Portuguese residence visa to enter Portugal and live there for an academic year. American students can apply to the Portuguese Consulate General in New York City or to the nearest Portuguese Consulate for the proper application forms. A statement of proof of financial support for the period of residence in Portugal will be required along with other documents. If a student has no sponsor living in Portugal (either American or Portuguese), a certificate of good conduct and a letter from the local police authorities are required. These documents are not required if the student has someone living in Portugal to vouch for him. The residence visa costs $3.67, which is payable at the time the visa is issued. At least six weeks to two months should be allowed for processing of the visa application because papers must be forwarded to Portugal and returned to the United States. Students must inform themselves of currency and customs regulations for entry to Portugal.

TUITION AND OTHER COSTS ... Tuition fees vary somewhat depending on the faculty a student enters. The range is from $42 to $55 per academic year. Students pay a small matriculation charge, fees for laboratory use, which are generally under $5 for the academic year, and examination fees. About $50 an academic year is the average amount spent on fees.

LIVING COSTS ... The Universities in Portugal do not provide living quarters for students. It is customary for a student to find his own living accommodations, perhaps in a boardinghouse, with a Portuguese family, or in a student house where he has a room only. A student can live on as little as $30 a month, but the average cost is about $65 per month for room and board. Incidental expenses must be added to this. There are cafeterias or student dining rooms where inexpensive meals can be obtained. The universities will help students by providing lists of possible lodgings. An American student should not plan to supplement his allowance by working in Portugal; it is almost impossible for a foreign student to hold a job.

University of Coimbra

COMMON COURTESIES AND LOCAL CUSTOMS ... A kind, warm greeting expressed by the handshake is a very important part of everyday life in Portugal and, in a way, an aid to understanding. The boss in an office shakes hands with his employees every morning. When Portuguese ladies go out in the evening, they are accompanied by some member of the family.

FOR FURTHER INFORMATION ... For complete information about a university and how to enroll, write to the university itself or the Casa de Portugal, 447 Madison Avenue, New York, N. Y. 10017.

For travel particulars and documentation, write to Educational Department, NHE, Pan American Airways, Pan Am Building, New York, N. Y. 10017.

HOW TO GET THERE ... By Pan American Jet Clipper, only 6¼ hours nonstop from New York to Lisbon, 10¼ hours from Miami, 2 hours from Paris, 1 hour from Madrid. By ship, 6 to 9 days.

UNIVERSITY OF COIMBRA

Tall, straight poplar trees line the banks of the Mondego River in Coimbra, one of Portugal's most romantic cities and the city that inspired the writer of "April in Portugal." Students of the University of Coimbra are a colorful and important part of the life of the city, and during the third week of May the "Burning of the Ribbons Festival" enlivens the city with serenades, dancing till dawn, athletic contests, and ceremonial bonfires in which ribbons representing the various faculties of the University are burned. Although the students do not dress exclusively in the traditional black suit, black tie, white shirt and huge black cape with ragged hem, this garb is still worn by some University students. Coimbra has two cathedrals of interest, the Monastery of Santa Cruz, the Convent of Santa Clara, and the Machado de Castro Museum, which has fine collections of jewelry, sculpture, paintings, pottery, and embroideries. The University of Coimbra was founded in Lisbon in 1290; it was moved to Coimbra in 1308, subsequently moved back to Lisbon twice, but finally came permanently to Coimbra in 1537. For five centuries it was the only university in Portugal.

SIZE ... About 5,800 students.

CALENDAR ... The academic year begins the first week in October and closes the end of July. A summer school, which is mainly for foreign students, is held in July and August.

COURSES OF STUDY ... Instruction is offered in the Faculty of Law, Faculty of Letters, Faculty of Medicine, Faculty of Sciences, and the School of Pharmacy.

SUMMER COURSES ... Portuguese language classes for beginning, intermediate, and advanced students are offered during the summer session.

TUITION ... Entrance fees for the summer course total $14; students may pay an additional $12 and take an examination which, if completed successfully, entitles the student to a diploma. Tuition fee for regular courses of the University is $42 per academic year; a matriculation fee of $3.50, and laboratory fees of $3.50 to $4.75 per year are also charged. There may be a charge of $3.50 for matriculation of a student transferring from another institution. An examination fee of $1.75 may be charged in some courses.

ADMISSION REQUIREMENTS ... To enroll in the University as a regular student one must meet the requirements set up by the faculty which one will enter. Entrance examinations may be given by that faculty as well as by the University. A student's complete academic record must be submitted to the Ministry of Education for evaluation; if these records are deemed acceptable the student will be eligible for admission to the University. See also the Admission Requirements section in the opening summary on Portugal.

LANGUAGE OF INSTRUCTION ... Portuguese.

ACCOMMODATIONS ... Students attending the summer courses will be housed with Portuguese families or in boardinghouses; the cost of room and board is $1.40 per day; accommodations in hotels may cost from $2.10 and up per day. Most students find their own living quarters, with families, in pensions, or in student homes. Room and board may cost as little as $45 per month.

AVERAGE COSTS ... Fees about $50 per academic year. Room and board about $65 per month.

STUDENT LIFE ... Social gatherings and excursions are a regular part of the summer school program. During the winter session there are also regular social gatherings and excursions for students. Coimbra has been for many years an attraction to poets and writers of Portugal and the Penedo da Saudade is a spot where students and poets traditionally have mingled. Foreign students will find a wide variety of subjects for sight-seeing in and near Coimbra. Portuguese students can give the best advice for wise use of leisure time. The University has various student groups which foreigners may join.

UNIVERSITY OF LISBON

Lisbon, the capital of Portugal, lies on the hilly northern bank of the Tagus River very near the Atlantic. It is a city of spacious squares, of pastel-colored buildings, tree-lined boulevards. Much of it is modern in appearance but the city still has ancient monuments and narrow streets here and there as remnants of its long history. The Belem Tower, an early sixteenth-century fortress, is an exquisite example of the Portuguese Manueline style of architecture blending Moorish and Gothic forms. The Jeronimos Monastery, also in Manueline style, and the Lisbon Cathedral of the thirteenth century are also notable. Lisbon's Zoological Garden and its Botanical Gardens together with many public gardens and parks are diverting or restful for visitors. Among the museums of note are the National Museum of Ancient Art, National Museum of Contemporary Art, Archaeological Museum, and the Museum of Folk Art. Lisbon is the home of the University of Lisbon, founded in 1911, and the Technical University of Lisbon, founded in 1930. The University of Lisbon can trace its history to 1290, when a University was established in Lisbon, but was transferred to Coimbra in 1308. Although the seat of this university moved several times between Coimbra and Lisbon, it remained in Coimbra after 1537. The Technical University of Lisbon brought together several institutions set up from 1830 to 1913.

SIZE ... There are about 7,200 students at the University.

CALENDAR ... The academic year begins the first of October and closes the end of July. Lectures are given during the period from the middle of October to June 20. A summer school, chiefly for foreign students, is held during July and August.

COURSES OF STUDY ... The University of Lisbon offers instruction in the Faculty of Law, Faculty of Medicine, Faculty of Science, Faculty of Letters, and the School of Pharmacy.

SUMMER COURSES ... The Faculty of Letters offers the summer program of study in the Portuguese language, art, history, geography, philology, thought, and culture. Language classes are offered for beginning, intermediate and advanced students.

TUITION ... Summer course enrollment fees are about $18, with an examination fee of $3.50 to $8.75, depending on the tests taken. Tuition and matriculation fees per academic year range from about $45 to about $53.

University of Lisbon, Faculty of Law

ADMISSION REQUIREMENTS ... See the Admissions Requirements section in the opening summary on Portugal.

LANGUAGE OF INSTRUCTION ... Portuguese.

ACCOMMODATIONS ... Students attending the summer courses may obtain housing and meals for $1.75 per day in student hostels. In general, students find accommodations in boardinghouses, in private homes, inexpensive hotels, or in student hostels. The cost of room and board is about $35 per month and up.

AVERAGE COSTS ... Fees about $50 per academic year. Room and board about $65 per month.

STUDENT LIFE ... A wide variety of events including festivals and fairs, exhibitions of paintings and sculpture, concerts, religious events, sailing, horse racing, football, golf, and rugby are on the calendar in Lisbon. The University itself has a program of cultural events besides recreational, social, and intellectual diversions for students. Bicycling and tennis are sports popular with students.

TECHNICAL UNIVERSITY OF LISBON

SIZE ... There are about 3,000 students attending the University.

CALENDAR ... The academic year opens the first week in October and closes the end of July. Classes run from mid-October to late June; there are vacations at Christmas, Easter and the end of February.

COURSES OF STUDY ... Instruction is offered in the School of Veterinary Medicine, the Institute of Agriculture, Institute of Economics and Finance and the Technical Institute.

TUITION ... Tuition fees for the academic year are about $50.

ADMISSION REQUIREMENTS ... See the Admission Requirements section in the opening summary on Portugal.

LANGUAGE OF INSTRUCTION ... Portuguese.

ACCOMMODATIONS ... Many students live in pensions, in student houses, or with families. Room and board may cost from $35 a month and up. The University will provide students with a list of possible living quarters.

AVERAGE COSTS ... Fees about $50 per academic year. Room and board about $65 and up per month.

STUDENT LIFE ... Lisbon offers students the advantages and variety of events of a large city; there are also fine libraries which are open to students and which have excellent exhibits of books and manuscripts from time to time. The University itself has a number of student organizations, often within the various faculties, which plan social, recreational, and cultural functions.

UNIVERSITY OF OPORTO

Oporto is Portugal's second city, a bustling seaport located where the mouth of the Douro River meets the Atlantic. The city is the center of Portugal's wine trade; port wine takes its name from this city. The population of 280,000 inhabitants is chiefly engaged in commerce and industry. The Cathedral and its cloister, the Church of Cedofeita, the Monastery of Leca do Bailio, and the Clerigos Church, from which a splendid view of Oporto can be seen, are among the city's important monuments. Notable museums include the Ethnographical Museum, the Museum of Ancient and Contemporary Art, and the Anthropological, Zoological and Geology Museums. The University of Oporto was founded in 1911; it was an outgrowth of the Polytechnic Academy founded in 1837 and the School of Medicine and Surgery which was set up in 1836.

SIZE ... There are about 3,250 students attending the University; this number includes about 20 foreign students.

CALENDAR ... The academic year begins the first week in October and closes the end of July; students have a 16-day vacation at Christmas and again at Easter and a week at the end of February.

COURSES OF STUDY ... Instruction is offered in the Faculty of Medicine, Faculty of Sciences, Faculty of Engineering, Faculty of Pharmacy, and the Faculty of Economics. The Sciences Faculty offers courses in Mathematics, Mechanics, Astronomy, Physics, Chemistry, Mineralogy, Geology, Botany, Anthropology, and Zoology. Courses in Civil, Hydraulic, Mining, Metallurgical, Mechanical, Electrical, and Chemical Industrial Engineering are offered by the Engineering Faculty.

TUITION ... The yearly tuition fee ranges from $42 to $49; there is a matriculation fee of $3.50. Small charges may be made for laboratory use.

ADMISSION REQUIREMENTS ... See the Admission Requirements section in the opening summary on Portugal.

LANGUAGE OF INSTRUCTION ... Portuguese.

ACCOMMODATIONS ... The University does not maintain residence halls for all students. There are dining rooms however where students can obtain meals. Most students live with families, in boardinghouses, or in student homes. Cost of room and board may be as low as $45 a month.

AVERAGE COSTS ... Fees about $50 per academic year. Room and board about $65 per month.

STUDENT LIFE ... Within each faculty of the University is an organization of students and faculty members which plans extracurricular activities of interest to both groups. There are also a number of clubs, organized by students with special interests in music, hobbies, science, or sports. Recreational and cultural events are planned for students by committees.

PUERTO RICO

SAN JUAN
PUERTO RICO
• SAN GERMAN

NOTE: Even though this book is concerned primarily with foreign universities, we have included schools in Alaska, Hawaii and Puerto Rico since they are "abroad" in the sense of being outside the continental United States. In these schools, entry requirements, transfers of credits, curriculums and methods of study are similar to those of all U.S. universities.

INTER AMERICAN UNIVERSITY OF PUERTO RICO, SAN GERMÁN

San Germán was founded on the southwest coast of Puerto Rico shortly after Ponce de León's first settlement near San Juan. The town moved inland to escape the raids of pirates and Indians fifty years later. Considered one of the best-restored and proudest towns on the island, San Germán is known for the second oldest church in the Western Hemisphere, Porta Coeli, as well as for the Inter American University of Puerto Rico. The main campus stretches over 251 acres of rolling, wooded land in the Santa Marta Hills above the lush Guanajibo Valley.

For 52 years Inter American has been dedicated to creative education and community service wherever it is most needed. Often, in the past half-century, the need has been greatest where there are few means. In 1912, J. Will Harris, a Texan missionary, responded to the needs of southwestern Puerto Rico and established a small school called Polytechnic Institute. Responding to the needs not only of Puerto Rico, but of developing areas throughout both hemispheres, Inter American has grown during the last eight years from 500 students to over 5,000.

The University became, in 1944, the first institution outside the continental U. S. to be accredited by the Middle States Association of Colleges. In 1956, under a new president, Dr. Ronald C. Bauer, the school entered a period of remarkable growth. Along with this growth the physical plant, the faculty and other areas have been greatly expanded.

SIZE ... About 5,500 students study on two main campuses with extensions in 14 towns. This number of students includes 228 foreign students representing 42 countries.

CALENDAR ... Three trimesters cover a full calendar year. Two trimesters make up the normal academic year. There is a summer session in June and July.

COURSES OF STUDY ... All sciences and humanities. Special area studies: Latin America, Caribbean, Africa and Middle East. Schools of Banking, Law, Architecture. Workshops in Spanish and French. Two-year courses in Secretarial Sciences and Education.

SUMMER COURSES ... Special summer programs: U. S. Position in the Caribbean—an institute to provide a better understanding of changes currently unfolding in the area. International Workshop in Musical Theater—a comprehensive study and production of musicals. There is also a special Laboratory for Youth, designed to bring together boys (age 14–18) to live, work, study and experience an international life together. Conducted by a noted teacher and international adviser.

Summer Course: A 6-week tour of little-known parts of Puerto Rico and the Caribbean, including special lectures, meetings with leaders and social functions.

TUITION ... Tuition is about $250 per semester.

ADMISSION REQUIREMENTS ... Inter American is fully accredited by the Middle States Accrediting Committee and therefore entrance standards are the same as at other U.S. schools.

LANGUAGE OF INSTRUCTION ... English.

ACCOMMODATIONS ... Modern dormitories located at San Germán and Barranquitas.

AVERAGE COSTS ... All living expenses per semester, $250; full academic year—all expenses, $1,000. Utilizing the full three semesters plus the summer trimester it is possible to graduate in three years for less than $5,000.

STUDENT LIFE ... A lovely campus in rural setting near beaches and mountains lends itself to student activities. New dormitories and a recently built million-dollar student center provide comfortable and pleasant facilities.

FOR FURTHER INFORMATION ... For complete information about the University and how to enroll, write directly to The President, INTER AMERICAN UNIVERSITY, San Germán, Puerto Rico.

For travel particulars and documentation, write to Educational Department, NHE, Pan American Airways, Pan Am Building, New York, N. Y. 10017.

HOW TO GET THERE ... By Pan American Jet nonstop from New York, 3½ hours; from Miami nonstop, 2¼ hours. Service also from Boston, Philadelphia and Baltimore-Washington, and direct flights from Europe, Central and South America.

SPAIN

In modern times, with people traveling more and taking greater interest in the cultures of other countries, the Spanish universities have organized courses for foreigners that range from elementary to advanced levels. Some of those courses are given in conjunction with music festivals. Music in Compostela courses, held in Santiago, designated especially for professional musicians and advanced students, claim some of the foremost professors and composers as lecturers.

The favorable rate of exchange of the American dollar and the fact that education in Spain is practically free make it a very desirable place to study. Also inspiring for the student is the traditionally artistic everyday life together with the historical background of the old cities and the most cosmopolitan way of living.

Antonio Espinosa
Cultural Attaché
Embassy of Spain
Washington, D. C.

UNIVERSITIES IN SPAIN ... Spain is divided into twelve educational districts by the Ministry of Education, a government unit which controls all education in Spain. Each of the twelve districts has a public university. These universities are the University of Barcelona, University of Granada, University of La Laguna, University of Madrid, University of Murcia, University of Oviedo, University of Salamanca, University of Santiago de Compostela, University of Seville, University of Valencia, University of Valladolid and the University of Saragossa. Spain also has three church and pontifical universities: at Pamplona, at Salamanca and at Santander; and three private universities: at Sacromonte, El Escorial, and Bilbao. Students must be examined by a public university, however, to receive a recognized degree.

Technical subjects such as engineering, architecture and dentistry are taught at university-level professional schools. Fine arts and music are both taught outside the university in Schools of Fine Arts (*Escuelas de Bellas Artes*), the most notable ones being the following: Escuela Superior de Bellas Artes San Jorge, in Barcelona; Escuela Superior de Bellas Artes San Fernando, in Madrid; Escuela Superior de Bellas Artes Santa Isabel de Hungría, in Seville; and the Escuela Superior de Bellas Artes San Carlos, in Valencia; and in the *Conservatorios de Música,* the most notable ones being the following: Conservatorios Superior de Música y Declamación in Barcelona, in Madrid, in Valladolid; and the summer course taught in Santiago de Compostela. Some of the public universities (i.e., Madrid, Barcelona and Valladolid) have a Faculty of Political Science, Economics and Commerce (*Facultad de Ciencias Políticas, Económicas y Comerciales*); the one of Valladolid is located in Bilbao. They offer courses in economics, politics, labor problems, social legislation and contemporary problems.

Also attached to each may be various institutes or research centers and sometimes professional schools. Foreign students are accepted by all the universities. Especially designed for foreign students are the summer courses offered in the Spanish language and culture by the various universities including those of Madrid, Barcelona, Saragossa (at Jaca), Oviedo, Santiago, Valladolid, La Laguna and Santander. There are various other summer courses for foreigners.

SPANISH UNIVERSITY SYSTEM ... When a student completes his secondary school education in Spain, he receives the *bachillerato* certificate, provided he has chosen the classical course of education as opposed to the pre-vocational training course. The *bachillerato* is generally considered to be equal to the American high school diploma. This certificate is required of Spanish students for admission to a university or other institution of higher education. Students specialize at the time of their enrollment in the university; they enter the faculty in which they wish to study and follow a highly specialized program of research and study. Because education in Spain is supervised by the Ministry of Education, the organization, administration and system of instruction are nearly uniform in all universities of the country. Each university is composed of a number of faculties, departments, schools, or institutes. Students enter one faculty and work toward a *licenciatura* degree requiring from five to seven years' study; one to two years' additional study is required for the *doctorado* degree. The public universities of Spain are co-educational. The academic year begins about the first week in October and ends June 30; students must register in the fall by September 20 for the academic year. Lectures are an important method of instruction in Spain.

ADMISSION REQUIREMENTS ... No special academic requirements must be met for admission to the special courses for foreigners set up during the academic year or the summer by the universities. Students must be at least 16 years old, however, to enroll in these courses, or in the regular courses of all the universities. Requirements for attending courses of the universities vary with the objective of the student. Students who are not seeking a degree from the Spanish university but who wish to attend as auditors certain university courses, whether they are graduate or undergraduate students, must apply directly to the dean of the chosen faculty of the university. Permission to attend the lectures for undergraduate students will be given by the dean upon payment by the student of the tuition fees. If the student completes the classroom work, attends classes regularly, and meets any other requirements of the course, he will receive a certificate of completion at the end of the course. Students who wish to work for a special diploma in Hispanic studies—not a university degree—should apply to the Spanish Embassy, Office of Cultural Relations, in Washington, for information and forms before August 31 for admission in the fall; proof of previous academic studies is not required for admission to this course of studies. An undergraduate American student who wishes to enroll as a regular student and work for a degree from a Spanish university must submit a legalized record of his former studies for evaluation by Spanish academic authorities. The student's academic record is evaluated against the standards of education required in Spain. The legalization of records and documents must be done by the nearest Spanish Consulate or by the Spanish Embassy. These documents must be translated into Spanish before they are sent to the consulate. The following are required: a legalized birth certificate, official transcripts of academic records, catalogues of the schools attended. Application forms may be obtained from the Spanish Embassy in Washington; when requesting the application blank, students should specify the type of study they wish to pursue (work for a degree or independent study and non-degree work), as application forms vary. The Spanish Embassy will forward the application and all documents to the proper university, through diplomatic channels. The student who is accepted will be notified by the Spanish authorities; students should begin application procedures at least four months before the start of the academic year. These procedures make it unnecessary for American students to take entrance examinations required of Spanish students. Students working toward a degree or auditing courses during the regular academic year must have a thorough knowledge of spoken and written Spanish as all instruction is in the Spanish language. Some of the beginning courses in the Spanish language in the summer schools are taught in English.

CREDIT TOWARD AN AMERICAN DEGREE ... A student must make arrangements for receiving credit toward an American degree from his own university or college before he leaves the United States. Because of the variations in credit systems within the universities and colleges in America, it is impossible to generalize about the number of credit hours a student may receive. Each student should discuss with his own dean or guidance counselor the requirements for receiving credit and the number of credit hours toward his American degree that may be awarded for study in Spain. Sometimes full credit may be given for the period of study in Spain if the student passes the Spanish examinations or completes the required assignments. But each American university or college will make its own evaluation of the study at each Spanish university. Certain certificates and diplomas can be earned from the Spanish universities.

TUITION ... Tuition and registration fees are low; they vary according to the length of the course and the category of study being followed, pursuit of a degree being more expensive than non-degree work. Summer courses cost from about $15 to $35. Regular courses cost about $50.

REGULATIONS ... American students need a valid passport for entry into Spain. A visa is not required for students who will be in Spain for less than six months. A student who plans to be in Spain for a longer period will need to register with the Spanish authorities before the end of the sixth month; the nearest Spanish Consulate can give students information on these regulations. Students should inform themselves of customs and currency regulations for entry into Spain.

LIVING COSTS ... During the summer many of the student residence halls of the universities are open to foreign students; room and board cost approximately $65 a month; some summer schools make an all-inclusive charge of about $65 for room, board, and tuition. During the academic year the residence halls are crowded and it is very difficult for foreign students to be admitted. These halls are called the *colegios mayores* and they are maintained by the Universities in Madrid, Barcelona, Granada, Valencia, Santiago de Compostela, Salamanca, Seville, Valladolid, and Saragossa. Many students live in pensions, boardinghouses, with private families, or in small hotels. The cost of living is somewhat higher in Barcelona and Madrid than in the smaller cities of Spain. Most American students will find that about $100–$150 will be sufficient for room and board per month. It is almost impossible for foreign students to have jobs in Spain, and students should not plan to supplement their income by working.

COMMON COURTESIES AND LOCAL CUSTOMS ... Spaniards are not too punctual, sometimes a little late for appointments. Students, however, are expected to be present at the time set for a professor's lecture to begin. Luncheon is late and long: in general from about 1 to 4 p.m.; dinner is usually served from 9 or 9:30 p.m. on, when the towns really become alive. The Spanish people shake hands when they are introduced. After having made friends with a Spaniard, when you leave him, tell him your name and address, thus offering your house. This is a common Spanish courtesy.

FOR FURTHER INFORMATION ... For complete information about a university and how to enroll, write to the Cultural Counselor, Spanish Embassy, Washington, D. C. 2009.

For travel particulars and documentation, write to Educational Department, NHE, Pan American Airways, Pan Am Building, New York, N. Y. 10017.

HOW TO GET THERE ... By Pan American Jet Clipper, elapsed time from New York, about 9 hours to Barcelona; Madrid is 1 hour by air from Lisbon, 2 hours from Rome, and 1½ hours from Barcelona. By ship, about 7 days to Lisbon, 6 to 8 days to Gibraltar.

UNIVERSITY OF BARCELONA

The University of Barcelona is located in the heart of Spain's most cosmopolitan and leading manufacturing and industrial city. With a population of 1,800,000 inhabitants, Barcelona is second in size in Spain and is the country's most important seaport, as well as one of the most historic ports of the Mediterranean. Barcelona has twelve museums, grand avenues, and outstanding bullfights. It is the place to eat seafood and many of its restaurants have music famous throughout Spain. The weather is hot in summer, mild in winter; spring, which begins in March, and autumn, which lasts into November, are the best seasons. The University of Barcelona was founded out of the *Estudios* of Barcelona and Lérida, which came together in 1377. Academic studies were set up in Barcelona in the twelfth century.

SIZE ... About 9,000 students, including foreign students, attend the University.

CALENDAR ... The academic year opens the first week of October and continues to the end of June. Summer courses are offered in August.

COURSES OF STUDY ... The University offers a course in Hispanic Studies especially designed for foreign students; it commences October 15 and ends May 31. General subjects are Spanish, Spanish Literature, Geography of Spain, History of Art, Spanish History, Spanish Political, Economic and Social Institutions, Spanish Popular Music, and courses in Commercial Correspondence, Translation Exercises, and Conversation in the Spanish Language. Students may follow lectures in these courses as auditors. The University is composed of the Faculty of Philosophy and Letters, the Faculty of Law, the Faculty of Science, the Faculty of Medicine, the Faculty of Pharmacy and the Faculty of Political, Economic and Commercial Science. Attached to the University are the School of Social Studies, School of Higher Commercial Studies, School of Industrial Engineering, School of Architecture and a School of Fine Arts.

SUMMER COURSES ... During July, the University of Barcelona offers a course for foreign students at Palma on the island of Majorca in the Balearic Islands; the same course is offered in August in Barcelona. Elementary, intermediate and advanced classes in the Spanish language are offered as well as courses in Spanish culture.

TUITION ... The registration fee for the academic year for the course of Hispanic Studies is $25, and for the whole diploma course is $100. Students matriculated for a degree pay various fees, depending on the faculty in which they are enrolled. In general, the tuition for courses in the Faculty of Philosophy and Letters is about $15.50; in the Faculties of Law, Medicine, Pharmacy, Science, Veterinary Medicine, Political Science and Economics, about $21.50 per academic year. A small matriculation fee may be charged as well as minimal fees for laboratory

University of Barcelona

and library use. The registration fee for either summer course offered by the University is about $17.

ADMISSION REQUIREMENTS ... Students who wish to enroll as regular students must submit their academic records and other documents to Spanish authorities for evaluation, as outlined in the Admission Requirements section in the opening summary of this chapter. Students do not need any special academic background for admission to the summer courses; language courses are divided into beginning, intermediate and advanced groups, and students are admitted to these groups according to their knowledge of the language.

LANGUAGE OF INSTRUCTION ... Spanish. Beginning courses in the Spanish language offered by the summer schools are taught in English.

ACCOMMODATIONS ... The University of Barcelona maintains several *colegios mayores* and university residences including Fray Junipero Serra, San Jorge, Ramon Llull, and San José for men students and the Angeles Mateu and the Virgen Immaculada for women students. The cost of a room and full board is under $10 per week. Requests for these accommodations must be made far in advance, however, because there are not enough rooms for all students. Most students live in pensions, with Spanish families, or in hotels. During the summer, room and board can be obtained with families for about $100–$150 per month and up; hotel costs are slightly higher than during the off season. Room and board at the college residences may be about $2.50 per day. The tourist bureau and various student groups will assist foreign students to find accommodations in Barcelona.

AVERAGE COSTS ... Fees about $25 per academic year. Room and board about $100 per month.

STUDENT LIFE ... The snack bar downstairs in the main building of the University is a gathering place for students and a place for foreign students, literally, to rub elbows with their Spanish counterparts, to exchange ideas and to discuss the problems of the world. Sidewalk cafés are scattered throughout the city, and certain ones are favorites of students. A wide range of cultural, social, intellectual, and recreational activities is offered to students. The University has its own swimming pool in a special park on a hillside overlooking the city. There are beaches too. The student card entitles one to free admission to several of the city's museums and monuments. Various student organizations and groups also have a planned program of activities.

UNIVERSITY OF GRANADA

Granada is the home of the famous red-walled Alhambra, the castle-fortress built from 1248 to 1354 by Moorish rulers. Washington Irving celebrates these historic grounds and buildings in his *Tales of the Alhambra*. Granada has another interesting section, the Albaicin, with its caves where gypsies are supposed to live. At night in summer they dance in gaily colored costumes to flamenco rhythms and the applause of tourists. The University of Granada dates back to 1526, when Carlos V created the Colegio de Lógica Filosofía e Teología e Canones.

SIZE ... About 5,000 students, including foreign students, attend the University.

CALENDAR ... The academic year opens the first week of October and continues to the end of June. From January to May the University offers a special course for foreign students. There is a summer session in July and August.

COURSES OF STUDY ... The University is composed of the Faculty of Philosophy and Letters, the Faculty of Law, Faculty of Science, Faculty of Medicine, Faculty of Pharmacy, the School of Soil Science and Plant Biology, the School of Nursing, the School of Social Work, the School of Arabic Studies, the Institute of Modern Languages, and other research institutes and centers. The Faculty of Philosophy and Letters offers the Winter Course for Foreign Students with instruction in the Spanish language (for elementary, intermediate, and advanced students), literature, art, geography, contemporary problems, Mussulman Spain, and Andalusia. The course begins in Málaga, and the last ten days are held in Granada. A spring course for foreigners is offered during the month of April.

SUMMER COURSES ... Various levels of the Spanish language and culture are offered in July and August at Fuengirola (Málaga).

TUITION ... Registration fee for the winter course is $15, which does not include the cost of the excursions. Tuition for the regular courses of the University is $15.50 for the academic year in the Faculty of Philosophy and Letters; $21.50 for the academic year in the Faculty of Law, Medicine, Science, or Pharmacy. A matriculation fee of about $2 and small library and laboratory fees are charged.

ADMISSION REQUIREMENTS ... An American student who wishes to become a regular student of the University working toward a degree must submit his academic record and other documents to the Spanish authorities for evaluation as outlined in the Admission Requirements section of the opening summary in this chapter.

LANGUAGE OF INSTRUCTION ... Spanish.

ACCOMMODATIONS ... A room and full board in the University dormitories is very inexpensive, under $15 a week. To secure these accommodations it is necessary to apply very early, however, as they are limited. Many students live in pensions, with families, in hostels, or in inexpensive hotels. The tourist office will assist students to find accommodations. There are student groups also which help foreigners to get settled. Room and board cost about $90 per month.

AVERAGE COSTS ... Tuition about $25 per academic year. Room and board about $90 per month.

STUDENT LIFE ... There are numerous parks, squares, and small streets fine for walking in Granada. The excursions for students to other parts of Andalusia are also rewarding; the winter festivals offer a wide range of entertainment and sports. The weather is warm enough in nearby Málaga for golf, tennis, and, for the hardy, swimming almost year round. There is a fine winter season of opera, concerts, and lectures. There is even a winter season of bullfights. A Spanish student will introduce foreign students to the folklore and fiesta traditions.

UNIVERSITY OF LA LAGUNA

La Laguna is the oldest city in the Canary Islands, off the west coast of Africa more than 800 miles from the Spanish mainland. Tenerife is the largest of the seven major and six smaller islands in the archipelago and it is in the interior of Tenerife that La Laguna is located, on the site of a former lake 2,000 feet above sea level. About five and a half miles away is the island's capital, Santa Cruz de Tenerife, a busy port city where ships from five continents call to load bananas, oranges, and tomatoes. The airport of Los Rodeos, about eight miles outside the capital, connects the islands with Europe. The curious landscape of the islands is a combination of snow-capped mountains, lush green valleys, plains, and beaches. The islands are rich in monuments and folklore and the people maintain a true "country life." The Canaries are said to enjoy eternal spring. The University of La Laguna was founded in 1701 as an affiliate of a university on the mainland; it became independent in 1920.

SIZE ... About 1,000 students attend the University.

CALENDAR ... The academic year opens the first week of October and continues to the end of June. There is a summer session held in July and August.

COURSES OF STUDY ... The University is composed of the Faculty of Philosophy and Letters, the Faculty of Law, and the Faculty of Science. The Faculty of Philosophy and Letters offers courses in Philosophy, Semitic Philology, History, History of America, and Pedagogy. The Faculty of Science offers a pre-Pharmacy course.

TUITION ... Tuition for the academic year for the Faculty of Philosophy and Letters is about $15.50 for credit students; for the Faculty of Law and the Faculty of Science about $21.50 for credit students. There is a small fee for matriculation, library use, and laboratory courses.

SUMMER COURSES ... Various levels of the Spanish language and culture are offered during July and August.

ADMISSION REQUIREMENTS ... An American student must submit to Spanish authorities his academic record and other documents as outlined in the Admission Requirements section in the opening summary on Spain to become a regular student working for a degree.

LANGUAGE OF INSTRUCTION ... Spanish.

ACCOMMODATIONS ... A dormitory for men is maintained by the University; a room and full board may cost under $10 per week. It is necessary to apply early to secure a room in the dormitory. Many students live in boardinghouses or with families. There are various student groups which will assist foreign students to find accommodations; the local tourist bureau also keeps lists of lodgings suitable for students. Room and board may cost about $90 per month.

AVERAGE COSTS ... Fees about $25 per academic year. Room and board about $90 per month.

STUDENT LIFE ... A tram links La Laguna with the capital and its beaches; the ride is a short and pleasant one. Students interested in meeting the people of these islands will have an opportunity to do so with the help of Spanish students. There are interesting places to walk, ride bicycles, to fish, and to rest. There are unusual excursions to be made, some on horseback, and the festival days and holidays are good occasions for sight-seeing. The University offers a program of cultural, social, and recreational activities.

UNIVERSITY OF MADRID

Spain's capital, Madrid, boasts broad, tree-lined avenues, boulevards, sidewalk cafés, plus quaint, "old city" squares lined with arcades. The Prado, one of the world's leading museums, has outstanding collections of Velázquez, Goya, El Greco, as well as other leading painters of various Spanish schools and old masters. The Retiro Park, with its man-made lake, colorful gardens, fountains, statuary is a relaxing place to stroll; the Plaza Mayor, built by Philip III as an arena for bullfights, is a huge square bounded by arcaded sidewalks. Ask a Spaniard to tell you its history. The Royal Palace has interesting gardens outside as well as superb collections of tapestries and paintings inside. Several modest "skyscrapers" have gone up along the streets of Madrid. But the University of Madrid itself is perhaps the center of modernity in the city. During the Civil War all the buildings of the University were completely destroyed, and the University has been rebuilt since 1939 on a large campus at the edge of the city. Considered one of the finest in Europe, the University of Madrid campus includes several residence halls and hostels for students as well as accommodations for the academic staff. The *Ciudad Universitaria* or University City is still in the process of growing and finishing new buildings. The University of Madrid is the outgrowth of the University of Alcalá de Henares founded in the sixteenth century.

SIZE ... About 24,000 students attend the University, including foreign students; there are about 500 American students in Madrid.

CALENDAR ... The academic year opens the first week of October and continues to the end of June. There is a summer session in July and August.

COURSES OF STUDY ... Various short courses, especially designed for foreign students interested in the Spanish language and culture, are offered during the regular academic year as well as the course leading to the Diploma of Hispanic Culture. From October 15 to December 15 the University offers the fall course in the Spanish language and culture with courses in the Spanish language, phonetics, grammar, morphology, and commentaries on literary texts, history, art, literature—including the Middle Ages, Renaissance, golden ages, modern and contemporary—Spanish music, geography, and philosophy. Visits and excursions are made along with the classroom studies. The same course is offered again in the spring, from February 15 to May 15. The Course of Hispanic Studies, which includes the study of Spanish language, Spanish literature, commentaries on the style of the Spanish writers, geography, history, and history of art, is offered from October to June. The University of Madrid is composed of the Faculty of Philosophy and Letters, Faculty of

Law, Faculty of Science, Faculty of Medicine and Dentistry, Faculty of Pharmacy, Faculty of Political Science, Commerce, and Economics, and the Faculty of Veterinary Medicine, and several schools including the School of Statistics, School of Psychology and Applied Psychology, School of Food Technology, and a School of Social Studies.

SUMMER COURSES ... The University of Madrid offers courses for foreigners during July and August. Subjects include the Spanish language, and culture. Students are divided into beginning, intermediate and advanced classes, according to their native languages in the case of beginners.

TUITION ... The spring course in the Spanish language and culture costs about $35 for the entire course, $25 for two months, and about $17 for one month. The fall course costs about $25 for the full session. Students following the course of Hispanic Studies as auditors pay $5 per subject attended; regular students pay $12.50 per subject or about $54 for the entire course from October to June. Students enrolled in the University as regular students working for a degree pay varying fees depending on the faculty in which they are enrolled: in Philosophy and Letters about $15.50; in Law, Medicine, Pharmacy, Sciences, Veterinary Medicine, Political Science, Commerce, and Economics about $21.50; in Dentistry about $5.75; all fees are charged once in the academic year. There is a small matriculation fee of about $2 and minimal laboratory and library fees. Summer school courses at the University cost about $25 for the course of seven weeks.

ADMISSION REQUIREMENTS ... No special academic requirements are set up for admission to the short courses in the Spanish language and culture. The summer schools are also open to all students without presentation of academic background. Students are admitted to the course of Hispanic Studies without proof of previous university studies; these courses are given in Spanish, however, so a thorough knowledge and understanding of the written and spoken Spanish language is required. Students in the Hispanic course may audit the courses without credit, or one may enroll as a regular student, take the examinations, and earn a diploma if the work is completed satisfactorily. To enroll as a regular student of the University, an American student must submit his academic record and other documents to the Spanish authorities for evaluation, as outlined in the Admission Requirements section in the opening summary on Spain.

LANGUAGE OF INSTRUCTION ... Spanish.

ACCOMMODATIONS ... Several dormitories are maintained at University City. There is still not enough space for all students, however, so one must apply very early to secure a room in one of the several *colegios mayores* intended for lodging. Many students live with families, in pensions, or in hostels. Cost of a room and full board in a University hall is under $10 per week. This is available in the summer only.

AVERAGE COSTS ... Fees vary with the course taken, but about $55 should be allowed by those taking the Hispanic Studies course; about $25 for other year-round students. Room and board about $100 per month.

STUDENT LIFE ... A part of many of the special courses for foreign students is a plan of excursions and visits to points of historical or artistic interest in and near Madrid. Students will find their student card a help in gaining admission, sometimes free of charge, to various museums and monuments. For activities that are truly free of charge the broad sidewalks and large parks are excellent for walking. Don't be surprised if someone charges you for sitting in a chair along the sidewalk—it is an established custom and the cost may be less than a penny. There are snack bars and student restaurants, certain sidewalk cafés and student lounges where American students can meet their Spanish counterparts. The bullfights will seem more interesting, perhaps, with a Spanish student to explain some of the activity. There are various student clubs and groups devoted to cultural, social, and intellectual as well as recreational activities; they welcome foreign students.

University of Madrid

UNIVERSITY OF MURCIA

Murcia, surrounded by a fertile plain, is a few miles inland from the Mediterranean Sea; it lies south of Alicante in a region of orange and lemon groves. The Holy Week celebration is considered one of the loveliest in Spain for its outstanding processions. The Cathedral of Santa Maria, the Provincial Archaeological Museum, and the city's Botanical Gardens are of special interest. The University of Murcia is a comparatively young institution, having been founded in 1915.

SIZE ... About 2,000 students attend the University, including foreign students.

CALENDAR ... The academic year opens the first week of October and continues to the end of June. A special course for foreigners is offered in April.

COURSES OF STUDY ... The special course offers classes in the Spanish Language and Literature, Cervantes, the Theater of Calderon, the Novel and Contemporary Theater, Dramatic Readings, Spanish Painting, Spanish Thought, and Recitals of Spanish Music. The University is composed of the Faculty of Philosophy and Letters, the Faculty of Law, and the Faculty of Science.

TUITION ... An inclusive fee of $50 is charged for the April course; this includes a room at the *colegio mayor,* Cardenal Belluga, full board, registration fees for all lectures, and the cost of excursions, musical events, and visits to monuments. The tuition fees for students who wish to enroll for work leading to a degree is about $15.50 for the academic year for students in the Faculty of Philosophy and Letters, about $21.50 for students in the Faculty of Law or the Faculty of Science. A matriculation fee of about $2 is charged along with small laboratory and library fees.

ADMISSION REQUIREMENTS ... No special requirements are set up for entrance to the special spring course for foreign students. No credit is given to auditors and they do not take examinations. Students who wish to enroll as regular students working toward a degree must submit various documents as well as an academic record to Spanish authorities, as outlined in the Admission Requirements section in the opening summary on Spain.

LANGUAGE OF INSTRUCTION ... Spanish.

ACCOMMODATIONS ... Students attending the special course will be housed in the *colegio mayor,* the fee for room and board being included in the inclusive admission fee. Many students live with families, in pensions, in small hotels, or in hostels. The cost of room and board is about $90 per month.

AVERAGE COSTS ... Fees about $25 per academic year. Room and board about $90 per month.

STUDENT LIFE ... The special course for foreign students is offered during the spring festival time in Murcia. Special arrangements are made for students to attend the festival with other Spanish students. There are excursions to nearby points of interest as well. Murcia, a small university, offers students an opportunity to meet and talk with Spanish students, to participate in student activities, and to join social, recreational, intellectual, or cultural groups of the University.

UNIVERSITY OF OVIEDO

Oviedo is an old Spanish city; it was the capital of the former kingdom of Asturias. Today it has a population of 90,000; the area is surrounded by agricultural activities—cattle raising, apple orchards, and grain-growing farms. Oviedo is about twenty miles from the port city of Gijon on the Bay of Biscay in the north of Spain. The city has a marvelous old quarter with a fine fifteenth-century Cathedral in pure Gothic design. Near the Cathedral is an eighth-century cloister which houses the Provincial Museum and its archaeological exhibits. The University of Oviedo was founded in 1604 by Royal Charter; instruction began in 1608. During the Civil War the University was seriously damaged but it has now been rebuilt.

SIZE ... About 3,500 students attend the University.

CALENDAR ... The academic year begins the first week in October and continues to the end of June. There is a summer session in August and September.

COURSES OF STUDY ... The University is composed of the Faculty of Philosophy and Letters, the Faculty of Law, the Faculty of Science and the Faculty of Veterinary Medicine, which is offered at León.

SUMMER COURSES ... Foreign students are offered a course in August and September in Spanish language, and culture. A series of concerts and tours is part of the program of study.

TUITION ... The summer course costs about $17 for lectures and tours. Tuition for regular students of the University who are working for a degree is about $15.50 per academic year in the Faculty of Philosophy and Letters and about $21.50 per academic year in the Faculty of Law, Faculty of Science, or the Faculty of Veterinary Medicine. Small fees are charged for matriculation, laboratory courses, and library use.

ADMISSION REQUIREMENTS ... No special academic requirements are set up for entrance to the summer course. To enroll as a regular student of the University an American student must submit his academic record and other documents to Spanish authorities for evaluation, as outlined in the Admission Requirements section of the opening summary of this chapter.

LANGUAGE OF INSTRUCTION ... Spanish.

ACCOMMODATIONS ... Some residential facilities are maintained for students—room and board cost less than $10 per week—but most foreign students live in boardinghouses or take a room with a Spanish family. The tourist bureau and student groups at the University will assist students to find suitable lodgings. Monthly cost of room and board is about $65.

AVERAGE COSTS ... Fees about $25 per academic year. Room and board about $65 per month.

STUDENT LIFE ... The north coast of Spain is one of the country's favorite summertime playgrounds and there are many fine beaches for sunbathing and swimming. Special tours, concerts, and excursions are arranged for students of the summer course; the same routes are open to students who stay the year round in Oviedo. Spanish students will give their foreign counterparts a cordial welcome to social, recreational, and cultural groups of the University.

UNIVERSITY OF SALAMANCA

The city of Salamanca, with its towers, domes, and mansions, rises from the banks of the Tormes River in western Spain about 75 miles from the Portuguese border. An outstanding artistic and historical center of Spain, Salamanca is considered the country's most beautiful city architecturally. The Old and New Cathedrals are magnificent examples of architecture, the Old Cathedral, Santa Maria de La Sede, representing the Romanesque style of the fourteenth century, the New Cathedral being an example of the latest period of Spanish Gothic design. They stand side by side. The Plaza Mayor with porticos in Baroque style is Salamanca's main square, and the Roman Bridge over the Tormes is also of note. The University of Salamanca is considered the oldest in Spain; it was founded sometime in the twelfth century. Alfonso X the Wise founded the University's library, which contains the best collection of works on humanism and sacred theology in Europe. Columbus lectured about his discoveries at Salamanca.

SIZE ... About 4,500 students, including 340 foreign students, attend the University.

CALENDAR ... The academic year opens the first week in October and continues to the end of June. There is a special course from March to late May. A summer session is held during July and August.

COURSES OF STUDY ... From March 1 to May 21 the Faculty of Philosophy and Letters of the University offers a course in Hispanic Philology including the Spanish Language, History of the Language, Spanish Literature, History of Spain, History of Spanish Art, Contemporary Spanish Thought, Popular Spanish Culture, and Spanish Folklore. Various excursions are offered with the study program. The University is composed of the Faculty of Law, Faculty of Science, and the Faculty of Medicine, as well as the Faculty of Philosophy and Letters.

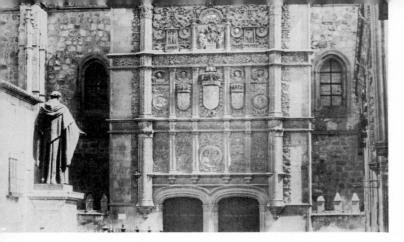

University of Salamanca

There is also an Institute of Languages and a School of Social Studies.

SUMMER COURSES ... Various levels of the Spanish language and culture are offered during July and August.

TUITION ... To enroll in the course in Hispanic Philology a registration fee of about $17 must be paid; this fee covers the costs of the excursions offered by the course. A fee of about $2 per subject enrolled in, or about $15.50 per academic year, is charged credit students in the Faculty of Philosophy and Letters; about $21.50 is charged credit students in the Faculty of Law, Science, or Medicine. Small matriculation, laboratory, and library fees may also be collected.

ADMISSION REQUIREMENTS ... To enroll in the Hispanic Philology course a student must be at least 16 years of age and must have a good working knowledge of the Spanish language, as all instruction is in Spanish. It is not necessary, however, to present one's academic records for admission to the course. To enroll as a regular student of the University, working for a degree, an American student must submit his academic record and other documents to Spanish authorities for evaluation as outlined in the Admission Requirements section in the opening summary on Spain. Students may attend classes as auditors, not working for credit, with the permission of the lecturer.

LANGUAGE OF INSTRUCTION ... Spanish.

ACCOMMODATIONS ... Students taking the special course are housed in boardinghouses and hotels; cost of a room and full board ranges from $1 to $2 per day, plus taxes. There are *colegios mayores,* intended for the lodging of students, at fair rates. Others live with Spanish families or in hostels and boardinghouses. Room and board may cost about $95 per month. The local tourist office and various University organizations will help foreign students to find lodgings.

AVERAGE COSTS ... Tuition fees about $25 per academic year. Room and board about $95 per month.

STUDENT LIFE ... The University of Salamanca has long had an important part in the life of the city, and foreign students will find themselves made at home there. The libraries, museums, the open markets are places to see and to meet Spanish students. There are various recreational and social groups which welcome foreign students and offer opportunities for international friendships.

UNIVERSITY OF SANTIAGO DE COMPOSTELA

Santiago de Compostela lies in the northwest corner of Spain, north of Portugal, in the province of Galicia. The city's Cathedral is considered the finest medieval monument in Spain and is one of the most celebrated in the world. St. James the Apostle, the patron saint of Spain, is entombed in the Cathedral, which is more than 900 years old. Since the ninth century, pilgrims have come to pay homage to the saint; the most famous pilgrimage and the solemn festival of Santiago takes place on July 25th. The great *botafumera,* a 250-pound silver incensory, is swung across the dome of the Cathedral on this special occasion. There are contests, parades, and fine fireworks and rocket displays. In front of the Cathedral is an enormous square. The

old buildings of the University are only a few yards from the Cathedral itself. The University was founded in 1501.

SIZE ... About 3,500 students attend the University, including foreign students.

CALENDAR ... The academic year begins the first week in October and continues until the end of June. There is a summer session from July to mid-September.

COURSES OF STUDY ... The University is composed of the Faculty of Philosophy and Letters, the Faculty of Law, Faculty of Science, Faculty of Medicine, Faculty of Pharmacy, and several schools and institutes including the Institute of Modern Languages, the Institute of Portuguese Studies, and the School of Social Studies. Students may sit in on classes of the Faculty of Philosophy and Letters as auditors.

SUMMER COURSES ... In July the University offers a special course for foreign students in Spanish language and culture. From late August to mid-September the University offers, in conjunction with the Cultural Relations office of Madrid, a course called "Music in Compostela." Guitar, Piano, Violin, Violoncello, Old Music, Popular Music, Singing and Chamber Music are offered. There are seminars in ancient and contemporary music of Spain.

TUITION ... A registration fee of about $9.50 is charged for the summer course. Students attending courses as regular students working for a degree pay about $15.50 tuition per academic year in the Faculty of Philosophy and Letters, about $21.50 per academic year in the Faculty of Law, Science, Medicine, or Pharmacy. A matriculation fee of about $2 and small laboratory and library fees are also charged.

ADMISSION REQUIREMENTS ... There are no special academic requirements for enrollment in the special courses of the University. To register as a regular student working for a degree, an American student must submit his academic record together with various documents to the Spanish authorities for evaluation. See the section on Admission Requirements in the opening summary on Spain.

LANGUAGE OF INSTRUCTION ... Spanish.

ACCOMMODATIONS ... Students taking the special courses for foreigners can live at the University residence halls. Many students live in pensions, in hostels, or with families. Room and board are about $85 per month in modest accommodations. The tourist bureau will assist students to find suitable lodgings. The University is separated into old and new campuses with the dormitory buildings on the new campus, which is on the opposite side of town.

AVERAGE COSTS ... Tuition about $25 for the academic year; about $50 for an inclusive summer course with excursions. Room and board about $85 per month and up.

STUDENT LIFE ... Excursions are planned so that students can see Galicia; neighboring cities are visited, including the walled city of Lugo, La Coruña, Betanzos, and Vigo. Monasteries, railroad bridges, beaches are also visited and show the wide variety of attractions in the countryside. The market and the street stands are a good place to learn the language;

University of Santiago de Compostela

Spanish students welcome the chance to make friends with American students.

UNIVERSITY OF SARAGOSSA (ZARAGOZA)

Saragossa is the capital of the former kingdom of Aragon; it is located in the center of a vast and fertile plain and it forms an important junction city between Madrid and Barcelona. One of the most important agricultural centers of Spain, it is also a city that has two cathedrals, a fine museum of tapestries, and a picturesque old market. The environs of Saragossa are rich in attractions: the Carthusian Monastery of Aula Dei a few miles from the city contains an outstanding collection of paintings by Goya; the Monastery of Cogullada dates back to 627. The University of Saragossa was founded in 1474.

SIZE ... About 3,700 students attend the University, including foreign students.

CALENDAR ... The academic year opens in the first week of October and continues until the end of June. There is a summer session from July to September.

COURSES OF STUDY ... The University of Saragossa is composed of the Faculty of Philosophy and Letters, the Faculty of Law, the Faculty of Medicine, Faculty of Science, and the Faculty of Veterinary Medicine. There is also a School of Social Studies. The Faculty of Philosophy and Letters offers the course of Hispanic Studies from November to the end of April. Subjects taught include Spanish language, literature, history, geography, history of art, art, and philosophy. Students may attend as auditors other courses in the Faculty of Philosophy and Letters.

SUMMER COURSES ... From July to September the University offers a course for foreign students in Spanish language and culture at Jaca. Language classes are offered for beginning, intermediate and advanced students. There are excursions, visits and musical events.

TUITION ... The registration fee for the academic year for the course of Hispanic Studies is about $25. Students matriculated for a degree pay fees varying with the faculty: students of the Faculty of Philosophy and Letters pay about $15.50; students of the Faculty of Law, Faculty of Medicine, Faculty of Science, or the Faculty of Veterinary Medicine pay about $21.50 per academic year. Small matriculation, laboratory and library fees are also charged. Registration fee for the summer terms is about $15 per term.

ADMISSION REQUIREMENTS ... No special academic requirements are set up for the summer courses. To pursue the course in Hispanic Studies students must have a good knowledge and understanding of the Spanish language as all instruction and examinations are given in Spanish; it is not necessary, however, to present one's academic credentials to enter the course. To enroll in the University as a regular student, an American must submit his academic record and other documents to the Spanish authorities, as outlined in the Admission Requirements section in the opening summary on Spain.

LANGUAGE OF INSTRUCTION ... Spanish.

ACCOMMODATIONS ... There are *colegios mayores,* intended for the lodging of students, at fair rates. Students should apply well in advance of registration for lodging in these. Many students live in pensions, in small hotels, in hostels, or with Spanish families. Room and board may cost about $53 per month in Jaca during the summer in a University residence hall. Accommodations during the school year may cost around $90 per month. *The Oficina de Turismo* keeps lists of accommodations suitable for students. There are also groups at the University which will assist students to find lodgings.

AVERAGE COSTS ... Tuition about $25 per academic year. Room and board about $90 per month.

STUDENT LIFE ... Excursions take visiting collegians to various points in Spain; the city's monuments are visited and the monasteries in the outlying district. Walks in the squares, along the river and in the parks are popular with students—as with all Spaniards. There are clubs for various recreational and social activities, and students may have an opportunity to learn songs and dances typical of the Aragonese.

UNIVERSITY OF SEVILLE

Seville is one of Andalusia's most important and artistic cites. Examples of Arabic architecture can be seen in the city, whose streets in summertime are covered with colorful awnings to protect against the hot sun. Some of the city's main streets are for pedestrian traffic only and sidewalk cafés add charm to this "most Spanish of Spanish cities." Patios decked with lush greenery, balconies of interesting iron grillwork, remnants of more than five hundred years of Moorish rule, small green squares and delightful public gardens attract visitors. The Gothic Cathedral, the Giralda Tower, the Alcazar, the Tower of Gold are handsome monuments. The University of Seville has the distinction of being founded in 1502 under the authority of Ferdinand and Isabella.

SIZE ... About 4,000 students, including foreign students, attend the University.

CALENDAR ... The academic year opens the first week of October and continues to the end of June. A special fall course for foreign students is held in August and September. A summer course in Spanish language and culture is held during July and August.

COURSES OF STUDY ... The fall course for foreign students offers classes in the Spanish language, literature, history, geography, art, music, Spanish thought and culture, history of the Spanish language, commercial Spanish and phonetics. The University offers courses in its Faculty of Philosophy and Letters which are open to auditors with the permission of the lecturer. Other faculties which make up the University are the Faculty of Science, Faculty of Law, Faculty of Medicine (at Cadiz and Seville), and the Faculty of Veterinary Medicine (at Cordoba). The University also has a School of Social Studies.

SUMMER COURSES ... A one-month course beginning in late August is offered in Spanish language and culture at Cadiz. Subjects taught are the Spanish language, culture, dance, literature, theater, lyric poetry of the Golden Age, and Spanish art. Various excursions and visits to monuments are included in the program.

TUITION ... Registration fee for the fall course for foreign students is $12.50; for the summer course the fee is about the same. The tuition fees for students who wish to attend courses of the Faculty of Philosophy and Letters during the regular academic year are about $2 per subject; for those working toward a degree, about $15.50 for the year. The fee is about $21.50 in Law, Medicine, Science, and Veterinary Medicine. A matriculation fee of about $2 is charged and there are small laboratory and library fees, from 40 cents to $1.35.

ADMISSION REQUIREMENTS ... No special academic requirements are set up for the fall or summer courses for foreigners. No credit is given for attendance as auditors and the usual admission requirements do not apply. To enroll as a regular student of the University, working for a degree, an American student must submit his academic record and other documents to Spanish authorities for evaluation, as outlined in the Admission Requirements section of the opening summary on Spain.

LANGUAGE OF INSTRUCTION ... Spanish.

ACCOMMODATIONS ... The *colegios mayores,* intended for student lodging, are maintained by the University at very fair rates, but in order to secure a room in one it is necessary to apply very early. Room and board are under $10 a week in these accommodations. Many students live in pensions, in hostels, or with Spanish families. Prices vary, of course, according to the elegance of the accommodations taken, but a room can be found for under $5 per week and meals in some restaurants are low, 80 cents to $1. The Tourist Office in Seville and various student groups will assist foreigners to get settled for the school year.

AVERAGE COSTS ... Tuition fees about $25 for the academic year. Room and board about $95 per month.

STUDENT LIFE ... In the spring Seville has a fair famous throughout Europe; flamenco dancing can be seen in the streets at night, the Spanish deck themselves out in colorful costumes, life is very gay. Students will find themselves welcome to participate in the festivities. There are frequent excursions for students to take to other parts of Andalusia; bicycle trips are popular, as are swimming, tennis, and golf. Various clubs within the University are devoted to special interests of an intellectual or recreational nature.

UNIVERSITY OF VALENCIA

Valencia, Spain's third largest city, lies on the Mediterranean coast, with a rich plain, covered with groves of lemon and orange, almond and olive trees, in the background. There are flowers everywhere in this colorful, beautiful, and ancient city; in July during the Festival for St. James there is a magnificent "Battle of Flowers." The *Fiestas de las Fallas* during the week of March 19 is a colorful occasion when cardboard figures are carried through the streets by torchlight. Once an area dominated by the Moors, Valencia has many examples of Moorish architecture as a reminder. The Cathedral, built on a former mosque, has fine paintings by Goya. The University of Valencia was founded in 1590; by that time Valencia had become one of the chief centers of learning in Spain. The first printing press in Spain was set up in Valencia in 1474, and printing flourished.

SIZE ... About 4,000 students, including foreign students, attend the University.

CALENDAR ... The academic year begins during the first week in October and continues to the end of June. Summer courses are offered in July and August.

COURSES OF STUDY ... The University is composed of the Faculty of Philosophy and Letters, Faculty of Law, Faculty of Science and the Faculty of Medicine.

SUMMER COURSES ... During July, the University offers a course in Spanish culture and language, including practical courses in pronunciation, composition and conversation. Excursions are part of the study program. During July and August, the University offers the same courses in Alicante and Peníscola.

TUITION ... Registration fee for the entire course at either Valencia or Alicante is about $11, for two weeks at Valencia about $7, for two weeks at Alicante about $8.50. Students attending the regular courses of the University pay about $15.50 tuition for the academic year in the Faculty of Philosophy and Letters, about $21.50 tuition for the academic year in the Faculty of Law, Medicine, or Science. A small matriculation fee is charged; laboratory courses and library use also carry small fees.

ADMISSION REQUIREMENTS ... No special academic background is required for admission to the summer courses. To enroll as a regular student, an American student must submit his academic record and other documents to Spanish authorities for evaluation, as outlined in the Admission Requirements section in the opening summary on Spain.

LANGUAGE OF INSTRUCTION ... Spanish.

ACCOMMODATIONS ... Three residences are maintained for men students and one for women students of the University. To secure a room, which with full board costs less than $10 per week, it is necessary to apply very early. Most students live in pensions, in hostels, or with Spanish families. The local tourist bureau and other groups will help students to find suitable accommodations. The cost for room and board is about $95 per month.

AVERAGE COSTS ... Fees about $25 per academic year. Room and board about $95 per month.

STUDENT LIFE ... There is much to see and do in Valencia and a student's spare time will easily be taken up. Sidewalk cafés are found about the city and certain ones are the favorites of students and the place for long discussions. Swimming, tennis, cycling are recreational activities of students. The festivals are important events, and students will soon feel at home in these gay celebrations.

UNIVERSITY OF VALLADOLID

Valladolid is about 125 miles northwest of Madrid, in the central region of Spain. Although there is an old section of the town, around the Cathedral and nearby churches, the city in general has a modern appearance. Valladolid has a busy Plaza Mayor, central square, as the city center. The city's museum of

University of Valladolid

religious sculpture is the only museum of its kind in the world. Throughout the city are churches of note, some of them containing important paintings or works of art. The University of Valladolid existed as a different institution before it was raised to university rank in 1346 by Clement VI; the University is thought to date back to the thirteenth century.

SIZE ... About 5,000 students, including 185 foreign students, attend the University.

CALENDAR ... The academic year opens during the first week in October and continues to the end of June. A summer course is offered in August and September.

COURSES OF STUDY ... The University is composed of the Faculty of Philosophy and Letters, the Faculty of Law, the Faculty of Science, the Faculty of Medicine, the Faculty of Political Science and Economics.

SUMMER COURSES ... The University offers a course in Spanish language and culture with classes in history, art, folklore, music and geography. Visits and excursions are part of the program of study.

TUITION ... Registration fee for the summer course is $12.50. Tuition fees for the regular University courses are about $15.50 for the Faculty of Philosophy and Letters; about $21.50 for the Faculty of Law, Science, Medicine, or Political Science and Economics, per academic year. A matriculation fee of about $2 is charged along with library and laboratory fees of under $2.

ADMISSION REQUIREMENTS ... No special academic background is required of students who wish to enroll in the summer courses. An American student who wishes to enroll for credit work must submit his academic record and other documents to Spanish authorities for evaluation, as outlined in the Admission Requirements section in the opening summary on Spain.

LANGUAGE OF INSTRUCTION ... Spanish

ACCOMMODATIONS ... Students of the summer course will be housed in the Santa Cruz residence hall for about $51 for the entire course, full board included. Many students of the University live with families or in pensions. The local tourist bureau will assist students to find suitable accommodations and the cost will be about $95 per month for room and board.

AVERAGE COSTS ... Fees about $25 per academic year. Room and board about $95 per month.

STUDENT LIFE ... During the summer, special excursions, tours, and musical events are arranged for the students. The Holy Week celebration in the spring is an interesting religious and artistic spectacle. The Spring Festival, held during the first half of May, and the Festival of San Mateo in September are also colorful. The city offers bullfights, a swimming pool, and tennis courts.

SWEDEN

SWEDEN

UPPSALA •
★
STOCKHOLM

• GÖTEBORG

• LUND

Sweden has always been dependent on exchange and co-operation with other countries in many fields, even though to some it may have appeared to be a country off the beaten track. Gradually, as the means of communication have improved, tourists and students from abroad have discovered the many different opportunities for recreation and study in Sweden. Now young students from all over the world are coming to our country in increasing numbers. The exchange in the field of scholarship and learning is expanding, and facilities for foreign students are increasing.

The Sweden-America Foundation had prepared a handbook for foreign students, Travel, Study and Research in Sweden, *and the Swedish Institute has issued a small pamphlet called* Studying in Sweden.

You may also write to the Swedish Institute for further information. We will do our best to facilitate your studies and to make you feel at home here. Sweden is anxious to welcome students and scholars from foreign countries.

Per-Axel Hildeman
Executive Director
Swedish Institute for Cultural Relations

Sweden's efficient and up-to-date educational system is one of the basic causes of her advanced position in the world today. There are five universities in Sweden; the oldest, at Uppsala, was founded in 1477 and revitalized in the early seventeenth century. The University at Lund was established in 1668, at Stockholm in 1877 and at Göteborg in 1891. The new University of Umeå started to operate on a limited scale in 1963. In addition, there are about twenty professional schools of university standing in the country which are, however, so crowded that very few foreign students are admitted, except on an advanced level.

The Stockholm University Institute for English-Speaking Students has two divisions: the International Graduate School, established at the University of Stockholm in 1947, and a Junior Year, which was organized at the Institute in the academic year 1959–60. In 1957, a Royal Decree created Master's degrees for foreign students of Social Science, Liberal Arts and Science.

Sweden has the Royal Institute of Technology in Stockholm and the Chalmers University of Technology in Göteborg. There are Schools of Social Work in Stockholm, Göteborg and Lund; Schools of Dentistry in Stockholm, Malmö and Umeå; Schools of Arts, Crafts and Design in Stockholm and Göteborg; Schools of Forestry, Veterinary Medicine, Pharmacy, Music, Fine Arts, etc., in Stockholm; a Royal School of Agriculture in Uppsala; and also Schools of Economics in Stockholm and Göteborg.

The Scandinavian Seminar offers a 9-month study program in Sweden based on the Folk High Schools. It extends from early August until May. During the years, the Seminar has become a recognized program for college undergraduates, graduates and other adults. Those interested in education as a profession find it a particularly rewarding experience. For a more detailed description, see under Denmark.

SWEDISH UNIVERSITY SYSTEM ... A characteristic of university study in Sweden, as in most Western European countries, is the relative freedom of the student. Attendance at lectures is often not compulsory, and the student determines the point at which he is ready for examinations. Independent study is encouraged, and most students specialize in one subject at a time as a result of the academic point system in Swedish universities.

The International Graduate School program and the Junior Year in Sweden are more closely organized and regulated.

ADMISSION REQUIREMENTS ... Swedish students are required to pass a student's exam to be admitted to a university. U.S. students are required to have at least a secondary school certificate (high school diploma) plus two years at an accredited college, and preferably a Bachelor's degree. Those students who do not wish to take a degree may attend lectures in various subjects in the Theological, Law, Arts and Science Faculties without being registered.

Foreign students who wish to study for an academic degree must apply to the Chancellor of the Swedish Universities for special permission. A basic knowledge of the Swedish language is essential, and a student may be required to pass a preliminary examination to establish his eligibility for admission.

Facilities in Swedish universities are especially good for postgraduate studies for foreign students, particularly in the fields of technology and natural sciences.

CREDIT TOWARD AN AMERICAN DEGREE ... Students who are candidates for a degree in an American university must make arrangements with their dean regarding transfer of credits.

SUMMER COURSES ... The Student Unions in Stockholm and Lund arrange international seminars on social, economic and political topics, usually during two weeks in August or September.

The Swedish Institute offers two courses each summer: Modern Sweden, a course on the economic, social and cultural life in Sweden today, at the University of Uppsala the first part of August; and Swedish Design and Architecture, a course intended to provide an opportunity for designers, architects, art students and teachers interested in meeting modern Sweden as it appears in design, architecture and town planning, in late August. The course includes study visits to museums, public establishments, workshops, etc. in Stockholm.

REGULATIONS ... A U.S. citizen needs no visa to stay in Sweden up to three months. After this period, a residence permit must be obtained from the State Aliens Commission.

In Sweden there is compulsory public health insurance for all residents. Students registered at a university are eligible for medical service at a reduced cost.

TUITION ... There is a small registration fee of $2 to $3, and no tuition fees at Swedish universities, but the student has to belong to the Student Union and pay entrance fees from $2 to $12, and registration fees of $8 to $12 each semester.

The International Graduate School course costs $145 for an academic year, or $90 for the fall semester. The tuition fee for the Stockholm Junior Year is $700. Folk High School costs vary; some charge no tuition, others may be up to $30, which may include board and room as well.

Summer courses vary in duration and cost, ranging from a few dollars per course to $120 for an all-inclusive course on modern Sweden.

LIVING COSTS ... Minimum living costs in Stockholm are about $130 per month—about the same in Göteborg.

Some of the summer courses estimate living costs at $2.20 to

$3.50 a day, including three meals.

Folk High School living costs range from $18 to $100 per month depending on location of school.

LOCAL CUSTOMS ... Visitors may find the Swedes somewhat reserved and formal at first. They are less impetuous, more deliberate than Americans are apt to be. However, they will find the Swedes warm and friendly on closer acquaintance.

Women do not smoke on the street in Sweden.

Don't miss a trip on the cruising train, Sunlit Nights, to Lapland.

Try Swedish delicacies in season: reindeer meat, *smultron* (wild strawberries), *hjortron* (cloudberries).

FOR FURTHER INFORMATION ... For complete information about a university and how to enroll, write to any of the following: The Swedish Institute, Box 3306, Stockholm 3; Sweden-America Foundation, Grev Turegatan 14, Stockholm O; Institute for English-Speaking Students, Sveavägen 166, Stockholm Va; America-Scandinavian Foundation, 127 East 73rd Street, New York, N. Y. 10021, and 1020 Lake Shore Drive, Chicago, Ill. Those interested in the Scandinavian Seminar program should contact Scandinavian Seminar for Cultural Study, 62 West 58th Street, New York, N. Y. 10019.

For travel particulars and documentation, write to Educational Department, NHE, Pan American Airways, Pan Am Building, New York, N. Y. 10017.

HOW TO GET THERE ... By Pan American's through-plane service from New York, about 9 hours to Stockholm, via Oslo, or connect from transatlantic Jet Clippers to London (6½ hours) or Copenhagen (9 hours). By ship, 8 to 10 days from New York to Göteborg.

UNIVERSITY OF GÖTEBORG

Göteborg, a great port and shipbuilding center, was founded in 1621. At that time it was Sweden's only outlet to the Atlantic, situated as it is on the Kattegat and just south of the Skagerrack. The first Swedish colonists in the United States sailed for Delaware Bay from Göteborg in 1637. Göteborg is in the province of Västergötland, which lies between the two largest lakes in Sweden, Vänern and Vättern. The fertile plains of this region are broken by heights which give variety to the landscape.

The University of Göteborg was founded in 1891.

SIZE ... There are about 4,500 students matriculated at the University of Göteborg, of which number 150 are foreigners.

CALENDAR ... The academic year is divided into two terms: the beginning of September to mid-December and mid-January to the end of May. There is a summer session held in August.

COURSES OF STUDY ... The University has Departments of Medicine, Humanities (divided into the Historical-Philosophical section and the Language section) and Mathematics and Science. There are independent Schools of Economics, History and Social Work, also a School of Arts, Crafts and Design. The Medical School was founded recently and is connected with the University.

The Chalmers University of Technology, an independent institution, is so crowded with Swedish students that it cannot take foreigners, except on an advanced level.

Language courses are arranged during the academic year.

SUMMER COURSES ... A course is conducted for medical students called Medical Summer School in Scandinavia.

TUITION ... The University charges no tuition or fees, but all students must belong to the Student Union. A membership fee of $4 to $15 is charged each term.

ADMISSION REQUIREMENTS ... See the Admission Requirements section in the opening summary on Sweden.

LANGUAGE OF INSTRUCTION ... Swedish.

ACCOMMODATIONS ... There is a shortage of student hostels in Göteborg, and foreign students cannot usually find a hostel room. However, U.S. students will find comfortable rooms in private homes, as do Swedish students. During July and August, Göteborg Kristliga Studenthem is open for foreign students at $1.20 to $1.40 per day.

AVERAGE COSTS ... The minimum cost of living is about $130 a month, with rent at about $35 and food about $45 to $50. Incidentals, books and supplies amount to about $50.

STUDENT LIFE ... The atmosphere of a busy port is a stimulating one, and students, both Swedish and foreign, learn each other's customs. The countryside round about will be interesting to the hiker or cyclist. A favorite excursion is the boat trip on Göta Canal between Stockholm and Göteborg, or a boat trip under the bridges in Göteborg.

UNIVERSITY OF LUND

The University of Lund is in southern Sweden in the province of Skane. This province is the granary of Sweden. It is dotted with castles and manor houses and surrounded by sunny beaches. The cathedral city of Lund is very old, and the University was founded in the year 1668. The present administration building dates from 1882. The Locus Peccatorum, in ancient times a students' hostel, is now part of the Cultural History Museum. It is here that the great botanist Carl von Linne worked.

SIZE ... There are about 7,400 students registered at Lund University, of whom about 300 are foreigners.

CALENDAR ... The academic year is divided into two terms: the beginning of September to mid-December, and mid-January to the end of May. There is an international student seminar in August and September.

COURSES OF STUDY ... The University of Lund has Departments of Theology, Law, Medicine, the Humanities (divided into the Historical-Philosophical section and the Language section), Mathematics and Science.

Two new schools, a College of Technology and a School of Business Administration, have recently been added to the University.

Courses in the Swedish language are arranged by the Extramural Department of the University during the year.

SUMMER COURSES ... The theme is on special social, political or economic subjects as related to Sweden. This is conducted in English.

TUITION ... None. However, all students must belong to the Student Union. At Lund, the entrance fee is about $2 and the semester fee about $12 per semester.

ADMISSION REQUIREMENTS ... See the Admission Requirements section in the opening summary on Sweden.

LANGUAGE OF INSTRUCTION ... Swedish.

ACCOMMODATIONS ... Applications may be made to the Internationelle Studenthuset, Lund, to obtain a hostel room. The minimum rent per month for a room in Lund amounts to $30. Board will be $45 to $50 per month, and an additional $30 to $40 for incidentals should be allowed.

STUDENT LIFE ... The Swedish National Union of Students arranges many student activities. Excursions and festivals provide a pleasant means of getting to know the people and learning the language.

The Student Union building, which is located in the downtown section of Lund, is the center of the very lively student activities in the city.

University of Lund

University of Stockholm

University of Uppsala

UNIVERSITY OF STOCKHOLM

Stockholm, the largest city in Sweden, covers a dozen islands, washed either by the Baltic Sea or by Lake Mälaren. The Royal Palace and the House of Parliament face the salt-water side, while the City Hall, whose tower is a symbol of the Swedish capital, is on Lake Mälaren.

The University of Stockholm was founded in 1877.

SIZE ... There are about 9,000 students at Stockholm University, of whom about 350 are foreigners.

CALENDAR ... The academic year is divided into two terms: the beginning of September to mid-December, and mid-January to the end of May. There are summer courses in Stockholm in September.

COURSES OF STUDY ... The University has Departments of Mathematics, Natural Science, Humanities, Law and Political Science. There are independent Schools of Medicine, Dentistry, Forestry, etc., also scientific institutes of note, in particular the Wenner-Gren Institute for Experimental Biology. The Institute for English-Speaking Students started an International Graduate School fifteen years ago and, since 1957, has awarded Master's degrees in Social Science, Arts and Sciences to foreign students. Annually, some fifty students from many countries are enrolled in the one-year diploma course. A second year is needed to complete the requirements for the Master's degree. Language of instruction: English.

The International Graduate School diploma course requires students to take a language course and two or three seminar courses. These deal with Swedish and comparative questions in economics, social welfare, government and administration and international relations. Each student must present a research paper in one of the seminars. The Master's degree program consists of graduate seminars, research work and independent reading.

The Junior Year in Sweden program consists of a Swedish language course and a number of lecture courses in the following subjects: modern history and international relations; economics; government; social structure and problems; literature and history of art. Each student must present a seminar paper on one of these subjects.

SUMMER COURSES ... The Central Organization of Student Unions in Stockholm conducts in English a 2-week international course in early September.

TUITION ... None. However, all students have to pay nominal fees to the Student Union. The courses for foreign students have special tuition fees. The International Graduate School fee is $145 for the academic year, or about $90 for the fall semester alone. Tuition for a Swedish language course only is about $95. Fees for the Junior Year program are $700 for the whole academic year. Some scholarships are available.

ADMISSION REQUIREMENTS ... Applicants for the special graduate program should have a degree from an accredited college or university. Foreign students—see also the Admission Requirements section in the opening summary on Sweden.

Applicants for the Junior Year program must have at least two years at an American college.

LANGUAGE OF INSTRUCTION ... Swedish. English for the Graduate School for English-Speaking Students and for the Stockholm Junior Year.

ACCOMMODATIONS ... There is a shortage of student hostels in Stockholm, and foreign students cannot, as a rule, obtain a room in a hostel. A U. S. student can find a comfortable room in a private home as Swedish students do.

AVERAGE COSTS ... Living costs in Stockholm are about $130 per month. Textbooks and supplies can run to about $60, but this can be kept to a minimum by using the libraries. An additional $20 to $30 per month should be allowed for incidentals.

STUDENT LIFE ... In Stockholm you will meet students from all over the world. Living with a family will make possible a real appreciation of Swedish life and customs. A favorite Easter holiday for Swedish students, in which an American might like to join, is a skiing trip to Lapland.

UNIVERSITY OF UPPSALA

Uppsala lies north of Stockholm in Uppland. This is a province of wide, fertile plains, broken by stony, wooded hills. Uppland was the core of the kingdom long ago and shows many ancient monuments. The town dates from around 500 A.D. The University was founded in 1477 and revitalized in the early seventeenth century. It is famous for its University Library, Carolina Rediviva.

SIZE ... There are about 10,500 students registered at Uppsala, of whom about 200 are foreigners.

CALENDAR ... The academic year is divided into two terms: the beginning of September to mid-December, and mid-January to the end of May. Courses in the Swedish language are arranged by the Extramural Department of the University during the year. There is a summer course at the University in August, and the Academic Summer School of Swedish every year.

COURSES OF STUDY ... The University has Departments of Theology, Law, Medicine, Humanities and Mathematics and Science. Especially interesting are the Department of Limnology (fresh-water biology), the Institute of Meteorology and the Gustav Werner Institute for Nuclear Chemistry.

Courses in the Swedish language are arranged by the Extramural Department of the University during the year.

SUMMER COURSES ... "Modern Sweden" in August is conducted in English. Courses in the Swedish language are offered in Uppsala and Gothenburg.

TUITION ... None. However, all students must belong to the Student Union. At Uppsala the semester fee is about $12.

ADMISSION REQUIREMENTS ... See the Admission Requirements section in the opening summary on Sweden.

LANGUAGE OF INSTRUCTION ... Swedish.

ACCOMMODATIONS ... Applications may be made to the International Secretary, Uppsala Students' Union, to obtain a hostel room. The minimum rent per month for a room in Uppsala amounts to about $30. Board will be about $50 per month, and an additional $30 to $40 for incidentals should be allowed.

STUDENT LIFE ... During the academic year, festivals and excursions attract students and make the process of language learning more interesting. Special student prices are charged for concerts and theaters. Winter sports are available almost everywhere in Sweden, although the climate is not extreme.

SWITZERLAND

Maybe you have been thinking of spending a year or more studying abroad, to widen your world knowledge, your command of languages, or simply to enjoy discovering new customs and ways of life.

The Swiss universities will open their doors to you as they have in the past to foreign students, some of whom became famous men, such as Albert Einstein. Among the many students from all over the world who attend courses in my country's universities, Americans come in increasing numbers.

I daresay you will find many interesting features in Switzerland which, in spite of its small size, is extremely varied and picturesque. Since a student ordinarily boards with a Swiss family he soon becomes part of it and shares its life, experiences and hopes. In this spirit of mutual understanding, I extend my hand to you and invite you to come and participate in the intellectual tradition of Switzerland.

Alfred Aehndev
The Ambassador of Switzerland
Washington, D. C.

UNIVERSITIES IN SWITZERLAND ... There are seven universities in Switzerland; each is maintained by the canton in which it is located, but each has complete independence and academic freedom. In the German-speaking part of Switzerland are the University of Basel, the University of Berne, the University of Zurich; in the French-speaking part of Switzerland are the University of Geneva, the Univesity of Lausanne, the University of Neuchâtel, and the University of Fribourg, which is actually bilingual, with courses offered in both French and German. There is no university in the Italian-speaking part of Switzerland. Besides these universities in the canton capitals, the Swiss Confederation maintains one institution of university rank, the Federal Institute of Technology, in Zurich. The Graduate School of Economics and Public Administration at St. Gall, in German Switzerland, and the Institute of Technology of the University of Lausanne in French Switzerland are also of university rank. There is also a graduate school, The Graduate Institute of International Studies, in Geneva. In addition to these institutions there are a number of music conservatories, art schools and specialized institutes. Swiss universities have been open traditionally to foreign students, and of 25,000 students enrolled, there were 7,050 foreign students in 1963; more than 50 nationalities were represented.

Special courses in language and literature are given by the Schools or Institutes of French Language at the Universities of Fribourg, Geneva, Lausanne and Neuchâtel. The Universities of Geneva, Lausanne and Neuchâtel also offer holiday courses in the French language and literature; these courses are designed for foreign students. The University of Geneva offers a summer course on international institutions; this course is translated into four languages, including English.

SWISS UNIVERSITY SYSTEM ... In Switzerland the universities are designed for work at the graduate level; each university has several faculties and the student enrolls in the faculty of his field of interest, works out his own plan of studies, chooses the lectures he will attend and works in the manner best suited to himself. Certain programs must be followed in medicine and technology. There is no differentiation between colleges and graduate schools in the Swiss university. Each university is divided into several faculties which fall under the general categories of Theology, Law, Medicine, Philosophy I (Letters, Philology, History) or Arts, and Philosophy II (Biology, Physics, Chemistry, Mathematics) or Science. The academic standard and the organization of each of the seven universities are much the same. Three offer courses in German, four in French, one in both French and German. Various specialized institutes are attached to each university. Most courses require four to five years of study for a degree; Medicine requires longer. With the exception of the Catholic Faculty of Theology at the University of Fribourg, all faculties of the universities are open to women. All students must be at least 18 years old to enter the universities. The Swiss Federal Maturity Certificate is required of Swiss students for admission.

Primary and secondary education are free and, usually for a period of eight to nine years, compulsory in Switzerland. Education at all levels is supervised by the Education Department of the canton.

ADMISSION REQUIREMENTS ... Four universities, Geneva, Lausanne, Fribourg, and Neuchâtel, offer holiday courses, usually in the French language and literature; these courses are generally open to all students over 18 years of age. Should a student desire to obtain a degree or a diploma from this course, he must have attended college previously. Students who wish to attend lectures at any of the seven universities may generally do so as auditors, if they have permission from the lecturer. Non-matriculated students, or auditors, are not subject to the admission requirements set up for matriculated students, do not take examinations or work toward a diploma or degree. To enroll as a regular, full-time student, a student must hold a Swiss Federal Maturity Certificate or the equivalent foreign certificate. Each overseas candidate is examined individually and must be accepted by the faculty he wishes to enter. Some faculties require satisfactory results on special entrance examinations. A B.A. or B.Sc. degree is acceptable and entitles the holder to enroll in any faculty.

Students attending universities in French-speaking Switzerland must be competent in the French language; those who enter universities in German-speaking Switzerland must be competent in the German language. The language of instruction is French or German in all universities, depending on geographical location.

CREDIT TOWARD AN AMERICAN DEGREE ... A student must make arrangements for receiving credit toward an American degree from his own university before he leaves the United States. Because of the variations in credit systems within American universities, it is impossible to generalize about the number of credit hours a student may receive. Each student should discuss with his own dean or guidance counselor the requirements for receiving credit and the number of credit hours toward his American degree that may be awarded for study abroad. Sometimes full credit may be given for the period of study in Switzerland if the student passes the Swiss examinations. Each American university will make its own evaluation of the study at each Swiss university. Certificates of completion of some special courses may be earned by foreign students at some Swiss universities.

REGULATIONS ... American citizens need only a valid passport to enter Switzerland. If a student intends to stay longer than three months in Switzerland, he must apply to the local police, the Aliens Police, for a permit of residence soon after his arrival in the country. The permit will be issued upon presentation of a university registration certificate.* Students should inform themselves about the regulations regarding the import of household equipment, motor vehicles or unusual or professional photographic equipment into Switzerland.

TUITION AND OTHER COSTS ... Although costs vary from one university to another the approximate minimum cost for one academic year for tuition as a regular student is about $200; with other fees for matriculation, library, laboratory, accident and sickness insurance, Student's Union, the total fees for the academic year may reach between $250 and $300.

LIVING COSTS ... American students will find that about $170 a month will be sufficient for room and board. Although some universities have student hostels with inexpensive accommodations, these accommodations are generally taken up by Swiss or European students. Students live with Swiss families or in boardinghouses. It is customary for students to arrange for their own living quarters. The various students' unions do, however, assist students with lists of suitable rooms. The Swiss National Tourist Office also publishes a pamphlet, *Accommodations for Students,* and will help students find lodgings. Working one's way through college is not unheard of in Switzerland, but foreign students may not earn incidental money while in the country.

COMMON COURTESIES AND LOCAL CUSTOMS ... The Swiss, although equally friendly, are a bit more reserved than Americans. Only members of the family and intimate friends are on a first-name basis. Men tip their hats to ladies and also to friends of the same sex. There's much more handshaking, too, in Switzerland. In general, however, the forms of etiquette and good manners are the same as in the United States. Excursions and holiday camping are a habit with Swiss students and foreign students are welcome on these student-organized jaunts.

FOR FURTHER INFORMATION ... For complete information about a university and how to enroll, write to the universities direct.

For travel particulars and documentation, write to Educational Department, NHE, Pan American Airways, Pan Am Building, New York, N. Y. 10017.

HOW TO GET THERE ... By Pan American Jet Clipper from New York to London, Paris or Frankfurt with connections to Zurich, 9 hours. Or from the U.S. West Coast about 10½ hours to London via Pan Am's polar route, then to Zurich. Zurich is 1½ hours from Rome by air. Geneva is a 1½-hour flight from London. By ship, 5 to 9 days to western Atlantic or Mediterranean ports and then overnight by train. Switzerland is the crossroads of the European railway network; from London and Paris the Simplon Express passes through Lausanne to Italy, and the Arlberg Express passes through Basel, with connections to Klosters, Davos, Arosa and St. Moritz, on the way to Vienna. Europabus from Amsterdam goes to Basel, Lucerne, Interlaken and Montreux, with connections to Milan or Nice. You can even go by Rhine boat from Rotterdam to Basel.

UNIVERSITY OF BASEL

Basel is the second largest city of Switzerland and serves as a gateway from France and Germany. It is a center of industry—especially the chemical industry—trade and banking, as well as intellectual life. The Rhine river flows through the city and provides a romantic setting for hotels and restaurants; its harbor takes an important place in Swiss economy. In spring each year the *Fasnacht*—carnival—is celebrated with much gaiety throughout the city. Among Basel's many excellent museums, the Art Museum has a fine collection of modern works as well as outstanding Holbeins. The Cathedral, surrounded by interesting medieval houses, is worth visiting.

Excellent modern hospitals and clinics and an outstanding library are connected with the University. Basel's modern social legislation is of special interest for its students.

The University of Basel is the oldest in Switzerland; it was

* However, a married student must apply at a consular representation of Switzerland for a visa for his family.

founded in 1459 by Pope Pius II, and had its first students in 1460. For nearly 500 years the University occupied buildings on the left bank of the Rhine; in 1939 new, modern buildings were taken over for classrooms; these are located throughout the city.

SIZE ... The University has about 3,150 students; this includes about 400 foreign students.

CALENDAR ... The academic year begins in mid-October and ends in mid-July. The year is divided into semesters: the winter semester from mid-October to the beginning of March, the summer semester from mid-April to mid-July.

COURSES OF STUDY ... The University of Basel has the following faculties: Faculty of Evangelical Theology, Faculty of Law, with its Institute of International Law and International Relations, Faculty of Medicine, including an Institute of Dentistry and several other institutes and clinics, departments and laboratories, Faculty of Arts, which includes courses in Political Science and in Economics, Faculty of Sciences, Swiss Tropical Institute, Institute of Pharmacology, Institute of Astronomy and Meteorology, Institute of Geology and Paleontology, Institute of Geography, Institute of Botany, Institute of Zoology, Institutes of Physics, Chemistry, and others.

TUITION ... Lecture fee for a 6-month course of one hour a week is about $1.50 per course for matriculated students. Non-matriculated students pay about $2.50 per semester for each lecture course. There are additional fees for registration, library use, laboratory supplies, health insurance, and Students' Union. Students should allow about $200 per academic year for tuition and various fees.

ADMISSION REQUIREMENTS ... American students must have a B.A. or a B.S. degree for admission as regular full-time students in most cases. Each foreign applicant is individually considered and examined and the faculty he wishes to enter may also examine him. Foreign students may enter as non-matriculated students, however, and may attend most of the lectures if the lecturer gives his consent.

See also the Admission Requirements section in the opening summary on Switzerland.

LANGUAGE OF INSTRUCTION ... German.

ACCOMMODATIONS ... The University does not maintain residence halls; however, it does operate a student cafeteria. Students live with Swiss families or in boardinghouses. The cost of room and board varies from about $130 to about $170 per month, depending on the accommodations. The Registrar's office of the University, the local tourist office and the Swiss National Tourist Office, SNTO, will supply students with information on accommodations.

AVERAGE COSTS ... Fees and room and board may cost about $170 per month, minimum; a student should allow from $1,600 to $1,800 for expenses per academic year.

STUDENT LIFE ... An active Students' Union organizes travel and holiday camps for students, as well as social activities; excursions are made outside Switzerland as well as within the country. There is good skiing not far from Basel; skating rinks and ice hockey clubs have been formed. There are several sports clubs, groups devoted to music, reading, and other intellectual pursuits, as well as to recreation. Fencing, riding, rowing, hiking, cycling, and tennis are popular with the students. The University owns its own house for skiers in the Alps. There are all-year-round swimming facilities. On the cultural side, Basel offers a rich concert, opera and theater life.

University of Basel

UNIVERSITY OF BERNE

Berne is the capital of Switzerland. A city founded in the twelfth century, Berne has still preserved much of its medieval character. Most famous attractions of the capital are the bear pits, which are said to have existed for hundreds of years, and the Clock Tower, which notes the hour by a display of mechanical figures. The arcaded streets, red-roofed buildings, the Rose Gardens and the splendid Gothic Cathedral make the city a true gem. The Aare river makes a picturesque loop as it flows through the city. There are scientific and historical museums, as well as the Swiss National Library, in Berne. The University of Berne was founded in 1528 as a school of theology, and in 1834 it became a university. Berne itself is a bridge between French and German Switzerland; the University is an important one in the country.

SIZE ... About 3,000 students attend the University; 400 are from foreign countries.

CALENDAR ... Mid-October to mid-July. The academic year is divided into the winter semester from mid-October to the beginning of March and the summer semester from mid-April to mid-July.

COURSES OF STUDY ... The University has the following faculties: Faculty of Law and Economics; Faculty of Medicine including an Institute of Dentistry and a School of Pharmacy; Faculty of Veterinary Science; Faculty of Sciences; Faculty of Letters and Philosophy, which offers Philology, Languages, History, Art, Music, Mathematics, and Science; Faculty of Protestant Theology; and the Faculty of Old Catholic Theology. Courses are also offered in Advanced Commercial Studies, Social Sciences, Political Science, and Education, and by various seminars, institutes, clinics and departments.

TUITION ... Non-matriculated students pay fees different from those for students working toward a degree. For credit students the fee for most 6-month lecture courses of one hour per week is about $1.50 per course. Non-matriculated students pay up to about $2.50 per course per semester. In addition there are fees covering health insurance, library use, laboratory use, registration, and Students' Union. A student should allow up to $200 per academic year for various fees, including tuition.

ADMISSION REQUIREMENTS ... Each candidate for admission as a regular student is examined individually. Besides the University-required entrance examination, the faculty which the student desires to enter may require a satisfactory mark on its own entrance examination. American students holding a B.A. or B.S. degree who have a good working knowledge of spoken and written German can enter as regular students. Non-matriculated students are permitted to attend most lectures with the consent of the lecturer. Medical students must have a good knowledge of Latin.

See also the Admission Requirements section in the opening summary on Switzerland.

LANGUAGE OF INSTRUCTION ... German. A few courses are given in French, Italian or English.

ACCOMMODATIONS ... The University does not maintain residence halls for students; however, it does operate a student restaurant. Most students live with Swiss families or in pensions. There is a Student Hostel, however, and the inquiry office of the Students' Union can furnish information on availability of accommodations there. Cost of board and room per month ranges from about $120–$170 for foreign students. The Swiss National Tourist Office will supply upon request a list of accommodations available to students.

University of Berne

AVERAGE COSTS ... Fees, room and board and incidental expenses for an academic year range from about $1,400 to about $1,900.

STUDENT LIFE ... Hub of student activity at the University is the Students' Union general center; scientific, literary and artistic groups are active as well as sports clubs. A fine sports ground and swimming pools are also maintained by the University. The Free Union of Students—an association including students from all faculties—plans social and cultural events. There are concerts, theater performances, lectures, exhibitions, and excursions; Berne has ice skating, ice hockey and, of course, skiing, soccer, swimming, horseback riding and so on.

SCHOOL OF ECONOMICS AND PUBLIC ADMINISTRATION, ST. GALL

Off the beaten path for tourists lies the northeastern part of Switzerland, where softly flows the great Rhine River; there lie green rolling pasturelands and countryside; its peasants have a rich tradition of folklore. St. Gall (St. Gallen) is the region's principal city and it is also Switzerland's textile and embroidery center. The St. Gall Cathedral and Abbey are considered outstanding examples of rococo architecture; the Abbey has a superb library. The School of Economics and Public Administration in St. Gall is one of the oldest institutions of its kind in Europe. It was founded in 1898.

SIZE ... About 900 students attend the School; 260 are from foreign countries.

CALENDAR ... The academic year is divided into the winter semester from mid-October to the beginning of March, and the summer semester from mid-April to mid-July. Summer language courses are offered each summer in St. Gall.

COURSES OF STUDY ... The School offers courses in the following departments: Department of Economics and Business Management, Industry, Trade, Banking, Insurance, Trusteeship and Accountancy, and Tourism; Department of Administration including General, Financial and Fiscal, and Traffic Administration, Social Insurance and Social Welfare, and Consular and Foreign Trade Service; Department of Commercial Teaching, which prepares students for teaching the commercial subjects on an advanced level. Among the seminars and institutes attached to the School are the Swiss Institute of Foreign Trade and Marketing, the Swiss Institute of Public Administration, the Seminar for Tourism and Politics of Transport, Swiss Institute of Industrial Economics, Institute of Insurance Economics, Institute for Research in Agricultural Economics and Land Law, Group for Research in Economics, and the Institute of Business Administration.

SUMMER COURSES ... German and French language courses are offered each summer in St. Gall.

TUITION ... Students pay about $1.50 per course of one hour per week, for a minimum of 25 hours. There may be small fees for health insurance, library use, Students' Union dues.

ADMISSION REQUIREMENTS ... Students may attend lectures as non-matriculated students, with the consent of the lecturer. Students should inquire of the School directly for detailed admission requirements. See also the Admission Requirements section in the opening summary on Switzerland.

LANGUAGE OF INSTRUCTION ... German.

ACCOMMODATIONS ... The Official Inquiry Office in St. Gall will help students to find living quarters. A room with full board in a boardinghouse costs from about $130 to $170 a month; prices for the same accommodations in a hotel or transient pension are slightly higher. A furnished room alone can be rented for about $50 a month. Some restaurants serve lunch or dinner for $1 to $1.50.

AVERAGE COSTS ... Tuition about $50 per academic year. Room and board about $170 per month.

STUDENT LIFE ... St. Gall is covered with snow for an average of 70 days each year; it is a winter sportsman's delight and the School has a special winter sports activities program. There is skiing, of course, and indoor social activities as well. In other seasons there are cycling, hiking and walking; there is a

University of Fribourg

season of excellent concerts and theatrical offerings. The School has an outstanding library, and there are three others of note in St. Gall. An art gallery and five museums are available for looking or browsing. A good many learned and intellectual societies beckon students to pursue any special interests.

UNIVERSITY OF FRIBOURG

Fribourg is situated on the borderline between French-speaking Switzerland and German-speaking Switzerland, and as a result the University of Fribourg, as well as the city, is bilingual. The University, a state institution, Catholic and international in character, the center of Catholic studies in the country, together with numerous other educational institutions, gives the city a special animation. The city has an important fine public library with over 800,000 volumes, art museums, and picturesque ancient houses, bridges, fountains, churches, and monuments from its medieval past. The University of Fribourg was founded in 1889; it grew out of St. Michael's College, which had been in existence in the 1600s. The University moved into new buildings, constructed according to modern designs, in 1938 and 1941. The city, with its population of 35,000 inhabitants, is considered a calm and quiet one, ideal for the pursuit of studies.

SIZE ... There are about 2,300 students at the University; about 800 students are from about 50 countries from the 6 continents.

CALENDAR ... The academic year runs from mid-October to mid-July with two semesters: mid-October to the beginning of March is the winter semester; mid-April to mid-July is the summer semester.

COURSES OF STUDY ... The University offers courses leading to graduate degrees (Licentiate and Doctor's degree) in the following faculties: Faculty of Jurisprudence, including the Departments of Law and Economics and Social Sciences; Faculty of Philosophy and Arts, including the Departments of Philosophy, Pedagogy, Languages and Literature, History, and Ethnology—this faculty also includes the Institute of the English Language and the Institute of the French Language—Faculty of Sciences including the Departments of Mathematics, Physics, Chemistry, Mineralogy, Geology, Geography, Botany, Zoology, Physiology, Biochemistry, Anatomy, and Histology; and the Faculty of Theology (Roman Catholic), including the Institute of Mission Studies and Eastern Languages Division. There are a number of related institutes attached to each faculty.

TUITION ... Tuition costs per semester are about $21 for the winter semester and about $18 for the summer semester for matriculated students. Non-matriculated students pay up to about $2.50 per semester for admission to each lecture course. In addition there are fees for matriculation, library use, laboratory sessions, health insurance and Students' Union. The approximate total for fees for a regular full-time student per academic year is $200, not including summer session, which is regulated separately.

ADMISSION REQUIREMENTS ... Students working for a degree will be matriculated if they are in possession of certificates of study at recognized institutions. Candidates from

the United States of America must be in possession of either a B.A. or a B.Sc. degree from a recognized college. Foreign students must have a good working knowledge of French and/or German. Latin is necessary for admission to the Faculty of Theology. Applicants whose certificates satisfy the above requirements are requested to send an authenticated copy or a photostatic copy of their diplomas and transcripts of record to the dean of the faculty concerned at Fribourg University. See also the Admission Requirements section in the opening summary on Swtizerland.

For admission to the summer courses, students must be at least 18 years old but do not need academic credentials.

LANGUAGES OF INSTRUCTION ... French, German, Latin (Faculty of Theology). The lectures on the various literatures are conducted in the original languages.

ACCOMMODATIONS ... The University does not maintain residence halls for students. Students live in student hostels, boardinghouses, or with Swiss families. A room with full board may cost about $145 to $170 a month and up. A furnished room alone may cost from about $30 to $50 per month. Students who eat out should expect to spend from about $1.50 to about $2 per day for meals. These are minimum figures, and students should allow up to $170 per month for room, board and incidental living expenses. The Office Fribourgeois du Tourisme (Official Enquiry Office) will supply students with a list of rooms and boardinghouses and will assist the student, when necessary, to get settled.

AVERAGE COSTS ... Fees about $200 per academic year. Room and board about $170 per month.

STUDENT LIFE ... Fribourg's splendid situation between the lake country and the lower Alps opens to the students the doors of numerous beaches along the lakes and famous skiing grounds in the nearby mountains. There are yachting, swimming, and fishing; skiing, ice skating, and winter sports. Tennis, golf, dancing, the theaters, concerts, and cinemas are also popular. Students organize excursions summer and winter, and there is almost never a time without an excursion in the offing. There are many treasures for art lovers to see. A special cosmopolitan atmosphere is added to the University because of its international character. Foreign students are very welcome.

UNIVERSITY OF GENEVA

Geneva is one of Europe's most cosmopolitan cities and has as romantic a setting as a fairy-tale town, with Lake Geneva at its foot and the Alps in the background. It is the home of the Peace Palace built for the League of Nations, now the European office of the United Nations.

There is a festival or celebration in every season of the year, with the *Fêtes de Genève* in August, the International Horse Show in November, Exposition of Watches and Jewelry in September, and the Automobile Show in February.

The University of Geneva, sometimes called "a mirror of the world," was founded in 1559 by John Calvin as the Schola Genevensis; it became the University in 1873.

SIZE ... 4,000 students attend the University; this figure does not include the non-matriculated students. About 2,200 foreign students are included in the student body.

CALENDAR ... The academic year begins in mid-October and ends in mid-July. There are two semesters: winter semester from October to March; summer semester from mid-April to July; summer courses especially for foreign students are offered from mid-July through October.

COURSES OF STUDY ... The University is composed of the following faculties: Faculty of Sciences, Faculty of Arts, Faculty of Economic and Social Sciences, Faculty of Law, Faculty of Medicine, including the Institute of Dentistry, Faculty of Protestant Theology, and the School of Pharmacy, Institute of Higher Commercial Studies, School of Architecture, Graduate Institute of Maritime Administration, Institute of Medical Biology and Chemistry, Institute of Physical Education and Sports, and the Department of Botany, and 35 other laboratories, institutes, departments, and clinics. The Faculty of Arts includes a Seminar of Modern French and a School of Practical French. This School is designed primarily for students whose native language is not French. Courses in literature as well as language are offered by the School of Practical French. Of special interest to foreign students may be the School of Interpreters, the Institute of Educational Sciences, and the Graduate Institute of International Studies, which is described below.

SUMMER COURSES ... The holiday course for foreigners offered by the University offers both language and culture courses in French; students may begin at an elementary or an advanced level. The University also offers a summer course in international institutions; with the collaboration of the School of Interpreters, and its facilities, this course is translated into four languages, including English.

TUITION ... Although fees vary with the faculties, many semester courses of one hour per week cost about $1.50 per course for matriculated students. Non-matriculated students pay from about $1.20 to about $2.50 per course. In addition, there are fees for health insurance, registration, laboratories, library, and Students' Union. Students should allow about $200 for tuition and various fees.

ADMISSION REQUIREMENTS ... American students who have completed their sophomore year in an accredited American college or university are eligible to enroll in the University as regular, full-time students, although a Bachelor's degree is preferable. Competence in the French language is required. The faculty chosen, as well as the University, give entrance examinations in French. The summer courses are open to all students who are at least 18 years of age; special academic training is not required for admission to these courses. See also the Admission Requirements section in the opening summary on Switzerland.

LANGUAGE OF INSTRUCTION ... French. The summer course on International Institutions is translated into English.

ACCOMMODATIONS ... The University does not maintain dormitories. There is a *restaurant universitaire*, however, where students can get meals for about 50 cents per meal. There is also a milk bar maintained by the University, where snacks are available. Most students live with Swiss families, in boarding-houses, or at International Student House, where full board is available for about $80–$100 per month. A room with full board at a pension costs from $145 to $170 per month; a room without meals costs from about $50 per month. Some furnished apartments are available in Geneva at prices above those for ordinary students' accommodations. The Association des Intérêts de Genève keeps a list of approved places for students to stay.

AVERAGE COSTS ... Fees about $250 per academic year. Room and board about $145 to $170 per month.

STUDENT LIFE ... The student cafeteria is a gathering place, and students can soon become part of an international group in Geneva. The variety of activities matches the variety of nationalities of Geneva's students. There are swimming, boating, sailing, debating, skiing, ice skating, sporting events, concerts, conferences, open-air theaters, yachting, summer pageants and celebrations. Geneva is an excursion center. One can visit mountains, forests, holiday resorts, spas, and vineyards. Walking is a special pleasure in Geneva, and the Quai du Mt. Blanc provides a special pleasure in early morning or a late summer evening.

University of Geneva

GRADUATE INSTITUTE OF INTERNATIONAL STUDIES, GENEVA

The Graduate Institute of International Studies is a foundation supported by financial grants from the Canton of Geneva, the Swiss Confederation, and private sources. Although it is independent of the University of Geneva, the Graduate Institute maintains a connection with the University, follows the same academic year, and suggests University courses which may be of benefit to its students.

CALENDAR ... The Institute follows the calendar of the University of Geneva; the winter semester begins about the middle of October and ends about the middle of March; the summer semester opens about the middle of April and closes about the middle of July.

COURSES OF STUDY ... The Institute is set up as a center for advanced study of contemporary international questions from the juridical, political, and economic points of view. It is a research and teaching institution and it confines itself to strictly international subjects not taught at the University of Geneva. The aim is not to cover the whole field of international questions, but to study in detail certain subjects which, hopefully, will throw light upon the general problems of international relations. Seminars, regular lectures, and "temporary" lecture courses are offered. Seminars are primarily intended for diploma and doctorate students and the number of their participants is strictly limited to those who take an active part in them. Seminars are concerned with the subjects of the regular lectures, or with the student's research. Particular importance is attached to this research: the number of courses and seminars is restricted in order to leave all the time necessary for individual work. "Temporary" lecture courses are offered once or twice a month by various professors from Switzerland or abroad and consist of three public lectures followed by a seminar for advanced students. Lectures are titled by their subject matter such as "The Origins of the Second World War," "The Role of Concepts in International Relations," "The Atlantic World: Its Internal and External Economic Relations," "International Trade and National Policies," "The Soviet Union Since Stalin," "Introduction to the Study of Civilizations," and "The Application and Interpretation of Modern International Law by the United States of America." To round out the student's study program, certain courses in the Faculty of Letters, Faculty of Law, and the Faculty of Economic and Social Studies of the University of Geneva are suggested to Institute students.

TUITION ... Regular students, those who are working for a degree from the Institute, pay about $30 per semester to attend lecture courses and seminars and to use the Institute library. In addition, fees amounting to about $25 must be paid to the University of Geneva each semester. Students who attend the lectures as auditors pay about $2.50 per semester for each lecture course attended and an additional fee of about $5 per semester if they wish to use the Institute library.

ADMISSION REQUIREMENTS ... A student holding a university or college degree may enroll as a candidate for one of the various degrees or diplomas offered by the Institute, depending on the student's background of study. Students thus enrolled are termed regular students. Their number is limited, preference being given to holders of an M.A. who are candidates for the Doctor's degree. Students who wish to attend lecture courses as auditors may do so, provided they are at least 18 years of age. Auditors do not participate in the course work, nor do they receive credit for attendance. Seminars are open only to regular students. See also the Admissions Requirements section in the opening summary on Switzerland.

LANGUAGES OF INSTRUCTION ... French and English. Lectures and seminars may be given in both languages and students must be able to understand and follow discussions in either French or English. French is the only language used at the University of Geneva.

ACCOMMODATIONS ... The Institute does not maintain living quarters for students. It does have available a list of boardinghouses and families recommended by former students. These accommodations cost about $5 to $6 per day for room and board. Students can obtain lodging information from the tourist bureau.

AVERAGE COSTS ... Fees about $50 per semester. Room and board about $145 to $170 per month.

STUDENT LIFE ... The Graduate Institute has a student association which maintains a committee which will help new students of the Institute to obtain practical information about Geneva and its cultural, social, recreational, and intellectual activities.

CENTRE D'ÉTUDES INDUSTRIELLES, GENEVA

The Centre d'Études Industrielles (CEI) is a postgraduate, international management development school for men aspiring to take executive responsibility in industry.

The objectives are threefold:

1. To develop a broad international industrial approach, not only to problems of a strictly business character, but of a general economic, technological, governmental and social character as well;

2. To develop the ability to arrive at, and convey, thoroughly considered decisions on a wide variety of industrial problems;

3. To develop the ability to work effectively and responsibly with other individuals of similar or considerably different backgrounds and points of view.

In the past fifteen years, CEI has grown and developed from an Aluminum Limited Training School (1946–47) to an International Management Development Institute offering a postgraduate university degree; its student body represents internationally renowned firms like Saint-Gobain, CIBA, IBM, etc., and 13 to 15 nationalities each year from all parts of the world. The CEI incorporated itself under Swiss law as an independent foundation, and established an official and formal connection with the University of Geneva in order to meet the needs of more and more organizations that have sent students from all parts of the world.

CALENDAR ... The program of study is eleven months long divided into three terms, designated the winter and spring terms, of four months each, and a 3-month summer term of field study and research. Regular courses, student projects and lectures by visiting and resident lecturers occupy the eight months of the first two terms. The 8-month period also includes three one-week industrial study trips. These trips are conducted all over Europe, including Scandinavia and the British Isles. There is a summer course in June.

SUMMER COURSES ... International Executive Course —management experience required.

TUITION ... The tuition fee, payable upon registration, is $1,163. Tuition fee covers course materials, the use of the library and of all other facilities at the CEI during the winter, spring and summer terms.

ADMISSION REQUIREMENTS ... Participants are either sponsored by an employer or may apply independently. Applicants are eligible for enrollment if they:

a) Have successfully completed a course of study at a recognized university or institution of higher learning at a similar level
b) Submit satisfactory character references
c) Submit a certificate of good health
d) Have a very good working knowledge of English
e) Pass an oral interview with one or more members of the CEI staff.

See also the Admission Requirements section in the opening summary on Switzerland.

ACCOMMODATIONS ... The CEI is not residential. Lists of boardinghouses and apartments in Geneva offering suitable accommodations for students may be obtained from the CEI. Board and lodging may be had in pensions from $170 a month upward.

CERTIFICATE AND DIPLOMA ... Students who satisfactorily perform the work of two terms of the normal curriculum and of the summer-term field study and research receive either a certificate from the CEI, or a Diploma in Industrial Administration, awarded jointly by the University of Geneva and the CEI.

All regular courses of the CEI are open to auditors, a maximum of three courses being available to each individual. Persons being accepted as auditors are expected to participate in class sessions and to prepare any work assigned. Auditing fees are about $9 per course term.

UNIVERSITY OF LAUSANNE

Lausanne is considered the cultural, educational, and medical center of French-speaking Switzerland. The city's lakeside suburb, Ouchy, is not only Lausanne's port, but also a charming waterfront village, and the home of boatmen and fishermen; the port is a place to row, swim, fish, and just stroll. Lausanne and its environs have attracted artists and writers and prominent teachers throughout the centuries. The city faces the Alps, looks out at Lake Geneva, or behind at a mass of verdant vines covering gentle slopes. There is a blend of urban and rural features in Lausanne; here and there about the city can be found a pleasant meadow or a wooded park. The "old town" has fountains, quaint houses, bookstalls, and markets. The bookstalls of the Place de la Riponne, open on market days, are a favorite haunt of students, and it's not unusual to see bearded bookworms studiously browsing. The University of Lausanne grew out of a theological seminary founded in 1537; the seminary grew into the Lausanne Academy, from which the University emerged in 1890.

SIZE ... About 3,300 students attend the University; this number includes 1,600 foreign students.

CALENDAR ... The academic year begins in mid-October and ends in mid-July; there are two semesters: winter semester from mid-October to the beginning of March; summer semester from mid-April to mid-July. Summer courses are held from mid-July to mid-October.

COURSES OF STUDY ... The University is composed of the Faculty of Protestant Theology; Faculty of Law, including the School of Social and Political Science, Department of Pedagogy, School of Higher Commercial Studies, and the Institute of Scientific Police Methods and Criminology; Faculty of Letters, including the School of Modern French designed primarily for those whose native language is not French; Faculty of Science, including the School of Pharmacy; and the Faculty of Medicine, which includes various institutes and clinics. There are also other institutes, clinics, and schools within the faculties of the University. The Institute of Technology of the University of Lausanne is described on page 168.

SUMMER COURSES ... Summer courses are offered in French language, and literature. The courses are designed primarily for foreign students and there are various levels at which a student may begin his studies.

TUITION ... Matriculated students pay about $1.50 per course per semester for 6-month lecture courses of one hour per week. Non-matriculated students pay up to about $2 per one-hour-per-week course, each semester. The matriculation fee may be about $5. In addition there are fees for library use, laboratories, health insurance, registration, and Students' Union. Students should allow about $225 per academic year for fees, including tuition.

ADMISSION REQUIREMENTS ... To attend the summer course students do not need academic certificates. American students who hold a B.A. or B.S. degree of a recognized college are eligible to enroll in any of the faculties of the University if their records show a satisfactory preparation. A good working knowledge of French is essential. Students whose qualifications are not sufficient to enroll as regular, full-time students may attend lectures of the University as non-matriculated students. Permission of the lecturer is required to attend. See also the Admission Requirements section in the opening summary on Switzerland.

LANGUAGE OF INSTRUCTION ... French.

ACCOMMODATIONS ... Residence halls are not maintained by the University and students must find their own lodgings. Most students live with Swiss families, in boardinghouses, or sometimes in apartments. In a boardinghouse a room and full board cost about $140 to $170 per month; a room alone costs about $50 per month. It is difficult to find a furnished apartment in Lausanne. The *foyer universitaire*, university canteen, serves meals for about 50 cents each, or snacks for about 40 cents. Some restaurants serve meals for about 85 cents each. The Lausanne Tourist Office publishes a list of boardinghouses with accommodations suitable for students. The *Association Générale des Étudiants* (AGE) also keeps a list of accommodations available to students.

AVERAGE COSTS ... Fees about $225 per academic year. Room and board about $170 per month.

STUDENT LIFE ... Not far from the main buildings of the University is the Place de la Riponne, a picturesque place on market days when the bookstalls are open and students from far and wide come to browse and have a good time. Intellectual interests of Lausanne's students are set off, on the other hand, by the wide recreational activities the ideal climate offers. There are swimming pools, golf courses, tennis courts, an artifical ice skating rink; there are concerts, theater performances; of course, skiing slopes are near. Students organize their own excursions.

INSTITUTE OF TECHNOLOGY OF THE UNIVERSITY OF LAUSANNE

COURSES OF STUDY ... The Institute of Technology of Lausanne is autonomous, although it is within the University of Lausanne; it was founded in 1853 and became part of the Academy of Lausanne in 1869. It offers courses in the following divisions: School of Engineering including the Department of Civil Engineering, Department of Mechanical Engineering, Department of Electrical Engineering, Department of Physical Engineering, Department of Chemical Engineering, and the Department of Land Surveying; the School of Architecture; and the Special Preparatory Course in Mathematics. The length of study varies from five to eight terms, plus a term for practice work.

TUITION ... The fees vary from about $50 to about $70 per semester in the School of Engineering and the School of Architecture; this amount includes laboratory fees. The Special Course in Mathematics costs about $93 per semester for matriculated students. In addition there are the usual university fees each semester for registration, health insurance, library use, and Students' Union dues.

ADMISSION REQUIREMENTS ... See the Admission Requirements section in the opening summary on Switzerland, as well as the preceding summary on the University of Lausanne.

LANGUAGE OF INSTRUCTION ... French.

UNIVERSITY OF NEUCHÂTEL

Neuchâtel is located in western Switzerland on the shores of Lake Neuchâtel; a fine view of the Alps stretches before the city itself. Since the days of the Reformation Neuchâtel has been an intellectual center; it has been called a "City of Studies," and in addition to its University it has many specialized schools, the Swiss Research Laboratory for Watchmaking, and an observatory. The city has an outstanding library which is open to students. Among the museums is the one which houses the three famous eighteenth-century mechanical dolls of Pierre Jaquet Droz and his son Henri Louis Jaquet Droz. The automata perform their skills of writing, drawing, and playing the piano on the first Sunday of each month. The city is also a popular holiday center in Switzerland. The University of Neuchâtel came into being in 1909; before that time it had been an academy, founded in 1838.

SIZE ... About 850 students attend the University; about 100 are foreign students.

CALENDAR ... Mid-October to mid-July. The academic year is divided into the winter semester from mid-October to the

University of Neuchâtel

beginning of March and the summer semester from mid-April to mid-July. A holiday course for foreign students is held from mid-July to mid-August.

COURSES OF STUDY ... The University has the following four faculties: Faculty of Theology, Faculty of Letters and Philosophy, Faculty of Sciences, and Faculty of Law. Also within the University are the Department of Higher Commercial Studies, Department of Economics, Department of Social Sciences, Department of Political Science, Chemical Engineering Course, and the School of Modern French Language. In addition there are a number of seminars and institutes. The School of Modern French is designed to teach students whose mother tongue is not French.

SUMMER COURSES ... The University holds a holiday course in French language and culture. The course is designed for foreign students.

TUITION ... These vary for matriculated and non-matriculated students. Matriculated students pay about $1.50 per course per semester for 6-month lecture courses of one hour per week. Non-matriculated students may pay about $2.50 per one-hour-per-week course, each semester. The matriculation fee is about $8.10. There are additional fees for library use, laboratories, health insurance, registration, and Students' Union. Students should allow about $200 per academic year for fees, including tuition.

ADMISSION REQUIREMENTS ... To attend the holiday course it is not necessary to present academic documents. Students primarily interested in attending the School of Modern French may find it possible to enroll under special circumstances without meeting the usual University requirements. To enroll as a regular, full-time matriculated student, an American student must hold a B.A. or B.S. degree and, of course, meet the French language requirements. He must also compete in the University entrance examinations and be accepted by the faculty he wishes to enter. A good working knowledge of the French language is essential for enrollment in any capacity. Non-matriculated students may attend lectures of the University by obtaining permission from the particular lecturer. See also the Admission Requirements section in the opening summary on Switzerland.

LANGUAGE OF INSTRUCTION ... French.

ACCOMMODATIONS ... Dormitories are not maintained by the University; there is, however, a students' refectory which provides meals very inexpensively. Most students live with Swiss families or in boardinghouses; some in apartments or small hotels. Boardinghouse prices for a room and three meals a day range from about $145 to $170 a month; a room alone may cost from $50 per month. A number of restaurants cater to students and serve them meals at reduced rates—from 50 cents to about 85 cents. The Secretary of the University keeps a list of rooms for students and assists students to get settled. The Official Inquiry Office (ADEN) also keeps a list of rooms and pensions for students.

AVERAGE COSTS ... Fees about $200 per academic year. Room and board about $170 per month.

STUDENT LIFE ... Its University has truly given Neuchâtel the atmosphere of a university town; its active intellectual life attracts leading theatrical groups and musicians of Europe. Foreign students will soon feel at home in the community and, summer or winter, will easily find recreation. The lake offers swimming, sun bathing on the beaches, yachting, boating, rowing, fishing, and cruising by motorboat or steamer to the sights along the shores. Golf, tennis, ice skating, skiing, and hiking are close at hand. Really energetic students can hike to Chaumont; for the less energetic there is a funicular. Near the city are the relics of prehistoric lake-dwellers, verdant vineyards, the picturesque Jura mountain range which is the city's background. Students can visit the Jaquet Droz dolls, use the reading room in the main University building, or take part in excursions planned by and for students.

UNIVERSITY OF ZURICH

A center of international banking, finance, and insurance, Zurich is also Switzerland's largest city. Besides the University of Zurich Medical School, which is well known, the city's hospitals and clinics have earned world-wide reputations. The Zurich Art Museum, which has an outstanding collection of modern French and German works, the Municipal Opera House where internationally famous stars perform in fall, winter and during the June Festival, the Civic Theater, and the Concert Hall all contribute to the city's well-developed cultural life. At the beginning of the nineteenth century, Zurich set up a new constitution, a new educational system, and by public vote established the University. In commemoration of this vote of 1832 an inscription translated "By the Will of the People" stands over the main entrance to the University. The University grew out of a school founded in 1523 and for 300 years thereafter the center of the city's intellectual life. The first university of Europe to open its doors to women students, the University of Zurich has always attracted foreign students and upheld a high degree of academic freedom.

SIZE ... About 4,400 students attend the University; about 850 students come from foreign countries.

CALENDAR ... Mid-October to mid-July. The year is divided into the winter semester from mid-October to the beginning of March, and the summer semester from mid-April to mid-July.

COURSES OF STUDY ... The University is composed of the Faculty of Medicine, Faculty of Veterinary Medicine, Faculty of Sciences, Faculty of Law, Faculty of Letters and Philosophy, and Faculty of Theology. The University has an Institute of Dentistry, Department of Advanced Commercial Studies, Department of Economics, Department of Social Sciences, Department of Political Science, and Department of Educational Sciences. There are also the following departments: Philosophy, Psychology, Pedagogy, Sociology, Philology (including classical and modern languages), History, Art History, Music, Mathematics, Physics, Chemistry, Astronomy, Geology, Mineralogy and Geography, Ethnography, Botany, Zoology, Paleontology, and Anthropology. There are a great many institutes and clinics attached to the University.

TUITION ... The matriculation fee is about $9. Lecture courses of one hour per week cost about $1.50 per course for matriculated and non-matriculated students. All students must pay each semester fees covering health insurance, registration, library use, laboratories, and Students' Union dues. Foreign students should allow about $200 per academic year for tuition and all other fees.

ADMISSION REQUIREMENTS ... To become a regular, full-time matriculated student, an American student must hold a B.A. or B.S. degree, or compete in the entrance examinations, and be accepted by the faculty in which he wishes to study. A good knowledge of the German language is, of course, essential. All entrance examinations are in German. Non-matriculated students are allowed to follow lectures if they have permission of the lecturers. See also the Admission Requirements section in the opening summary on Switzerland.

LANGUAGE OF INSTRUCTION ... German.

ACCOMMODATIONS ... Residence halls are not maintained by the University. Students live in pensions, with Swiss families, or in the student hostels, the *Studenten—und Studentinnenheimen*. It is necessary to apply long in advance to secure a room at the hostels. The cost is low, about $17 to $19 per month. Meals are served at the hostels for $1.45 to $1.65 a day. A room alone in Zurich may cost about $50 per month; in winter the cost

of heating must be added; this usually amounts to anything from $1.50 to $7.50 per month. There are a few restaurants in the university district which serve meals for about 75 cents to $1. The Secretary of the University keeps a list of rooms available to students and will assist those looking for lodgings. The newspaper *Tagblatt der Stadt Zürich* publishes the official list of rooms and apartments for rent for students on the third Tuesday of each month.

AVERAGE COSTS ... Fees about $225 per academic year. Room and board about $170 per month.

STUDENT LIFE ... Recreation-minded students may take part in swimming, tennis, golf, rowing, boating, ice skating, skiing, mountain climbing, horseback riding, or gymnasium sports. Spectators can enjoy cross-country bicycle races, soccer, and football. Student unions of the University offer artistic, social, intellectual, political, and religious activities. There are skiing trips, mountain-climbing excursions, hikes for all students. For those who enjoy strolling, Lake Zurich provides a suitable background.

SWISS FEDERAL INSTITUTE OF TECHNOLOGY, ZURICH

SIZE ... About 4,500 regular students and 500 postgraduate students are enrolled in the Swiss Federal Institute of Technology; there are about 2,130 non-matriculated students, about 950 foreign students.

COURSES OF STUDY ... The Institute is composed of the School of Architecture, School of Civil Engineering, School of Mechanical Engineering, School of Electrical Engineering, School of Chemistry, School of Pharmacy, School of Forestry, School of Agriculture, School of Rural Engineering and Surveying, School of Mathematics and Physics, School of Natural Science and School of Military Science (for Swiss officers only). Courses for Special Studies in Metallurgy, Aeronautics, Country Planning, Meteorology, Reactor Technology, Wood Technology. Courses in Gymnastics and Sports are also offered.

In addition there are numerous institutes and laboratories attached to the various schools. A general section of the Institute offers courses in Literature, Philosophy, Pedagogics, History, Political Science, Arts, Economics, Law, and Languages (German, French, Italian, English, Spanish, Chinese, Russian).

TUITION ... Tuition is about $47 per semester; laboratory charges are extra. There are also charges for health and accident insurance, registration, library use, and student organization dues.

ADMISSION REQUIREMENTS ... All students must have a good working knowledge of the German language. In order to be admitted to the first semester, American students must be holders of the B.Sc. certificate and eventually also sit for an entrance examination. Postgraduate students intending to work out a thesis leading to the Doctor's degree must be holders of the Master's degree and must pass an examination of admittance after two terms' study before being admitted to the doctorate. For further information, apply to the Rector of the Institute.

See also the Admission Requirements section in the opening summary on Switzerland.

LANGUAGE OF INSTRUCTION ... German. Some courses given in French.

ACCOMMODATIONS ... The same housing facilities open to students of the University of Zurich are available to students of the Swiss Federal Institute of Technology. The Institute does not maintain accommodations and students must find their own lodgings. See Accommodations section of the University of Zurich.

AVERAGE COSTS ... Fees about $200 per academic year. Room and board about $170 per month.

STUDENT LIFE ... In some years the percentage of foreign students at the Institute is as high as 20 per cent and even more. This gives a truly cosmopolitan atmosphere to the Institute. There is an opportunity for the international exchange of ideas. All the recreational and cultural activities open to students of the University of Zurich are available to the Institute's students. See Student Life section, University of Zurich.

TURKEY

Turkey, situated with a foot in each of two continents—Europe and Asia—has been the birthplace of several civilizations, and the bridge between the ancient and modern civilizations of the world.

Istanbul, with its marvelous natural beauty and unique historical interest, and many other cities are fields of research and sources of knowledge with their ancient ruins, monuments, mosques and rich museums.

Istanbul University, founded more than 500 years ago, and the modern universities and institutions of higher education in Ankara and Izmir train not only several thousands of young Turkish men and women but many hundreds of foreign students, especially from the Near and Middle East and Balkan countries.

Turkey is a country ever eager to share her historical heritage and riches and natural beauties and recreational facilities with her friends, and with the youth of friendly countries.

For the Turks, who are by nature hospitable, it is the greatest pleasure to welcome again old friends whose one desire has been to revisit this lovely land.

No country can rival Turkey for a tranquil and peaceful holiday in all seasons of the year. In summer, sunny weather, hundreds of miles of beaches, mostly free, extending all around Marmara with their clear golden sands, make a real paradise for sea and water-sport lovers.

Mr. Muhittin Akdik
Inspector
Turkish Ministry of Education

Turkey's universities are independent institutions governed by the staff (professors' council), the senate, the University executive committee and the Rector. They are supported by the government, by foundations and by private donations. The universities of Turkey number as follows: the University of Aegea (Izmir), which has Faculties of Agriculture, Medicine and Science; the University of Ankara; the Middle East Technical University at Ankara; the University of Ataturk (Erzurum), which has Faculties of Agriculture, Science and Letters; the Technical University of Karadeniz (Black Sea), located in Trabzon on the coast of the Black Sea and opened for the academic year 1963–64; Istanbul University; the Technical University of Istanbul; and Robert College of Istanbul.

ADMISSION REQUIREMENTS ... United States students must be at least 18 years of age and, in general, should have had at least two years of college or a Bachelor's degree. All candidates for the freshman class must pass an entrance examination which is given in Turkish. There is a quota for foreign students.

FOR FURTHER INFORMATION ... For complete information about a university and how to enroll, write to the Registrar at each of the colleges.

For travel particulars and documentation, write to Educational Department, NHE, Pan American Airways, Pan Am Building, New York, N. Y. 10017.

HOW TO GET THERE ... By Pan American Jet Clipper from New York to Istanbul, 13 hours; 45 minutes more to Ankara, which is also served by Middle East Airlines—routings via London, Paris, Frankfurt, Munich, Belgrade, Vienna and Rome. By ship, about 15 days.

UNIVERSITY OF ANKARA

Ankara is the capital of modern Turkey and has a population of 646,000. The residence of the President of Turkey at Çankaya, government buildings and monuments are of interest, as well as numerous mosques, including the Arslanhane Mosque and the Ahi Evran Mosque. For a spectacular sight, the sunset at Akkale should be seen from the fortress near Ankara. The tomb of Ataturk is in Ankara and so is the Turkish National Theater. The University of Ankara was founded in 1946 as a state institution; it brought together several faculties which had existed since as early as 1925.

SIZE ... Over 15,000 students attend the University; of this number about 500 are from foreign countries.

CALENDAR ... The academic year runs from November to July; there are two semesters: November–February and March–July.

COURSES OF STUDY ... The University has the following faculties: Faculty of Letters, Faculty of Law, Faculty of Science, Faculty of Medicine, Faculty of Veterinary Medicine, Faculty of Agriculture, Faculty of Theology and Faculty of Political Science.

ADMISSION REQUIREMENTS ... See the Admission Requirements section in the opening summary on Turkey.

LANGUAGE OF INSTRUCTION ... Turkish. Language classes are sometimes taught in the language being studied.

ACCOMMODATIONS ... The University does not maintain dormitories or restaurants for students; it is necessary to find lodgings for oneself.

AVERAGE COSTS ... Fees about $2 per academic year. Room and board about $75 per month.

MIDDLE EAST TECHNICAL UNIVERSITY, ANKARA

The Middle East Technical University in Ankara was founded in 1957; the United Nations and UNESCO assisted greatly and continue to do so in the planning and development of the University, a state institution supported by the Government of Turkey.

SIZE ... About 1,200 students; about 12 per cent of the total student body are foreign students.

CALENDAR ... The academic year is divided into two semesters and runs from the last week in September to the first week in June.

COURSES OF STUDY ... The Middle East Technical University has four schools at the present time: Engineering School, School of Arts and Sciences, School of Architecture, and School of Administrative Sciences. Bachelor's and Master's degrees are offered in Mathematics, Physics, Chemistry, Social Sciences, Civil Engineering, Mechanical Engineering, Electrical Engineering, Chemical Engineering, Mining Engineering, Architecture and Administrative Sciences. At this time the Ph.D. is offered only in the School of Arts and Sciences in the Depart-

Middle East Technical University

ments of Mathematics, Physics and Chemistry.

The University emphasizes basic and applied research in every field.

TUITION . . . Total cost for the academic year from about $800.

ADMISSION REQUIREMENTS . . . The University can accept any number of American students, provided they pass the entrance examination. See also the Admission Requirements section in the opening summary on Turkey.

LANGUAGE OF INSTRUCTION . . . English.

ACCOMMODATIONS . . . The University provides housing and dining facilities for the students.

ISTANBUL UNIVERSITY

Istanbul University was founded in 1453, following the conquest of the city by Sultan Mehmet II, the Conqueror. The first major courses were given by two well-known scholars of the time, namely Molla Husrev at Saint Sophia Mosque, and Molla Zeyrek at Zeyrek Mosque.

Eighteen years after the conquest, the Conqueror founded the University as a complete unit and the largest and most advanced educational establishment of the century, with its sixteen *medreses* (schools), free public kitchen and hospital, in the part of the city bearing his name. He brought the greatest scholars of his time to teach in eight of these *medreses,* and by so doing made Istanbul the most important center of culture and science in the East. At the University then, law, history, medicine, mathematics, physical sciences and astronomy were studied, as well as theology; and an observatory also was established connected with the department of astronomy. The University was quite independent and was supported by foundations and private donations awarded to it by citizens.

The University stands today in the middle of the city, in a most interesting historical setting with its exquisitely artistic, splendid gateway overlooking the ancient Bayezit Square. As with the other universities in Turkey, it is an independent institution governed by the staff (professors' council), the senate, University executive committee and the Rector. Education at Istanbul University is completely free except for a very small registration fee and a small fee for laboratories of some faculties. Successful students who cannot afford to pay these fees may be exempted from them by the professors' committee. There are also yearly scholarships for these students to help them with their personal living expenses.

Istanbul University has an international student pattern somewhat like that of many American universities; not only Turkish citizens, but many young men and women from the Balkan countries and from countries of the Middle and Near East, such as Iran, Pakistan, Afghanistan, Iraq, Libya, etc., attend all departments. Those especially attended are the Schools of Medicine, Dentistry, Pharmacy and the Faculty of Science.

CALENDAR . . . There is a summer session from July through September.

COURSES OF STUDY . . . The University has the following faculties: Medicine, Law, Science, Letters, Economics and Forestry, the School of Pharmacy and the School of Dentistry.

SUMMER COURSES . . . Turkish language and culture.

ADMISSION REQUIREMENTS . . . See the Admission Requirements section in the opening summary on Turkey.

UNITED KINGDOM

All the universities in Britain have always accepted some students from overseas, but the number of vacancies available to students from other countries is inevitably small, owing to the heavy demand for admission from British students, with whom the competition for entry is severe.

Few vacancies are available for overseas students at the undergraduate level; most of these are in the humanities, mathematics and the social sciences. There are opportunities for postgraduate work, which usually involve independent work on an approved topic under supervision.

UNIVERSITIES OF THE UNITED KINGDOM ... The opening of the new Universities of Essex and Lancaster in October 1964 brought the number of universities in Britain to 29. Oxford and Cambridge are the oldest, and the University of London the largest. Each university has its own individuality and has evolved according to historical needs. There is no uniformity nor are they subject to the control of any central body.

Some of the universities are prepared to consider applications from students who are already undergraduate members of an American college or university, and who wish to take a one-year course in Britain, usually during their junior year, returning to their own college or university to take their degrees. Occasional students who desire to receive credit from their home university for any work they may do at a British university should arrange this in advance with their own university authorities. Such students can usually be supplied with certificates of satisfactory attendance and performance by the British university.

Universities which are prepared to consider applications from occasional students are: University of Birmingham, University of Bristol, University of Durham, University of East Anglia, University of Essex, University of Hull, University of Leeds, University of Leicester, University of Liverpool, University of Manchester, University of Newcastle-upon-Tyne, University of Nottingham, University of Reading, University of Sheffield, University of Southampton, University of Sussex, University of Wales; as well as the four Scottish universities (St. Andrews, Glasgow, Aberdeen and Edinburgh) and the Royal College of Science and Technology, Glasgow.

Information concerning lecture programs, tuition fees, admission requirements, etc., can be obtained by writing the Registrar of the university concerned.

ENGLISH UNIVERSITY SYSTEM ... Each university is a completely independent body; each awards its own degrees, decides the entrance qualifications and appoints its own teaching staff. This allows a wide choice for a student, who should always be able to find a course which appeals to him from the wide variety offered.

Undergraduates receive instruction by means of lectures and classes, but there is an increasing amount of teaching to individuals and small groups. Great importance is attached to the student's own initiative in planning his course and preparing for his final examination under the guidance of his tutor. The undergraduate course lasts for three or four years, as a rule, apart from Medicine, where it is longer. Two years of further study are needed for a Master's degree and three years for a Ph.D.

Communal life is provided by the Students' Unions, where some meals can be obtained, and where various literary, religious and political societies meet. No student is expected to attend lectures without taking part in the social life of the university. Broadly speaking, half the students live in lodgings for which they make their own arrangements, aided by the university lodgings officer; about a quarter live at home and travel daily to the university, and the remainder live in halls of residence.

Undergraduates never work their way through college. British students work during the summer vacation, but never in term time.

CREDIT TOWARD AN AMERICAN DEGREE ... A student from an American university who wishes to spend part of his time at a British university should discover from his own college how many credits he will receive for the course of study which he intends to follow, since the credit system does not operate at British universities.

U.C.C.A., THE UNIVERSITIES CENTRAL COUNCIL ON ADMISSIONS (First [Bachelor's] degree and First Diploma Courses only) ... The Council was founded in 1962 as a central organization to handle applications for admission to undergraduate courses in the United Kingdom universities, except the Universities of Oxford, Cambridge, Belfast and the medical and dental schools in London. Applications should be submitted through the central office of the U.C.C.A., 29/30 Tavistock Square, London, W.C. 1.

It should be stressed that the scheme does not apply to postgraduate students nor to occasional students, who will continue to apply direct to the university.

A handbook explaining the central admission scheme is obtainable from the U.C.C.A., price 2 shillings and 6 pence (35 cents). A postal fee of 10 shillings is payable by overseas applicants ($1.40). Please do not send transcripts to the U.C.C.A.

ADMISSION REQUIREMENTS ... Each university in the United Kingdom may decide which students it will accept. Admission is on a competitive basis and, as there are more applicants than places, a student generally applies to several universities or separate colleges at Oxford, Cambridge and London.

Certain minimum entrance qualifications are required: a minimum of two years of college and preferably a college degree. However, most universities expect candidates to have other qualifications, and a student should always inquire about conditions of admission when he makes his application.

Applications from an overseas student will always be considered provided he has the necessary qualifications for university entrance in his own country. Normally, though, each overseas application is judged on its merits, and there is no general rule for all universities.

It is important that preliminary inquiries should be addressed to the University *at least one full year* (at Oxford and Cambridge at least 18 months) before the proposed date of entry, and final applications should be made *not later* than the beginning of December for admission in the following October.

In order to be eligible for study for a higher degree, or in order to undertake advanced study or research at a British university, the applicant needs, in general, to be a graduate of a recognized college or university, must be proficient in spoken and written English, must be able to present evidence to the effect that he will major and has received grades averaging not below B in the field in which he intends to specialize, and that he is well equipped to undertake advanced and independent research in that field. The universities of Oxford, Cambridge and Durham admit only their own graduates to the degree of M.A.

TUITION ... Fees are not high and range from about $110 to $420 for the academic year. Fees for the science courses, including medicine and engineering, are slightly higher than those for liberal arts students. Depending on the university, these costs may or may not include examination fees.

LIVING COSTS ... No definite figure can be given. As a rough guide, living costs at Oxford and Cambridge are higher than elsewhere, and $1,700 to $2,000 would cover expenses for the academic year. This would allow for some traveling during the vacations.

At London University the cost of living would range between $1,400 and $1,700 a year, and for most other universities about $1,400.

If possible, overseas students should live in the college or in a university hostel. As accommodations are very limited, it is best to make inquiries when applying for admission to the university. If it is necessary to find lodgings, which are usually a little cheaper than hostels, the university lodgings officer will be able to give advice and practical help. It is often *extremely difficult* to find suitable accommodations for married couples, and what can be found is generally very expensive.

REGULATIONS ... A student from the United States who plans to spend more than three months in Britain must have a residence permit. A letter from his British university and a bank statement of financial independence will insure that the Home Office gives the permit. The nearest British Consulate will give more information.

Students should also check on customs regulations. Such items as cameras and typewriters may be duty free, but they should be declared.

TECHNICAL EDUCATION ... The increasing demand for higher technical educational standards is reflected in the growth of technical colleges throughout the United Kingdom.

As with the universities, their organization is very decentralized, and therefore extremely varied.

Broadly, they provide an opportunity for students to study for higher professional qualifications on a whole or part-time basis.

At the colleges of advanced technology there are many courses at the undergraduate and postgraduate levels similar to university courses.

HANDBOOK ... *Higher Education in the United Kingdom: A Handbook for Students from Overseas* may be ordered from Sales Section, British Information Services, 845 Third Avenue, New York, N. Y. 10022; price $1.50, including postage. The handbook, which is published in London for the British Council and the Association of Commonwealth Universities by Longmans, Green and Co., contains a "Directory of Subjects and Facilities for Study" and other useful information on the organization of the universities.

FOR FURTHER INFORMATION ... For complete information about a university and how to enroll, write to the Office of the Registrar of the university concerned.

For travel particulars and documentation, write to Educational Department, NHE, Pan American Airways, Pan Am Building, New York, N. Y. 10017.

HOW TO GET THERE ... By Pan American's Jet Clipper service, 6½ hours to London from New York and Boston. Jet Clipper service also from Philadelphia, Baltimore/Washington, Atlanta, Detroit, New Orleans, Dallas and Houston; direct from Chicago (7¾ hours), or via Detroit. Jet Clippers fly from U.S. West Coast via the polar route in 10½ hours. Clippers serve Glasgow through Prestwick Airport. By ship, about 5 days.

UNIVERSITY OF EDINBURGH

Scotland's university tradition has been widespread for longer than that of England and Wales. When England, with a higher population, had only two universities, Scotland had four.

Edinburgh, the historic capital of Scotland, has had a university for nearly 400 years. The youngest of the four Scottish universities, it was founded in 1583, and is older than all the English and Welsh universities except Oxford and Cambridge.

Situated in the heart of the city, the University plays a very important part in the life of Edinburgh. Students are not isolated as they often are in other British universities which are built on the outskirts of a town.

Edinburgh is rich in opportunities for theater- and concert-going, and the countryside is easily accessible and very lovely.

The Edinburgh International Festival in August and September falls during the vacation, but its importance has grown since it was founded after the last war. Any student at Edinburgh University should try to be there for at least some of the musical or theatrical events, or see the art exhibitions which are always arranged.

SIZE ... There are about 7,500 undergraduates at Edinburgh University, of which 10 per cent come from overseas.

CALENDAR ... The academic year, which begins in October and ends in June, is divided into three terms, each lasting about ten weeks. Dates vary slightly each year. The Department of Extramural Studies arranges summer vacation courses.

SUMMER COURSES ... See page 19.

TUITION ... University fees are from $100 per annum for an arts course to $204 for medicine and sciences. In addition, cost of books and special equipment is $28–$84, according to the subject.

ADMISSION REQUIREMENTS ... The University of Edinburgh is prepared to consider applications from occasional students from overseas in the Faculties of Arts, Divinity, Music, and Science. The Scottish Universities Entrance Board has been set up to determine entrance requirements. No applicant may be accepted for a First degree course until he possesses the Board's Certificate of Fitness. Exemption from its Preliminary Examination may be obtained if the applicant 1) has approved degree (other than honorary) of an accredited university or college, or 2) has completed satisfactorily the second year either of a course leading to a degree in arts or pure science or of a pre-medical course at such a university or college. See also the Admission Requirements section in the opening summary on the United Kingdom.

ACCOMMODATIONS ... The Department of Student Accommodation and Welfare, Pollock Institute, 46 Pleasance, Edinburgh 8, will help the student find a room when he arrives, and also gives advice on financial and other matters.

There are a number of University halls of residence, where costs are from $280 to $410 for the academic year. Although it sometimes costs more to live in a hall of residence, overseas students should try to do so because they will have the great advantage of a busy social life revolving round the hostel.

AVERAGE COSTS ... A foreign student in Edinburgh should have at least $1,500 a year, which should cover university fees and living costs and leave some money for a little traveling.

STUDENT LIFE ... The University Union, which is open to all men students, is the center of the student's social life. This society, which is run by the students themselves, was formed in 1889, and was the forerunner of similar student unions at every other university in Great Britain.

The Union building has space for diverse activities. There are rooms for debates, dances, a library, quiet rooms, a snack bar and a billiard room.

Most social, sports and faculty societies are affiliated with the Union, and they can use the premises for meetings. The Union subscription is about $8.40 a year.

The University Women's Union has similar facilities, including a large dining hall, dance hall, lounges, library and television room. Students who live outside the center of Edinburgh may stay for a few days at the Union, and charges are moderate. Membership is about $5.90 a year.

University of Edinburgh

EXETER UNIVERSITY

Exeter is one of the oldest and loveliest country towns in the United Kingdom. Its cathedral dates from the thirteenth and fourteenth centuries, and the beauty of old buildings and the surrounding countryside make it a busy tourist center. There are a few light industries, including papermaking and printing and the leather and clothing industries.

Exeter University was founded in 1901 as the University College of the Southwest of England. It received its charter to grant degrees in 1955, but until then students used to sit for the external degrees of the University of London.

Exeter is a small city, with a population of well under 100,000, so that transport is easier than in many larger university towns. As the only university in southwest England it attracts students from a wide area, and there is a high proportion of overseas students. In a small university students make friends quickly and it is very rare for a newcomer to be lonely for long, as everyone soon knows everyone else.

Each year more and more postgraduate and part-time students are attracted to Exeter.

Besides the University, there are many schools in the neighborhood, among them a well-known art school and a firmly established teachers' training college. All these make Exeter an important educational center.

SIZE ... There are 1,600 students in the University, 10 per cent of them from overseas.

CALENDAR ... In common with most universities in the United Kingdom, except Oxford and Cambridge, there are three 10-week terms in the academic year.

The session begins on the first Thursday of October, and includes two vacations of four weeks, at Easter and Christmas.

TUITION ... Fees vary. An arts course costs about $168 a year, and science $210. Fees for postgraduate tuition are from $84 to $112 a year.

Books and scientific equipment cost extra, and there is a compulsory annual Students' Guild membership fee of $15.

Fees for occasional students are $56 a term.

ADMISSION REQUIREMENTS ... The University of Exeter is prepared to consider applications from occasional students in the Faculties of Arts, Social Studies and Law, but the number of such students who can be accepted is small. Such students should already have completed two years of undergraduate study.

There are certain further entry qualifications imposed by the Faculties of Arts and Science. See also the Admission Requirements section in the opening summary on the United Kingdom.

UNIVERSITY OF LONDON

London was one of the last great capitals of the world to have a university. The University of London was formed in 1836 to grant degrees to students of two existing colleges, Kings and University College, which had been founded a few years before, but which had not been given the power to grant degrees.

Since then the University has grown into the largest in the United Kingdom, at which a huge variety of subjects can be studied. Today there are 26 colleges, including medical and other specialized schools, in the federation of the University of London.

Full-time undergraduates are taught in their own colleges, although occasionally two or three colleges may combine for part of their program. They are known as internal students and must usually spend a minimum of three years in the University for a First degree.

Postgraduates working for higher degrees or doing research may be attached to one of the specialized schools of advanced study, such as the Institute of Historical Research. At the schools of research, postgraduates have the advantages of teaching and advice from specialists of every college of the University.

Because of the size, the decentralization and the distance between constituent schools of the University, students often find that they have little contact with members of other colleges, even within the same faculty. This can be a disadvantage for those who have to live in the suburbs, away from their colleges and the

University Union. Strangers to London can be very lonely at first, and of all universities in the United Kingdom the greatest individual effort is needed here to get to know a wide circle of friends, and overcome the feeling of being lost among 29,000 other students, and 9 million other people.

SIZE ... There are about 29,000 full-time internal students of the University, of whom about 5,000 come from overseas. There are about 27,000 external students.

All of the colleges are co-educational.

CALENDAR ... The academic year runs from early October to the end of June. There are three terms of ten weeks each, although for some subjects students are expected to follow a prescribed course of study during their vacations.

Most students have matriculated before they are accepted by the University; a year is added to the course if they are accepted before matriculation.

COURSES OF STUDY ... The Department of Extramural Studies organizes courses of degree standard in vocational studies such as nursing and drama, and in the humanities, history, and so on. Further teaching is given to those with diplomas and degrees in some subjects.

SUMMER COURSES ... See page 19. In conjunction with other universities in the United Kingdom, the Department of Extramural Studies organizes a 6-week summer school for foreign students in the summer vacation. One course of study is chosen each year: for example, in 1964, Twentieth-Century English Literature was the course selected.

The summer school is intended for graduates, though undergraduates with suitable qualifications may be considered.

TUITION ... University registration is $8. Examination fees for First degrees vary: Arts and Science, about $50 to $56; Dentistry, $92; and Medicine, $131.

Undergraduate tuition fees range from about $140 per annum to $210, according to the subject. Postgraduate fees are less.

ADMISSION REQUIREMENTS ... Many overseas students, especially from the Commonwealth countries, come to London for their entire degree course. The Faculties of Law, Economics and Medicine have a large number who return to practice in their own countries.

All overseas students must prove their eligibility for admission as internal students before they are considered for admission.

The entrance requirements are similar to those demanded by other universities in the United Kingdom, namely a minimum of two years of college and preferably a college degree.

Undergraduate places are so scarce, and competition is so strong, that an overseas student who already has a degree from his own country and wishes to undertake advanced study or research here has a much better chance of being accepted.

University of London

ACCOMMODATIONS ... The Lodgings Bureau, University of London Union, Malet Street, London W.C. 1, will give practical advice on where to live. Only the three women's colleges are residential. Most colleges have halls of residence attached, and there are a few university hostels. Most of these hostels are full long before any overseas students know they are accepted. They therefore have to live in lodgings. Fees in the halls of residence are $420 for a session of 30 weeks.

The colleges are scattered over a wide area, and it is very difficult to find rooms in the center of London. Students may have to travel 45 minutes each way if they live in the suburbs, and even there costs are high. Partial board in lodgings with a family will cost $11 to $12 a week, plus fares. A room with cooking facilities will probably cost about $8.50. London, for students living in lodgings in the suburbs, can be a lonely place, particularly at weekends away from the college and fellow students. Those who can share with a colleague will be much happier at first.

AVERAGE COSTS ... $1,540 to $1,680 is necessary for board, lodging, tuition and examination fees. A little traveling should be possible in the vacations with this amount of money. American students will find it difficult to supplement their incomes by working in the vacations, so they should not be tempted to spend all their money during the term, hoping to live on their earnings on holiday.

STUDENT LIFE ... Each college has its own union, run by the students themselves. At the larger colleges the premises are extensive, and include meeting rooms, canteens and bars. Sports, drama, social and faculty societies are affiliated with the college unions.

In addition, the University of London Union is open to every student. In the great new building in the University Precinct, there is an assembly hall for plays and large meetings and debates, a swimming pool, lounges, canteen and bar. The University Union publishes a newspaper during term time, and several of the college unions have their own publications.

QUEEN'S UNIVERSITY OF BELFAST

Queen's College, Belfast, was established in 1845 as a constituent college of the Royal University of Ireland. It became the Queen's University of Belfast under the Irish Universities Act of 1908, dissolving alliance with the Royal University of Ireland.

SIZE ... The University has about 4,000 full-time students enrolled, including 370 students from outside Ireland.

CALENDAR ... The academic year is divided into three terms of ten weeks each, starting the first of October and ending early July.

COURSES OF STUDY ... The University is composed of several faculties: The Faculty of Arts, Faculty of Science, the Faculty of Law, the Faculty of Economics, the Faculty of Agriculture, the Faculty of Medicine, the Faculty of Theology and the Faculty of Applied Science and Technology.

TUITION ... Each student in attendance at the University for any course leading to any degree shall pay (a) an annual enrollment fee of $8.40–$16.80, (b) an annual composite fee of $33.60–$182, and (c) such other charges as may be prescribed. Composite annual fees cover tuition, exams (but not re-exams), graduation, hire of microscopes and premium for personal accident insurance. There is also a convocation fee on graduation.

ADMISSION REQUIREMENTS ... Entrance to all the British universities is obtained only by passing an entrance examination, or by establishing a claim to exemption from the examination. Overseas students who reach standards equivalent to those required for the appropriate University entrance examination are eligible to be considered for admission. The Queen's University of Belfast is prepared to consider applications from occasional students in the Faculties of Arts (including Music and Education), Economics (excluding Social Studies) and Law. Applications from overseas undergraduate students should be received as soon as possible after January for the academic year following. In the case of candidates who do not apply through the Education Department of the Colonial Office or the appropriate department of the government of the country in which the candidate obtained his qualifications, the University may require certificates of character and educational qualifications to be authenticated by such an authority. Applications should be addressed to the Clerk of Admissions.

LANGUAGE OF INSTRUCTION ... English.

ACCOMMODATIONS ... Undergraduate students are required to reside in lodgings recognized by the University; students who wish to consult the list of recognized lodgings or who wish to have lodgings recognized should apply to the Welfare Officer at 25 University Square. There are a number of university halls of residence where costs are about $112 per term (ten weeks).

AVERAGE COSTS ... Room and board will probably not exceed $1,500 per academic year.

STUDENT LIFE ... There is a Students' Representative Council and a Student Health Service. Athletic facilities include 25 acres of playing fields at Cherryvale, Belfast, for rugby, association and Gaelic football, hurling, hockey and cricket, tennis and track. The boat house at Lockview Road provides facilities for pairs, fours and eights.

URUGUAY

URUGUAY

★ MONTEVIDEO

UNIVERSITY OF URUGUAY ... Uruguay has only one university, the Universidad de la Republica, which is located in Montevideo. In addition to the University, Uruguay has several very fine educational institutions. The University itself maintains a total of 65 vocational schools in Montevideo and in the interior of the country. Included in the list of higher educational institutions is the Instituto Normal de Maestros, the national teachers college; the Instituto de Profesores, the national high school teacher-training college; and the Escuela Municipal de Arte Dramático, a drama school which is supported by the city of Montevideo. There are no private educational institutions at the college level.

URUGUAYAN UNIVERSITY SYSTEM ... All Uruguayan schools and universities are tuition free. In accordance with the country's constitution, education is also free of all religious influence in the official schools. There are numerous private schools, however, which offer a religious education.

The main difference between the University of Uruguay and universities in the United States corresponds to the differences existing between American and European systems of higher education—and it is evident that Uruguay's system has followed, basically, the European educational pattern. For example, the University has no campus, as its schools are scattered throughout the city of Montevideo. There are no dormitories, and students live at home or in boardinghouses. Little supervision on the part of the teacher exists, and attendance is not strictly controlled. In many cases there is only one examination a year, given at the end of the year.

The University of Uruguay is controlled by the Central University Council, which is made up of governing councils from the various schools. These school councils include professors, graduate students, and undergraduate students. The individual school councils appoint the dean of each school, whereas the Rector of the University, who is the equivalent to a president of a university in the United States, is elected by the Assembly of all the Councils. Both the Rector and the deans are elected for 4-year terms. In addition to the governing councils and the Central University Council, there are two consultative bodies, one for each school and one for the University.

ADMISSION REQUIREMENTS ... Each school at the University admits Uruguayan students who certify by having completed four years of high school and two years of preparatory courses. Students from the United States are required to revalidate their high school and preparatory school degrees as well as pass an examination on Uruguayan history administered by the Secondary Education Board before they can be admitted to the University. Students already admitted to an American university are automatically accepted for enrollment at the University of Uruguay.

The various auxiliary and non-University schools require only a high school diploma. No preparatory courses are necessary for entrance.

REGULATIONS ... For student visa and entrance procedure, see the For Further Information heading at the end of this section.

CREDIT TOWARD AN AMERICAN DEGREE ... At the present time, university credits and degrees cannot be exchanged between Uruguay and the United States because of the

differences in curriculum. If, however, a large number of American students were to study in Uruguay, this matter could be subject to inter-government agreements. Under the present conditions, it is felt that the most suitable candidates for attending university courses in Uruguay are college students who already have taken a year or two at an American university or those who have graduated and want to specialize or acquire extra experience in their particular fields of study. The educational level is quite high, particularly in the Schools of Medicine, Dentistry, and Architecture.

TUITION ... There are no tuition fees in any school. With the exception of minor fines for tardy registration, the only legal charge for education in Uruguay is a $10 fee for a diploma. In those instances where a student has achieved exceptionally high grades, he is issued a diploma free of charge. Education expenses, then, are limited to the purchase of materials and books.

LIVING COSTS ... Most students will find that living costs in Uruguay are comparatively low. A student can rent an apartment and live comfortably on $200 a month. Room and board in a good boardinghouse will cost about $100 a month. One can eat lunch in a nice restaurant for $2.50 or less, ride on a bus for less than a nickel, and make a local telephone call for 3 cents. It is possible to receive complete medical attention by securing membership in a co-operative health insurance association at the rate of $4 per month.

COMMON COURTESIES AND LOCAL CUSTOMS ... The dinner hour is very late, generally from 9:00 to 11:00. There is a central information number to dial in Montevideo, 213, which gives information on train, airplane and bus schedules, weather reports, movie programs and other pertinent information about the city.

FOR FURTHER INFORMATION ... For complete information about the University and how to enroll, write to the UNIVERSIDAD DE LA REPUBLICA ORIENTAL DEL URUGUAY, Avenida 18 de Julio 18 24, Casilla No. 450, Montevideo, Uruguay.

For travel particulars and documentation, write to Educational Department, NHE, Pan American Airways, Pan Am Building, New York, N. Y. 10017.

HOW TO GET THERE ... By Pan American Jet Clipper, 14 hours from New York; or 35 minutes from Buenos Aires, which by Pan Am Jet is only 10½ hours from New York. By ship from New Orleans or New York, 13 days.

UNIVERSITY OF THE REPUBLIC, MONTEVIDEO

The University of the Republic, at Montevideo, was founded in 1833. Although completely government supported, it is a fully autonomous organization. Today the University has numerous schools scattered throughout the city of Montevideo.

SIZE ... There are approximately 10,000 students enrolled in the ten schools of the University.

CALENDAR ... The school term begins in March and terminates in November. There are three vacation periods

University of Uruguay, School of Architecture

throughout the year: winter holiday in July (2 weeks), Holy Week, and spring holiday (beginning September 21). The seasons in Uruguay are the opposite of ours. Their summer is our winter and vice versa. Summer school courses are offered during the month of February.

COURSES OF STUDY ... The University maintains the Schools of Agriculture, Architecture, Chemistry and Pharmacy, Dentistry, Economics, Engineering, Humanities, Law, Medicine, and Veterinary Medicine. These schools issue regular diplomas to practice the various liberal professions. The average length of study for each profession is five years. In addition, the University offers courses in 16 auxiliary careers. One can study to be a music teacher, painter, sculptor, social assistant, librarian, nurse, dietitian, laboratory assistant, rural technician, etc.

These careers usually require no more than two years of study at the college level.

SUMMER COURSES ... Tuition is free and attendance is unrestricted. There are no degrees or diplomas issued. Guest professors from foreign countries are invited in the summer to conduct round-table discussions. Subjects treated in these discussions include: juvenile delinquency, youth and politics, science in Latin America, atomic energy, agricultural development, society and culture, etc.

LANGUAGE OF INSTRUCTION ... All University courses are conducted in Spanish. Examinations, research papers and theses must all be written in Spanish.

ACCOMMODATIONS ... There are no dormitory facilities at the University of Uruguay. Therefore a student must rent his own apartment or take a room in a boardinghouse. Students may eat in the University cafeteria where good meals are served for about $1.

AVERAGE COSTS ... A student may rent an apartment and live comfortably on $200 a month; room and board in a good boardinghouse will cost about $100 a month or less.

STUDENT LIFE ... Students at the University tend to be active not only in University matters but also in national and international politics. Each school has its own student organization and all of these are represented in the Federation of University Students of Uruguay (FEUU). The FEUU generally takes a stand on all international matters.

VENEZUELA

UNIVERSITIES OF VENEZUELA ... Venezuela has seven universities, four of which are national and autonomous; these are the Central University in Caracas, Zulia University in Maracaibo, Los Andes in Mérida, University of Valencia in Carabobo State and University of Oriente in Cumaná, Sucre State. Both of the private institutions, Andres Bello University and Santa Maria University, are located in Caracas. In addition, there is the National Teachers College in Caracas which trains high school teachers.

VENEZUELAN UNIVERSITY SYSTEM ... The Ministry of Education has charge of all official schools except the universities, which are autonomous. The educational system is divided into preschool, primary, secondary, normal, special and technical, and artistic. Venezuela's schools are classified as federal, state, municipal, or private faculties according to whether they are founded and supported by the federal government, the states, the municipalities, or by private persons or institutions. Education in all of the official institutions is free.

ADMISSION REQUIREMENTS ... In order to be eligible for admission to a Venezuelan university, a student must have successfully completed his high school education and two years of college. He must present his high school diploma along with a record of grades.

REGULATIONS ... For student visa and entrance procedure see the For Further Information heading at the end of this section.

CREDIT TOWARD AN AMERICAN DEGREE ... Arrangements for credit toward an American degree must be arranged through the student's home university.

TUITION ... The national universities in Venezuela are all tuition free. Some, however, do charge a matriculation fee and a nominal fee for a diploma.

LIVING COSTS ... The cost of living in Venezuela is quite high today in comparison with other Latin American countries. For example, first class hotels operate on the European Plan and daily rates begin at about $10 for a single room and $15 for a double room. Living accommodations can be arranged for in private homes at moderate rates. Taxis are plentiful but expensive; admission to a movie costs about $1.

COMMON COURTESIES AND LOCAL CUSTOMS ... Caracas, because of its cool climate, has an unusual amount of formality. Shorts and sports shirts are not seen in the streets but are restricted to the beaches and private clubs. Dinner in private homes is generally between 8:30–9:00 p.m. or often later.

FOR FURTHER INFORMATION ... For complete information about a university and how to enroll, write to the individual university. For information on the Central University of Caracas, write to: UNIVERSIDAD CENTRAL DE VENEZUELA, Ciudad Universitaria, Caracas, Venezuela.

For travel particulars and documentation, write to Educational Department, NHE, Pan American Airways, Pan Am Building, New York, N. Y. 10017.

HOW TO GET THERE ... By Pan American Jet Clipper, only 4¼ hours from New York to Caracas. Flights from Miami, 3¼ hours. Caracas is 1¾ hours from Panama, where connections are made with Pan Am flights from New Orleans, Houston, San Francisco and Los Angeles, via Central America and Mexico. Exactly 1 hour nonstop from Trinidad. By ship, about 5 days, with stops, from New York.

CENTRAL UNIVERSITY OF CARACAS

The Central University of Caracas, founded in 1696 as a seminary, was originally housed in a Franciscan convent. In 1722 it was authorized to award degrees and in 1725 it was actually established as a university. The University is an autonomous state institution with a University Council serving as the governing body.

Today the University is located on the outskirts of Caracas in what is known as University City.

SIZE ... There are approximately 18,000 students enrolled in the University's 11 faculties, various schools and institutes.

CALENDAR ... The academic year begins in September and ends in July. The month of July is devoted to examinations. As for the climate, Caracas is springlike all year. Weather is perfect even in the rainy season, June to December.

COURSES OF STUDY ... The Central University offers courses in the Faculties of Economics and Social Sciences, Law, Philosophy, Letters, Chemistry and Pharmacy, Mathematics and Natural Sciences, Medicine, Dentistry, Veterinary Medicine, Agriculture, Architecture, Engineering, and Journalism.

TUITION ... Tuition and registration are free but students must pay a nominal fee in order to receive their diploma.

ADMISSION REQUIREMENTS ... In addition to the admission requirements as described in the opening summary on Venezuela, a student must also present two photographs, birth and vaccination certificates and a health certificate.

LANGUAGE OF INSTRUCTION ... All classes are conducted in Spanish.

ACCOMMODATIONS ... Housing facilities are rather limited at the University. There are, however, several student residences now available on the campus. The remaining students live in private homes.

AVERAGE COSTS ... A student will find that the cost of living in Caracas is quite high. He should be prepared to have $225 a month to cover his total expenses.

STUDENT LIFE ... The students at the University participate in sports events which are held in the beautiful Olympic Stadium, which has a seating capacity of 35,000. The stadium and adjacent baseball parks, gymnasium, swimming pools and tennis courts were all built by the Venezuelan government for the students of the University.

Due to the changing political scene in Latin America, University students are very active and interested in all phases of politics.

Central University of Caracas

Summer Sessions

Note: Summer sessions at most universities are conducted in English.

PART II

*A Guide to Day and
Boarding Schools Abroad –
Selected Day and Boarding Schools
in Africa, Europe, the Middle East,
the Far East, and Latin America*

Study Abroad–A Developing Trend

by JOHN J. BROOKS, Ph.D., former *President, The International Schools Services* •

Studying abroad is an ancient tradition, now assuming vast proportions. Long before the Christian era, young men walked and rode weary distances to enroll in Plato's Academy or Aristotle's Lyceum.

Foreign students were so numerous at the University of Paris in the twelfth century that the University was divided into different schools—one for the English, Germans, and Scandinavians; one for the French, and so on.

A contemporary tells us that in the thirteenth century most of the 10,000 students at the University of Bologna were "foreigners" from neighboring city-states or from "overseas."

In more recent times, study abroad was the privilege of pomp and good circumstance. In some instances it was necessary to seek overseas opportunities not available at home.

Today, however, few Americans study overseas because good facilities do not exist at home. American students go abroad in search of *different* values, not better ones. They look for opportunities in linguistics or in first-hand cultural experience. Travel itself represents an expanding personal curriculum.

Study abroad was once largely limited to older youth. Today, the imperatives of history and the force of current events have combined to send thousands of younger students to lands other than their own.

About 160,000 American children are enrolled in some 290 military dependents' schools set up by the Department of Defense throughout Europe and the Middle East. Thousands of other children are attending local schools or American-sponsored civilian schools in some 90 nations of the world.

While most of these young people are studying abroad because their parents are assigned to overseas areas, hundreds of others leave their home communities in the United States for a year or two of schooling overseas to gain, while young, some of those skills, backgrounds, and attitudes required of every citizen of a national or international community tomorrow.

While developing its plan for preparing this directory of overseas boarding schools enrolling Americans and nationals of many other countries, the International Schools Services has received encouragement from a number of sources:

Mr. Arthur K. Watson, President, IBM World Trade Corporation, writes that "the increasing importance of a real international awareness on the part of today's citizens is becoming more and more apparent. Certainly with the present interdependencies of nations of the world, the leaders, planners, and thinkers of tomorrow should have a real understanding of other people and cultures.

"A valuable opportunity is afforded the American youth who has occasion to attend school abroad to learn through personal experience some fundamentals in this direction, in addition to his regular academic pursuits."

Mr. Francis Parkman, former president of the National Association of Independent Schools, writes: "I think that the project is of great interest, and that the resulting publication will be most useful."

Mr. Philip H. Coombs, former Assistant Secretary of State for Educational and Cultural Affairs and an official of the Ford Foundation for many years, believes that this directory will serve as a helpful guide to opportunities abroad. Study overseas, notes Mr. Coombs, is "a potent means for developing mutual understanding among today's young people from many lands who must lead the world toward greater co-operation and peace tomorrow."

No single academic or other experience holds the same value for all students. There are many young people who would not profit from an overseas educational experience. There are, also, many overseas schools which would not provide a worthwhile experience for many young Americans.

However, the "internationalizing" of American education—the growing contacts that are developing between our schools and those of other nations—is most dramatically demonstrated by the swelling numbers of young people who are studying abroad.

We hope that this directory will serve a useful purpose for those young people who wish to extend their schooling experience beyond their national boundaries.

International Schools Services

147 East 50th Street, New York, N.Y. 10022; 2000 P Street, N.W., Washington, D.C. 20036 •

International Schools Services provides educational services to overseas elementary and secondary schools which support programs of international industry, diplomacy and technical aid by enrolling the children of personnel assigned to such programs overseas. ISS has non-profit, tax-exempt status.

Major ISS programs on behalf of overseas schools include, but are not limited to, recruitment of teachers and administrators; curriculum and administrative advisory services, including publications; field consultation; educational conferences for overseas school principals and staff members; liaison among the overseas schools and between them and individuals in the United States.

ISS gives services most substantially to some 150 community-sponsored schools in Asia, Africa, the Middle East, Europe and

Latin America, and to 60 additional schools around the world which are company-sponsored or church-related.

ISS draws its support from foundations, the U.S. government and international industry. Special efforts are exerted to help overseas schools realize the unique educational and international potential which they possess by reason of location and the multinational nature of their communities.

EDITOR'S NOTE ... *This secondary school guide does not attempt to provide counsel for the decision to study abroad, or for final selection of overseas boarding schools to which a particular student should apply in geographic areas where many schools are available. That decision, and the selection of a proper school, are matters which should be worked out through the best wisdom of the home and the guidance of a counselor closely familiar with this expanding field.*

Among the professional counselors with a comprehensive and intimate knowledge of boarding schools in Europe are Mrs. George J. Nelson, Consultant on European Schools, 12 East 93rd Street, New York City, and Mr. John Oliver Rich, Box 1968, Annapolis, Maryland.

Specific mention is made here of Mr. Rich and Mrs. Nelson not only because of their work as boarding school placement specialists but because in late 1962, along with other ISS staff members, they accomplished a field survey in Europe through which evaluative data were gathered for the first edition of this guide. In addition, they have provided substantial counsel and information for this revised edition.

Current enrollment data, fees and other changes of fact since the first edition were secured chiefly through questionnaire by Pan American Airways, not by ISS.

The purpose of this and of the first edition of the guide are the same: to present a panorama of secondary and elementary boarding and day schools throughout Africa, Europe, the Middle East, the Far East and Latin America which share one characteristic: each annually enrolls among its students a proportion of U.S. students. These young overseas Americans number as few as 5 per cent in several schools to 100 per cent in two schools, and constitute about 50 per cent of the total over-all enrollment.

Prior knowledge of the host country language is not required for admission to any of these schools, most of which are highly multinational. In almost all the schools, strong emphasis is placed upon study of the local language; most have social studies and activities programs which are also designed to help students gain those educational values that are most readily available through overseas study.

COURSES OF STUDY ... The academic programs of the schools vary greatly. One-fourth of them have solely American curricula. A few have British programs. Others follow a "multi-track" system: two or more fairly separate curricula, each based upon the educational patterns of a different country. Such a school may, for example, offer one curriculum in French, another in German, a third in English.

The English-speaking section may consist of an American school program; or the section may be "Anglo-American," preparing some children for British school or university entrance, others for U.S. undergraduate study.

The French-speaking section may include French and/or Swiss university preparation, courses toward French language proficiency certificates, and/or a finishing school program—generally consisting of some traditional academic subjects, including languages, plus home economics and perhaps some commercial subjects. The offerings within the German-speaking section may be similarly numerous.

Among the "multi-track" schools described in this directory —all of them in Europe—a considerable number offer two courses of study: one curriculum taught in the local language, and a second, taught in English, designed to enable students to return to U. S. schools or enter American colleges.

Other schools, particularly in Switzerland, offer a few subjects in English, but provide all new students with especially intensive language training, and either integrate them fully into the basic French or German curriculum of the school or, at least, limit English-language course work to an hour or so daily.

The Course of Study section in the description of each school defines which of the above programs, or combinations of those or others, is offered at that school. Each description also furnishes information about school location, staff, size and composition of student body, activities and sports, college admissions where applicable, fees, and summer programs.

The 2–2½-month summer courses given by many of the schools located in Europe provide opportunity for brief study abroad to many students for whom a secondary or post-high school year overseas is not practical. Language study, cultural orientation, and sports are the constituent parts of most of the summer sessions.

The academic year in these boarding schools opens between the first and middle of September, unless another date is stated. In Europe, most of the schools follow a trimester year, with the first term ending at Christmas, the second at Easter, the third around the first of July.

ADMISSION REQUIREMENTS ... There are such wide variations among the schools in admissions standards, availability of boarding space, nature of policies and types and caliber of programs offered that, especially in Europe, the effort to determine the best school for a given student should not be made solely on the basis of the introductory overview provided by this publication.

International Schools Services

Overseas Day Schools Enrolling American Students

This list of day schools enrolling American students is intended to supplement those schools described in the section on elementary and secondary boarding schools. This list does not include company-operated schools, which are frequently restricted to dependents of the company running the school, and it gives only basic information about each school. Further information can be obtained from the International Schools Services. Generally, the schools on this list have the following characteristics in common: they have a history of enrolling American students; they offer a complete curriculum in English; and there has been a reciprocal relationship between the schools and the International Schools Services in accepting services and supplying requested information.

KEY TO THE LIST

AC   Accredited by a U. S. regional organization
Bdg.   Boarding
CR   Church related
PR   Proprietary

Department of Defense operated schools are not listed, except where they are the only facility available for American education.

LOCATION		NAME OF SCHOOL	DATE FOUNDED	TUITION RANGE ($)	GRADE RANGE	U.S. ENROLL- MENT	TOTAL ENROLL- MENT
AFRICA							
ALGERIA	Algiers	English Speaking Schools of Algiers	1964		K– 5	6	21
ANGOLA	Luanda	English Speaking School of Luanda	1959	260	K– 8	1	36
CAMEROUN	Yaoundé	American International School	1964		K– 6	19	19
CANARY ISLANDS	Las Palmas	Gran Canaria International School (reorganized)	1964		1–12	30	38
CONGO	Leopoldville	American School of Leopoldville	1961	160–425	K–12	130	225
ETHIOPIA	Addis Ababa	American Dependent School	1958	340	1– 9	150	160
	Addis Ababa	Bingham Academy (CR)	1945	500	1– 9	80	125
	Addis Ababa	Good Shepherd School (CR)	1960	300–360	1–11	123	131
	Dire Dawa	American Dependent School of Alemaya	1959	455	1– 8	15	15
	Jimma	Jimma American School	1960	350–475	1– 6	8	8
GHANA	Accra	Christ the King School (CR)	1956	144–180	K– 6	20	380
	Accra	Ghana International School	1955	135–225	N–12	68	502
	Accra	Ridge Church School (CR)	1957	170–228	N– 6	10	300
IVORY COAST	Abidjan	Abidjan American School	1963		1– 9	11	11
KENYA	Nairobi	Hospital Hill School	1948	230	1– 8	25	200
LIBERIA	Roberts Field	Farmington Community School	1960	225–450	K– 8	16	18
	Monrovia	American Cooperative School	1960	585	1– 9	134	140
LIBYA	Benghazi	American Community School of Benghazi	1958	650	1– 9	200	231
MALI REPUBLIC	Bamako	American Cooperative School	1950	500	1– 7	12	12
MOROCCO	Rabat	Rabat American School	1962	380	1– 8	81	93
	Tangier	American School of Tangier	1950	100–300	K–12	28	221
NIGERIA	Jos	Hillcrest School (Bdg.-CR)	1942	225–340	1–12	180	270
	Lagos	Corona Society Schools (3)	1955	220	1– 8	48	1,060
	Lagos	American International School	1964		K– 8	95	125
SENEGAL	Dakar	Dakar Academy (CR)	1961	300	K– 8	15	15
SIERRA LEONE	Freetown	Service Children's School	1947	100	1– 9	8	136
	Kabala	Rupp Memorial School (Bdg.-CR)	1956	125	1– 8	35	35
SOMALI REPUBLIC	Mogadiscio	American School of Mogadiscio	1959	400	1– 8	75	92
SOUTHERN RHODESIA	Umtali	Marymount College (girls) (CR-Bdg.)	1958	330–924	5–11	3	200
SUDAN	Khartoum	Khartoum American School	1960	630	1– 8	54	54
TANGANYIKA	Dar-es-Salaam	International School of Tanganyika	1963	245	1– 8	55	225
	Mwanza	Victoria Primary School	1954	36	1– 5	11	13
TUNISIA	Tunis	American Cooperative School of Tunis	1959	525	1– 8	62	67
EUROPE							
AUSTRIA	Vienna	The English School of Vienna	1959	280–320	K–12	25	150
BELGIUM	Brussels	International School of Brussels	1951	360–640	1–12	500	600
CZECHOSLO- VAKIA	Prague	English Speaking School in Prague	1950	196–210	K– 6	18	98

LOCATION		NAME OF SCHOOL	DATE FOUNDED	TUITION RANGE ($)	GRADE RANGE	U.S. ENROLL-MENT	TOTAL ENROLL-MENT
DENMARK	Copenhagen	International Section of Danish High School	1962	270	9–12	15	30
	Hellerup	Bernadotteskolen (The International School in Denmark)	1949	120	1– 9		500
FINLAND	Helsinki	The English School (CR)	1945	60–130	K–10	80	520
FRANCE	Paris	American School of Paris (AC)	1946	640–895	1–12	465	513
	Paris	École Active Bilingue (PR)	1954	160–240	K– 8	100	421
	Paris (Port-Marly)	The English School of Paris	1954	96–150	K–12	120	165
	St. Germain-en-Laye	SHAPE, Lycée International de l'OTAN	1952	none	1–12	140	1,475
GERMANY	Berlin	John F. Kennedy School	1960	none	K– 6	174	400
	Frankfurt	The Frankfurt International School	1961	250–525	K–12	250	450
	Hamburg	Hamburg International School	1957	300–330	1–11	80	200
ITALY	Florence	St. Michael's Country Day School (PR)	1963	600	1– 8	54	60
	Milan	American Community School of Milan	1963	315–530	N–11	110	124
	Milan	International School of Milan	1959	292–664	K–12	115	275
	Rome	The Parioli International Day School	1952	400–500	N– 8	60	120
	Rome	Overseas School of Rome	1947	528–624	K–12	600	700
	Turin	The American School of Turin	1963	520	1–12	65	71
LUXEMBOURG	Luxembourg	Schola Europaea	1953	30– 60	K–12	56	1,400
NETHERLANDS	Dordrecht	The International School	1961	500	1– 9	51	51
	The Hague	International School of The Hague (American Division)	1953	262–425	K–12	400	460
	The Hague	American School	1950	320	K– 8	100	200
	Rotterdam	American School of Rotterdam	1959		1– 8	11	15
POLAND	Warsaw	Warsaw Elementary School (AS of Warsaw)	1953	345	1– 6	25	65
SPAIN	Barcelona	The American School of Barcelona	1962	300–550	N–12	51	263
	Castelldefels	The Anglo-American School (PR) (Bdg.)	1958	220–600 (Bdg. 1,500)	K–10	62	77
	Palma de Majorca	Baleares International School	1957	90–225	K–12	38	45
	Madrid	The American School of Madrid	1961	200–450	N–12	306	490
SWEDEN	Stockholm	The Anglo-American School	1950	300	1– 8	86	148
SWITZERLAND	Berne	English-Speaking School of Berne	1961	165–375	K– 8	31	58
	Geneva	International School of Geneva (AC)	1924	350–600	1–12	700	1,500
	Lausanne	Commonwealth-American Primary School	1962	309–450	K– 7	75	90
	Zurich	The Inter-Community School	1960	105–133	K– 7	100	180
	Zurich	The American International School of Zurich	1963	1,500	8–12	40	45
UNITED KINGDOM	London	The American School in London (PR)	1951	420–756	1–12	240	242
USSR	Moscow	Anglo-American School	1949	315–405	K– 8	46	132
YUGOSLAVIA	Belgrade	International School of Belgrade	1948	160–321	K– 8	49	124

NEAR EAST AND SOUTH ASIA

LOCATION		NAME OF SCHOOL	DATE FOUNDED	TUITION RANGE ($)	GRADE RANGE	U.S. ENROLL-MENT	TOTAL ENROLL-MENT
AFGHANISTAN	Kabul	Ahlman Academy (PR)	1957	360–525	K– 8	70	82
	Kabul	American International School (reorganized)	1964		K–12	172	284
	Kandahar	American Community School of Kandahar	1962	500	1– 8	32	41
	Lashkar Gah	American Community School of Lashkar Gah	1958	675	3– 8	13	13
CEYLON	Colombo	American Community Center	1959	250–420	K–12	34	50
	Colombo	Overseas Children's School, Ltd. (PR)	1957	110–240	1– 8	30	195
CYPRUS	Nicosia	The Junior School	1944	468–858	K– 8	130	300
GREECE	Athens	American Community Schools of Athens	1947	385–435	1–12	925	1,050
	Thessaloniki (Salonika)	Pinewood Elementary School (Bdg.)	1950	150–380	N– 6	45	75
	Thessaloniki (Salonika)	Thessaloniki International High School (Bdg.)	1959	415	7–12	52	64
INDIA	Bombay	Bombay International School	1962	100	1– 7	26	163
	Darjeeling	Mount Hermon School (CR-Bdg.)	1895	450–540	1–13	10	350
	Kodaikanal	Kodaikanal School	1901	162–504	1–12	247	321
	Mussoorie	Vincent Hill School (CR-Bdg.)	1922	405	1–12	77	102
IRAN	Shiraz	Shiraz Community School	1960	412	1– 9	27	39
	Tehran	American School	1954	468	1–12	907	907
	Tehran	Community School (CR)	1935	250–300	N–12	125	600
IRAQ	Baghdad	American Community Center	1953	640	1– 9	54	68
ISRAEL	Haifa	Convent of Nazareth (CR-Bdg.)	1898	30–230	K–12	7	604
	Petach Tikvah	Baptist Center High School (CR)	1958	233	9–12	3	40
	Tel Aviv	American International School	1958	400–500	1– 9	80	105

LOCATION		NAME OF SCHOOL	DATE FOUNDED	TUITION RANGE ($)	GRADE RANGE	U.S. ENROLL- MENT	TOTAL ENROLL- MENT
JORDAN	Amman	American Community School	1956	530	K- 8	71	76
KUWAIT	Kuwait	American International School of Ku- wait	1964	252–402	1- 8		
NEPAL	Kathmandu	Lincoln School	1956	545	K- 9	82	87
PAKISTAN	Dacca	Dacca American Society School	1958	190–500	K–10	120	140
	Karachi	Karachi American School	1953	225–500	N–12	297	390
	Lahore	Lahore American Society School	1956	225–500	K–12	209	256
	Quetta	Quetta American School	1961	450	1- 8	20	20
SAUDI ARABIA	Dhahran	Dhahran Academy	1961	900	1- 8	14	32
	Jidda	Parents' Cooperative School	1953	120–345	K- 8	133	133
SYRIAN ARAB REPUBLIC	Damascus	Damascus Community School	1950	264	K- 7	29	87
TURKEY	Istanbul	Robert College Community School	1919	250–500	K- 9	90	97
UNITED ARAB REPUBLIC	Alexandria	American School (CR)	1924	515 1,145 (Bdg.)	1–12	93	127
	Cairo	Cairo American College	1945	360–420	K–12	212	312
YEMEN	Taiz	Taiz American School	1961		1- 8	16	40

FAR EAST

BURMA	Rangoon	International School	1955	270	K- 8	63	126
INDONESIA	Djakarta	The International School	1951	40	K- 8	142	305
	Djakarta	Regina Pacis School (CR)	1954	80–100	K–11	40	680
JAPAN	Hiroshima	Hiroshima American School	1962	312	1- 6	21	21
	Kobe	Marist Brothers School (CR)	1951	252	K–12	35	250
	Kobe	Canadian Academy (CR)	1913	231–572	K–12	275	460
	Nagoya	Nagoya International School	1963	545–655	1- 9	90	95
	Sapporo	Hokkaido International School	1958	424–480	1- 9	55	55
	Tokyo	American School in Japan (AC)	1902	285–685	K–12	659	926
	Tokyo	Christian Academy in Japan (CR)	1950	320–370	1–12	300	330
	Tokyo	International School of the Sacred Heart (CR)	1948	400–450	K–12	120	430
	Tokyo	Nishimachi School	1949	264–443	K- 7	68	150
	Yokohama	Yokohama International School	1924	160–350	K- 7	164	264
	Yokohama	St. Joseph College (CR)	1901	178–223	1–12	172	499
KOREA	Taejon	Korea Christian Academy (CR)	1958	350–400	1–12	43	55
LAOS	Vientiane	American School of Vientiane	1958	500	1–12	116	118
MALAYSIA	Singapore	Singapore American School	1956	200–425	K–12	250	354
MIDWAY ISLAND		George Seitz School	1956	464	K–12	632	632
PHILIPPINES	Cebu City	Cebu American School	1924	80–103	K- 7	29	40
	Manila (Rizal)	American School	1920	167–295	K–12	1,071	1,389
	Manila	Faith Academy (CR)	1957	80–145	K–11	231	232
RYUKYU ISLANDS	Okinawa	Christ The King International School (CR)	1957	90–135	K- 8	95	570
TAIWAN	Taipei	Taipei American School	1949	100–348	K–12	1,700	1,900
THAILAND	Bangkok	International School (AC)	1951	300–407	1–12	1,107	1,307
VIETNAM	Saigon	American Community School	1954	350–475	1–12	620	720

LATIN AMERICA

ARGENTINA	Buenos Aires	American Community School (AC)	1913	140–500	K–12	735	925
	Buenos Aires	Colegio Ward	1913	210–290	1–12	10	860
	Córdoba	Argüello Academy	1955	150–235	K–12	120	276
BOLIVIA	Cochabamba	Cochabamba Cooperative School	1958	135–270	K–10	55	125
	La Paz	Franklin D. Roosevelt School	1954	120–350	K–12	138	250
	Oruro	Colegio Anglo-Americano	1941	33- 55	K–12	0	920
	Santa Cruz	Santa Cruz Cooperative School	1959	135–450	K–12	40	90

LOCATION		NAME OF SCHOOL	DATE FOUNDED	TUITION RANGE ($)	GRADE RANGE	U.S. ENROLL-MENT	TOTAL ENROLL-MENT
BRAZIL	Belém	Amazon Valley Academy	1959	225	1– 8	47	56
	Belo Horizonte	American Cooperative School	1957	155–265	1– 8	16	27
	Campinas	Escola Americana de Campinas	1957	258–379	K–10	115	126
	Curitiba	American Cooperative School	1960	95–190	K–12	29	40
	Recife	American School of Recife	1957	200–450	K–12	130	160
	Rio de Janeiro	Escola Americana do Rio de Janeiro (AC)	1937	234–684	K–12	473	680
	Rio de Janeiro	Our Lady of Mercy (CR)	1952	80–183	K–12	177	347
	Salvador	Escola Pan Americana de Bahia	1961	50–200	N– 8	25	100
	Santos	Escola Americana de Santos	1958	142–152	K– 8	20	78
	São Paulo	American Elementary and High School (AC)	1921	200–600	K–12	550	1,010
CHILE	Osorno	Corporacion Educacional Osorno College	1954	60– 90	K–11	3	242
	Santiago	Colegio Nido de Aguilas	1934	180–447	K–12	75	367
	Santiago	Santiago College (CR) (AC) (girls)	1880	330–360 800 (Bdg.)	K–12	180	1,087
COLOMBIA	Barranquilla	Escuela Karl C. Parrish	1938	145–360	N– 9	90	360
	Barranquilla	Marymount School (CR) (Bdg.) (girls)	1953	100	1–12	8	370
	Bogotá	Colegio Estados Unidos (PR)	1941	125–200	K–12	10	400
	Bogotá	Colegio Abraham Lincoln	1955	165–461	K–12	190	535
	Bogotá	Colegio Nueva Granada (AC)	1938	180–465	N–12	412	750
	Bucaramanga	Colegio Panamericano	1963	130–150	K– 5	9	114
	Cali	Colegio Bolívar (AC)	1948	144–378	N–12	213	530
	Cartagena	Escuela Jorge Washington	1952	157	K– 9	66	185
	Medellín	Columbus School	1956	185–300	K–12	80	430
COSTA RICA	San José	The Lincoln School (AC)	1944	170–320	K–12	45	585
DOMINICAN REPUBLIC	Santo Domingo	Colegio Santo Domingo (CR) (girls)	1946	160	1–12	60	850
	Santo Domingo	Carol Morgan School of Santo Domingo	1933	190–560	K–12	137	328
ECUADOR	Guayaquil	Colegio Americano de Guayaquil	1942	150	K–12	70	765
	Quito	Colegio Americano de Quito (AC)	1940	106–540	K–12	122	1,345
	Quito	The Alliance Academy (CR) (Bdg.)	1929	360	1–12	245	245
EL SALVADOR	San Salvador	Escuela Americana (AC)	1946	200–660	K–12	204	786
GUATEMALA	Guatemala	The American School of Guatemala (AC)	1945	210–440	1–12	79	738
	Guatemala	The Mayan School	1958	165–315	K– 8	146	180
HAITI	Port-au-Prince	The Union School (AC)	1919	198–360	K–12	92	150
HONDURAS	San Pedro Sula	Escuela Internacional Sampedrana	1953	90–158	1– 8	60	206
	Tegucigalpa	Escuela Americana (AC)	1946	225–400	K–12	127	550
MEXICO	Durango	Colegio Americano de Durango	1954	36–144	K– 9	23	285
	Guadalajara	American School	1956	120–360	K–12	171	474
	Monterrey	American School Foundation (AC)	1928	161–320	K–12	202	680
	Monterrey	Pan American School (AC)	1952	180–360	K– 9	108	450
	Mexico City	American School Foundation (AC)	1888	160–340	N–12	600	1,550
	Pachuca	Escuela Americana	1948	62	N– 6	0	170
	Puebla	The American School Foundation	1943	48–100	K–11	50	1,050
	Tampico	American School of Tampico	1917	124–168	K–10	75	379
	Torreón	Colegio Americano de Torreón (AC)	1950	100–200	K–12	44	521
NETHERLANDS ANTILLES	Aruba	Seroe Colorado Schools (CO) (AC)	1929	540–1,080	K–12	308	328
NICARAGUA	Managua	American-Nicaraguan School	1946	180–225	K–12	188	625
PARAGUAY	Asunción	The American School of Asunción	1955	90–450	K–12	100	150
PERU	Lima	Abraham Lincoln School	1950	134–159	K–12	36	478
	Lima	The American School of Lima (AC)	1946	195–365	K–12	603	1,014
	Lima	Colegio Villa Maria (CR) (AC) (girls)	1923	120	K–12	13	1,333
URUGUAY	Mercedes	Uruguayan-American School of Mercedes	1958	21– 53	K– 6	2	64
	Montevideo	Uruguayan-American School	1958	206–270	1– 9	85	256
	Montevideo	Instituto Crandon (CR)	1879	80–200	N–12	20	1,000
VENEZUELA	Caracas	Academia La Castellana (AC)	1956	331–729	N–12	168	316
	Caracas	Colegio Americano (CR) (AC)	1896	190–700	K–12	90	580
	Caracas	Escuela Campo Alegre	1937	269–820	K– 9	540	625
	Maracaibo	Escuela Bella Vista (AC)	1934	630–998	K– 9	275	325
	Maracay	Academy Las Delicias	1960	390–800	K–12	45	60
	Valencia	Colegio Internacional de Carabobo (AC)	1955	243–594	K–12	155	188

AUSTRIA

AMERICAN INTERNATIONAL SCHOOL, VIENNA

Co-educational day school, ages 5–18. Boarding arrangements for limited number of students 12 and over ·

PRINCIPAL . . . Dr. Gordon Parsons.

A non-profit organization founded by the American and Canadian Ambassadors to Austria. With the academic year beginning in September 1964, the school occupied its new $1.5 million structure located on a beautiful 17-acre site on the edge of the famed Vienna Woods. The new building incorporates the latest and best features of modern school architecture including laboratories, gymnasium, cafeteria and large library. Some 12 acres are devoted to playing fields, tennis courts, baseball and soccer fields, outdoor basketball courts, track and other athletic and recreational facilities. The new school accommodates about 500 boys and girls.

The school is about 25 minutes by car from the downtown business district. School buses service the entire city.

Two principal facilities are available for out-of-town students requiring boarding facilities:

(1) A *Schülerheim,* operated by the City of Vienna, for girls up to age 18 and boys up to age 14; and

(2) a School Villa on the grounds of the new school for boys 14 and over.

Although the majority of the students are American, 28 nationalities are represented. The staff of 27 teachers includes 12 Americans; the others are drawn from Canada, Austria, Australia, the United Kingdom and other countries.

COURSES OF STUDY . . . The program extends from kindergarten through the 12th grade. The curriculum in the secondary grades is primarily college preparatory. English is the language of instruction throughout the school except for foreign language courses. Methods and materials are based on U.S. and Canadian systems of education. Courses designed to develop the international nature of the school include Austrian history and geography, European history, Asian and African history. Study of German is required through the 10th grade; it is recommended through the 12th. French and Latin are also offered.

American International School, Vienna

COLLEGE ADMISSIONS . . . The Preliminary Scholastic Aptitude Tests and the National Merit Scholarship Qualifying Test are administered to all 11th grade students, and College Entrance Examination Boards are administered in Vienna twice annually. Recent graduates have been accepted at Columbia, Harvard, Cornell, Georgetown, Stanford, Smith, Wellesley, McGill, Northwestern, Whitman, Mills, Carleton and various state universities.

The school is accredited by the Austrian Federal Ministry of Education, which permits students of this school who have been in attendance for the last four years prior to graduation to attend Austrian universities upon satisfactory completion of the school requirements.

SPORTS AND ACTIVITIES . . . Winter sports and other athletics; scouting program; excursions to museums, palaces, art galleries and government offices; attendance at local theaters and concerts. In addition to the sports program available on the new playing fields, student activities include school paper and yearbook, Student Council, National Honor Society, Austro-American exchange groups and many special interest clubs; an annual ski trip of about 10 days in February.

FEES . . . Tuition from $250 to $750 annually, according to grade; board and lodging between $500 and $750 a year. The February ski trip costs about $25, plus equipment rental. Costs of academic tutoring and private music and dancing lessons are extra.

HOW TO GET THERE . . . By Pan American Jet Clipper, 11 hours (elapsed time) to Vienna from New York via Frankfurt. By ship, 5 to 9 days to Le Havre, France, then about 28 hours by train to Vienna. Western Austria is most easily reached by Pan Am to Munich and thence a 2½-hour train ride to either Innsbruck or Salzburg. Austrian Airlines provides frequent service by connecting with Pan Am in many European cities. During the summer, there is also daily air service to Salzburg, Innsbruck, Graz, Linz and Klagenfurt.

FOR FURTHER INFORMATION . . . For complete information about the School and how to enroll, write to the AMERICAN INTERNATIONAL SCHOOL, Salmannsderferstrasse 47, Vienna XIX, Austria. For general information (in addition to the facts given on pages 184 to 185), write to the International Schools Services, Department PA, 147 East 50th Street, New York, N. Y. 10022. For travel particulars and documentation, write to Educational Department, NHE, Pan American Airways, Pan Am Building, New York, N. Y. 10017.

FRANCE

COLLÈGE CÉVENOL

Co-educational boarding and day school, ages 10–19. Established 1938 ·

DIRECTOR . . . Pasteur M. Roland Leenhardt.

ADMINISTRATOR . . . Mme. Lavondes.

U.S. REPRESENTATIVE . . . Rev. R. Unsworth, Dartmouth College, Hanover, New Hampshire.

Located in the Haute-Loire region of France, about 30 miles from the small town of Le Puy and 150 miles south of Lyon. The school is under the sponsorship of the Reformed Church of France, United Church of Christ, and United Presbyterian Church in the U. S. All students receive religious as well as academic instruction and are required to attend chapel.

The student body of 470, of whom 250 are boarders, is composed of many nationalities, with students coming from Asia, Africa, Europe and the U. S. Americans constitute about 5 per cent of the group. A teaching staff of 30 (mainly French; 2 Americans and 3 other nationalities). The 25-acre campus has playing fields for soccer, basketball, volleyball, track, ski track and ski jump, four tennis courts. Accommodations are simple;

most of the buildings have been erected on foundations dug by summer work campers.

COURSES OF STUDY ... Mainly preparatory work for the French *baccalauréat,* taught in French, but with a limited amount of special tutoring in English for U.S. college entrance examinations. Most of the American students come to the school with only 2 or 3 years' prior study of French; an intensive course in the language is provided to enable them to adapt as quickly as possible to the French curriculum and participate in the life of a French school.

Required courses for American students are world history and other social studies courses, general physical science, mathematics, French, English, gymnastics.

Standardized academic aptitude and achievement tests are administered.

COLLEGE ADMISSIONS ... Colleges in the U. S. which have accepted graduates of Cévenol include Harvard, Radcliffe, Swarthmore.

SPORTS AND ACTIVITIES ... Soccer, basketball, volleyball teams, track team, orchestra, choir, dramatics, literary group, radio set repairs, ceramics, painting. Students are required to participate in one activity. Excursions to historical sites, industrial centers, etc.

FEES ... Total expenses run to about $1,000 for the academic year.

SUMMER PROGRAM ... Two courses of four weeks each. One begins the second week in July: French language and civilization, music, painting, ceramics, dramatics, sports, excursions; $190. Second begins the second week in August: refresher course in French; French language and civilization for foreign students; fees approximately the same as for first course.

HOW TO GET THERE ... By Pan American Jet Clipper, nonstop to Paris, about 7 hours from New York and Boston, about 15¼ hours from Los Angeles via Jet connection in New York, 10½ hours from U.S. West Coast via polar route to London, then by easy connection to Paris. Through Jet Clipper service to Nice on the Riviera via Lisbon and Barcelona, about 10¾ hours from New York. Connections at Lisbon for Paris (2¼ hours). By ship, 5 to 9 days.

FOR FURTHER INFORMATION ... For complete information about the school and how to enroll, write to the COLLÈGE CÉVENOL, Le Chambon-sur-Lignon (Haute-Loire), France.

For general information (in addition to the facts given on pages 184 to 185, write to the International Schools Services, Department PA, 147 East 50th Street, New York, N. Y. 10022. For travel particulars and documentation, write to Educational Department, NHE, Pan American Airways, Pan Am Building, New York, N. Y. 10017.

Collège Cévenol

Cours Maintenon

COURS MAINTENON, CANNES

Girls' boarding and day school, ages 4–20. Limited number of boys admitted as day students in grades 1–6. Founded 1919 ·

DIRECTORS ... Mme. Palet and Mme. Blay.

Located in the center of Cannes, this privately owned school provides a program for kindergarten through grade 12. Students number about 300. Most students are French, but there are 40 American girls and some from the United Kingdom and other European countries. About 50 girls are boarders.

COURSES OF STUDY ... Two academic sections: (1) A full American curriculum, with intensive French language instruction in small groups. (2) A French, *lycée* curriculum, followed mainly by the large group of French students. There is a faculty of 30 teachers and 5 supervisors, mostly French.

COLLEGE ADMISSIONS ... American juniors and seniors take the tests of the College Entrance Examination Board, including language comprehension. Credit is given for all regular high school subjects successfully completed.

Full transcripts are supplied for transfer students. Applications for admission to U.S. colleges are carefully supervised by the special counselor for American students.

In recent years, Cours Maintenon graduates have been admitted to Wellesley, Smith, Antioch, Mt. Holyoke, Hendrix, Western, etc., and to several state universities and junior colleges.

SPORTS AND ACTIVITIES ... Visits to Islands of St. Honorat and Ste. Marguerite, museums in Cannes and Antibes, local industries, art exhibitions, concerts, theaters, International Film Festival, etc. Excursions to Monaco, Nice Carnival, etc. Sports include swimming, tennis and volleyball. Facilities for gymnastics, ballet, music, etc.

FEES ... For day students, $650–$750 annually; for boarders, $1,350–$1,500 annually. Small additional fees for trips, riding, tennis instruction.

Summer program: July and August. French language, literature, civilization. Mainly designed to instruct non-French students in the French language. About 50 boarders enroll.

HOW TO GET THERE ... By Pan American Jet Clipper, nonstop to Paris, about 7 hours from New York and Boston, about 15¼ hours from Los Angeles via Jet connection in New York, 10½ hours from U.S. West Coast via polar route to London, then by easy connection to Paris. Through Jet Clipper service to Nice on the Riviera via Lisbon and Barcelona, about 10¾ hours from New York. Connections at Lisbon for Paris (2¼ hours). By ship, 5 to 9 days.

FOR FURTHER INFORMATION ... For complete information about the school and how to enroll, write to the COURS MAINTENON, Cannes (Alpes Maritimes), France.

For general information in addition to the facts given on pages 184 to 185, write to the International Schools Services, Department PA, 147 East 50th Street, New York, N. Y. 10022. For travel particulars and documentation, write to Educational Department, NHE, Pan American Airways, Pan Am Building, New York, N. Y. 10017.

MARYMOUNT INTERNATIONAL SCHOOL, PARIS

Girls' boarding and day school, ages 13–17. Founded 1960 ·

PRINCIPAL ... Rev. Mother M. Aquinas.

Affiliated with Marymount in Tarrytown, New York, and under the direction of the Sisters of the Sacred Heart of Mary (Roman Catholic Church). The school is located in a suburb of Paris on a former country estate, with spacious grounds which include tennis courts and playing fields. Students may go into the city on Saturday and Sunday, and in the evenings with a chaperone.

The total enrollment is 80, of whom 24 are boarders. There are 56 American girls; the others are of a variety of nationalities. Staff of seven teachers includes five Americans.

COURSE OF STUDY ... An American secondary curriculum, with college entrance requirements stressed. Special emphasis is given to study of the French language. Study of religion optional for non-Catholic students (for whom attendance at school chapel is not required).

Standardized academic achievement and aptitude tests are administered by the school.

COLLEGE ADMISSIONS ... All 14 American students in the most recent graduating class took College Entrance Examination Board tests; 13 entered colleges in the U. S., including George Washington University, Hanover, Marymount (New York and Virginia), Middlebury, Stetson University, University of Kansas.

SPORTS AND ACTIVITIES ... School paper and literary magazine; dramatics in both French and English; choral club. School plans five trips each year, including a ski trip in February. Sports include tennis, volleyball.

FEES ... Annual tuition $550; board and lodging $1,575. Fees for trips are extra (weekend trips about $50; Easter holiday trip $100–$300). Transportation, lunches, book rental, and allowances are supplementary expenses.

HOW TO GET THERE ... By Pan American Jet Clipper, nonstop to Paris, about 7 hours from New York and Boston, about 15¼ hours from Los Angeles via Jet connection in New York, 10½ hours from U.S. West Coast via polar route to London, then by easy connection to Paris. Through Jet Clipper service to Nice on the Riviera via Lisbon and Barcelona about 10¾ hours from New York. Connections at Lisbon for Paris (2¼ hours). By ship, 5 to 9 days.

FOR FURTHER INFORMATION ... For complete information about the school and how to enroll, write to the MARYMOUNT INTERNATIONAL SCHOOL, Chemin du Mur du Parc, Bougival (Seine-et-Oise), France.

For general information (in addition to the facts given on pages 184 to 185), write to the International Schools Services, Department PA, 147 East 50th Street, New York, N. Y. 10022. For travel particulars and documentation, write to Educational Department, NHE, Pan American Airways, Pan Am Building, New York, N. Y. 10017.

Marymount International School, Paris

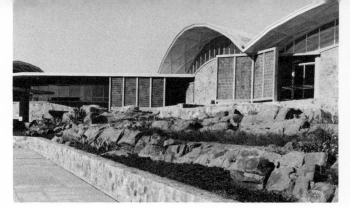

American International School, New Delhi

INDIA

AMERICAN INTERNATIONAL SCHOOL, NEW DELHI

Co-educational day and boarding school, ages 6–18. Boarders are currently admitted in grades 9–12, but proposed new facilities will permit inclusion of 7th and 8th graders. Founded 1952 ·

SUPERINTENDENT ... Dr. Lawrence E. Newberry.

Housed in newly constructed buildings which are located in a strongly international section of New Delhi, the school enrolls about 600 students, of whom 45 are Indian, 495 American, the others of several nationalities. Boarders number 55. When new residential quarters are completed in 1967, boarding capacity will be 160. Teaching staff of 34 includes 23 Americans, 10 Indians, 1 Swiss.

COURSES OF STUDY ... The school offers a complete range of courses parallel to U.S. elementary and secondary school programs, with English the language of instruction. Required courses are English, social studies (including world and U.S. history), general science and biology.

Standardized academic aptitude and achievement tests are administered.

COLLEGE ADMISSIONS ... College Entrance Examination Board and National Merit Scholarship Qualifying Tests are among those used in college admissions program. Graduates in 1963 continued their studies at the American College in Paris, College of William and Mary, Rice University, the Universities of Colorado and South Carolina and Delhi University in New Delhi.

SPORTS AND ACTIVITIES ... Athletic program includes swimming, softball, basketball, tennis, volleyball, soccer, track and field. There are several student organizations, with plans for more as demand arises and staff increases.

FEES ... Annual tuition of $500 includes basic supplies and use of textbooks. Annual cost of room and board is $1,400.

HOW TO GET THERE ... By Pan American Jet Clipper, through-plane service from New York to Delhi, 22¾ hours (elapsed time); Delhi is 1¾ hours by air from Karachi, 3½ hours from Calcutta. Bombay is 2 hours from Karachi via Middle East Air Liban. By ship, 25 to 45 days.

FOR FURTHER INFORMATION ... For complete information about the school and how to enroll, write to the AMERICAN INTERNATIONAL SCHOOL, Panchsheel Marg, Chanakyapuri, New Delhi 21, India.

For general information (in addition to the facts given on pages 184 to 185), write to the International Schools Services, Department PA, 147 East 50th Street, New York, N. Y. 10022. For travel particulars and documentation, write to Educational Department, NHE, Pan American Airways, Pan Am Building, New York, N. Y. 10017.

Kodaikanal School

KODAIKANAL SCHOOL

Co-educational boarding and day school, ages 6–18. Minimum age for boarders is 7. Founded 1901 ·

PRINCIPAL . . . Mr. Herbert L. Krause.
VICE-PRINCIPAL . . . Mr. Stephen E. Root.

The school is located in the extreme southern part of India, about 300 miles southwest of Madras. The town of Kodaikanal is at an altitude of about 7,000 feet; the climate is temperate. The 18-acre school grounds include ten playing fields and courts and are bordered by a lake.

The education of children whose parents serve the 15 sponsoring Protestant missionary groups is a primary aim of the school; however, children of parents affiliated with governmental, industrial and other international programs are also accepted. There are about 340 students, of whom 256 are Americans; others are Indian, Canadian, German, Austrian, Burmese. Approximately two-thirds of the students are boarders; many applicants must be turned down for lack of further dormitory space. Most of the 29 members of the teaching staff are Americans; others are of 4 different nationalities, including Indian.

The school year opens June 1 and ends about May 10, with a long vacation from mid-October through the second week in January.

COURSES OF STUDY . . . A complete American elementary and secondary program, with English the language of instruction. Required courses in the high school are American history, English (4 years), religious education and physical education. Standardized academic aptitude and achievement tests are administered.

COLLEGE ADMISSIONS . . . Students may take College Entrance Examination Board tests; National Merit Scholarship Qualifying Tests are also given. U.S. colleges entered the past two years by graduates include Asbury, Brigham Young, Centralia Junior College, Shimer, Swarthmore, Taylor, Wheaton, and the Universities of the Pacific, Miami, Syracuse, Virginia, Washington, Mills, Beloit, Oberlin, University of Redlands, University of Michigan, Lewis and Clark, Valparaiso University, American College for Women, Beirut.

SPORTS AND ACTIVITIES . . . Debating, dramatics, special field trips for Indian social studies class, camping and hiking, intramural and interschool athletics. Sports program includes soccer, track and field, football, basketball, softball.

FEES . . . Tuition $165 annually for children from sponsoring mission group families; $500 for non-sponsoring mission groups; $600 for all others. Boarding fee $215 annually for all children. Small additional fees for field trips, special tutoring.

HOW TO GET THERE . . . By Pan American Jet Clipper, through-plane service from New York to Delhi, 22¾ hours (elapsed time); Delhi is 1¾ hours by air from Karachi, 3½ hours from Calcutta. Bombay is 2 hours from Karachi via Middle East Air Liban. By ship, 25 to 45 days.

FOR FURTHER INFORMATION . . . For complete information about the school and how to enroll, write to the KODAIKANAL SCHOOL, Kodaikanal, Madras State, India.

For general information (in addition to the facts given on pages 184 to 185), write to the International Schools Services, Department PA, 147 East 50th Street, New York, N. Y. 10022. For travel particulars and documentation, write to Educational Department, NHE, Pan American Airways, Pan Am Building, New York, N. Y. 10017.

WOODSTOCK SCHOOL, MUSSOORIE

Co-educational boarding and day school, ages 5–18. Minimum age for boarders is 6. Founded 1854. Accredited by the Middle States Association of Colleges and Secondary Schools ·

PRINCIPAL . . . Rev. Canon Samuel R. Burgoyne.

Mussoorie is one of the old hill stations of India, located about 165 miles from New Delhi and accessible by train and car.

The education of children whose parents serve the 16 sponsoring Protestant missionary groups is a primary aim of the school; however, children from many non-missionary families are also accepted. Enrollment is 461, of whom 75 per cent are American; there are also a number of Canadian and Indian students, and a few from Austria, Burma and Germany. Boarders number 385; many applicants must be turned down for lack of further dormitory space. Most of the 34 teachers are Americans.

School grounds cover some 123 acres; there are tennis and basketball courts, playing fields and a swimming pool.

The academic year runs from June 15 through the last week of May, with a 3-month vacation from early December to early March.

COURSES OF STUDY . . . A complete elementary and secondary program, paralleling that of U.S. schools, with English the language of instruction. A standard range of academic subjects is required, as is religious education (chapel attendance is mandatory). A course in Indian social studies is given; Hindustani is among language offerings. The school administers a program of standardized academic aptitude and achievement tests.

COLLEGE ADMISSIONS . . . Students may take College Entrance Examination Board tests; the National Merit Scholarship Qualifying test is also given. U.S. colleges entered this year by graduates are Amherst, Baldwin-Wallace, Bethel, California State Polytechnic, Chico State, Duke University, Emory University, Florida Presbyterian, Greenville, Grove City, Linfield, Malone, McPherson, Princeton University, San Francisco State, Simpson, University of Michigan, Westmont, Wooster, Whitworth.

SPORTS AND ACTIVITIES . . . Dramatics, orchestra, chorus, yearbook. Sports competitions with other schools in Mussoorie and in New Delhi; athletic program includes swimming, soccer, tennis, basketball, track and field.

FEES . . . Scaled to grades and according to whether children are from sponsoring missionary groups. Annual tuition all grades $108 to $450. Annual boarding fees from $256 to about $585. Student allowances are extra, as are small additional fees for special tutoring and music lessons.

Woodstock School

HOW TO GET THERE ... By Pan American Jet Clipper, through-plane service from New York to Delhi, 22¾ hours (elapsed time); Delhi is 1¾ hours by air from Karachi, 3½ hours from Calcutta. Bombay is 2 hours from Karachi via Middle East Air Liban. By ship, 25 to 45 days.

FOR FURTHER INFORMATION ... For complete information about the school and how to enroll, write to the WOODSTOCK SCHOOL, Landour, Mussoorie, U.P., India.

For general information (in addition to the facts given on pages 184 to 185), write to the International Schools Services, Department PA, 147 East 50th Street, New York, N. Y. 10022. For travel particulars and documentation write to Educational Department, NHE, Pan American Airways, Pan Am Building, New York, N. Y. 10017.

ITALY

MARYMOUNT INTERNATIONAL SCHOOL, ROME

Co-educational elementary and girls' boarding high school. Founded 1946 ·

PRINCIPAL ... Reverend Mother Elizabeth.

The school is affiliated with Marymount in Tarrytown, New York, and is under the direction of the Sisters of the Sacred Heart of Mary (Roman Catholic Church). Extensive campus, located on the outskirts of Rome, includes playing fields and courts. There is a modern new classroom building; a second residence hall is under construction.

Current enrollment is nearly 400, including about 100 boarders. The great majority of students are American; there are 35 Italians, and small groups of Australians, Indians and other nationalities. Teaching staff of 26 (including 18 lay teachers) consists of 8 Americans, 5 Italians and others of 4 different nationalities.

COURSES OF STUDY ... American elementary and secondary school program, taught in English, with emphasis at high school level upon college entrance requirements. Required courses include history (European, world and American); general physical science, biology; elementary algebra and plane geometry; gymnastics; religion or, for non-Catholic students, courses in ethics. The school administers a program of standardized academic aptitude and achievement tests.

COLLEGE ADMISSIONS ... Almost all American students take College Entrance Examination Board tests; National Merit Scholarship Qualifying Test is given. U.S. colleges entered this year by graduates include the American College of Paris, Denison University, Mount Holyoke, Russell Sage, Oberlin; and the Universities of Maryland (Munich), Michigan State, Portland, Santa Clara and Vermont.

Marymount International School, Rome

SPORTS AND ACTIVITIES ... Volleyball, basketball tournaments, skiing weekends, debates, dramatics (in English, French and Italian). Thanksgiving weekend is spent in Florence; there is a week-long trip at Easter.

FEES ... Annual tuition varies from $200 to $500 depending upon grade level; annual boarding fee is $1,300, plus $25 registration fee and $100 room deposit. School uniform, athletic uniform and equipment cost about $80; laboratory fees about $15. Student allowances extra.

HOW TO GET THERE ... By Pan American Jet Clipper, only 8 hours direct from New York; service also via Paris, or via Lisbon, Barcelona and Nice. By ship to Venice, Naples or Genoa, 8 to 14 days.

FOR FURTHER INFORMATION ... For complete information about the school and how to enroll, write to the MARYMOUNT INTERNATIONAL SCHOOL, Via di Villa Lauchli, 180, Rome, Italy.

For general information (in addition to the facts given on pages 184 to 185), write to the International Schools Services, Department PA, 147 East 50th Street, New York, N. Y. 10022. For travel particulars and documentation, write to Educational Department, NHE, Pan American Airways, Pan Am Building, New York, N. Y. 10017.

NOTRE DAME INTERNATIONAL SCHOOL, ROME

Boys' boarding and day school, ages 9–18. Minimum age for boarders is 13. Founded 1952 ·

HEADMASTER ... Brother Robert Fontaine, C.S.C.

Under the direction of the Brothers of Holy Cross (Roman Catholic), the school is located on eight acres of rolling land about five miles from the center of Rome. The recently constructed buildings which house the school are of modern design and include 2 residence halls with a capacity of 140. Campus contains tennis court, football, baseball and soccer fields.

Enrollment of 450, including 140 boarders, is almost 85 per cent American; there are 20 Italian boys, and a few students from each of 30 other countries. Teaching staff of 35 consists mainly of Americans from the sponsoring Congregation of Holy Cross, plus a few qualified lay teachers.

COURSES OF STUDY ... Elementary school curriculum (grades 4–8) is based on New York State syllabus. The secondary school program is college preparatory. Required courses are ancient, European and American history, and American government and social structure; general science, biology, chemistry and physics (school has laboratory facilities for these sciences); complete new math program, elementary and intermediate algebra, plane and solid geometry, trigonometry, calculus, one foreign language, English (4 years), creative writing, gymnastics. English is the language of instruction.

The school administers standardized academic aptitude and achievement tests.

COLLEGE ADMISSIONS ... Almost all American students take College Entrance Examination Board tests; National Merit Scholarship Qualifying Test is given. U.S. colleges entered this year by graduates include California Institute of Technology, Georgetown University, Notre Dame University, Rensselaer Polytechnic Institute, Massachusetts Institute of Technology, Harvard, Villanova and Yale.

Notre Dame International School

SPORTS AND ACTIVITIES ... Intramural sports include swimming, soccer, tennis, baseball. There are special interest clubs, student publications. Scheduled trips include visits to museums and to nearby places of interest, longer excursions for skiing. Attendance at school chapel is required of Catholic boys.

FEES ... Annual tuition for elementary school is $450; for high school, $550. Annual board and lodging $1,800. School trip during Christmas costs $150; spring trip $150. Other trips during academic year are at no cost for boarders. Student allowances and tutoring are extra.

HOW TO GET THERE ... By Pan American Jet Clipper, only 8 hours direct from New York; service also via Paris, or via Lisbon, Barcelona and Nice. By ship to Venice, Naples or Genoa, 8 to 14 days.

FOR FURTHER INFORMATION ... For complete information about the school and how to enroll, write to the NOTRE DAME INTERNATIONAL SCHOOL, Via Aurelia 796, Rome, Italy.

For general information (in addition to the facts given on pages 184 to 185), write to the International Schools Services, Department PA, 147 East 50th Street, New York, N. Y. 10022. For travel particulars and documentation, write to Educational Department, NHE, Pan American Airways, Pan Am Building, New York, N. Y. 10017.

SAINT FRANCIS INTERNATIONAL SCHOOL, ROME

Girls' elementary boarding school, ages 5–14, and co-educational day school, boys 5–9. Founded 1960 •

HEADMISTRESS ... Sister M. Dolora.

Owned by the Generalate of the Congregation of the Sisters of St. Francis and Christian Charity (Roman Catholic Church), and affiliated with the Diocese of Buffalo, New York. The school accepts non-Catholic students; all take part in Catholic religious exercises. School is located in a quadrangle of buildings. A 6-acre campus includes a large playing field.

Enrollment is about 92, of whom 70 per cent are Americans. Full boarding capacity of 40; at present some 10 students live in the recently opened residence quarters. Teaching staff of six, of whom four are sisters of sponsoring order; five teachers are American, one Dutch.

COURSE OF STUDY ... American elementary school curriculum, grades 1–8, following that of diocese of Buffalo, New York. Emphasis upon Christian social principles. Courses in addition to traditional academic subjects are vocal music and music appreciation, crafts, ballet, gymnasium. Grades are multigrouped as follows: grades 3–4, 5–6, 7–8. English is the language of instruction.

St. Francis International School

ACTIVITIES ... Plays, ballets, and operettas are offered several times yearly for parents and friends; students are required to participate. There are annual excursions in Rome and nearby.

FEES ... Annual tuition is $250; annual boarding fee, $1,400 ($1,150 if child lives at home on weekends). Transportation for day students is $80 yearly; school uniform $25; and about $30 for books, application and library fees, athletic uniform.

HOW TO GET THERE ... By Pan American Jet Clipper, only 8 hours direct from New York; service also via Paris, or via Lisbon, Barcelona and Nice. By ship to Venice, Naples or Genoa, 8 to 14 days.

FOR FURTHER INFORMATION ... For complete information about the school and how to enroll, write to the SAINT FRANCIS INTERNATIONAL SCHOOL, Via Cassia 645, Rome, Italy.

For general information (in addition to the facts given on pages 184 to 185), write to the International Schools Services, Department PA, 147 East 50th Street, New York, N. Y. 10022. For travel particulars and documentation, write to Educational Department, NHE, Pan American Airways, Pan Am Building, New York, N. Y. 10017.

ST. STEPHEN'S SCHOOL, ROME

Co-educational boarding and day school; grades 9–12, with plans for addition of a postgraduate year in 1965. Minimum age for boarders is 13. School incorporated in 1962 as a non-profit, tax-exempt organization in the State of Connecticut •

RECTOR AND HEADMASTER ... Dr. John O. Patterson.

Located in a 73-room villa in Parioli, set in 2½ acres of landscaped gardens, this new school enrolls approximately 150 students, of whom two-thirds are boarders. (Two nearby pensions serve as boarding quarters.) There are twelve teachers, two with experience in leading European schools, the other ten experienced in American boarding schools. (Dr. Patterson was for 13 years rector and headmaster of Kent School, Connecticut.) The school is a short walk from athletic facilities used for the 1960 Olympics; the training fields, pool and gymnasiums of Acqua Acetosa are among sports areas used by students under staff supervision.

St. Stephen's School

COURSE OF STUDY ... A rigorous program in the traditional American secondary school disciplines, including comprehensive courses in English and history. Mathematics (including algebra, geometry, trigonometry and calculus) is taught from a contemporary point of view; for qualified students there is opportunity to study probability and statistics, linear algebra and matrices. Using the modern laboratory approach to the sciences, the school offers courses in biology, chemistry, physics. All students take either Latin or Greek, plus one modern language—Italian, French or German.

Studies in fine arts are available to all students, with the intent of giving each a practical, appreciative understanding of art. Strong use is made of the cultural riches of Rome. Music studies have a similar orientation both in resources and purpose.

The school administers standardized academic aptitude and achievement tests, including entrance examinations.

COLLEGE ADMISSIONS ... College Entrance Examination Board tests will be employed, with special emphasis upon Advanced Placement Program. (School will have its first graduating class in 1966.)

SPORTS AND ACTIVITIES ... School policy requires of all students a choice of athletic activity. Sports such as tennis, swimming, riding, skiing which can be pursued in adult life will be encouraged.

Students may choose from among a variety of extracurricular clubs, which, whenever possible, will draw heavily upon the cultural environment which Rome offers.

FEES ... Annual tuition is $2,500 for boarding students and $1,000 for day students.

HOW TO GET THERE ... By Pan American Jet Clipper, only 8 hours direct from New York; service also via Paris, or via Lisbon, Barcelona and Nice. By ship to Venice, Naples or Genoa, 8 to 14 days.

FOR FURTHER INFORMATION ... For complete information about the school and how to enroll, write to the ST. STEPHEN'S SCHOOL, Via Pietro Paolo Rubens 21, Rome, Italy.

For general information (in addition to the facts given on pages 184 to 185), write to the International Schools Services, Department PA, 147 East 50th Street, New York, N. Y. 10022. For travel particulars and documentation, write to Educational Department, NHE, Pan American Airways, Pan Am Building, New York, N. Y. 10017.

JAPAN

CANADIAN ACADEMY, KOBE

Co-educational boarding and day school, ages 5–18. Minimum age for boarders is 9. Founded 1913 ·

PRINCIPAL ... Mr. Gilbert E. Bascom.

Situated near Mt. Rokke in the seaport city of Kobe, the school is not far from the city center and only two miles from the Inland Sea. Facilities include a main academic hall and new classroom wing, separate library-art department building, auditorium, and two residence halls with combined capacity of 75 students. Four-acre campus includes tennis courts, playing fields.

Major sponsoring group is the Inter-Board Committee for Christian Work in Japan; the school is open to students of all nationalities, religions, and parental affiliations. Enrollment of approximately 460 is distributed evenly from kindergarten through grade 12. About 20 different national groups are represented: 65 per cent American, 5 per cent each Japanese and Chinese, 3 per cent each British and Canadian, 2 per cent each Israeli and Iranian. Twelve of the thirty-two teachers are Americans, four are Japanese.

Canadian Academy, Kobe

COURSES OF STUDY ... Elementary curriculum is American. Secondary curriculum, based on the Canadian system, is modified to meet the needs of American students. High school students take a usual range and number of subjects; emphasis is upon college entrance requirements. Advanced placement courses are given in mathematics, French. Study of the Bible and chapel attendance are required. Japanese language study is offered in both elementary and secondary school. English is the language of instruction. Standardized academic aptitude and achievement tests are administered.

COLLEGE ADMISSIONS ... Most of the U.S. students take College Entrance Examination Board tests. Graduates of a recent class entered the following U.S. colleges: Agnes Scott, American University, California Lutheran, Carleton, Davidson, Glendale, Johns Hopkins, Kenyon, Lewis and Clark, Milligan, Mount Holyoke, Pacific Christian, Park, Southwestern at Memphis, Vanderbilt University.

SPORTS AND ACTIVITIES ... Basketball, soccer, baseball teams. Athletic competitions with local teams. Student council; school paper; drama club, debates and oratory contests; radio, science, and art clubs; choir. An extensive scouting program, day hikes, overnight trips, summer camps, games. Social parties and dances once a month.

FEES ... Tuition according to grades, from $175 in kindergarten to $460 annually for grades 9–12; board and lodging $730 a year. Small fees for laboratory equipment, trips, transportation, lunches, laundry. Charge for staying at school during vacations is $3 daily.

HOW TO GET THERE ... By Pan American Jet Clipper to Tokyo from United States West Coast via "Great Circle" route, 13 hours; via Honolulu, about 14½ hours (elapsed time); 3¾ hours from Hong Kong. Tokyo is on Pan American's Round-the-World Route. By ship the journey from the United States West Coast takes about 12 to 14 days.

FOR FURTHER INFORMATION ... For complete information about the school and how to enroll, write to the CANADIAN ACADEMY, Nada-ku, Kobe, Japan.

For general information (in addition to the facts given on pages 184 to 185), write to the International Schools Services, Department PA, 147 East 50th Street, New York, N. Y. 10022. For travel particulars and documentation, write to Educational Department, NHE, Pan American Airways, Pan Am Building, New York, N. Y. 10017.

ST. JOSEPH COLLEGE, YOKOHAMA

Boys' boarding and day school, ages 6–19. Founded 1901 ·

PRINCIPAL ... Rev. Francis T. Nakagawa, S.M.

Under the sponsorship of the Society of Mary (Marianists), Roman Catholic Church. Located on a 12-acre campus in the large seaport town of Yokohama, the school is about 20 miles from Tokyo. There are 2 major student groups: Japanese children totaling about 240, and some 170 Americans. Total enrollment of over 500 includes children from China, Germany, India, Pakistan, the Philippines, Portugal, and the United Kingdom. There are 8 Americans among 60 boarders. The teaching staff of 25 includes 12 Americans and 5 Japanese.

COURSES OF STUDY ... Curriculum in both elementary and secondary school is American, approved by the Catholic University of America. English is the language of instruction. Required subjects for high school students are European and world history; elementary algebra and plane geometry; English (4 years); one science; and typing. Each student must choose a course in Christian doctrine or general ethics. Japanese is offered in grades 2–8. The school administers standardized academic aptitude and achievement tests.

COLLEGE ADMISSIONS ... A number of students take College Entrance Examination Board tests. Colleges in the U. S. entered this year by graduates include Georgetown, Seton Hall, St. Mary's, Loyola, Stanford, and the University of Cincinnati. Other graduates continued their education in Japan, France, Switzerland.

SPORTS AND ACTIVITIES ... Intramural and interscholastic sports. Offerings include soccer, baseball, basketball, volleyball, handball. Scouting, international choir, school paper, student council, dramatics, chapel service (not required for non-Catholic students). Several excursions to local places of interest are scheduled each year.

FEES ... Tuition for the elementary school is about $180 annually; for the high school, about $225. Board and lodging cost $400 a year. Student allowances are extra; there are supplementary charges for laundry, medical treatment, tutoring, and laboratory materials.

HOW TO GET THERE ... By Pan American Jet Clipper to Tokyo from United States West Coast via "Great Circle" route, 13 hours; via Honolulu, about 14½ hours (elapsed time); 3¾ hours from Hong Kong. Tokyo is on Pan American's Round-the-World Route. By ship the journey from the United States West Coast takes about 12 to 14 days.

FOR FURTHER INFORMATION ... For complete information about the school and how to enroll, write to the ST. JOSEPH COLLEGE, 85 Bluff, Yokohama, Japan.

For general information (in addition to the facts given on pages 184 to 185), write to the International Schools Services, Department PA, 147 East 50th Street, New York, N. Y. 10022. For travel particulars and documentation, write to Educational Department, NHE, Pan American Airways, Pan Am Building, New York, N. Y. 10017.

St. Joseph College

Seoul Foreign School

KOREA

SEOUL FOREIGN SCHOOL

Co-educational day school, ages 5–18, with on-campus dormitory for 16 students, ages 12–18. Founded 1912 ·

HEADMASTER ... Mr. Richard F. Underwood.

Sponsored by several Protestant church organizations in the U. S. to serve the English-speaking community in Seoul. Enrollment is 180, of whom about 125 are Americans (most are children of co-operating missionary groups); there are 10 Koreans and small groups of British, Canadian, Chinese and German students. Largest concentration of children is in kindergarten through grade 6. Fourteen of the seventeen teachers are Americans, others Canadian and Australian. Campus includes tennis court, gymnasium, playing fields.

COURSES OF STUDY ... An American elementary and secondary school curriculum, kindergarten through grade 12, based upon New York and California school standards and taught in English. The secondary school program is college preparatory. Korean is among the foreign language offerings. Local history and geography are also studied. School administers standardized academic aptitude and achievement tests.

COLLEGE ADMISSIONS ... Students take College Entrance Examination Board tests. Among U.S. colleges entered by recent graduates are Asbury, Berea, Dickinson, Hamilton, Wheaton, Whitworth, and the University of California.

SPORTS AND ACTIVITIES ... Intramural and inter-school sports: baseball, basketball, football, swimming. Student council, chapel committee, school chorus and dramatic society. School paper and yearbook. Annual week-long tour of South Korea by junior and senior classes.

FEES ... Annual tuition is $385 in the elementary grades, $485 at secondary level. Annual fee for board and lodging is $600.

HOW TO GET THERE ... By Pan American Jet Clipper direct to Tokyo from United States West Coast via "Great Circle" route, 13 hours; then 2½ hours from Tokyo to Seoul via connecting airline.

FOR FURTHER INFORMATION ... For complete information about the school and how to enroll, write to the SEOUL FOREIGN SCHOOL, 55 Yunhi Dong, Suhdaemun-ku, Seoul, Korea.

For general information (in addition to the facts given on pages 184 to 185), write to the International Schools Services, Department PA, 147 East 50th Street, New York, N. Y. 10022. For travel particulars and documentation, write to Educational Department, NHE, Pan American Airways, Pan Am Building, New York, N. Y. 10017.

LEBANON

AMERICAN COMMUNITY SCHOOL, BEIRUT

Co-educational boarding and day school, ages 5–18. Boarding for students in grades 7–12. Founded 1904 ·

HEADMASTER ... Dr. Dwight E. Knox.

Chartered by the New York State Board of Regents and sponsored by the American University of Beirut, American Presbyterian Commission, and Arabian American Oil Company. The 4-acre school campus adjoins the American University of Beirut.

The enrollment is 650, of whom about 90 per cent are Americans; others are of a wide range of nationalities. The majority of students are between 14 and 18 years old. Dormitories accommodate 170 students; admissions standards are high, and many applicants must be turned away for lack of further boarding space. Staff of 41 teachers includes 23 Americans, 5 Lebanese, others of 4 different nationalities.

COURSE OF STUDY ... An American curriculum, kindergarten through grade 12, taught in English and designed to enable students to re-enter U.S. schools or enter U.S. colleges. French is taught from kindergarten through grade 12, along with a standard range and number of other academic subjects, including two sciences and two mathematics courses at secondary level. Advanced placement work is offered in English, French, chemistry, mathematics. School administers standardized academic aptitude and achievement tests.

COLLEGE ADMISSIONS ... All juniors and seniors take College Entrance Examination Board tests. All students graduated last year entered college, 14 per cent gaining advanced placement in one or more subjects. The colleges are Barnard, Oberlin, Ohio Wesleyan, Princeton, Yale, and the Universities of Arizona, Chicago, Connecticut, Cornell, Georgetown, Maryland, Oklahoma, Pennsylvania, and Syracuse.

SPORTS AND ACTIVITIES ... Intramural and interscholastic competition in softball, basketball, volleyball, track, touch football, tennis. Also available are badminton, skiing, swimming, archery, shuffleboard, ping-pong, square dancing. Organized groups pursue such interests as chorus, orchestra, school newspaper and yearbook, stamp collecting, archaeology, photography, dramatics, debating, art. Weekend dances, parties, teas, picnics, and other social activities.

The school encourages attendance at church services, and provides bus service on Sundays to local churches. Boarding students are required to attend chapel services at the school.

FEES ... Tuition from $300 to $650 annually, depending upon grade; board and lodging $825 annually. A deposit of $25 is required to cover medical expenses; student allowances are extra.

HOW TO GET THERE ... By Pan American Jet Clipper service from New York to Beirut, only 13¾ hours. By ship, about 14 to 21 days depending on the steamship line.

FOR FURTHER INFORMATION ... For complete information about the school and how to enroll, write to the AMERICAN COMMUNITY SCHOOL, Beirut, Lebanon.

For general information (in addition to the facts given on pages 184 to 185), write to the International Schools Services, Department PA, 147 East 50th Street, New York, N. Y. 10022. For travel particulars and documentation, write to Educational Department, NHE, Pan American Airways, Pan Am Building, New York, N. Y. 10017.

MALAYSIA AND SINGAPORE

SINGAPORE AMERICAN SCHOOL

Co-educational day school, founded 1956, offering kindergarten through 12th grade. Academic year consists of three terms, September–July. Of the 390 students, a limited number (ages 7–16) live as boarders in separately operated Singapore hostels ·

PRINCIPAL ... Dr. Harold M. Elsbree.

A non-profit, community-supported, non-sectarian school incorporated under the laws of Singapore; located on a 7½-acre campus in buildings constructed during 1962. Sponsoring American Association of Singapore appoints the members of the governing board of directors.

A majority of the students are U.S. citizens; also represented by sizable numbers of children are Canada, England, Indonesia, Japan, Singapore; smaller groups from France, Germany, Israel, Norway, the Philippines, Thailand, Yugoslavia, other countries. Staff of about 28 includes Americans, British, Malayans, French.

There are two hostels in Singapore: the Methodist Hostel, which takes children of many nationalities, ages 7–16; and the Lutheran Hostel, primarily for American missionary children. As space permits, these hostels accept a few students who attend Singapore American School while their parents serve in Asian locations where no appropriate schooling is available.

COURSES OF STUDY ... The school provides a full American curriculum, kindergarten through high school, with emphasis at secondary level upon college preparatory standards. Graduates have been admitted to many American colleges.

COLLEGE ADMISSIONS ... Write to the Principal for information on College Entrance Examination Board tests.

SPORTS AND ACTIVITIES ... Physical education program operates at all grade levels. Student Body Association has jurisdiction over a variety of extracurricular projects, clubs.

FEES ... Registration fee of approximately $30 per child, plus annual tuition of $200–$425, depending upon grade level. Hostel charges are additional, and must be worked out by the family with the hostel.

HOW TO GET THERE ... By Pan American Jet Clipper, Singapore is 24¾ hours from San Francisco, with stopovers in Honolulu, Manila and Saigon. There are regular Malayan Airways flights to Malacca, Kuala Lumpur and Penang in Malaya; to Kuching, Jesselton, Sandkan and Brunei Town in Borneo.

FOR FURTHER INFORMATION ... For complete information about the school and how to enroll, write to the SINGAPORE AMERICAN SCHOOL, 60 King's Road, Singapore 10, Malaysia.

For general information (in addition to the facts given on pages 184 to 185), write to the International Schools Services, Department PA, 147 East 50th Street, New York, N. Y. 10022. For travel particulars and documentation, write to Educational Department, NHE, Pan American Airways, Pan Am Building, New York, N. Y. 10017.

Singapore American School

Uplands Preparatory School

UPLANDS PREPARATORY SCHOOL, PENANG

Co-educational boarding school, ages 5–12. Founded 1955 ·

HEADMASTER ... Mr. S. T. Thurley.

Sponsored by the Incorporated Society of Planters School Association. Penang is a beautiful tropical island, separated by a few miles from the mainland of Malaya. The school is located near the top of Penang Hill, where the climate is temperate, a 30-minute ride by cable car from the city of George Town. The enrollment is just over 100, and most of the students are British; there are about 15 Americans, and a few students from countries of Southeast Asia. The school maintains an international character and welcomes American students. The teaching staff of eight includes one Malayan; the others are British. The school year runs from late September through late July, with long winter and spring vacations. Boarders may not stay at the school during the holidays.

Attendance at morning and evening prayers is required of all students; the Sunday service is compulsory for Protestants.

COURSE OF STUDY ... A standard British curriculum, with the addition of French, study of which is begun at age 8, and Latin at age 9. Students are prepared for admission to preparatory and public schools in England. Mandatory courses include English history, world geography, general mathematics and elementary algebra, French, Latin, English and gymnastics. An effort is made to adjust teaching for individual students to the requirements of the educational systems into which they will go later. English is the language of instruction.

SPORTS AND ACTIVITIES ... Facilities for playing organized games are limited, but maximum use is made of a small padang and a hard tennis court. Piano lessons.

FEES ... $700 annually, with additional fees for school uniform, use of linens, medical checkups, and student allowances.

HOW TO GET THERE ... By Pan American Jet Clipper, Singapore is 24¾ hours from San Francisco, with stopovers in Honolulu, Manila and Saigon. There are regular Malayan Airways flights to Malacca, Kuala Lumpur and Penang in Malaya; to Kuching, Jesselton, Sandkan and Brunei Town in Borneo.

FOR FURTHER INFORMATION ... For complete information about the school and how to enroll, write to the UP-LANDS PREPARATORY SCHOOL, Penang Hill, Penang, Malaysia.

For general information (in addition to the facts given on pages 184 to 185), write to the International Schools Services, Department PA, 147 East 50th Street, New York, N. Y. 10022. For travel particulars and documentation, write to Educational Department, NHE, Pan American Airways, Pan Am Building, New York, N. Y. 10017.

THE NETHERLANDS

INTERNATIONAL QUAKERSCHOOL BEVERWEERT

Co-educational boarding and day school, ages 12–18. Founded 1934 ·

RECTOR ... Dr. Wytze C. Bakker.

Under sponsorship of the Society of Friends (Quaker) and affiliated with the International Quakerschool Vilsteren (elementary school), which has the same board of management. Located in a rural, agricultural area about 20 minutes by car from Utrecht. Three of the major school buildings, including the "Castle" (Kasteel Beverweert), date back to the twelfth century. There are playing fields, garden plots and a stream on the estate.

Enrollment of 140 includes some 100 Dutch and about 40 American students; others are from Canada, England, Germany, Iraq, Venezuela. Five day students. Of the 37 teachers, 18 are Dutch, 3 Americans, the others of 4 different nationalities.

COURSES OF STUDY ... Two programs are offered: (1) a Dutch curriculum, taught in Dutch, which prepares students for entrance to the last year or two of *Gymnasium;* (2) an English-language curriculum, which is divided into a Junior Section, similar to a U. S. junior high school program, and a Senior Section, preparing for return to U.S. schools, U.S. college entrance, or British examinations. Required courses for American secondary level students in the English-language curriculum are American history and world geography, general biological science, elementary and intermediate algebra, plane and solid geometry, English (3–4 years) and gymnastics. Study of Dutch is optional.

An excellent arts program is offered, with work in ceramics, weaving, woodwork, metalwork, drawing and painting, sewing. Students from the Dutch- and English-language programs mix in arts, physical education, dining, music and other activities; most English-speaking students soon become bilingual.

COLLEGE ADMISSIONS ... College Entrance Examination Board tests are taken by some students each year. Of six Americans graduated in a recent class, two entered U.S. colleges, others continued their education in Europe.

SPORTS AND ACTIVITIES ... Hockey league competitions and many other sports, including swimming, soccer, tennis, judo, basketball, baseball, volleyball. Drama group. Excursions to concerts, museums, tulip fields, industrial plants, nearby cities such as Amsterdam. Attendance at church or Quaker meeting required once a week.

International Quakerschool, Beverweert

FEES ... Annual tuition $697, boarding $697. Supplemental fees amount to about $223 yearly.

HOW TO GET THERE ... By Pan American Jet Clipper, nonstop flights to Amsterdam from New York, 8 hours; 1 hour from London. By ship from New York, 7 to 11 days.

FOR FURTHER INFORMATION ... For complete information about the school and how to enroll, write to the INTERNATIONAL QUAKERSCHOOL BEVERWEERT, Kasteel Beverweert, Werkhoven, Netherlands.

For general information (in addition to the facts given on pages 184 to 185), write to the International Schools Services, Department PA, 147 East 50th Street, New York, N. Y. 10022. For travel particulars and documentation, write to Educational Department, NHE, Pan American Airways, Pan Am Building, New York, N. Y. 10017.

INTERNATIONAL QUAKERSCHOOL VILSTEREN

Co-educational elementary boarding school, ages 6–13. Founded 1946 ·

HEADMASTER ... Mr. A. W. de Landgraaf.

Located about three hours' drive from Amsterdam. Under sponsorship of the Society of Friends (Quaker) and with the same board of management as International Quakerschool Beverweert (secondary school). The school occupies two buildings: the main house containing student living quarters, dining hall, offices, recreation area; the second building, newly constructed, consists of two large classrooms. There is a back garden leading onto a stand of trees, and a stream which is used for swimming.

The 30 students are mostly Dutch, plus a few children from each of several other countries, including the U. S., England and Pakistan. The headmaster is assisted by a staff of five; Mrs. de Landgraaf serves as housemother. All students attend Quaker meeting on Sunday.

COURSE OF STUDY ... An elementary curriculum, conducted in Dutch and English. Using American texts, the headmaster gives the several English-speaking children individual attention in the various elementary school subjects.

SPORTS AND ACTIVITIES ... Soccer and swimming team. Students present a play at Christmas time. There is an annual 3-day trip by bicycle to a youth hostel.

FEES ... Total annual cost is about $835.

HOW TO GET THERE ... By Pan American Jet Clipper, nonstop flights to Amsterdam from New York, 8 hours; 1 hour from London. By ship from New York, 7 to 11 days.

FOR FURTHER INFORMATION ... For complete information about the school and how to enroll, write to the INTERNATIONAL QUAKERSCHOOL VILSTEREN, Ommen, Netherlands.

For general information (in addition to the facts given on pages 184 to 185), write to the International Schools Services, Department PA, 147 East 50th Street, New York, N. Y. 10022. For travel particulars and documentation, write to Educational Department, NHE, Pan American Airways, Pan Am Building, New York, N. Y. 10017.

International Quakerschool, Vilsteren

International School, Eerde

INTERNATIONAL SCHOOL EERDE

Co-educational boarding school, ages 12–19. Founded 1951 · Castle Eerde, Ommen, Netherlands.

HEADMASTER ... Mr. Cornelius Oudshoorn.

Eerde, a secondary school, is located near Ommen, in the eastern part of Overijssel province, about 2 hours from Amsterdam. The school takes its name from the former country estate on which it is located. The school is surrounded by extensive woods, which offer natural playgrounds. Enrollment at Eerde is 104 students, including 10 Americans. Ten other nationalities are represented. There are 27 teachers, whose nationalities are Dutch, British, American and Canadian. Staff interns from Antioch College, Ohio, are used regularly.

COURSES OF STUDY ... Two curricula are offered, one in Dutch, the other in English. At Eerde pupils may complete a 4-year course, which is equivalent to 3 years' instruction in a normal Dutch grammar school. The two curricula are parallel in content up to the final two secondary school years, during which all students receive all instruction in English. Non-Dutch students follow the English-language curriculum, which is based on the British pattern, and prepare for the General Certificate of Education examinations.

COLLEGE ADMISSIONS ... Those few students with reason to do so take College Entrance Examination Board tests in The Hague. Those who have wished to enter U.S. colleges have generally had no difficulty in securing admission.

SPORTS AND ACTIVITIES ... Nationalities are intermixed in as many aspects of the program as possible. There are frequent excursions. Believing in development of manual skills, the school offers typing, weaving, ceramics, model construction, technical drawing, printing and sewing. There are musical and theatrical activities. Full range of sports including swimming, hockey, football, baseball, handball, tennis.

FEES ... Tuition, room and board at Eerde are about $1,400. Small entrance and recreation fees are additional, as is medical insurance. Basic fees do not include laundry, books, writing materials and personal expenses.

HOW TO GET THERE ... By Pan American Jet Clipper, nonstop flights to Amsterdam from New York 8 hours; 1 hour from London. By ship from New York 7 to 11 days.

FOR FURTHER INFORMATION ... For complete information about the school and how to enroll, write to the INTERNATIONAL SCHOOL EERDE, Castle Eerde, Ommen, Netherlands.

For general information (in addition to the facts given on pages 184 to 185), write to the International Schools Services, Department PA, 147 East 50th Street, New York, N. Y. 10022. For travel particulars and documentation, write to Educational Department, NHE, Pan American Airways, Pan Am Building, New York, N. Y. 10017.

INTERNATIONAL SCHOOL RHEDEROORD

De Steeg (Gld.), Netherlands.
Co-educational elementary boarding school, ages 5–13. Founded 1951 ·

HEADMASTER ... Mr. Werner Hermans.

Rhederoord is in the province of Gelderland, on the main road from Zutphen to Arnhem, a Renaissance town on the Rhine. The school takes its name from a former country estate on which it is located. The school is surrounded by extensive woods, which offer natural playgrounds. Enrollment is 35, including 4 Americans. There are four teachers; their nationalities are Dutch and British.

COURSES OF STUDY ... Two curricula are offered, one in Dutch, the other in English.

SPORTS AND ACTIVITIES ... Nationalities are intermixed in as many aspects of the program as possible. There are frequent excursions. School offers handicraft, model building, etc. Sports include swimming during the whole year.

FEES ... Tuition, room and board at Rhederoord total about $1,000 annually. Small entrance and recreation fees are supplementary, as is medical insurance. Basic fees do not include laundry, books, writing materials, personal expenses.

HOW TO GET THERE ... By Pan American Jet Clipper, nonstop flights to Amsterdam from New York, 8 hours; 1 hour from London. By ship from New York, 7 to 11 days.

FOR FURTHER INFORMATION ... For complete information about the school and how to enroll, write to the INTERNATIONAL SCHOOL EERDE, Castle Eerde, Ommen, Netherlands.

For general information (in addition to the facts given on pages 184 to 185), write to the International Schools Services, Department PA, 147 East 50th Street, New York, N. Y. 10022. For travel particulars and documentation, write to Educational Department, NHE, Pan American Airways, Pan Am Building, New York, N. Y. 10017.

International School, Rhederoord

International School of Ibadan

NIGERIA

INTERNATIONAL SCHOOL OF IBADAN

Co-educational boarding and day school, grades 7–12. Minimum age for boarders is 12 years. Founded 1963 ·

HEADMASTER ... Mr. S. D. Snell.

Situated in Ibadan, the school shares the rich resources of the University of Ibadan, and the diverse educational facilities available on that campus.

There are 90 boarding students at the school, which enrolls a total of 240 students, 95 of whom are American, 23 British, and 103 Nigerian. Five of the teachers are American, five British and the remaining ten of various nationalities.

COURSE OF STUDY ... The curriculum is built around a common core of studies leading to Nigerian, British and American qualifications for further education in those countries. Subjects required of all students are English, modern languages, history, geography, mathematics, science, music, art and physical education. There is a wide variety of additional subjects available, plus special advanced studies in several academic areas.

Standardized testing program is a combination of British and American examinations, developed to meet differing needs of the major national groups enrolled in the school.

COLLEGE ADMISSIONS ... Graduates will enter a range of U.S. and British colleges and universities; a number will attend the University of Ibadan.

SPORTS AND ACTIVITIES ... Sports include basketball, soccer, softball, swimming. Field trips are made periodically, and students are encouraged to participate in community service projects.

FEES ... Tuition is $600, room and board $750, which does not include the cost of uniforms.

HOW TO GET THERE ... About 15½ hours by Pan American Jet Clipper direct from New York.

FOR FURTHER INFORMATION ... For complete information about the school and how to enroll, write to the INTERNATIONAL SCHOOL OF IBADAN, University of Ibadan, Ibadan, Nigeria.

For general information (in addition to the facts given on pages 184 to 185), write to the International Schools Services, Department PA, 147 East 50th Street, New York, N. Y. 10022. For travel particulars and documentation, write to Educational Department, NHE, Pan American Airways, Pan Am Building, New York, N. Y. 10017.

Murree Christian School

Brent School

PAKISTAN

MURREE CHRISTIAN SCHOOL

Co-educational boarding school, ages 6½–18. Founded 1956 ·

PRINCIPAL ... Mr. Charles Roub.

Upper Topa is about 70 miles from Rawalpindi, the new capital of Pakistan. The school is intended primarily for children from the seven sponsoring Christian missionary groups, but accepts increasing numbers of students (about 25 at present) from non-missionary families. Total enrollment is 150, of whom 135 are Americans; others are from Australia, New Zealand, Scotland. Most students are under 14 years of age. There are ten teachers, seven of whom are Americans, the others from Canada, England, Scotland.

School year opens in June and closes the last of May. A 3-month break is taken from early December to early March; students may not remain at the school during this or other holidays.

The former British Garrison Church houses the school's 12 classrooms, science laboratory and library; work is progressing on construction of a new boarding hostel, and staff housing is planned, as well as a new classroom block to house elementary grades. Campus has a basketball court, tennis court and playing field.

COURSES OF STUDY ... An American curriculum, grades 1–12, with instruction in English. Special assistance is given to students who must meet British Commonwealth requirements. In the secondary school, required courses include world and American history, American government, general physical science, general mathematics or elementary algebra and English (4 years). Urdu is among the language offerings.

COLLEGE ADMISSIONS ... Graduates have gained admission to Purdue University, Grand Rapids Junior College, Moody Bible School.

SPORTS AND ACTIVITIES ... Basketball, tennis, other games. Field trips in conjunction with local social studies.

FEES ... Annual tuition is about $468; annual boarding fee is $325.

HOW TO GET THERE ... By Pan American Jet Clipper, about 21½ hours (elapsed time) to Karachi from New York; 24 hours from San Francisco. Karachi is on Pan American's Round-the-World Jet route. By ship, about 23 days.

FOR FURTHER INFORMATION ... For complete information about the school and how to enroll, write to the MURREE CHRISTIAN SCHOOL, Upper Topa, West Pakistan.

For general information (in addition to the facts given on pages 184 to 185), write to the International Schools Services, Department PA, 147 East 50th Street, New York, N. Y. 10022. For travel particulars and documentation, write to Educational Department, NHE, Pan American Airways, Pan Am Building, New York, N. Y. 10017.

THE PHILIPPINES

BRENT SCHOOL, BAGUIO

Co-educational boarding and day school, ages 5–18. Minimum age for boarders is 10. Founded 1909 ·

HEADMASTER ... The Reverend Alfred L. Griffiths, D.D.

Sponsored by the Philippine Episcopal Church, the school is located at an elevation of 5,000 feet in a climate resembling that of the temperate zones. School buildings, on a pine-studded 24-acre campus near the center of Baguio, include an academic hall, dining hall, chapel, gymnasium, boys' dormitories, girls' dormitory and library. There are playgrounds, tennis courts and an athletic field.

The enrollment of 330 includes 230 Americans. Fifty students are Filipino; other countries represented include Australia, China, England. About 40 per cent of the students are boarders, most of them between the ages of 14 and 18; largest number of day students is in the age range 5–11. Boarders may stay on at the school during spring and Christmas holidays if necessary. Admission to the school is difficult because of the pressure of applications from throughout Southeast Asia. Staff of 40 includes 27 Filipinos, 13 Americans.

COURSES OF STUDY ... A Fil-American elementary and secondary school curriculum, following the pattern of private preparatory schools in the United States. English is the language of instruction. For high school graduation, a student must have 4 credits in English; 3 credits in one foreign language or 2 in each of two languages; 3 in mathematics; 2 in science; 2 in history and 2 electives. School administers standardized academic aptitude and achievement tests.

Courses related to location of school are Asian and Philippine history, Philippine government and social life, international relations, Filipino folk dances and the national Filipino language, Tagalog.

COLLEGE ADMISSIONS ... Most secondary students take College Entrance Examination Board tests. Colleges entered by recent graduates include American University, Antioch, California State Polytechnic, Case Institute of Technology, College of Marin, George Washington University, Hobart College, Howard College, Hope College, Montana State University, Lake Erie College, MacMurray College, McGill University, Northwestern University, Oregon State University, Reed College, Stevens Institute of Technology, Whittier College, and the Universities of Maryland, Michigan, Southern California, Tennessee, Virginia and the Philippines.

SPORTS AND ACTIVITIES ... Basketball, tennis, golf, baseball, volleyball. Students are required to participate in physical education. Dramatic club. Excursions are made by small groups into mountains north of Baguio, famous for their rice terraces. Attendance is required at Episcopal chapel on campus.

FEES ... Annual tuition ranges from $154 to $340, depending upon grade level. Annual boarding fee is $1,090. Charge for staying on during holidays is $5 daily. There are supplemental charges for insurance, laboratory materials, music or art lessons, special tutoring.

HOW TO GET THERE ... By Pan American Jet Clipper from Los Angeles via Honolulu, about 18½ hours (elapsed time) to Manila. Saigon is 2½ hours and Singapore is another 1¾ hours. By ship from San Francisco, 17 to 21 days.

FOR FURTHER INFORMATION ... For complete information about the school and how to enroll, write to the BRENT SCHOOL, Baguio City, Philippines.

For general information (in addition to the facts given on pages 184 to 185), write to the International Schools Services, Department PA, 147 East 50th Street, New York, N. Y. 10022. For travel particulars and documentation, write to Educational Department, NHE, Pan American Airways, Pan Am Building, New York, N. Y. 10017.

SPAIN

MARYMOUNT INTERNATIONAL SCHOOL, BARCELONA

Girls' boarding school, ages 11–18; day school for girls 6–18 years old ·

PRINCIPAL ... Reverend Mother M. Mercedes.

The school is a branch of Marymount College, Tarrytown, New York, and is under the direction of the Sisters of the Sacred Heart of Mary (Roman Catholic Church). Both Catholic and non-Catholic children study religion. Non-Catholics may attend Sunday services at a church of their own choice.

The school is situated in a hilly residential section of northwest Barcelona. There are four buildings, an outdoor swimming pool and a tennis court. The student body is composed of many nationalities including a majority of girls from North and South America and the Philippine Islands. The Junior School consists of grades 1–6. No child is accepted until she has attained the age of 6. A knowledge of English is required from the 4th grade onwards. On the faculty are religious and lay teachers with native speakers for the language department.

COURSES OF STUDY ... The elementary curriculum is based on U.S. patterns; the secondary curriculum follows requirements of the New York State Board of Regents. English is the medium of instruction. Required secondary school courses include history (ancient, world and American) and world economic geography; general physical science, biology and chemistry; algebra and plane geometry; French; Spanish; English (4 years); religious instruction and gymnastics.

COLLEGE ADMISSIONS ... Students are prepared for College Entrance Examinations, for which Marymount is the center. Graduates are awarded either a High School or a College Entrance Diploma.

SPORTS AND ACTIVITIES ... Varsity basketball, volleyball, cheerleading, swimming, dramatic club, glee club. Trips of religious and cultural interest are arranged annually. Such trips include Tarragona, Lourdes, La Molina, Costa Brava, Andorra, Montserrat and skiing trips to Nuria. Art museums in and around Barcelona are visited regularly throughout the year.

FEES ... Tuition of $200 annually for grades 1–6, and $300 annually for higher grades. Board and tuition $1,500 annually, school uniform $100. A room deposit for resident students is required before August 15 ($100). There is a registration fee of $35. Trips are extra, as are courses in typing, dancing, music, tennis, riding. Students are not permitted to remain at the school during vacation periods. Special trips are arranged at Thanksgiving and Easter for students who cannot return to their homes.

HOW TO GET THERE ... By Pan American Jet Clipper (elapsed time) from New York, about 9 hours to Barcelona; Madrid is 1 hour by air from Lisbon, 2 hours from Rome, and 1½ hours from Barcelona. By ship, about 7 days to Lisbon, 6 to 8 days to Gibraltar.

FOR FURTHER INFORMATION ... For complete information about the school and how to enroll, write to the MARYMOUNT INTERNATIONAL SCHOOL, Calle San Pedro Claver 17, Barcelona 17, Spain.

For general information (in addition to the facts given on pages 184 to 185), write to the International Schools Services, Department PA, 147 East 50th Street, New York, N. Y. 10022. For travel particulars and documentation, write to Educational Department, NHE, Pan American Airways, Pan Am Building, New York, N. Y. 10017.

SWITZERLAND

AIGLON COLLEGE

Boys' boarding school, ages 11–19. Founded 1948 ·

HEADMASTER ... John H. C. Corlette, M. A. Oxon.

Located in the Swiss Alps some 4,000 feet above the Rhone Valley, an hour by car from Lausanne and half an hour from Montreux. The school is patterned after the British public school; there are houses with masters and proctors, and a merit system with promotions for qualities of character and responsibility as well as for academic excellence. The school emphasizes development of responsibility, good citizenship, cultural interests and sound academic training. Although it is not a church school, chapel attendance is mandatory, as are daily meditation periods. French is a required language; it must be spoken at certain specified times.

Marymount International School, Barcelona

Aiglon College

About 45 per cent of the enrollment of 160 boys are American, with an equal number of British and small numbers of each of many nationalities. Teaching staff of 22 is all British; all but one are men. Two of the school buildings were hotels that have now been converted into living quarters. The campus has playing fields for basketball, soccer, volleyball; tennis courts; an orchard and vegetable and flower garden. A swimming pool is available nearby.

COURSES OF STUDY ... Aiglon College is divided academically into Lower, Middle and Upper Schools, and the courses are given in English except for foreign language instruction. Students in the Lower School pursue studies in English language, English literature, scripture, French, Latin, geography, history, mathematics, science. In the Middle School, the same subjects are pursued at higher levels: physics and chemistry are begun by those with suitable ability, and biology by the others. When a boy moves into Upper School, he specializes in six (occasionally five) of the previously mentioned subjects for the General Certificate of Education Examinations, Ordinary Level. After passing these, he pursues 2 years' further study of three subjects for G.C.E. Advanced Level Examinations.

American boys who return to U.S. schools from Aiglon before completing the course of study there often gain grade placement in advance of their contemporaries.

COLLEGE ADMISSIONS ... American students take College Entrance Examination Board tests at the school (often in addition to taking G.C.E. examinations along with their English colleagues). Colleges and universities in the U.S. to which Aiglon has sent boys recently include Bowdoin, California, Colby, Colorado, Columbia, Harvard, Lawrence, Michigan State, Middlebury, Nichols, Olivet, Pennsylvania, Princeton, Rollins, Rutgers, St. Lawrence and Tulane.

SPORTS AND ACTIVITIES ... Required outdoor exercise under the direction of a sports master trained in "Outward Bound" concepts. Students must participate in all sports; school has its own swimming and skiing tests. A 3-day camping expedition is taken once each term. Hobbies are encouraged, and an exhibition of projects is held three times annually. Illustrated lectures, debates, concerts are scheduled one evening each week; on Sunday evenings boys may go to Headmaster's apartment to read, talk, play chess or cards, or listen to records. Parties and dances held with neighboring girls' schools.

FEES ... From $1,600 to $1,800 annually, depending upon age level. Allow another $100 for miscellaneous costs. Allowances are based on school rank, and range from $1–$2 weekly.

HOW TO GET THERE ... By Pan American Jet Clipper from New York to London, Paris or Frankfurt with connections to Zurich, 9 hours. Or from the U.S. West Coast about 10½ hours to London via Pan Am's polar route, then to Zurich. Zurich is 1½ hours from Rome by air. Geneva is about a 1½-hour flight from London. By ship, 5 to 9 days to western Atlantic or Mediterranean ports and then overnight by train.

FOR FURTHER INFORMATION ... For complete information about the school and how to enroll, write to the AIGLON COLLEGE, Chesières-Villars (Vaud), Switzerland.

For general information (in addition to the facts given on pages 184 to 185), write to the International Schools Services, Department PA, 147 East 50th Street, New York, N. Y. 10022. For travel particulars and documentation, write to Educational Department, NHE, Pan American Airways, Pan Am Building, New York, N. Y. 10017.

American School in Switzerland

AMERICAN SCHOOL IN SWITZERLAND, LUGANO

Co-educational boarding school, grades 9–12 and postgraduate year. Established 1955 ·

DIRECTOR ... Mrs. M. Crist Fleming.

Located just outside Lugano in the southeastern part of Switzerland, near the Italian border overlooking Lake Lugano. Milan is 60 miles distant. The area is trilingual, with French, Italian and German used interchangeably. The school admits 180 students; 80 are in the postgraduate section. The student body is almost entirely American, as is the staff of 25 teachers, except in the language department. The school is housed in historic villas. A soccer field, tennis courts and the lake waterfront for swimming, sailing and water skiing are nearby.

COURSE OF STUDY ... American high school college-preparatory curriculum. Courses include ancient and modern world history and American history; biology, chemistry, physical science and physics; algebra I and II, geometry, advanced math; 3 years of language; 4 years of English; art history.

POSTGRADUATE COURSE ... Also for college-bound students; offers history, languages, history of art and music, literature and composition, advanced mathematics, French, German, Spanish, or Italian. Travel in Europe included (6 weeks of field trips).

COLLEGE ADMISSIONS ... Students may take College Entrance Examination Board tests, and the majority enter U.S. colleges. Some of the colleges entered by 1964 graduates are Barnard, Briarcliff, Brown, Drexel, Lake Forest, Dickinson, Northwestern, Occidental, Ohio Wesleyan, Purdue, Rensselaer, Scripps, Skidmore, Smith, Sweet Briar, Trinity, Wellesley, Whitman, and the Universities of California, Colorado, Georgia, Michigan, Oregon, Pennsylvania.

The school administers standardized academic aptitude and achievement tests.

SPORTS AND ACTIVITIES ... Two hours of sports five afternoons each week. For six weeks in winter the high school moves to Andermatt, in the Alps, where there is skiing and skating every afternoon; classes in the mornings. Frequent Saturday excursions and overnight trips to nearby cities. Optional vacation trips to Florence or Rome, Spain or Egypt, and Greece or Egypt. Clubs: music, art, drama, debating, workshop, Alpine. Student government committees organize travel, social events, sports.

FEES ... For grades 9–12, tuition and board $2,750. Postgraduate, tuition, board and 6 weeks' travel, about $3,250. Vacations are additional and range from $100 to $450.

SUMMER PROGRAM ... During July and August a "Swiss Holiday" program is offered. Largely travel, with intervening weeks spent on the campus at Montagnola, where morning classes are held in languages, art, history related to next trip. Cost is $1,995 including transatlantic round trip.

HOW TO GET THERE ... By Pan American Jet Clipper from New York to London, Paris or Frankfurt with connections to Zurich, 9 hours. Or from the U.S. West Coast, about 10½ hours to London via Pan Am's polar route, then to Zurich. Zurich is 1½ hours from Rome by air. Geneva is about a 1½-hour flight from London. By ship, 5 to 9 days to western Atlantic or Mediterranean ports and then overnight by train.

FOR FURTHER INFORMATION ... For complete information about the school and how to enroll, write to the AMERICAN SCHOOL IN SWITZERLAND, Lugano/Montagnola (Tessin), Switzerland.

For general information (in addition to the facts given on pages 184 to 185), write to the International Schools Services, Department PA, 147 East 50th Street, New York, N. Y. 10022. For travel particulars and documentation, write to Educational Department, NHE, Pan American Airways, Pan Am Building, New York, N. Y. 10017.

Institute de Beaulieu

Collège Alpin Beau Soleil

INSTITUT DE BEAULIEU

Boys' boarding school, ages 8–19. Founded 1961 •

DIRECTOR ... M. Pierre Fleury.

La Tour de Peilz is near Montreux, on Lake Geneva, about 50 miles from the city of Geneva. The school building is a large château. Campus is well away from the main roads; sports facilities are available nearby. In its first year, the school enrolled 20 boys; 6 were Americans, and others came from Canada, the Congo, France, Italy, the Netherlands, Portugal, Spain and the United Kingdom. The majority of students were between the ages of 14 and 19. New construction allows space for 40 students. Teaching staff of 12, some part-time, includes 4 Swiss, 4 other nationalities, no Americans. Staff member responsible for development of American program is French, but well acquainted with U.S. school patterns.

COURSES OF STUDY ... Elementary school curriculum is on the Swiss pattern, with instruction in French. Secondary curriculum is primarily in French at present. As enrollment grows, the English-language program, with courses leading to British examinations and preparing for U.S. college entrance, will be further developed. Small groups will make individualized programs possible. Depending upon needs of the students, the following courses are available in the American section: American history and government, world geography, chemistry, elementary and intermediate algebra, plane and solid geometry, trigonometry, English, gymnastics, typing and shorthand.

COLLEGE ADMISSIONS ... Write directly to the Director for information on College Entrance Examination Board tests.

SPORTS AND ACTIVITIES ... Swimming, water skiing, rowing, riding, tennis, skating, skiing. Excursions for skiing, visits to other cities, museums, attendance at concerts.

FEES ... $1,635–$1,985 annually. Holiday boarding fees: $150 for Christmas; $85 for spring vacation. Allowances, tutoring, supplies, sports fees extra.

SUMMER PROGRAM ... July–September, 2½ months. Two hours' daily instruction in French, other European languages, or English as a foreign language. Fees are about $150 monthly.

HOW TO GET THERE ... By Pan American Jet Clipper from New York to London, Paris, or Frankfurt with connections to Zurich, 9 hours. Or from the U.S. West Coast, about 10½ hours to London via Pan Am's polar route, then to Zurich. Zurich is 1½ hours from Rome by air. Geneva is about a 1½-hour flight from London. By ship, 5 to 9 days to western Atlantic or Mediterranean ports and then overnight by train.

FOR FURTHER INFORMATION ... For complete information about the school and how to enroll, write to the INSTITUT DE BEAULIEU, Chemin de Béranges 29, La Tour de Peilz (Vaud), Switzerland.

For general information (in addition to the facts given on pages 184 to 185), write to the International Schools Services, Department PA, 147 East 50th Street, New York, N. Y. 10022. For travel particulars and documentation, write to Educational Department, NHE, Pan American Airways, Pan Am Building, New York, N. Y. 10017.

COLLÈGE ALPIN BEAU-SOLEIL

Co-educational boarding and day school. Ages: boys 6–18; girls 6–16. Founded 1920 •

DIRECTOR ... M. Pierre de Meyer.
ADMINISTRATOR ... M. Christian de Meyer.

Located in a winter sports area, at an altitude of 4,500 feet, the school can be reached by train from Aigle, about 75 miles east of Geneva. The enrollment of 100 includes 35 Americans, 5 Swiss, sizable numbers of children from France, Belgium and other European countries, and a few from the Middle East and Latin America. There are about a dozen day students. Age spread is large, and the number in each age group is about the same. The 22 teachers, both men and women, include 10 Swiss and 4 Americans. The large, modern school building has boys' and girls' dormitory wings; classrooms are in the same building. School grounds have a swimming pool and play areas for sports.

COURSES OF STUDY ... For the younger children there is a French-language curriculum combining elements of French, Swiss and Belgian national systems of education. At the secondary level, there are a French-language curriculum, preparing for the *baccalauréat,* and an Anglo-American curriculum, preparing for the British General Certificate of Education examinations. Required courses in the latter curriculum, for which English is the language of instruction, include European and American history, French, English (4 years), fine arts and woodshop.

COLLEGE ADMISSION ... Write directly to the Director for information on College Entrance Examination Board tests.

SPORTS AND ACTIVITIES ... Swimming, field sports, tennis, skiing, skating, hockey, games for the younger children. Excursions are arranged from time to time.

FEES ... $2,000 a year depending on age. Additional charges for staying at school during vacations are about $7 a day. Tuition for day students, $315. Student allowances not included in these fees.

SUMMER PROGRAM ... July and August. Refresher courses in French and English, and a full range of summer sports. Fees total about $515 for the 2 months.

HOW TO GET THERE ... By Pan American Jet Clipper from New York to London, Paris or Frankfurt with connections to Zurich, 9 hours. Or from the U.S. West Coast about 10½ hours to London via Pan Am's polar route, then to Zurich. Zurich is 1½ hours from Rome by air. Geneva is about a 1½-hour flight from London. By ship, 5 to 9 days to western Atlantic or Mediterranean ports and then overnight by train.

FOR FURTHER INFORMATION ... For complete information about the school and how to enroll, write to the COLLÈGE ALPIN BEAU-SOLEIL, Villars-sur-Ollon (Vaud), Switzerland.

For general information (in addition to the facts given on pages 184 to 185), write to the International Schools Services, Department PA, 147 East 50th Street, New York, N. Y. 10022. For travel particulars and documentation, write to Educational Department, NHE, Pan American Airways, Pan Am Building, New York, N. Y. 10017.

INSTITUT BÉNÉDICT

Girls' boarding school, ages 14–19. Founded 1956 ·

DIRECTOR . . . Mr. Denis de Meyer.

Situated at Montana/Cran, 80 miles from Lausanne and 115 miles from Geneva, the school can be reached by road or train following the shores of Lake Geneva, then going up the Valais (Simplon Line). There is a magnificent view of the mountains. Enrollment of 30 girls; 12 are American, the others European. The teaching staff of five includes three nationalities.

COURSES OF STUDY . . . French and American secondary programs, and secretarial courses combined with languages. American girls are asked to bring their textbooks as a guide to their programs at home. The American program offers English (4 years), French, history (3 years), sciences (3 years), mathematics (elementary and intermediate algebra, plane and solid geometry, trigonometry) taught in a combination of French and English. Also offered are singing, drawing, sewing and cooking, typing, shorthand, bookkeeping. Subjects are taught in French and English, with French preferred for as many courses as possible.

COLLEGE ADMISSIONS . . . Arrangements can be made for College Entrance Examination Board tests in Geneva. The school reports that a number of students have continued their education in U.S. colleges. Recent college admissions include Smith and the Universities of California and South Dakota.

SPORTS AND ACTIVITIES . . . Skiing, skating, tennis, swimming, hiking. Concerts, theater. During the year there are seven to ten excursions.

FEES . . . About $1,650 annually. Additional charges for laundry, books and supplies, entertainment, excursions and ski clothes and equipment and private lessons.

SUMMER PROGRAM . . . July and August. About 40 girls enrolled for language courses. Fees are $280. For students who wish to stay on in September, there is a trip to Italy or Spain. Cost for this is extra.

HOW TO GET THERE . . . By Pan American Jet Clipper from New York to London, Paris or Frankfurt with connections to Zurich, 9 hours. Or from the U.S. West Coast about 10½ hours to London via Pan Am's polar route, then to Zurich. Zurich is 1½ hours from Rome by air. Geneva is a 1½-hour flight from London. By ship, 5 to 9 days to western Atlantic or Mediterranean ports and then overnight by train.

FOR FURTHER INFORMATION . . . For complete information about the school and how to enroll, write to the INSTITUT BÉNÉDICT, Montana/Cran (Valais), Switzerland.

For general information (in addition to the facts given on pages 184 to 185), write to the International Schools Services, Department PA, 147 East 50th Street, New York, N. Y. 10022. For travel particulars and documentation, write to Educational Department, NHE, Pan American Airways, Pan Am Building, New York, N. Y. 10017.

Institut Bénédict

Institut Bleu Léman

INSTITUT BLEU LÉMAN

Girls' boarding school, ages 13–20. Founded 1954 ·

DIRECTOR . . . Mme. Dorette Faillettaz.

ASSISTANT DIRECTOR . . . Mrs. M. Jackson.

A small French-Swiss school, international in character, established by the present director. Located between Montreux and Villeneuve, near Lake Geneva and the Château of Chillon. The distance to Geneva is 55 miles. Because of the limited over-all enrollment and a desire to maintain a wide representation of nationalities, the number of Americans accepted each year is small. Of a student body of 60, 15 are Americans. Five of the seventeen teachers are Swiss, two are American. The 3-acre campus has tennis courts and playing fields for volleyball and basketball.

COURSES OF STUDY . . . Programs available are French and (1) domestic science; (2) secretarial; (3) modern languages and literature; (4) general cultural education, including American 8th, 9th, 10th, 11th grade programs. Required subjects in the American curriculum are French, general mathematics, elementary and intermediate algebra, plane and solid geometry, biology, world history, American history. English and French are the languages of instruction. Courses in 12th grade are virtually on a tutorial basis. Emphasis on language study (French, German, Italian, Spanish, Latin are available).

COLLEGE ADMISSIONS . . . The one or two Americans graduated each year almost always continue their education in American colleges. College Entrance Examination Board tests may be taken at Geneva.

SPORTS AND ACTIVITIES . . . Tennis, riding, swimming, gym, skiing, dancing. During the winter, 3 weeks are spent at Leysin for winter sports. Trips to nearby towns and to the mountains.

FEES . . . About $2,500, with extra charges for riding lessons, medical fees, allowances and field trips.

SUMMER PROGRAM . . . July to mid-September. About 60 to 70 students enroll. Intensive French language instruction in the afternoon; sports in the morning. Cost is $300 per month with excursions.

HOW TO GET THERE . . . By Pan American Jet Clipper from New York to London, Paris or Frankfurt with connections to Zurich, 9 hours. Or from the U.S. West Coast about 10½ hours to London via Pan Am's polar route, then to Zurich. Zurich is 1½ hours from Rome by air. Geneva is about a 1½-hour flight from London. By ship, 5 to 9 days to western Atlantic or Mediterranean ports and then overnight by train.

FOR FURTHER INFORMATION . . . For complete information about the school and how to enroll, write to the INSTITUT BLEU LÉMAN, Villeneuve-Montreux (Vaud), Switzerland.

For general information (in addition to the facts given on pages 184 to 185), write to the International Schools Services, Department PA, 147 East 50th Street, New York, N. Y. 10022. For travel particulars and documentation, write to Educational Department, NHE, Pan American Airways, Pan Am Building, New York, N. Y. 10017.

CHÂTEAU BRILLANTMONT, LAUSANNE

A boarding school for girls of all nationalities, aged from 14 to 18 ·

PRINCIPAL . . . Mademoiselle L. Freymond.
DIRECTOR OF STUDIES . . . Madame A. de Montmollin.
COURSES OF STUDY . . . The school, which is in beautiful surroundings overlooking the Lake of Geneva, accepts from 65 to 70 pupils who desire to acquire a good knowledge of French, at the same time continuing their other studies.

The specialized and highly qualified staff prepares the girls for the Certificat Cantonal Supérieur de Français, awarded by the Department of Public Instruction of the Canton of Vaud. This certificate enables a recipient to enter the School of Modern French at Lausanne University.

COLLEGE ADMISSIONS . . . The College Entrance Examination Board, including the Advanced Placement Test in French. The General Certificate of Education (Oxford and Cambridge Joint Board) O and A levels.

SPORTS AND ACTIVITIES . . . There is a large garden with facilities for games and tennis. The girls have the opportunity to participate in the principal summer and winter sports.

Excursions and voyages are organized to various centers of art in Europe and to picturesque parts of Switzerland. The students spend some time in the mountains in winter.

Special attention is paid to the cultural development of the pupils: theater club, music society, arts and crafts club, debating society, etc. The school reserves seats for all the worthwhile entertainments which are given in the city.

FEES . . . Approximately $2,500, plus $50 monthly for excursions, pocket money, personal expenses, etc. Sports lessons, music and art extra. Christmas stay in the mountains, $140; two weeks' stay there during the winter term, $95.

HOW TO GET THERE . . . By Pan American Jet Clipper from New York to London, Paris or Frankfurt with connections to Zurich, 9 hours. Or from the U.S. West Coast about 10½ hours to London via Pan Am's polar route, then to Zurich. Zurich is 1½ hours from Rome by air. Geneva is about a 1½-hour flight from London. By ship, 5 to 9 days to western Atlantic or Mediterranean ports and then overnight by train.

FOR FURTHER INFORMATION . . . For complete information about the school and how to enroll, write to the CHÂTEAU BRILLANTMONT, Av. Secrétan 16, Lausanne, Switzerland.

For general information (in addition to the facts given on pages 184 to 185), write to the International Schools Services, Department PA, 147 East 50th Street, New York, N. Y. 10022. For travel particulars and documentation, write to Educational Department, NHE, Pan American Airways, Pan Am Building, New York, N. Y. 10017.

Château Brillantmont

Prof. Buser's Voralpines Töchterinstitut

PROFESSOR BUSER'S VORALPINES TÖCHTERINSTITUT

Girls' boarding school, ages 11–18. Founded 1908 ·

PRINCIPAL . . . Frau H. B. Hofstetter.
Located in the village of Teufen, a health resort situated between Lake Constance and the Säntis Mountains, in German-speaking Switzerland. About 20 minutes by mountain railway from St. Gallen. The enrollment of 100 includes 10 Americans, 35 Swiss, 30 Germans and others of many nationalities. There are 19 teachers, including one English-speaking teacher who gives all courses for which English is the language of instruction. School grounds include two tennis courts, playing fields, a large garden, dairy and a vegetable farm.

COURSES OF STUDY . . . The primary and secondary programs are based on Swiss standards; courses are offered (in German) in commercial subjects, domestic science and German higher general education subjects.

About 12 girls are enrolled in an English-language section, which provides instruction in general academic subjects. Stress is laid on the study of foreign languages (French, Italian, Spanish, Latin and especially German).

The school does not prepare for American college or British university examinations, and is not designed for American girls beyond the 10th grade unless they wish to follow the German finishing school course which constitutes the major program of the school.

The school will presently accept applications only from girls between 12 and 15 years old.

COLLEGE ADMISSIONS . . . Write directly to the Principal for information on College Entrance Examination Board tests.

SPORTS AND ACTIVITIES . . . Emphasis on outdoor physical exercise: hiking and mountaineering expeditions, skiing, skating, swimming. Three to four excursions monthly. Visits to St. Gallen for concerts, theater, museums, lectures, libraries.

FEES . . . $1,625–$1,850 annually, plus $280–$350 for personal expenses. Tutoring, piano lessons extra.

SUMMER PROGRAM . . . July 15–August 25. Intensive language courses for about 60 girls, ages 12–16. Excursions, games, tennis, swimming. Costs $5 a day plus $23 for each language course; extra charges for private lessons.

HOW TO GET THERE . . . By Pan American Jet Clipper from New York to London, Paris or Frankfurt with connections to Zurich, 9 hours. Or from the U.S. West Coast about 10½ hours to London via Pan Am's polar route, then to Zurich. Zurich is 1½ hours from Rome by air. Geneva is about a 1½-hour flight from London. By ship, 5 to 9 days to western Atlantic or Mediterrean ports and then overnight by train.

FOR FURTHER INFORMATION . . . For complete information about the school and how to enroll, write to PROFESSOR BUSER'S VORALPINES TÖCHTERINSTITUT, Teufen (Appenzell), Switzerland.

For general information (in addition to the facts given on pages 184 to 185), write to the International Schools Services, Department PA, 147 East 50th Street, New York, N. Y. 10022. For travel particulars and documentation, write to Educational Department, NHE, Pan American Airways, Pan Am Building, New York, N. Y. 10017.

La Châtelainie

LA CHÂTELAINIE

Saint-Blaise, Neuchâtel, Switzerland.
Girls' boarding school, ages 13–20. Founded 1880 ·

HEADMASTER ... Dr. R. A. Dupuis.

St. Blaise is just outside the university town of Neuchâtel, some 75 miles from Geneva. The school is situated on the shores of Lake Neuchâtel, at the foot of the Jura mountains. Of the 170 girls enrolled, 50 are Americans, 30 are Germans, and 25 are British. Many other nationalities (European, Asian, African) are also represented. The teaching staff of 44 includes 5 Americans; the others are of various European nationalities. The school buildings are remodeled 18th-century houses, attractive and comfortable. An effort is made to group different nationalities together in the living quarters. There are playing fields and 3 tennis courts on the campus.

COURSES OF STUDY ... The school offers an American college preparatory program; preparation for the British General Certificate of Education examinations; preparation for the French *baccalauréat;* and a German-language commercial and secretarial course. About 60 per cent of the girls are enrolled in the English-language curriculum. Required courses in this section are American history, biology, elementary and intermediate algebra, plane geometry, French, English (4 years), and gymnastics. Sixteen credits are necessary for graduation. French is a major subject for all students; they must study it 12 hours weekly, and are encouraged to speak it outside class.

A branch of the school at Vermala, Crans-sur-Sierre, provides an additional 80 girls of many nationalities with a finishing course consisting of work in languages, domestic science, commercial subjects, art and music.

COLLEGE ADMISSIONS ... Almost all girls in the American section take College Entrance Examination Board tests. Colleges entered by recent graduates include Bradford, Grinnell, Skidmore, Wellesley, Vanderbilt, Washington State College, and the Universities of Arizona, Michigan and Maryland.

SPORTS AND ACTIVITIES ... Tennis, netball, basketball, rowing, swimming, riding, golf, hockey, skiing, skating. Girls may spend one month skiing at Vermala. Day excursions made to nearby cities and lakes. There are trips to Greece and Spain during Easter vacation; to France and Italy during May and June.

FEES ... About $2,400. Holiday trips are extra.

SUMMER PROGRAM ... Early July to mid-September. Program consisting of 3 hours' daily instruction in French, or, on request, in other languages or subjects, is offered at both St. Blaise (150 girls) and Vermala (80 girls). Costs about $185 per month at St. Blaise, $210 per month at Vermala.

HOW TO GET THERE ... By Pan American Jet Clipper from New York to London, Paris or Frankfurt with connections to Zurich, 9 hours. Or from the U.S. West Coast about 10½ hours to London via Pan Am's polar route, then to Zurich. Zurich is 1½ hours from Rome by air. Geneva is a 1½-hour flight from London. By ship, 5 to 9 days to western Atlantic or Mediterranean ports and then overnight by train.

FOR FURTHER INFORMATION ... For complete information about the school and how to enroll, write to LA CHÂTELAINIE SAINT-BLASEI, Neuchâtel, Switzerland.

Maison de la Harpe

For general information (in addition to the facts given on pages 184 to 185), write to the International Schools Services, Department PA, 147 East 50th Street, New York, N. Y. 10022. For travel particulars and documentation, write to Educational Department, NHE, Pan American Airways, Pan Am Building, New York, N. Y. 10017.

MAISON DE LA HARPE

Girls' boarding school, ages 13–18. Founded 1918 ·

DIRECTOR ... Mme. Suzanne Amiguet.

Located in a resort area about an hour's drive from Lausanne and two hours from Geneva. Long established, and with great continuity of directorship, the school draws most students from European countries; special values of a family atmosphere are preserved through limiting enrollment to 35 girls. Half a dozen of them are Americans. Eleven teachers are in charge of classes, of whom five are residents.

The school buildings are chalets; the grounds include a tennis court and a playing field.

COURSES OF STUDY ... A General Culture Section, taught in French, and an Anglo-American section, taught in English. Required courses in the latter are French, English, European history and world geography, general biological science, intermediate algebra, plane and solid geometry, fine arts and sewing. Also offered are other languages, piano, typing and shorthand.

The curriculum is not designed for college-bound American girls beyond the tenth grade. Americans intending to enter college generally enroll for a year or two, then transfer to other schools for the final years of college preparatory work. Only students with high scholastic averages should apply.

COLLEGE ADMISSIONS ... Write directly to the Director for information on College Entrance Examination Board tests.

SPORTS AND ACTIVITIES ... Skiing, skating and tennis. Trips to places of interest in Switzerland. The school is non-denominational but requires church attendance.

FEES ... About $1,550 for the academic year; excursions and field trips are extra.

SUMMER PROGRAM ... From the beginning of July to the end of August. About 30 girls are generally accepted. Program consists mainly of language courses; other subjects given on request. Cost: $350 for the entire course.

HOW TO GET THERE ... By Pan American Jet Clipper from New York to London, Paris or Frankfurt with connections to Zurich, 9 hours. Or from the U.S. West Coast about 10½ hours to London via Pan Am's polar route, then to Zurich. Zurich is 1½ hours from Rome by air. Geneva is a 1½-hour flight from London. By ship, 5 to 9 days to western Atlantic or Mediterranean ports and then overnight by train.

FOR FURTHER INFORMATION ... For complete information about the school and how to enroll, write to the MAISON DE LA HARPE, Villars-sur-Ollon (Vaud), Switzerland.

For general information (in addition to the facts given on pages 184 to 185), write to the International Schools Services, Department PA, 147 East 50th Street, New York, N. Y. 10022. For travel particulars and documentation, write to Educational Department, NHE, Pan American Airways, Pan Am Building, New York, N. Y. 10017.

ÉCOLE D'HUMANITÉ

Co-educational boarding school, ages 2–20. Founded 1910 ·

DIRECTORS . . . Edith Geheeb and Armin Lüthi.

Situated in the Bernese Oberland near the Brünig pass, at an altitude of 3,500 feet, the village of Goldern is about an hour's drive from Interlaken and 2–2½ hours from Bern or Zurich. Founded by Dr. Paul Geheeb more than 50 years ago in Germany, the school was moved to Switzerland in 1934 and continued under his directorship until his death in 1961.

The school enrolls about 100 students, the majority in the upper grades. One-third of the children are Swiss; 27 are American; there are also sizable numbers of children from Germany, France, England, Scandinavia, Israel and other countries. The staff of 20 teachers includes 6 Swiss and 4 Americans.

Each student above the elementary grades studies three subjects intensively for a 6-week period, then moves for the next 6 weeks to more advanced material in the same subjects or changes to others. Emphasis is placed upon independent study under staff guidance. Formal instruction is given in the mornings; afternoons are devoted to handicrafts, art, music, open-air activities. Every child contributes to the communal life, working in the house and garden.

COURSES OF STUDY . . . In the elementary school, development of reading, writing, arithmetic skills is particularly stressed; these and other subjects are taught in German, but are generally available in English as well. The secondary school offers three curricula: Swiss (German), British and American. In the American section, required courses are American history, algebra, plane and solid geometry, German, English composition and literature. German is the language of the school; while French and English are also used, course offerings in English are limited. Most students soon become bi- or trilingual on at least a conversational level.

COLLEGE ADMISSIONS . . . There are few American graduates; however, several in recent years have entered U.S. colleges, including Antioch, Earlham, North Carolina Women's College, Rhode Island School of Design, Swarthmore, University of the City of New York and Vassar.

SPORTS AND ACTIVITIES . . . All students are expected to ski and hike; other athletics are optional. There are several 2- to 3-day skiing and hiking excursions annually, and a 6-day hike each spring. The activities program is considered an integral part of the curriculum; it is organized entirely by the students under teachers' guidance.

FEES . . . About $1,380 for the academic year. Allowances vary by age, with a maximum of $2.34 per month. There is no charge for tutoring.

HOW TO GET THERE . . . By Pan American Jet Clipper from New York to London, Paris or Frankfurt with connections to Zurich, 9 hours. Or from the U.S. West Coast about 10½ hours to London via Pan Am's polar route, then to Zurich. Zurich is 1½ hours from Rome by air. Geneva is a 1½-hour flight from London. By ship, 5 to 9 days to western Atlantic or Mediterranean ports and then overnight by train.

École d'Humanité

FOR FURTHER INFORMATION . . . For complete information about the school and how to enroll, write to the ÉCOLE D'HUMANITÉ, Goldern-Hasliberg (Berne), Switzerland.

For general information (in addition to the facts given on pages 184 to 185), write to the International Schools Services, Department PA, 147 East 50th Street, New York, N. Y. 10022. For travel particulars and documentation, write to Educational Department, NHE, Pan American Airways, Pan Am Building, New York, N. Y. 10017.

LE LYCÉE JACCARD

Le Lycée Jaccard

Boys' boarding school, ages 6–19 (a few boys and girls admitted as day students). Founded 1900 ·

HEADMASTER . . . M. Marius Jaccard.
ASSISTANT HEADMASTER . . . M. Marius Jaccard, Jr.

Located on Lake Geneva near Lausanne, about 40 miles from the city of Geneva. The school was established by the father of the present headmaster. Enrollment is about 100; some 40 per cent are Americans, 15 per cent British, 10 per cent Italian. Fourteen other nationalities are represented. Teaching staff of 16 includes 6 Swiss and usually 2 or 3 Americans. The small campus has tennis courts and a swimming pool; a soccer field is available nearby. The majority of students are between the ages of 14 and 18.

COURSES OF STUDY . . . The school offers two curricula: (1) French, with preparation for the Swiss *maturité*; (2) Anglo-American, with preparation for return to U.S. schools or colleges, and for the British General Certificate of Education examinations (chiefly Ordinary Level). The English-language elementary curriculum is based largely upon U.S. standards, but with emphasis upon French as a second language. Required courses at secondary level are American history, elementary and intermediate algebra, plane and solid geometry and French. School administers standardized academic aptitude and achievement tests.

COLLEGE ADMISSIONS . . . Most American students take College Entrance Examination Board tests. All students graduating from the Anglo-American section in a recent class were American; they entered the following colleges in the U. S.: Brown, Cornell, Dartmouth, and the Universities of Michigan and Washington.

SPORTS AND ACTIVITIES . . . Tennis, rowing, swimming (lake and indoor pool), football, skating, skiing, ice hockey; interscholastic sports. In the middle of the winter term, the school moves to Montana/Cran at 5,000 feet, for a stay of 15 "White Days," where skiing and skating can be intensively practiced. Skiing, skating, ice hockey are the main extracurricular activities during this term.

FEES . . . About $2,000. Additional expenses are for Easter trip ($120–$140), private lessons, allowances, laundry, insurance, books, sports equipment. School estimates that these and other small fees amount to approximately 15 per cent of tuition and boarding fees. Fees for Day School (admission restricted to residents of Lausanne): under 12, $95; 12 to 16, $155; 16 and up, $215.

SUMMER PROGRAM ... Second week in July through first week of September. French language instruction; sports and excursions. Usually about 70 students enroll. Costs $6 a day.

HOW TO GET THERE ... By Pan American Jet Clipper from New York to London, Paris or Frankfurt with connections to Zurich, 9 hours. Or from the U.S. West Coast about 10½ hours to London via Pan Am's polar route, then to Zurich. Zurich is 1½ hours from Rome by air. Geneva is a 1½-hour flight from London. By ship, 5 to 9 days to western Atlantic or Mediterranean ports and then overnight by train.

FOR FURTHER INFORMATION ... For complete information about the school and how to enroll, write to LE LYCÉE JACCARD, Avenue Général-Guisan, Pully Près Lausanne (Vaud), Switzerland.

For general information (in addition to the facts given on pages 184 to 185), write to the International Schools Services, Department PA, 147 East 50th Street, New York, N. Y. 10022. For travel particulars and documentation, write to Educational Department, NHE, Pan American Airways, Pan Am Building, New York, N. Y. 10017.

COLLÈGE DU LÉMAN, GENEVA

Co-educational day and boarding school, ages 6–18. Minimum age for boarders is 7. Founded 1959 •

DIRECTORS ... M. and Mme. Francis Clivaz.

HEADMASTER OF ENGLISH LANGUAGE SECTION ... Mr. A. D. Campbell.

Located on the outskirts of Geneva, this recently established school is under the directorship of a member of the Clivaz family, which also directs Institut Alpin les Roches and Institut Près Fleuris. Although about one-third of the student body of 380 is American, the school is strongly multinational, with children from 48 nations enrolled. There are 74 boarders. Teaching staff of 47 includes 12 Swiss and 2 Americans. Campus includes tennis courts and playing fields for football, volleyball, basketball; there is swimming in nearby Lake Geneva.

COURSES OF STUDY ... The program is divided into two main sections: (1) French-language section, preparing for the *baccalauréat*, the Swiss *maturité*, and a commercial certificate; (2) English-language section, preparing for the British General Certificate of Education examinations and for return to U.S. schools or entrance into U.S. colleges. Grades 1–6 include the subjects offered in most American schools; grades 7–9 have courses in English, mathematics, general science, history or geography, French, Latin or a second foreign language, physical education, and art. Grades 10–12 have English, French, Latin (or second language), mathematics, sciences, social studies, physical education. Languages offered include Russian, German, Italian, Spanish.

College Du Léman

Study of French as a foreign language is emphasized in the English language section; the school aims to provide enough French for students to become practically bilingual in 2 years.

The school administers standardized academic aptitude and achievement tests.

COLLEGE ADMISSIONS ... Almost all U.S. secondary students take College Entrance Examination Board tests. Eight to ten graduates annually gain advanced placement in one or more subjects in U.S. colleges. The colleges entered by graduates last year include California Institute of Technology, Massachusetts Institute of Technology, and the Universities of Connecticut, Michigan, and Pennsylvania.

SPORTS AND ACTIVITIES ... Interschool sports (skiing, tennis, volleyball, basketball). Dramatics, music. Students are required to participate according to interests and abilities. Skiing trips; regularly scheduled excursions to museums, art galleries, points of historical interest.

FEES ... Tuition for day students ranges from $425–$590 annually; tuition and boarding annually from $1,635 to $2,000, depending upon grade level. Extra charge for staying at school during Christmas holiday, $140; during spring holiday, $165. Additional charges for laundry, lunches, athletic uniform and equipment, medical fees, insurance. Field trips are extra.

SUMMER PROGRAM ... July and August. Instruction in languages; sports, social and cultural events; refresher courses in various academic subjects when needed. Usual enrollment is 80. Cost: $225 for entire course.

HOW TO GET THERE ... By Pan American Jet Clipper from New York to London, Paris or Frankfurt with connections to Zurich, 9 hours. Or from the U.S. West Coast about 10½ hours to London via Pan Am's polar route, then to Zurich. Zurich is 1½ hours from Rome by air. Geneva is about a 1½-hour flight from London. By ship, 5 to 9 days to western Atlantic or Mediterranean ports and then overnight by train.

FOR FURTHER INFORMATION ... For complete information about the school and how to enroll, write to the COLLÉGE DU LÉMAN, Versoix-Geneva, Switzerland.

For general information (in addition to the facts given on pages 184 to 185), write to the International Schools Services, Department PA, 147 East 50th Street, New York, N. Y. 10022. For travel particulars and documentation, write to Educational Department, NHE, Pan American Airways, Pan Am Building, New York, N. Y. 10017.

LEYSIN AMERICAN SCHOOL

Leysin American School

Co-educational boarding school, ages 14–18 (grades 9–12), and postgraduate year. Founded 1961 •

HEADMASTER ... Mr. José Martinez.

Located in skiing area at an altitude of 5,000 feet above the Rhone Valley and Lake Geneva; half an hour by train from Aigle, and 2 hours from Geneva.

Enrollment of approximately 120; all are Americans. Parents of a majority of the students live in the Far East, Middle East, Africa, Europe, on assignment to international programs of diplomacy, technical aid, industry. School reports a waiting list; plans call for increasing enrollment to 150. Staff includes 12 teachers, 2 dormitory counselors, nurse, all American except for French language teachers.

The 10-acre grounds include ski slopes and playing fields for basketball, volleyball. Students use town pool and gymnasium.

COURSE OF STUDY ... An American college preparatory program. Required courses: English (4 years); mathematics (2 years); social studies (3 years); laboratory sciences (2 years); foreign languages (study of French required; German also offered). Advanced placement courses offered in mathematics, French. All students must participate in physical education program, including skiing.

Standardized academic aptitude and achievement tests are administered.

COLLEGE ADMISSIONS ... All students take College Entrance Examination Board tests. All students in the graduating classes entered colleges.

SPORTS AND ACTIVITIES ... Group and team sports; skiing, skating, tobogganing, swimming, water skiing, boating, tennis, golf, riding, riflery, mountain climbing, hiking and camping. Dancing, folk festivals, dramatics and debating, glee club and instrumental ensemble, newspaper and student government. Clubs and hobby groups. Trips to nearby points of interest, and weekend excursions to cultural centers in France, Italy, Germany.

FEES ... Approximately $2,400 a year, exclusive of fees for tutoring, art and music lessons, laboratory fees, skiing instructions and 3-day excursions.

HOW TO GET THERE ... By Pan American Jet Clipper from New York to London, Paris or Frankfurt with connections to Zurich, 9 hours. Or from the U.S. West Coast about 10½ hours to London via Pan Am's polar route, then to Zurich. Zurich is 1½ hours from Rome by air. Geneva is a 1½-hour flight from London. By ship, 5 to 9 days to western Atlantic or Mediterranean ports and then overnight by train.

FOR FURTHER INFORMATION ... For complete information about the school and how to enroll, write to the LEYSIN AMERICAN SCHOOL, Leysin (Vaud), Switzerland.

For general information (in addition to the facts given on pages 184 to 185), write to the International Schools Services, Department PA, 147 East 50th Street, New York, N. Y. 10022. For travel particulars and documentation, write to Educational Department, NHE, Pan American Airways, Pan Am Building, New York, N. Y. 10017.

INSTITUT MONNIVERT

Boys' boarding school, ages 9–18. Founded 1924 ·

DIRECTORS ... M. and Mme. Marc Rivier.

The school is located on spacious grounds at the shore of Lake Geneva, about 10 miles west of Lausanne and 40 miles from the city of Geneva. The enrollment of 50 students usually includes 5 to 10 Americans, and boys from many countries of Europe, Latin America, and the Middle East. The 14 teachers are almost all Europeans (no Americans). Campus includes playing fields and courts for football, basketball, volleyball, and tennis.

Institut Monnivert

COURSES OF STUDY ... The school offers preparation for the Swiss *maturité,* French *baccalauréat,* British General Certificate of Education examinations, and American college entrance.

The American college preparatory program is combined with the British program, and includes the following subjects taught in English: mathematics, chemistry and physics, American and European history, grammar, composition, literature. All other courses for the English-speaking students are given in French, which is the basic language of the school; there is intensive instruction in the language for students who are not fluent in it on admission.

COLLEGE ADMISSIONS ... In 1962, three students took College Entrance Examination Board tests and entered Harvard, Princeton University, and the University of California.

SPORTS AND ACTIVITIES ... Tennis, basketball, football, volleyball, riding, water skiing, rowing, gymnastics, swimming, skiing. Ski trips are scheduled each weekend during the winter, and one full week in February is spent at a ski resort such as Zermatt, Cran, Murren, Villars.

FEES... Total annual cost, including personal expenditures and excursions, is about $3,500.

SUMMER PROGRAM ... Mid-July through August. Intensive French language instruction. Cost of tuition, room and board only is approximately $275.

HOW TO GET THERE ... By Pan American Jet Clipper from New York to London, Paris or Frankfurt with connections to Zurich, 9 hours. Or from the U.S. West Coast about 10½ hours to London via Pan Am's polar route, then to Zurich. Zurich is 1½ hours from Rome by air. Geneva is about a 1½-hour flight from London. By ship, 5 to 9 days to western Atlantic or Mediterranean ports and then overnight by train.

FOR FURTHER INFORMATION ... For complete information about the school and how to enroll, write to the INSTITUT MONNIVERT, St. Prex (Vaud), Switzerland.

For general information (in addition to the facts given on pages 184 to 185), write to the International Schools Services, Department PA, 147 East 50th Street, New York, N. Y. 10022. For travel particulars and documentation, write to Educational Department, NHE, Pan American Airways, Pan Am Building, New York, N. Y. 10017.

INSTITUT MONTANA

Boys' boarding school, ages 11–18. Founded 1926 ·

HEADMASTER ... Dr. Josef Ostermayer.

DEAN OF AMERICAN SCHOOL ... Mr. Glenn Robertson.

The school is 25 miles south of Zurich, 3,000 feet above the Lake of Zug and 15 minutes by cable car from the city of Zug. The 75-acre campus has sports fields for soccer, baseball, basketball, hockey and boccia, 5 tennis courts, and ski runs.

The enrollment of 230 boys includes 63 Americans (of whom 60 are of secondary school age), 30 Swiss, and students from 20 other countries, with especially sizable groups of German, Dutch and Italian boys. The 44 teachers include 20 Swiss, 8 Americans and 5 other nationalities.

COURSES OF STUDY ... The school has American, Dutch, German-Swiss and Italian curricula. Each is university preparatory for its respective country. The American program follows the pattern of preparatory schools in the U. S., within the framework of the school's international character. Grades 7–12 are offered. Required courses at secondary level are history (ancient, European and American), world geography, American government and social structure; general physical and biological science, chemistry and physics with laboratory; general mathematics, elementary and intermediate algebra; plane and solid geometry, trigonometry and analytical geometry; French and German (4 years of 2 languages recommended); and English (4 years). Advanced placement work is offered in mathematics, English, French, German and history. One hour of religious

Institut Montana

Institution Château Mont-Choisi

instruction, according to faith, is required each week. English is the language of instruction in the American program.

The school administers a full program of standardized academic aptitude and achievement tests. The National Merit Scholarship Qualifying Tests are given annually to juniors.

COLLEGE ADMISSIONS ... Students in the American program take College Entrance Examination Board tests. Several students annually gain advanced placement in American colleges in one or more courses. U.S. colleges admitting recent graduates are Beloit, Brown University, Duke University, Brandeis, Massachusetts Institute of Technology, Georgetown, Purdue, Stanford, and the service academies.

SPORTS AND ACTIVITIES ... Intramural sports. Skiing trips to Engelberg and Andermatt, visits to Basel, Zurich, Berne, Fribourg; bimonthly excursions to Zurich for theater, concerts and opera. Clubs: dramatics, literary, science, international, photography, chess; choral group, debating society, language societies. There is a "travel workshop," which consists of a 2- to 3-week tour to one or another European country, planned according to academic interests (cost is $200–$300). Church attendance is required at church of student's faith.

FEES ... About $2,000 annually, exclusive of excursions and personal allowances. A deposit of $235, required for personal expenditures, is refunded if not used. Extra charges for staying on during vacations are $7 daily.

SUMMER PROGRAM ... July and August. Program of language instruction (French, German, English, Italian), private tutoring and sports. Approximately 100 boys attend; applications from American students for the summer program are not encouraged. Costs are about $40 weekly.

HOW TO GET THERE ... By Pan American Jet Clipper from New York to London, Paris or Frankfurt with connections to Zurich, 9 hours. Or from the U.S. West Coast about 10½ hours to London via Pan Am's polar route, then to Zurich. Zurich is 1½ hours from Rome by air. Geneva is a 1½-hour flight from London. By ship, 5 to 9 days to western Atlantic or Mediterranean ports and then overnight by train.

FOR FURTHER INFORMATION ... For complete information about the school and how to enroll, write to the INSTITUT MONTANA, Zugerberg (Zug), Switzerland.

For general information (in addition to the facts given on pages 184 to 185), write to the International Schools Services, Department PA, 147 East 50th Street, New York, N. Y. 10022. For travel particulars and documentation, write to Educational Department, NHE, Pan American Airways, Pan Am Building, New York, N. Y. 10017.

INSTITUTION CHÂTEAU MONT-CHOISI, LAUSANNE

Girls' boarding school, ages 10–21. Founded 1885 ·

DIRECTORS ... M. and Mme. François Pusztaszeri-Gayrhos.

The school is located about 10 minutes from the center of Lausanne, at an altitude of 2,000 feet with a commanding view of Lake Geneva and the Alps. The campus includes a large garden, tennis courts, playground, miniature golf, ping-pong tables and swimming pool.

Enrollment of 100 includes about 20 American girls, and nationals of some 25 to 30 other countries. The teaching staff of 27 includes 8 Swiss, 1 American, 2 British.

COURSES OF STUDY ... The basic language of instruction is French; except as noted below, students must speak French at all times except on Sundays. Predominantly a finishing school based on Swiss standards, with the addition of commercial subjects, advanced language programs in French and English, and optional American courses.

All students of elementary school age are taught in French except in spelling and grammar, history and arithmetic, which are given in English to English-speaking students.

In the secondary school, English-speaking girls may take the following subjects in English: grammar and literature, mathematics, biology and American history. As these courses are given on a tutorial basis by specially contracted teachers, extra tuition is charged.

COLLEGE ADMISSIONS ... American students may take College Entrance Examination Board tests at Geneva. However, preparation for college is not a major aim of the school; few graduates seek college entrance. Many students return to U.S. secondary schools after enrolling for 1 or 2 years.

SPORTS AND ACTIVITIES ... Concerts, theater, school movies, annual dance given with a boys' school. Excursions for winter sports to Zermatt; Easter trip to Spain or France, trips to Geneva, Berne, Neuchâtel, Interlaken. Skiing weekend in the mountains. Visits to art exhibitions.

FEES ... About $2,000. Supplemental charges for trips ($140 for winter sports in Zermatt; about $260 for tour to France, Italy, or Spain), charges for painting and drawing, piano, shorthand, typing. Cost of each English-language course is $20.

SUMMER PROGRAM ... From second week of July through August. About 30 American girls enroll. French lessons in mornings; sports, excursions in afternoons. Costs $200 for 4 weeks, $400 for 8 weeks. Additional expenses for 8 weeks total about $100.

HOW TO GET THERE ... By Pan American Jet Clipper from New York to London, Paris or Frankfurt with connections to Zurich, 9 hours. Or from the U.S. West Coast about 10½ hours to London via Pan Am's polar route, then to Zurich. Zurich is 1½ hours from Rome by air. Geneva is a 1½-hour flight from London. By ship, 5 to 9 days to western Atlantic or Mediterranean ports and then overnight by train.

FOR FURTHER INFORMATION ... For complete information about the school and how to enroll, write to the INSTITUTION CHÂTEAU MONT-CHOISI, Lausanne–La Rosiaz (Vaud), Switzerland.

For general information (in addition to the facts given on pages 184 to 185), write to the International Schools Services, Department PA, 147 East 50th Street, New York, N. Y. 10022. For travel particulars and documentation, write to Educational Department, NHE, Pan American Airways, Pan Am Building, New York, N. Y. 10017.

MONTE ROSA AND CHILLON COLLEGE

Co-educational boarding school, ages 7–18. Enrolls a limited number of day students. Founded 1874 ·

DIRECTOR ... Dr. K. Gademann.

The school is located in the town of Territet, which is near Montreux on the shores of Lake Geneva. While the school has existed since 1874, the present Monte Rosa and Chillon College was established in 1955, in co-operation with Rosenberg College, St. Gallen. Chillon is the Junior School (ages 7–10) and Monte Rosa the Senior School (ages 11–18).

Current enrollment is 300 (including 45 day students), of whom 146 are at secondary school level. Student body is international, with 81 American students (of whom 71 are at secondary level) and sizable groups from many countries of Europe, the Middle East, Far East, and South America. Teaching staff of 51 includes 9 nationalities (there are British but no American teachers).

The campus, though not large, has tennis and basketball courts and a practice track.

COURSES OF STUDY ... A number of curricular patterns are followed: American, British, Swiss, Austrian, German; a commercial course is also given. In the English-speaking Section, students are taught together in preparation for British General Certificate of Education examinations and U.S. college entrance.

The elementary school in the English-speaking Section offers a standard program based upon American and British curricula. At the secondary level, required courses are European history and world geography (American history is available); chemistry and physics; elementary and intermediate algebra, plane and solid geometry, analytical geometry, trigonometry, and introduction to calculus; French; English (4 years); music courses, religious instruction (1 period weekly), art appreciation, physical education.

COLLEGE ADMISSIONS ... Most U.S. students take College Entrance Examination Board tests. U.S. colleges entered by recent graduates include Colby, Cornell, Northwestern University, Reed, and the Universities of Arizona, California, Colorado, and Tulane.

SPORTS AND ACTIVITIES ... Skiing, ice skating, tobogganing; basketball, tennis, hikes, football. Two- or three-day outings to nearby resorts during the winter. Swimming at Montreux Plage during summer. Historical and cultural excursions, dramatic society, bridge club, stamp club; films and theater in Lausanne and Montreux. Students are required to participate in certain activities according to program and grade.

FEES ... Annual tuition and boarding, $1,400–$1,700; tuition for day students, $525–$600, depending upon age. Extras include laboratory and handwork fees, tutoring, music lessons, personal expenditures. Excursions, including all field trips, amount to $25–$50 per term.

SUMMER PROGRAM ... July and August. Excursions, sports, language courses. About 200 students enroll. Fees $65 a week.

HOW TO GET THERE ... By Pan American Jet Clipper from New York to London, Paris or Frankfurt with connections to Zurich, 9 hours. Or from the U.S. West Coast about 10½ hours to London via Pan Am's polar route, then to Zurich. Zurich is 1½ hours from Rome by air. Geneva is a 1½-hour flight from London. By ship, 5 to 9 days to western Atlantic or Mediterranean ports and then overnight by train.

FOR FURTHER INFORMATION ... For complete information about the school and how to enroll, write to the MONTE ROSA AND CHILLON COLLEGE, Territet-Montreux (Vaud), Switzerland.

For general information (in addition to the facts given on pages 184 to 185), write to the International Schools Services, Department PA, 147 East 50th Street, New York, N. Y. 10022. For travel particulars and documentation, write to Educational Department, NHE, Pan American Airways, Pan Am Building, New York, N. Y. 10017.

View of Territet, Site of Monte Rosa and Chillon College

Institut Alpin, Montesano

INSTITUT ALPIN MONTESANO

Girls' boarding school, ages 14–19. Founded 1951 ·

DIRECTORS ... M. and Mme. Henry Bauchau.

Located in a resort area at an altitude of 3,450 feet, the school is 100 miles from Geneva and can be reached by train via Montreux. Enrollment of 90 includes 30 girls from the U.S., 26 from England, 11 from France; the others are from a variety of European countries and Latin America. There are 21 teachers, including 5 Swiss, 3 Americans, 4 French, 2 English, 2 Spanish. Campus has a basketball court and general sports field. Facilities of the Palace Hotel in Gstaad are used for tennis, swimming, skating.

COURSES OF STUDY ... The girls are divided into two main sections: (1) Secondary Education; (2) a finishing school program (foreign language study, general cultural courses, domestic science).

Girls in the Secondary Education section may follow any of five programs: (1) preparation, in French, for the French *baccalauréat;* (2) French language and cultural studies, leading to the *certificat de français* of the University of Nancy; (3) English language and cultural studies (for girls whose native language is not English); (4) preparation for French language examinations, General Certificate of Education, Ordinary and Advanced levels; (5) an American college preparatory program, described below.

The American program is for grades 9–12. Girls pursuing this curriculum may take the following subjects in English: American and English literature and composition; American and European history; social studies, biology and physics; algebra, geometry, and trigonometry. The remainder of their courses are taken in French; intensive instruction is provided in that language for those who require it.

COLLEGE ADMISSIONS ... Girls in the American program take College Entrance Examination Board tests in Geneva. Of nine U.S. students in a recent graduating class, seven entered U.S. colleges: Barnard, Middlebury, Randolph Macon, Skidmore, and the Universities of California, Oregon, Puget Sound.

SPORTS AND ACTIVITIES ... Skiing and tennis competitions with other schools. Intramural sports: skiing, swimming, basketball, ping-pong. Riding and rock climbing. Clubs: theater, music, political, photography, botany, bridge. Reading French plays, prose, poetry. Girls attend theatrical performances in Lausanne. At the half-term holiday in November, a visit to Paris is arranged. There is a trip to Italy during spring holidays. Students visit Berne, Lausanne, Geneva, and Lucerne during the term.

FEES ... $2,325 for the year. Ski uniform and equipment about $235. Local excursions cost about $50 annually; trips during vacations to other countries are extra.

HOW TO GET THERE ... By Pan American Jet Clipper from New York to London, Paris or Frankfurt with connections to Zurich, 9 hours. Or from the U.S. West Coast about 101½ hours to London via Pan Am's polar route, then to Zurich. Zurich is 1½ hours from Rome by air. Geneva is a 1½-hour flight from London. By ship, 5 to 9 days to western Atlantic or Mediterranean ports and then overnight by train.

FOR FURTHER INFORMATION ... For complete information about the school and how to enroll, write to the INSTITUT ALPIN MONTESANO, Gstaad (Fribourg), Switzerland.

For general information (in addition to the facts given on pages 184 to 185), write to the International Schools Services, Department PA, 147 East 50th Street, New York, N. Y. 10022. For travel particulars and documentation, write to Educational Department, NHE, Pan American Airways, Pan Am Building, New York, N. Y. 10017.

INSTITUT MONTJOIE

Montjoie

Co-educational boarding and day school; boys 9–14, girls 9–13. Founded 1940 ·

DIRECTOR ... M. Sergio Emery.

The school occupies a large chalet overlooking Villars, which is about 13 miles southeast of Montreux. A new academic building is under construction. The enrollment of 32 includes about equal numbers of boarders and day students. Half the students are Swiss; there are six Americans; others are French, Italian. Teaching staff of eight includes four Swiss.

COURSES OF STUDY ... A French-language academic program, with a limited amount of instruction given in English to enable English-speaking children to return to English-language schools at grade level commensurate with age. Concentrated courses in French are organized for non-French students. Classes are small; teaching is virtually on a tutorial basis.

SPORTS AND ACTIVITIES ... Supervised physical training and sports, including tennis, riding, skiing, skating, swimming. Dramatics, choral groups, school newspaper. Discussion groups on family life, social relations, international problems. Excursions to the mountains.

FEES ... About $155 monthly. Excursions extra.

SUMMER PROGRAM ... July and August. French language instruction. Costs about $155 monthly.

HOW TO GET THERE ... By Pan American Jet Clipper from New York to London, Paris or Frankfurt with connections to Zurich, 9 hours. Or from the U.S. West Coast about 10½ hours to London via Pan Am's polar route, then to Zurich. Zurich is 1½ hours from Rome by air. Geneva is a 1½-hour flight from London. By ship, 5 to 9 days to western Atlantic or Mediterranean ports and then overnight by train.

FOR FURTHER INFORMATION ... For complete information about the school and how to enroll, write to the INSTITUT MONTJOIE, Villars-sur-Ollon (Vaud), Switzerland.

For general information (in addition to the facts given on pages 184 to 185), write to the International Schools Services, Department PA, 147 East 50th Street, New York, N. Y. 10022. For travel particulars and documentation, write to Educational Department, NHE, Pan American Airways, Pan Am Building, New York, N. Y. 10017.

ÉCOLE NOUVELLE PRÉPARATOIRE

Boys' boarding and day school, ages 8–18. Founded 1926 ·

DIRECTOR ... Mme. May Jomini.

Situated on Lake Geneva, about 20 minutes by car from Lausanne. Enrollment is 110, of whom 60 are boarders. Americans number about 16; Swiss about 61; a variety of other nationalities are represented. Teaching staff of 20 includes 15 Swiss, 2 Americans, 1 French. Campus has facilities for tennis, soccer, basketball; swimming in the lake.

COURSES OF STUDY ... Three curricula are offered: (1) preparation for the Swiss *maturité* and French *baccalauréat;* (2) an American curriculum, taught in English and French; (3) a commercial course. Depending upon number, ages and academic needs of the English-speaking students in a given year, the following courses are offered in English: American history; general biological science; general mathematics, elementary and intermediate algebra, plane and solid geometry, trigonometry, analytical geometry, introduction to calculus. The balance of the academic programs of English-speaking boys is in French, which is the basic language of the school. Languages offered are French, German, Italian, Latin, Greek, English. Typing, bookkeeping, shorthand are available.

In the elementary school, instruction corresponds to that of Lausanne public schools, with teaching in French. Study of German is begun at about the age of 11.

COLLEGE ADMISSIONS ... While preparation for American college entrance is not a major emphasis of the school, a few students take College Entrance Examination Board tests, and one or two annually gain advanced placement in American colleges in one or more subjects. The two American students in a recent graduating class entered Georgetown University and the University of Montreal.

SPORTS AND ACTIVITIES ... Interschool academic competitions; interschool sports; gymnastics, swimming, soccer, rowing, basketball, tennis, skating. Excursions include a Christmas skiing trip, Sunday outings and a 1-week trip in March.

FEES ... Tuition for day students ranges between $550 and $950; tuition and boarding amount to $2,200, depending upon age. Cost of Christmas trip (skiing) is $234; cost of spring trip to another country is the same. Student allowance and fees for tennis, rowing, tutoring are extra.

SUMMER PROGRAM ... July to early September. Usually about 50 students. Program of French language instruction; other courses on demand. Costs $175 a month, plus extras amounting to about $50 for the entire course.

HOW TO GET THERE ... By Pan American Jet Clipper from New York to London, Paris, or Frankfurt with connections to Zurich, 9 hours. Or from the U.S. West Coast about 10½ hours to London via Pan Am's polar route, then to Zurich. Zurich is 1½ hours from Rome by air. Geneva is a 1½-hour flight from London. By ship, 5 to 9 days to western Atlantic or Mediterranean ports and then overnight by train.

École Nouvelle Préparatoire

FOR FURTHER INFORMATION ... For complete information about the school and how to enroll, write to the ÉCOLE NOUVELLE PRÉPARATOIRE, Paudex près Lausanne (Vaud), Switzerland.

For general information (in addition to the facts given on pages 184 to 185), write to the International Schools Services, Department PA, 147 East 50th Street, New York, N. Y. 10022. For travel particulars and documentation, write to Educational Department, NHE, Pan American Airways, Pan Am Building, New York, N. Y. 10017.

INSTITUT PRÉS FLEURIS

Girls' boarding school, ages 9–18. A few day students accepted. Founded 1956 ·

DIRECTORS ... M. and Mme. Roger Clivaz-Monnier.

INSTITUT ALPIN LES ROCHES

Boys' boarding and day school, ages 9–18. Founded 1955 ·

DIRECTORS ... M. Marcel Clivaz and M. Jean-Pierre Clivaz.

INSTITUT PRÉS FLEURIS and INSTITUT ALPIN LES ROCHES are located on adjoining grounds; both are under direction of members of the Clivaz family. The village of Bluche is in a mountain resort area, about 100 miles east of Geneva and 35 miles southeast of Montreux.

The academic programs of the two schools are virtually identical; teachers and classrooms are shared. Facilities include girls' living quarters at Prés Fleuris, an administrative building, a new classroom building, boys' dormitory quarters, and staff housing. Boarding quarters contain ample space for studying and lounging. A current construction program includes new chemistry and physics laboratories suitable for individual work with class of 12 students at a time. The 20-acre campus includes tennis courts, a ski lift and ski slopes, and a new swimming pool.

Enrollment at Prés Fleuris is 44; all students but one are boarders. Americans constitute slightly more than half the student body; there are also sizable proportions of Italian and French students.

Les Roches has 81 students, including 30 Americans, 10 Swiss, a number of French and Italian children, and representatives of some 20 other nationalities. There are 6 day students.

Teaching staff of 27 includes 6 Swiss, 1 American, others of 6 different nationalities, including a number of British teachers for the Anglo-American program.

COURSES OF STUDY ... Four programs are provided: (1) French program (primary school, commercial studies, languages); (2) Italian program (primary school, commercial studies, languages); (3) German program (languages, commercial studies); (4) Anglo-American program, detailed below.

The Anglo-American program enrolls about 80 children in grades 6 through 12. Preparation is given for U.S. college entrance, and for the British General Certificate of Education examination, Ordinary Level. Required subjects in the college preparatory program are history (3 years) and world geography; mathematics (3 years); English (4 years); at least one science; and French. (The official language of the school is French; a minimum of 8 hours' weekly study of the language is required for each student.) Advanced placement courses are offered in sciences, mathematics, English, French, and history. Standardized academic aptitude and achievement tests are given.

COLLEGE ADMISSIONS ... English-speaking students may take College Entrance Examination Board tests. Among colleges admitting recent graduates are Amherst, Hamilton, Hampden-Sydney, Harvard, Massachusetts Institute of Technology, Middlebury, Northwestern, and Yale.

SPORTS AND ACTIVITIES ... For Prés Fleuris: special interest groups in literature, music, ballet, art, ceramics; ski competitions, mountain climbing. For Les Roches: literature, debating, agriculture, carpentry, mechanics; ski competitions, mountain climbing. Other sports offered are swimming, golf, basketball, volleyball, riding, skating. Annually scheduled trips for both schools include Zermatt, Geneva, Lausanne, Italy.

FEES ... $1,400 annually at each school. Charges for staying on during Christmas holiday are about $100. Ski and sports equipment total about $200. Other usual annual expenses: skiing excursions, $50; cultural trips, $25; school materials, $50. Personal allowances extra.

SUMMER PROGRAMS ... July and August. About 50 girls and 70 boys are enrolled. Program of language study (French, English, Italian, German, Spanish), sports, games, excursions, social and cultural activities. Costs about $150 a month.

HOW TO GET THERE ... By Pan American Jet Clipper from New York to London, Paris or Frankfurt with connections to Zurich, 9 hours. Or from the U.S. West Coast about 10½ hours to London via Pan Am's polar route, then to Zurich. Zurich is 1½ hours from Rome by air. Geneva is a 1½-hour flight from London. By ship, 5 to 9 days to western Atlantic or Mediterranean ports and then overnight by train.

FOR FURTHER INFORMATION ... For complete information about the school and how to enroll, write to the INSTITUT PRÈS FLEURIS or INSTITUT ALPIN LES ROCHES, Bluche-sur-Sierre (Valais), Switzerland.

For general information (in addition to the facts given on pages 184 to 185), write to the International Schools Services, Department PA, 147 East 50th Street, New York, N. Y. 10022. For travel particulars and documentation, write to Educational Department, NHE, Pan American Airways, Pan Am Building, New York, N. Y. 10017.

Institut Prés Fleuris

Les Roches

Institut Auf Dem Rosenberg

Institut Le Rosey

INSTITUT AUF DEM ROSENBERG, ST. GALL

Boys' boarding and day school, ages 10–18. English-speaking section accepts limited number of girl boarders, ages 10–18. Founded 1870 ·

DIRECTORS ... Dr. K. Gademann, Dr. W. Reinhard, Dr. C. Lattmann.

DIRECTOR, ENGLISH-SPEAKING SECTION ... Dr. Ivor Widlake.

Located in German-speaking Switzerland within sight of Lake Constance. Enrollment of 500, of whom 130 (110 boys, 20 girls) are in the English-speaking section. A majority of these students are between the ages of 14–18. Students are grouped by age in dormitories, but effort is made to mix nationalities. Teaching staff of 86 includes 20 Swiss, 12 Americans. Large campus has tennis courts, playing fields for soccer, rugby, cricket, and a swimming pool.

COURSES OF STUDY ... Swiss, German, Italian, and Anglo-American programs are offered. The English-speaking section prepares students for U.S. college entrance or for British General Certificate of Education examinations. English is the language of instruction in this section, but stress is placed upon acquiring multilingual facility, especially in German. Required courses are history (2 years) and world geography; chemistry and physics; German; English (4 years); and mathematics. Advanced placement courses are offered in mathematics, physics, languages. Standardized academic aptitude and achievement tests are given.

COLLEGE ADMISSIONS ... Most American students take College Entrance Examination Board tests. Recent graduates were admitted to the following U.S. colleges: Columbia, Cornell, Dartmouth, Georgetown, Massachusetts Institute of Technology, and the University of Pennsylvania.

SPORTS AND ACTIVITIES ... Among the range of activities offered are dramatics, literary club, gymnastics, field games, tennis, swimming, skiing, tobogganing, skating, woodwork, metal work. Excursions are made regularly to the mountains, Lake Constance, and to museums, libraries, concerts, theater, and industrial and commercial firms in St. Gallen. The house unit is a basis for intramural athletics. There is a "school state" with a president, student council, justice court and committees to plan community life and develop civic responsibility.

FEES ... $1,500–$1,800 exclusive of tutoring, music lessons, personal allowances, excursions, insurance.

SUMMER PROGRAM ... Program of language study (Latin, Greek, Arabic, Hebrew, Russian, French, Italian, Spanish and German). Sports, games, excursions. Costs about $50 a week.

HOW TO GET THERE ... By Pan American Jet Clipper from New York to London, Paris or Frankfurt with connections to Zurich, 9 hours. Or from the U.S. West Coast about 10½ hours to London via Pan Am's polar route, then to Zurich. Zurich is 1½ hours from Rome by air. Geneva is a 1½-hour flight from London. By ship, 5 to 9 days to western Atlantic or Mediterranean ports and then overnight by train.

FOR FURTHER INFORMATION ... For complete information about the school and how to enroll, write to the INSTITUT AUF DEM ROSENBERG, St. Gall, Switzerland.

For general information (in addition to the facts given on pages 184 to 185), write to the International Schools Services, Department PA, 147 East 50th Street, New York, N. Y. 10022. For travel particulars and documentation, write to Educational Department, NHE, Pan American Airways, Pan Am Building, New York, N. Y. 10017.

INSTITUT LE ROSEY

Boys' boarding school, ages 9–19. Founded 1880 ·

DIRECTORS ... Dr. Louis Johannot and Mlle. Helen Schaub.

Rolle is a small town on the shores of Lake Geneva, less than 20 miles distant from Lausanne and Geneva. Le Rosey, part of an ancient domain of the thirteenth century, has a campus of 66 acres where the students spend most of the academic year. During the winter months the students and staff move to Gstaad in the mountains, where the school has a number of chalets and the academic program is combined with two hours of skiing daily.

The enrollment is international, with students from 35 countries, including 75 American and 10 Swiss boys. The school is always filled to its maximum of 190 students; applications must be made a year or two in advance. Most of the 25 full-time and 7 part-time teachers are men; 8 are Swiss, 1 is American, and 7 other nationalities are represented. The school emphasizes academic excellence, languages, and physical culture.

COURSES OF STUDY ... French is the official language of the school. Students who do not know French are given intensive courses in the language on entrance. The lower grades are taught in French; the upper in English and French.

In the elementary school courses are given in English, German, Latin, arithmetic, history, geography, drawing, general science. Each boy learns at least two languages.

For the American secondary program the required subjects are history (4 years), geography (2 years), science (4 years), mathematics (4 years), English (4 years), French, fine arts, philosophy, gymnastics, swimming and skiing. Many other languages are offered: German, Italian, Spanish, Russian, Latin, Arabic, Persian, Modern Greek, Swedish, Finnish.

The school offers preparation for American college entrance tests, the Swiss *maturité*, British General Certificate of Education (Ordinary and Advanced levels), and the Canadian Matriculation.

COLLEGE ADMISSIONS ... American colleges entered by recent graduates: Boston University, Dartmouth, Harvard, Yale, Princeton, Stanford, Williams, and the Universities of Michigan, Pennsylvania, Virginia.

SPORTS AND ACTIVITIES ... Each day the boys have two hours of sports (those offered are football, basketball, tennis, skiing, track, rowing, swimming). Younger boys spend three hours a week in the workshop. The school has musical assemblies, lectures on art history, concerts, movies, lantern-slide programs.

St. George's School in Switzerland

Villa St. Jean International School

Students may attend religious services at local churches. Sunday Mass is compulsory for Catholics. Religious instruction is given at the school.

FEES ... $2,825 annually. No extra cost for staying on at the school for Christmas and spring holidays unless a trip is organized. Extra charges for excursions, sports equipment, books and school materials, pocket money, personal expenses, medical treatment, private lessons.

HOW TO GET THERE ... By Pan American Jet Clipper from New York to London, Paris, or Frankfurt with connections to Zurich, 9 hours. Or from the U.S. West Coast about 10½ hours to London via Pan Am's polar route, then to Zurich. Zurich is 1½ hours from Rome by air. Geneva is a 1½-hour flight from London. By ship, 5 to 9 days to western Atlantic or Mediterranean ports and then overnight by train.

FOR FURTHER INFORMATION ... For complete information on the school and how to enroll, write to the INSTITUT LE ROSEY, Rolle (Vaud), Switzerland.

For general information (in addition to the facts given on pages 184 to 185), write to the International Schools Services, Department PA, 147 East 50th Street, New York, N. Y. 10022. For travel particulars and documentation, write to Educational Department, NHE, Pan American Airways, Pan Am Building, New York, N. Y. 10017.

ST. GEORGE'S SCHOOL IN SWITZERLAND

Girls' boarding school (limited number of day students accepted), ages 12–20. Founded 1927 ·

HEADMISTRESS ... Miss G. A. Codrington, B.A.

The school is situated 150 feet above Lake Geneva, some 50 miles from the city of Geneva. The 12-acre campus includes a large, modern school building with accommodations for 100 girls, and a chalet with additional boarding space. The curriculum is British; about half the total enrollment of 155 girls (of whom 120 are boarders) come from the United Kingdom. At present there are 15 Americans (the second largest group); the others are from 30 different countries. Number of Americans and other non-British students admitted is limited, since school intends to preserve its English character. Only students of outstanding academic achievement should apply. Staff of 28 teachers, mainly British but with some Swiss, French, German, Italian, Spanish, and Russian nationals.

COURSES OF STUDY ... Middle School program, for girls 12–15 years old, includes English language and literature, modern languages and Latin, history and geography, mathematics, biology, Divinity, art and handwork, class singing, gymnastics, national dancing.

The Senior School program offers history, world affairs, English, modern languages and Latin, Divinity, art and handwork, class singing, gymnastics, national dancing, dressmaking, shorthand, typing. In the first year students normally take the General Certificate of Education, Ordinary Level; in the second year, they may prepare in French for the *certificat* or *diplôme*

offered by the University of Nancy; in English, for the Certificate of Proficiency, University of Cambridge, or for G.C.E. Advanced Level examinations.

There is no specific preparation for U.S. college entrance examinations. However, students who have taken G.C.E. Advanced Level examinations are often admitted to American colleges with advanced standing in those subjects.

COLLEGE ADMISSIONS ... Write directly to the Headmistress for information on College Entrance Examination Board tests.

SPORTS AND ACTIVITIES ... Part of each afternoon is devoted to games and sports (tennis, netball, rounders, swimming, winter sports, hockey, volleyball). Other outdoor occupations include walks, gardening. Literary, dramatic, debating, music societies. Chapel attendance is required, and religious instruction is provided for different religious groups.

FEES ... $1,600–$1,700. Extra charges for tennis, dancing, and piano lessons, and for certain academic subjects at an advanced level. The school aims at a simple standard of personal expenditures; luxuries are not encouraged.

HOW TO GET THERE ... By Pan American Jet Clipper from New York to London, Paris or Frankfurt with connections to Zurich, 9 hours. Or from the U.S. West Coast about 10½ hours to London via Pan Am's polar route, then to Zurich. Zurich is 1½ hours from Rome by air. Geneva is a 1½-hour flight from London. By ship, 5 to 9 days to western Atlantic or Mediterranean ports and then overnight by train.

FOR FURTHER INFORMATION ... For complete information about the school and how to enroll, write to the ST. GEORGE'S SCHOOL IN SWITZERLAND, Clarens (Vaud), Switzerland.

For general information (in addition to the facts given on pages 184 to 185), write to the International Schools Services, Department PA, 147 East 50th Street, New York, N. Y. 10022. For travel particulars and documentation, write to Educational Department, NHE, Pan American Airways, Pan Am Building, New York, N. Y. 10017.

VILLA ST. JEAN INTERNATIONAL SCHOOL, FRIBOURG

Boys' boarding and day school, ages 12–18. Founded 1903 ·

PRINCIPAL ... Bro. Wilfred P. Moran, S.M., M.S., Ph.D.

Located in a bilingual city famous for its Catholic schools and university, Villa St. Jean was converted in 1962 from a French college to an English-language international school. It is sponsored by the Society of Mary (Marianists), Roman Catholic Church.

Enrollment in the first year after the reorganization was about 55 (including 27 boarders), of whom 42 were Americans, most in the 14–18 age range. Other nations represented: Argentina, Austria, Canada, Peru, Spain, Southern Rhodesia, Switzerland, Thailand. Staff of 15 includes 8 Americans, 3 Swiss.

Facilities include six buildings, of which one houses classrooms and laboratories, and three are dormitories accommodating 150 students in all. Campus contains tennis courts, playing fields.

COURSES OF STUDY ... An American college preparatory curriculum, grades 7–12, taught in English. Required courses are European, World, and American history; general science; elementary and intermediate algebra, plane and solid geometry, trigonometry; French, Latin; English (4 years); religion (for Catholics) or ethics (for non-Catholics). Among other offerings are additional courses in social studies, sciences, mathematics, languages, music, fine arts, typing. School administers a program of American standardized academic aptitude and achievement tests. Chapel attendance is required for Catholics.

COLLEGE ADMISSIONS ... The school graduated its first class in June, 1963. All are attending colleges in the U.S. or abroad.

Write directly to the Principal for information on College Entrance Examination Board tests.

SPORTS AND ACTIVITIES ... Skiing, skating, judo, swimming, tennis, volleyball, basketball, soccer, baseball, softball. Clubs for dramatics, languages, choral and instrumental music, photography, radio, science projects, crafts.

FEES ... $1,400–$1,500 annually, depending upon grade level. Tuition for day students is $350–$450 annually. Insurance, student allowances, tutoring, use of school linens extra. Cost for staying at school during holidays is about $6 daily.

HOW TO GET THERE ... By Pan American Jet Clipper from New York to London, Paris or Frankfurt with connections to Zurich, 9 hours. Or from the U.S. West Coast about 10½ hours to London via Pan Am's polar route, then to Zurich. Zurich is 1½ hours from Rome by air. Geneva is a 1½-hour flight from London. By ship, 5 to 9 days to western Atlantic or Mediterranean ports and then overnight by train.

FOR FURTHER INFORMATION ... For complete information about the school and how to enroll, write to the VILLA ST. JEAN INTERNATIONAL SCHOOL, Fribourg, Switzerland.

For general information (in addition to the facts given on pages 184 to 185), write to the International Schools Services, Department PA, 147 East 50th Street, New York, N. Y. 10022. For travel particulars and documentation, write to Educational Department, NHE, Pan American Airways, Pan Am Building, New York, N. Y. 10017.

INSTITUT DR. SCHMIDT

Boys' boarding school, ages 12–18. Founded 1889–91 ·

PRINCIPALS ... Dr. H. C. Schmidt, Mme. Schmidt-Rossi, M. and Mme. Thuri Schmidt.

The school has been under the direction of the same family since its inception by Dr. John Ulrich Schmidt 75 years ago. Lutry is near Lausanne, on Lake Geneva, less than 50 miles from the city of Geneva. The enrollment of 60 boys includes sizable percentages from the U. S., France, Germany, Italy, Portugal, Spain, the Netherlands, Belgium, Scandinavia and Latin America. There are 12 teachers, all men, including 3 Swiss and others of 7 different nationalities. Campus has courts and fields for tennis, basketball, soccer; there is swimming in the lake.

Institut Dr. Schmidt

COURSE OF STUDY ... The basic curriculum is French, but a limited number of courses are taught in English. American students are encouraged to follow the French curriculum as soon as possible; intensive French instruction is provided for all students insofar as necessary; French is the conversational language of the school. Required courses include ancient, European, and world history, and world geography; general physical and biological science, biology, chemistry, physics, physiology, general mathematics, elementary and intermediate algebra, plane and solid geometry, trigonometry, English, French, athletics. There is no course work in English for older students in mathematics or sciences.

COLLEGE ADMISSIONS ... A high proportion of the American students take College Entrance Examination Board tests. Four or five students each year gain advanced placement in U.S. colleges in one or more subjects. Among colleges entered by recent graduates are American University, Brown University, Emory, Massachusetts Institute of Technology, Princeton University, University of Texas, Yale, Harvard, Oregon, Columbia, Johns Hopkins.

SPORTS AND ACTIVITIES ... School day starts with early morning exercises. Some afternoons are free for games: swimming, rowing, tennis, football, basketball, gymnastics, winter sports. In the evenings boys organize lectures, plays, and entertainments, or go into Lausanne to the theater, movies, concerts, or lectures at the University. In January and February, the school moves to the mountains for skiing and skating instruction, combined with the usual academic program.

FEES ... For students under 16, $2,450 annually; over 16, $2,800. Trip to Italy or Spain during Easter vacation around $210, plus daily rate of $7 to $8. Same daily rate for students staying at school during holidays.

SUMMER PROGRAM ... Early July to second week of September. Study of modern languages. Costs $280 per 4 weeks.

HOW TO GET THERE ... By Pan American Jet Clipper from New York to London, Paris or Frankfurt with connections to Zurich, 9 hours. Or from the U.S. West Coast about 10½ hours to London via Pan Am's polar route, then to Zurich. Zurich is 1½ hours from Rome by air. Geneva is a 1½-hour flight from London. By ship, 5 to 9 days to western Atlantic or Mediterranean ports and then overnight by train.

FOR FURTHER INFORMATION ... For complete information about the school and how to enroll, write to the INSTITUT DR. SCHMIDT, Château de la Rive, Lutry (Vaud), Switzerland.

For general information (in addition to the facts given on pages 184 to 185), write to the International Schools Services, Department PA, 147 East 50th Street, New York, N. Y. 10022. For travel particulars and documentation, write to Educational Department, NHE, Pan American Airways, Pan Am Building, New York, N. Y. 10017.

ÉCOLE NOUVELLE DE LA SUISSE ROMANDE, LAUSANNE

Boys' boarding and co-educational day school, ages 5–19. Minimum age for boarders is 8. Founded 1906·

DIRECTOR ... Dr. Aloys de Marignac.

Situated slightly above Lausanne, a cultural and educational center of French-speaking Switzerland, the school is owned by a group of parents of present and former students. A majority of the 380 students are Swiss, with Americans forming the next largest group (about one-third) and a few children from each of many other countries. There are 32 teachers (2 Americans, 1 Italian, 1 French, all others Swiss). Dormitories have a capacity of 98.

COURSES OF STUDY ... The curriculum is Swiss; French is the language of instruction, with the important exceptions noted below. Intensive French language courses are provided as needed for all students whose native language is not French; as language capability increases, students are gradually integrated into the regular program. However, for Americans who plan to re-enter U.S. schools or gain admission to American colleges, English is the language of instruction in literature and composition, and in certain courses in mathematics, sciences, social studies.

COLLEGE ADMISSIONS ... Students may take College Entrance Examination Board tests. U.S. colleges entered by recent graduates include Amherst, Brown, Harvard, Massachusetts Institute of Technology, University of Pittsburgh, Williams, and Yale.

SPORTS AND ACTIVITIES ... Many intramural and interscholastic sports. Campus includes two tennis courts and a playing field. Skiing and coasting in winter, with an annual 2-week stay during winter vacation in school chalet at Champéry. Sports participation is voluntary. There are several expeditions each year related to classwork, and trips to Lausanne for theater, lectures, and exhibitions.

FEES ... About $2,100 annually; extra charges for students who stay at school during vacations. Supplemental fees for laundry, school supplies, riding lessons, and excursions do not exceed $25 a month.

SUMMER PROGRAM ... July and August; held at Champéry. A maximum of 40 boys, ages 11–17, are admitted. Two hours' daily instruction, usually courses in French language; remainder of time devoted to sports, excursions. Costs: about $5 a day.

HOW TO GET THERE ... By Pan American Jet Clipper from New York to London, Paris or Frankfurt with connections to Zurich, 9 hours. Or from the U.S. West Coast about 10½ hours to London via Pan Am's polar route, then to Zurich. Zurich is 1½ hours from Rome by air. Geneva is a 1½-hour flight from London. By ship, 5 to 9 days to western Atlantic or Mediterranean ports and then overnight by train.

FOR FURTHER INFORMATION ... For complete information about the school and how to enroll, write to the ÉCOLE NOUVELLE DE LA SUISSE ROMANDE, Chailly-sur-Lausanne (Vaud), Switzerland.

For general information (in addition to the facts given on pages 184 to 185), write to the International Schools Services, Department PA, 147 East 50th Street, New York, N. Y. 10022. For travel particulars and documentation, write to Educational Department, NHE, Pan American Airways, Pan Am Building, New York, N. Y. 10017.

ÉCOLE PRIVÉE TOURNESOL

Co-educational boarding and day school, ages 5–12. Founded 1954 •

DIRECTOR ... Mme. Doris E. Müllener-Hess.
Located in a famed skiing area about 100 miles northeast of Geneva. Enrollment of 35 (plus 6–8 day students), of whom 80 per cent are U.S. nationals. Staff of six teachers, including one

École Privée Tournesol

Swiss, two British, two French. The school is housed in a large, comfortable chalet, with playing field in front.

COURSE OF STUDY ... American elementary school program (grades 1–8), taught in English. A major goal of the curriculum is to enable the students, most of whom are abroad for only one or two years, to re-enter U.S. schools at grade level commensurate with age. The goal is attained through use of American correspondence course materials, enriched and supplemented by language teaching (special stress is placed upon learning French) and an advanced level of instruction in mathematics and certain other subjects. Grades 1–4 meet as one group, grades 5–8 as a second group. There are few students in grades 1 and 8.

SPORTS AND ACTIVITIES ... Hiking, gymnastics, swimming, tennis, skiing (during winter months a midday period is regularly devoted to skiing practice and instruction). Fall visits are made to Berne, and a special 3-day trip is a reward for seniors of outstanding character and development.

FEES ... About $1,310 for the academic year, with supplemental charges for medical insurance, sports equipment, excursions, special tutoring, and sports instruction.

SUMMER PROGRAM ... July and August. Twenty students are accepted. Daily classes in French language for beginning and advanced students, plus such activities as excursions, games, hiking tennis, riding, swimming. Cost: approximately $142 for room, board and tuition. Summer school closes September 1. School begins around mid-September.

HOW TO GET THERE ... By Pan American Jet Clipper from New York to London, Paris or Frankfurt with connections to Zurich, 9 hours. Or from the U.S. West Coast about 10½ hours to London via Pan Am's polar route, then to Zurich. Zurich is 1½ hours from Rome by air. Geneva is a 1½-hour flight from London. By ship, 5 to 9 days to western Atlantic or Mediterranean ports and then overnight by train.

FOR FURTHER INFORMATION ... For complete information about the school and how to enroll, write to the ÉCOLE PRIVÉE TOURNESOL, Gstaad (Berne), Switzerland.

For general information (in addition to the facts given on pages 184 to 185), write to the International Schools Services, Department PA, 147 East 50th Street, New York, N. Y. 10022. For travel particulars and documentation, write to Educational Department, NHE, Pan American Airways, Pan Am Building, New York, N. Y. 10017.

TAIWAN

MORRISON ACADEMY

Co-educational boarding and day school (Grades, kindergarten–12). Minimum age for boarders is 6. Founded 1953 •

SUPERINTENDENT ... Mr. C. E. Redfield.
Established and operated by five Protestant missionary groups. Though primarily for children of missionary families, the school enrolls a number of children whose parents serve Ameri-

Morrison Academy

can governmental, corporate and other programs on Taiwan. The total enrollment of 255 is predominantly American; there are small groups of European and Canadian students. The majority of students are between the ages of 5 and 11. Seventy-five children are boarders. Teaching staff of 28, of whom 10 are part-time, consists of 4 Chinese, 24 Americans. The 12-acre campus has a tennis court and playing fields for soccer, basketball and baseball.

COURSES OF STUDY ... The elementary school curriculum is American, with the addition of courses in Chinese language, history, geography. The secondary program is also patterned on U.S. school standards. Required subjects are world history, American history, American government and social structure, general physical and biological sciences, biology with laboratory, two mathematics courses, and English (4 years). Study of Bible and church history and chapel attendance are required.

COLLEGE ADMISSIONS ... Students may take College Entrance Examination Board tests. From a recent graduating class, nine students entered U.S. colleges, including Asbury, Belhaven, Bowling Green, Furman University, Seattle Pacific, and Texas Technological College.

SPORTS AND ACTIVITIES ... Full program of intramural sports. Vocal and instrumental concerts.

FEES ... Annual tuition is $370; lodging $105 per year. Board is computed at 75 cents daily for grades 1–6, $1 daily for grades 7–12. Charges for laundry, school athletic uniform and equipment are covered by these fees.

HOW TO GET THERE ... By Pan American Jet Clipper direct to Tokyo from United States West Coast via "Great Circle" route, 13 hours; then 4 hours to Taiwan via connecting airline.

FOR FURTHER INFORMATION ... For complete information about the school and how to enroll, write to the MORRISON ACADEMY, 100 Morrison Road, Taichung, Taiwan.

For general information (in addition to the facts given on pages 184 to 185), write to the International Schools Services, Department PA, 147 East 50th Street, New York, N. Y. 10022. For travel particulars and documentation, write to Educational Department, NHE, Pan American Airways, Pan Am Building, New York, N. Y. 10017.

and physical education.

School administers academic aptitude and achievement tests in alternate years.

FEES ... Special rates for children of missionary groups; for others, annual tuition of $275, annual fee for room and board of $375.

HOW TO GET THERE ... By Pan American Jet Clipper, Bangkok is 2½ hours' flying time from Hong Kong and approximately 28 hours eastbound from New York. By ship, 50 to 60 days from New York.

FOR FURTHER INFORMATION ... For complete information about the school and how to enroll, write to the CHIENGMAI CHILDREN'S CENTER, Box 38, Chiengmai, Thailand.

For general information (in addition to the facts given on pages 184 to 185), write to the International Schools Services, Department PA, 147 East 50th Street, New York, N. Y. 10022. For travel particulars and documentation, write to Educational Department, NHE, Pan American Airways, Pan Am Building, New York, N. Y. 10017.

Chiengmai Children's Center

THAILAND

CHIENGMAI CHILDREN'S CENTER

Co-educational day and boarding school, ages 6–14. Minimum age for boarders is 8. Founded 1954.

PRINCIPAL ... Miss Lorene McNutt.

The school is under auspices of the Church of Christ in Thailand. It is situated in the northern part of the country, where the climate is temperate, about 3 hours' flight from Bangkok. The school year runs from September to late August; Christmas vacation is 4 weeks, spring vacation 6 weeks.

Enrollment is about 50; almost all are Americans. The school is primarily for missionaries' children, but also serves a limited number of families who are in Thailand under other programs. A new school building, recently completed, has space for 16 boarders; there are 9 boarders this year. Six of the teaching staff of eight are Americans, with one Thai and one British. School grounds have facilities for badminton, basketball, softball.

COURSE OF STUDY ... American elementary school program, taught in English. Grades 1–3 are in self-contained classrooms; grades 4–8 are semi-departmentalized. All students are required to take mathematics, English, Thai language, general physical science, social studies, art, chorus, music appreciation,

UNITED ARAB REPUBLIC (EGYPT)

AMERICAN SCHOOL, ALEXANDRIA

Co-educational boarding and day school, ages 6–18. Minimum age for boarders is 9. Founded 1922 ·

PRINCIPAL ... Mr. George W. Meloy.

Located in the Schutz district of Alexandria, about 6 miles east of the center of the city, the school is less than half a mile from the Mediterranean. It was established by the United Presbyterian Church in the U. S. primarily for children of American missionaries serving in North Africa, but other American children and those of other nationalities are welcomed. The student body of 150 includes about 100 Americans; other students come from Greece, Italy, the United Kingdom, India, Turkey and Scandinavia. Most of the students are boarders, a majority of them between 14 and 18 years old. A teaching staff of 18, most of whom are appointed by the United Presbyterian

American School, Alexandria

Atlantic College

Church. The 2-acre campus has a tennis court and a basketball court; the facilities of a nearby camp are used for other sports. Classroom space for 200 students; boarding for 100.

COURSES OF STUDY ... The elementary curriculum parallels that of schools in the United States, with the addition of courses related to the school environment. Grades 3–8 have instruction in French and Arabic.

A college preparatory program is offered in grades 9–12. Required subjects are Middle Eastern history, Near Eastern geography, American government and social structure, general physical and biological science, general mathematics or algebra, foreign language (2 years), English (4 years), research writing and religious education.

The school administers standardized academic aptitude and achievement tests. English is the language of instruction.

COLLEGE ADMISSIONS ... In a recent graduating class, all students took College Entrance Examination Board tests, and the majority entered colleges in the U. S., including Hope, Muskingum, Miami University, Oregon State, Princeton University, Sterling and Tarkio.

SPORTS AND ACTIVITIES ... Basketball, tennis, scouting groups. Dramatic clubs, choral group, youth fellowship, school newspaper and yearbook. Students are encouraged to participate in school and community religious programs. A trip to Cairo is arranged each year, and there are frequent excursions to places of historical interest nearby. Students are assigned certain routine chores in the dormitory and may also take paid jobs such as waiting on table and running the school post office and bank.

Chapel attendance is required.

FEES ... Annual tuition for all grades $515; board and lodging for all grades $630. No supplemental fees. No charge for staying at school during holidays.

HOW TO GET THERE ... By Pan American Jet Clipper to Rome, about 8 hours from New York. Then by connecting airline, about 2½ hours to Cairo. For Middle East travelers, Cairo is 1½ hours via Middle East Air Liban from Beirut, and may be included at no extra cost if you purchase in advance a ticket covering your full itinerary. By ship to Alexandria, 13 to 17 days from New York.

FOR FURTHER INFORMATION ... For complete information about the school and how to enroll, write to the AMERICAN SCHOOL, 51 Rue Shutz, Alexandria, Egypt (United Arab Republic).

For general information (in addition to the facts given on pages 184 to 185), write to the International Schools Services, Department PA, 147 East 50th Street, New York, N. Y. 10022. For travel particulars and documentation, write to Educational Department, NHE, Pan American Airways, Pan Am Building, New York, N. Y. 10017.

UNITED KINGDOM

ATLANTIC COLLEGE, THE UNITED KINGDOM

Boys' university preparatory boarding school, ages 16–19. Founded 1962. International ·

HEADMASTER ... D. J. Hoare, C.B., M.I., Mech. E., M.R.I.N.A.

Located on a wooded 112-acre estate near Bristol Channel on the coast of South Wales; housed in St. Donat's Castle (begun in twelfth century, modernized in 1920s) and auxiliary buildings.

Atlantic College (U. K.) is the first of six international university preparatory schools started by British Air Marshal Sir Lawrance Darvall and now being established as the Atlantic College Project, furthered by an international council whose members include Dr. Kurt Hahn, formerly headmaster of Salem and Gordonstoun Schools. Anticipated locations of the other colleges: Canada, France, Germany, Greece, the United States.

Because of differences among national systems of education, a student obtaining his secondary schooling in any one country of the Atlantic Community cannot easily obtain higher education in the universities of another country. A major purpose of Atlantic College (U. K.) is to provide a curriculum that meets the university entrance needs of all the various Atlantic Community nationals enrolled. Graduates will be able to return to universities in other Atlantic Community countries without further preparation.

Enrollment in the first year of operation was 55 boys from 12 countries, including 8 from the U. S. It is expected that by 1966 enrollment will total 300, with 30–50 U. S. boys. The national group of each Atlantic Community country will be large enough (at least 20 boys) to represent adequately its own history and customs. Group teachers will ensure that no boy is estranged from the traditions of his home country.

Staff of 20, mostly British, French, German, and Scandinavian masters have been added. Faculty will become more fully multinational as enrollment is increased.

COURSE OF STUDY ... About 35 class periods weekly, with each boy studying mathematics, sciences, European history, the literature, language and history of his own country and two languages other than his own. In American terms, the work of the College begins at 11th grade level (high school graduation is preferred as a prerequisite to application). All students at the British Atlantic College will follow courses leading to the General Certificate of Education, Advanced Level examinations. Three passes at Advanced Level are recognized as university matriculation qualification in American and Canadian universities and in a number of other countries.

Influence of the "Outward Bound" concept developed by Dr. Kurt Hahn and others is seen in that development of students' confidence and sense of obligation, which is achieved partly through use of their sense of adventure in ways that also provide physical development. A daily program of physical education is an integral part of the curriculum; this includes not only team games, but full training in seamanship with the aim of developing "the human qualities which the sea demands."

The main theme of all physical activities is preparation for and participation in rescue services. All boys are taught first aid and life saving, and may then volunteer to join the various corps of beach-rescue, canoe lifeguard, coast guard and safety boat and other rescue services which are being established.

School year consists of 2 terms; there is an 8-day break during each for "mid-term expedition"—accomplishment of individual student projects not directly covered in classroom and designed as an additional means of fostering initiative and self-reliance intellectually, physically, and socially.

COLLEGE ADMISSIONS . . . Write directly to the Head-master for information on College Entrance Examination Board tests.

FEES . . . $1,400 annually for tuition, room and board; an additional $112 annually for clothing and equipment.

HOW TO GET THERE . . . By Pan American Jet Clipper services, 6½ hours to London from New York and Boston. Jet Clipper service also from Philadelphia, Baltimore/Washington, Atlanta, Detroit, New Orleans, Dallas and Houston; direct from Chicago (7¾ hours), or via Detroit. Jet Clippers fly from U.S. West Coast via the polar route in 10½ hours. Clippers serve Glasgow through Prestwick Airport. By ship, about 5 days.

FOR FURTHER INFORMATION . . . For complete information about the school and how to enroll, write to the ATLANTIC COLLEGE IN THE UNITED KINGDOM, St. Donat's Castle, Llantwit Major, Glamorgan, Wales.

For general information (in addition to the facts given on pages 184 to 185), write to the International Schools Services, Department PA, 147 East 50th Street, New York, N. Y. 10022. For travel particulars and documentation, write to Educational Department, NHE, Pan American Airways, Pan Am Building, New York, N. Y. 10017.

Marymount International School, London

MARYMOUNT INTERNATIONAL SCHOOL

Girls' boarding and day school, ages 10–18. Minimum age for boarders is 11. Founded 1955 ·

PRINCIPAL . . . Rev. Mother M. Finbarr, R.S.H.M.

Located in a Surrey suburb, about 45 minutes from London by train or bus.

The school is a branch of Marymount in Tarrytown, New York, and is under the direction of the Sisters of the Sacred Heart of Mary (Roman Catholic Church). There is a school chapel; attendance is required.

The enrollment of 150 includes 70 U.S. students, 32 British, and others from European, Latin American and Far Eastern countries. Most of the girls are between the ages of 14 and 18. About two-thirds of the students are boarders. Teaching staff of 13 includes 6 Americans.

COURSES OF STUDY . . . The Junior School (grades 5–8) provides a thorough foundation in mathematics, social studies, science, foreign languages and Christian doctrine. The Senior School (secondary program) offers two main courses, one a general academic and the other a college preparatory curriculum. Required courses in the latter are world and American history; biology, chemistry or physics; elementary and intermediate algebra and plane geometry; French and Latin; 4 years of English; speech; Christian doctrine; gymnastics; ballet. The school also prepares girls for the British General Certificate of Education examinations at Ordinary Level. English is the language of instruction; special programs available for students whose native language is not English. School administers standardized academic aptitude and achievement tests.

COLLEGE ADMISSIONS . . . Colleges in the U. S. admitting recent graduates include College of William and Mary, Marquette, Manhattanville, Mary Baldwin, Marymount, Middlebury, Smith and the University of Colorado.

SPORTS AND ACTIVITIES . . . Extracurricular societies and clubs include athletic association, debating, dramatics, French, poetry, glee club. There are a school paper, student council and charitable works program. Visits are made to major points of historical and literary interest; students attend Shakespearean plays at Stratford or the Old Vic. At Easter an educational trip is usually organized for students staying on at the school.

FEES . . . About $1,280 annually for boarding and tuition, plus approximately $230 for excursions, school uniform and miscellaneous other charges, excluding personal allowances and special tutoring.

HOW TO GET THERE . . . By Pan American Jet Clipper services, 6½ hours to London from New York and Boston. Jet Clipper service also from Philadelphia, Baltimore/Washington, Atlanta, Detroit, New Orleans, Dallas and Houston; direct from Chicago (7¾ hours), or via Detroit. Jet Clippers fly from U.S. West Coast via the polar route in 10½ hours. Clippers serve Glasgow through Prestwick Airport. By ship, about 5 days.

FOR FURTHER INFORMATION . . . For complete information about the school and how to enroll, write to the MARYMOUNT INTERNATIONAL SCHOOL, George Road, Kingston Hill, Surrey, England.

For general information (in addition to the facts given on pages 184 to 185), write to the International Schools Services, Department PA, 147 East 50th Street, New York, N. Y. 10022. For travel particulars and documentation, write to Educational Department, NHE, Pan American Airways, Pan Am Building, New York, N. Y. 10017.